Prelude to Analysis

PRENTICE-HALL INTERNATIONAL, INC.   *London*
PRENTICE-HALL OF AUSTRALIA, PTY., LTD.   *Sydney*
PRENTICE-HALL OF CANADA, LTD.   *Toronto*
PRENTICE-HALL OF INDIA (PRIVATE), LTD.   *New Delhi*
PRENTICE-HALL OF JAPAN, INC.   *Tokyo*

PRENTICE-HALL MATHEMATICS SERIES

Prelude to Analysis
Prelude to Analysis
Prelude to Analysis
Prelude to Analysis
Prelude to Analysis
Prelude to Analysis
Prelude to Analysis
Prelude to Analysis
Prelude to Analysis
Prelude to Analysis

Prelude to Analysis

Analysis

Paul C. Rosenbloom / Seymour Schuster

Professor of Mathematics
and Mathematics Education
Columbia University

Associate Professor of
Mathematics
University of Minnesota

PRENTICE-HALL, INC, ENGLEWOOD CLIFFS, NEW JERSEY

510
R813p

Preface *Thumbing through just a few of its pages will convince the prospective reader that this* Prelude to Analysis *is unusual in many of its features. It therefore behooves us, the authors, to explain and perhaps justify the departure from the norm.*

First, it should be said that the book is not a treatise, but rather a textbook. *Hence, questions of content, order of presentation, style, and format have been governed by pedagogical considerations rather than by a desire to present a neat, logical package of theorems and proofs. With this said, we move on to specifics.*

10 4/5

Mathematical Content   This is a pre-calculus book for students with a background of three or more years of high school mathematics, including algebra, geometry, and a few of the elements of trigonometry (say, the trigonometry of right triangles). The choice of mathematical material for an audience of this type has been based on answers to questions like: What bridges the gap between this background and a strong up-to-date course in calculus and analytic geometry? What are the principal difficulties of calculus for which students should be prepared? Thus, preparation for the limit concept has been made a principal theme that permeates the entire book. In fact, we have chosen to give a thorough treatment of limits of sequences at this stage, leaving the more general notions of limit to a *bona-fide* calculus course.

But, how is the study of limits motivated before encountering calculus? Why would anyone wish to study limits of sequences? The answer, for us, seems to come, quite naturally, from the problem of solving equations (which students already believe to be an important mathematical activity). At an early stage of the book, we study methods for solving equations and we are led to various methods of approximating solutions. Methods of iteration yield *sequences*, about which we ask: Is the sequence converging to a number? Is it converging to the desired solution? And, if so, what is the error at the nth step of the iteration? These questions give rise to all the important points to be studied in connection with limits of sequences: a precise definition of convergence, completeness of the real numbers, and error estimates.

A secondary, but nonetheless central, theme is that of *approximation*. In the foregoing paragraph we mentioned its role in motivating the study of limits. But, quite independent of this, the subject of approximations is worthy for any user of mathematics. One of the characteristics that distinguishes mathematical analysis of today from mathematics of a century ago is the prevalence of *estimates* and the instrument for their expression, namely *inequalities*. Today, we realize that relations of equality are rare—the exception rather than the rule—so that much of the heart of modern analysis lies in the attempt to obtain estimates: estimates to solutions, error estimates, and the like. (In particular, the problem of finding a δ corresponding to a given ε is one of determining an estimate.)

Now that we have established the need for studying solutions of equations, approximate methods, error estimates, and inequalities in order to prepare for limits, we remark that all of this material rests heavily on an understanding of the real numbers. Hence, a study of the *real number system* becomes another one of our principal themes.

Many of the recently written textbooks that wish to incorporate "modern mathematics" with some rigor have emphasized (and over-emphasized) the algebraic aspects of the real number system. That is, they devote a good deal of attention to the fact that the real numbers constitute an example of a field, but pay little attention to the analytic properties of the real number system. It is our view that both the algebraic and the analytic properties of real numbers deserve thorough treatment, with the latter receiving strong emphasis to strengthen the student's background for future analysis courses. To be specific, the questions of *order* and *completeness* deserve far more attention than they have hitherto been given. Hence, we attempt to provide a fairly thorough description of the real number system, discussing the significance of Archimedean order and the relatively sophisticated topics relating to completeness: Cauchy convergence, nested intervals, monotonic bounded sequences, and least upper bounds.

A few of the other mathematical topics not discussed in the above scheme of principal themes, but worthy of mention, are *functions, vectors*, and *mathematical induction*. These, too, are chosen because of their importance in any up-to-date calculus course.

The *function concept* is one of the most important of all ideas in modern mathematics. Every branch of mathematics rests heavily on it. We therefore begin to utilize it, intuitively, in Chapters 1 and 2. Chapter 3 makes extensive use of the algebra of functions and functional notation. Finally, Chapter 5 attempts a more formal and complete treatment, wherein the student shall learn how functions may be used to define ideas such as *property, ordered pair, relation*, and *sequence*.

The notion of *vector* is introduced as a translation, thus relating it to geometry. In Chapter 6, we apply vectors to geometry, both in a coordinate setting and in a coordinate-free fashion. The following chapter gives rise to applications of vectors to linear transformations and to the solutions of linear systems of equations, including a brief introduction to matrices.

Mathematical induction is still a subject that plagues both students and teachers. There are various conjectures on why this is so. We attempt to eliminate, or at least minimize, the difficulty by not formalizing the notion until quite late—the very last chapter, in fact—but by creating the need for induction, and utilizing it throughout earlier stages of the book. Recursive definitions and recursion relations begin to appear in Chapter 5, and are used in the iteration processes of Chapter 7. The questions surrounding convergence of iterations require induction, so the student becomes actively involved in its use from Chapter 7 onward. After the formal treatment of induction, we discuss its relation to well-ordering and make further varied applications of the idea, including many to number theory.

Motivation The preceding discussion of mathematical content, the interconnection of topics, and the order of presentation was, to some extent, a discussion of motivation. We have attempted to go beyond and consider questions of motivation at each stage of the writing. Every new topic is introduced through a problem that gives rise to the topic and creates a need for the new ideas. An abstract notion is presented only after the reader has become familiar with concrete examples to abstract from; in short, generalizations arise to effect logical economy for the study of particular cases, and postulates are set forth to put in logical form that which has been studied heuristically.

Sections 1.1 and 1.2, in discussing the nature of mathematics and its role in modern society, are attempting to give general motivation for the study of mathematics. Section 1.3 presents a brief encounter with calculus, which, in a general way, serves to motivate the main ideas of the *Prelude*. Section 1.4 uses a problem in economics to motivate the study of order properties. And so, throughout the book, this spirit continues: functions are motivated by their use in describing physical phenomena (Chapter 1), in studying the geometry of the real line (Chapter 2), and in developing the algebra of real numbers (Chapter 3); coordinate systems arise from the need to visually comprehend masses (or messes) of data; vectors are motivated by translations (displacements); linear systems are encountered in the study of electrical networks; convergence questions come from the study of numerical methods; the Cauchy criterion (our completeness postulate) is motivated by the intuitively acceptable idea that a sequence whose terms "bunch up," as does $\{\sum \frac{1}{n!}\}$, ought to converge to a real number; Archimedes' order postulate arises from its need in showing that monotonic bounded sequences converge; and so on.

We have tried to make *applications of mathematics* an integral part of the book. Students who pursue the standard elementary courses in mathematics often ask, "What can I use this for?" or "What good will this do me?" No matter how abhorrent these questions may be to the mathematics teacher, it must be admitted that they are legitimate for a student to ask. It is a bit unfair to expect the student, at this stage, to share the instructor's enthusiasm for a quest for knowledge, an appreciation of the fact that fundamental knowledge will "someday" pay off; and it is certainly unfair to expect the student to have an appreciation of the abstract beauty of mathematical knowledge when his experience in the field has been meager and, most often, dull. It seems to us that providing applications of interest should be one of the primary responsibilities of both the textbook (not the treatise, perhaps) and the instructor. We have therefore attempted to insert more applications than are usual, and it is our hope that they are more interesting than those found in the standard book at this level. There are applications to physics, chemistry, social science, work with mathematical machines, and back to mathematics itself.

In the final chapter of the book, when (we hope) the reader has reached a more mature level and has developed some appreciation for pure mathematics, we give him a dessert in the form of applications to the theory of numbers.

Novelty While, in some sense, all that has been said above has concerned the novelty of the work, we want to dwell here upon the particular novelty in introducing and developing individual topics.

The population in pre-calculus courses today contains students of varied backgrounds. Some may be quite unfamiliar with all of the content of our *Prelude to Analysis*; yet others may have touched on—or even studied—several of the major topics. The latter group is the more dangerous. A student who has "seen this subject before" may be his own worst enemy. This is borne out by many of the studies of students who enter college calculus, having had some calculus in high school; in general, they don't fare well. Therefore, we have tried to save these people from themselves by presenting fresh approaches whenever possible. We hope that this has the additional effect of injecting some interest and excitement into their intellectual lives.

The development of the real numbers in Chapters 2 and 3 should be novel to students who have seen the material before. The field postulates probably differ from those seen in any elementary study of abstract algebra; in Chapter 4, the treatment of the straight line is not a rehash of what one sees in the standard analytic geometry books; taking the idea of function, in Chapter 5, to be undefined should be new to the student; treating vectors as translations (Chapter 6) is rarely done at this level; and skipping to Chapter 9, the use of the Cauchy criterion as a completeness postulate is unusual. (In fact, we don't know of any textbook that attempts so thorough a treatment of limits and completeness below the advanced calculus level.)

Another novel feature that might be classed as development of topics is the review of algebra. It is nearly all hidden. The usual obvious review of high school algebra is a deadly dull subject. So, again trying to protect students from themselves while keeping life interesting, we have sneaked into exercises all the necessary review of exponents, fractions, radicals, inequalities, functional notation, etc. The hiding places for some specific topics are given in the *Teacher's Manual*, so that instructors may be assisted in constructing assignments.

General Format and Style We have tried to write in a manner that simulates classroom teaching. Perhaps eloquence has been sacrificed, but we prefer direct and informal language that conveys the spirit of conversation.

The best classroom teachers are those who succeed in involving their students in the discovery and development of the mathematics. For, in the final analysis, mathematics is learned by doing. Our efforts to get the reader involved permeate the text as well as the exercises. The text is partially programmed, consisting of portions of exposition interspersed with questions so that the reader, while studying, should become actively involved in mathematical activity. The answers to most of these questions appear in the right hand margin. Many of the questions we ask are of the sort that a critical reader should be asking himself as he reads a mathematical textbook. It is our hope, therefore, that we are inculcating, in the student, a critical awareness that will enable him to approach further mathematical literature without a feeling of trepidation.

Many of the proofs are constructed in a "natural" way, so that the reader can feel that he might have thought of the idea, if he hasn't already done so before the appearance of the punch line. Much mathematics writing has the effect of giving the student an inferiority complex and/or the feeling that divine revelation is what it takes to become a creative scientist; so he packs his bags and heads for the sociology department, or elsewhere. We have tried our best to convey the impression that mathematicians and scientists struggle and sometimes flounder a good deal before making discoveries; they must investigate, examine special cases and "play" before the insights come. Moreover, they must ask themselves the "right questions" in order to get results. From our vantage point, we try to assist the student to discover by asking many of the "right questions."

Finally, we mention the exercises. They constitute an integral part of the book. In fact, we believe the exercises to be the heart of the book. Most of them are nonroutine. Often, the main points of a topic are contained in the exercises. And, quite frequently, we rely on a result that was contained or was to be proven in an earlier exercise. Still another departure is that exercises sometimes appear in blocks, so that as many as four or five (or more) in sequence develop an important idea. This means that the reader should do most of the exercises. Occasionally, the sets are so long that the instructor may feel that a selection is necessary in order to finish the course in a finite time. In making such a selection for assignment purposes, he should take care and consult the *Teacher's Manual* when in doubt.

Omissions For many years the pre-calculus sequence has consisted of algebra, trigonometry, and analytic geometry. Earlier, we mentioned the inefficacy of a blatant review of high school algebra and the desirability of absorbing this subject within other topics; analytic geometry is already absorbed— though not adequately treated—in most calculus courses, but we do present some introduction to the subject from Chapter 4 onward. However, *trigonometry* is definitely absent from our textbook.

The explanation for this omission is threefold: (1) Most students who enter a pre-calculus course have already had a high school course in trigonometry. (2) Many of the calculus and analytic geometry books, currently in use, include a treatment of trigonometry in connection with the study of the calculus of transcendental equations. (3) Finally, it is our opinion that trigonometry, if not studied in early high school work, is more satisfactorily studied in connection with calculus and differential equations, where the trigonometric functions arise as solutions to differential equations that derive from physical problems. An excellent treatment of trigonometry from this point of view appears in a forthcoming work on calculus by a pair of authors whose names we are too modest to mention.

The only other omission worth commenting upon is a chapter on formal logic. Since the mid-1950's it has become fashionable for American textbooks to include such a chapter that treats the propositional calculus via truth tables, some study of quantification and a fair amount of formal manipulation of logical symbolism. We take issue with this fashion, feeling that such a treatment of logic, with its emphasis on formalism, is not well motivated. Its usefulness in the mainstream of a mathematical student's training has been exaggerated; for example, it can never show a student how to construct a proof of a nontrivial theorem in analysis.

This is not to say that logic doesn't merit any attention at all. We do, in fact, treat those elements of logic that we think are necessary for the chosen mathematical content, but we treat it gradually, and in the context of its usefulness. The *nature of a deductive science* (postulate system) and the *role of definitions* are discussed from the first section of the book through the last. The meanings of *and, or, not,* and *implies* are studied as the need arises—in the statements and proofs of the field properties of the real numbers (Chapter 3). The construction of proofs of inequalities is a subject particularly rich in examples that can impress the student with the importance of these logical ideas. Although we have never exhibited the truth tables, we have presented the reader with as much about logical connectives as he can possibly use in his undergraduate analysis courses. *Quantification* and the method of *negating quantified statements* are useful ideas that are also motivated by mathematical need. We begin this, also gradually, in Chapter 3 and, as a climax in the final chapter, we present a nontrivial application to the study of logical equivalents of the principle of mathematical induction.

Acknowledgments Now that we have more or less presented our case for the book, it is time to acknowledge the assistance we received along the road to its publication.

First, we wish to acknowledge the inspiration of two works of art in mathematical textbook writing: *Mathematical Methods in Engineering* by T. von Karman and M. A. Biot, and *Aufgaben und Lehrsätze* by G. Pólya and G. Szegö. These served as models and goals for the sort of book we desired to write at a more elementary level. We shall be pleased if our effort is in any way comparable to these fine works.

During the academic year 1963–64, a class of freshman students at Carleton College volunteered to be guinea pigs for the preliminary version of the manuscript (which included seven more chapters on calculus and differential equations). Since neither of us have met any of the students in the class, we wish to seize this opportunity—our only one—to express our thanks. Professor Frank Wolf taught the class and faithfully communicated to us the student reactions and opinions as well as expressing his own. He pointed out errors and made suggestions for improvement.

After extensive revisions that resulted from the Carleton trial, Professors Frank Wolf and Donald Taranto of Carleton then read the new version and once again pointed out errors and gave us the benefit of their judgment. To them, also, we express our sincere thanks.

At this stage we had the good fortune of assistance from two University of Minnesota freshmen: Catherine Geise and Carolyn Malm. They read the manuscript, worked through all the programmed text, filled the blanks, and attempted all of the exercises. This student judgment was invaluable "feedback," especially because we received it daily while it was still hot. Needless to say, this led to still further revision, particularly of Chapter 8. (Chapter 8 is still a difficult one, but we want still more feedback from you, the reader, before we tamper with it further.)

Finally, the manuscript was given to Professor Joseph D. E. Konhauser of the University of Minnesota, who read it so carefully that he presented us with over forty pages of corrections and comments! "Thanks" seems like a weak word to express our appreciation for such painstaking care.

Perhaps we owe our greatest debt of gratitude to Karen Stevens Fleischhacker. She masterfully typed the manuscript and its several revisions. While doing so, she caught many of our slip-ups that were mathematical and otherwise, and she helped, immeasurably, to bring about consistency. She brought a note of order into the lives of two disorganized mathematicians.

If errors still remain—and it is likely that there are at least a few—then, of course, the responsibility is ours.

Minneapolis, Minnesota   PAUL C. ROSENBLOOM

                                                             SEYMOUR SCHUSTER

To the Student *This book is written for you. It is meant to be read and studied. We have tried to minimize some of the difficulties in your mathematical life by assisting you over some of the rough territory. This has been done by helping you take small steps with firm footing. But* you *must take the steps;* you *must do the work.*

Mathematical skill and power are developed by doing mathematics. We have therefore written a book that seeks to get you involved in "doing mathematics." It is a book that is, literally, loaded with exercises, ranging from the relatively simple to extremely difficult. Do as many as you can in each set. You will find this one of the most rewarding activities in your academic training.

We have not provided answers to the exercises, feeling that answers in back of the book often do the student more harm than good. However, a compromise has been effected. The main body of the text is written with questions interspersed in the exposition. Answers to these questions are given in the right-hand margin. Portions of text with questions and blanks to be filled are called "programmed." We suggest that you read such programmed sections with the answers covered, filling the blanks and then checking your answers as you move down the page. (In general, you should read mathematics with pencil and paper handy, working as you read.) In order to help you gain the full benefit of your willpower, we give a warning, "Programmed Text Follows," at the bottom of an odd-numbered page that is to be followed by one with programmed text.

Have fun.

PAUL C. ROSENBLOOM
SEYMOUR SCHUSTER

Contents

Contents

Symbols

Prelude to Analysis

Chapter One **Introduction** *Here we are concerned with orientation—orientation to mathematics in general, and orientation to this particular book. Section 1.1 presents the reader with some ideas concerning the nature of mathematics as a science, a language, an art, and as an instrument for analysis in other branches of human knowledge. In Sec. 1.2, career opportunities in mathematics and related fields are discussed in the light of the increased number of applications of mathematics and the increased number of fields that now utilize mathematics.*

Although the intuitive introduction to calculus in Sec. 1.3 is designed to give the motivation for the principal ideas of the Prelude to Analysis, *it may furnish the reader with sufficient knowledge to understand the applications of calculus in first courses in subjects such as physics, chemistry, and economics. The chapter closes with the construction of a mathematical model of an economic theory of utility. This example serves to illustrate a meaningful application of mathematics and to provide the reader with a strong reason for carefully studying the notions of order (greater than and less than). The concept of* linear order, *which is introduced here, will be used throughout the remainder of the book.*

1.1

Nature of Mathematics   Scientific thinking is generally divided into two categories, *inductive* and *deductive* reasoning. While both types of reasoning are common to the sciences, and indeed to nearly all human endeavors which require thought, mathematics, particularly, works in the realm of deductive reasoning. In fact, among the many definitions—none of them entirely satisfactory—that have been given for mathematics is the following: *Mathematics is the science of deductive reasoning.*

We shall expand on the methods of scientific thinking.

Consider the student of chemistry who knows that adding a few drops of hydrochloric acid to a test tube containing a silver nitrate solution produces a clumpy white precipitate. How does he "know" this before mixing? In explicit terms he might state that he has tried this experiment many times, perhaps ten, and each time the hydrochloric acid was poured into the silver nitrate, there appeared clumps of white precipitate; and if he performs the experiment an eleventh time, he is sure that a similar result will follow. This line of reasoning is called inductive. *Induction* is the method of observation and experimentation: You experiment and observe enough times to convince yourself that the same outcome (a white precipitate) is so very likely, that you predict it with assurance.

Inductive reasoning is often described as reasoning *from particular cases to a general conclusion.* This is in contrast to reasoning *from a general result to a particular case.* The famous syllogism:

> All men are mortal.
> Socrates is a man.
> Socrates is mortal.

is an illustration of reasoning from a general proposition (All men ...) to the particular case of Socrates being mortal. This type of reasoning is *deductive* or logical reasoning. A *deduction* is a statement of what *must* logically follow with *complete certainty* from a given assumption (or assumptions).

It is with complete certainty that we conclude for a particular member (e.g., Socrates) that which is the case for all members of the general class (e.g., men). Reasoning from general to particular is one of the most important patterns of *deductive inference.*

The physical, biological, and social sciences all make use of both methods. We shall describe a somewhat idealized picture of the scientific method: A beginning is made with the observation of phenomena. This is followed by a search for general laws that fit the data. After the "guesses" of general laws are formulated, an attempt is made to set up a theory in which the laws appear as part of a sensibly organized body of knowledge. The observation and the formulation of a law that fits the data form the inductive aspect of the scientific method, whereas the theory in which logical consequences are drawn from certain assumptions is the deductive aspect of the scientific method.

Before we go any farther, we shall try to clarify the meaning of deduction by leading you through an example that is a bit more elaborate than the simple syllogism.

Suppose you are at a party at which introductions are made and some hand-shaking takes place. After the introductions, you classify the people at the party into two categories, or *sets*, in the following way: If a person has shaken hands with an odd number of people, then call him an *odd fellow*; if he has shaken hands with an even number of people, then he is an *even fellow*. Our claim is that *the number of odd fellows at the party must be even*.

For the sake of simplicity, we shall assume that any two people at the party shake hands with each other at most once.

Jim shook hands with two people.	
Two is an _____ (even/odd) number.	*even*
Therefore, Jim is an _____ (even/odd) fellow.	*even*
Tom shook hands with five people.	
Therefore, Tom is an _____ (even/odd) fellow.	*odd*

Imagine that each person at the party makes a list of all the people with whom he has shaken hands. If Bill shakes hands with Joe, then Bill's name appears on Joe's list and Joe's name appears on Bill's list.

Since each handshake involves *two* people, then each handshake is recorded _____ times, once on each shaker's list. → *two*

(1) Therefore, the total number of names on the lists is _____ times the number of handshakes. → *two*

Two times a whole number yields an _____ number. → *even*
Therefore, the total number of names on all the lists is _____ (even/odd). → *even*

Every *even* fellow has an _____ (even/odd) number → *even*
of names on his list. Every *odd* fellow has an _____ → *odd*
number of names on his list.

The total number of names on the *even* fellows' lists is the sum of several _____ (even/odd) numbers. Compute 4 + 12. The answer is _____ (even/odd). Compute 4 + 12 + 28 + 392 + 6. The answer is _____ (even/odd). Did you really have to compute to answer the last question to decide whether the sum was even or odd? → *even* / *even* / *even*

The sum of any number of *even* numbers is _____. → *even*

(2)   The total number of names on the *even* fellows' lists is _____.   *even*

The total number of names on the *odd* fellows' lists is the sum of as many _____ (even/odd) numbers as there are _____ fellows.   *odd* *odd*

Write any two odd numbers and add: ____ + ____. The sum is _____ (even/odd).   *even*

Write any three odd numbers and add:

____ + ____ + ____.

The sum is _____ (even/odd).   *odd*

The sum of an *even* number of odd numbers is _____ (even/odd).   *even*

The sum of an *odd* number of odd numbers is _____ (even/odd).   *odd*

If the sum of a sequence of odd numbers is *even*, then the number of numbers in the sequence is _____ (even/odd).   *even*

If the sum of a sequence of odd numbers is *odd*, then the number of numbers in the sequence is _____ (even/odd).   *odd*

(3)   Therefore, the total number of names on the odd fellows' lists is *even* if there is an _____ (even/odd) number of odd fellows, and *odd* if there is an _____ (even/odd) number of odd fellows.   *even* *odd*

(4)   The total of the numbers on all the lists is the sum of the total number of names on the even fellows' lists and the total number of names on the _____ fellows' lists.   *odd*

(5)   If the sum of an even number and some other number is *even*, then the other number must be _____.   *even*

By statements (1), (2), (4), and (5), the total number of names on the odd fellows' lists must be _____ (even/odd).   *even*

Therefore, by statement (3), there is an _____ (even/odd) number of odd fellows.   *even*

We have thus led you through a chain of *deductive reasoning*. We chose this particular example in order to illustrate that deduction can be applied to a variety of subject matter.

Before saying any more on this topic we present a few problems on which you may sharpen your (deductive) wits.

1. Suppose the sum of n numbers is even. What do you deduce about the number of odd numbers among the given n?

2. Professor Murray Klamkin, of the University of Minnesota, claims that he can always win in the following two-person game, provided that he makes the first move.

The game is played on a circular table. Players A and B, alternately, place a single penny anywhere on the table, such that it neither extends over the edge nor overlaps a penny already on the table. Once placed, a penny may not be moved. The player who places the last penny wins.

Justify Klamkin's claim. What if the table is square? Can you make some generalization as to the allowable shape of the table which will still permit player A (who makes the first move) to win every time?

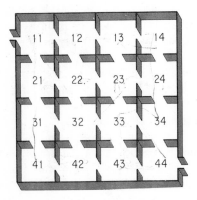

Figure 1-1

3. Referring to Fig. 1-1, if the numbers represent room numbers and the openings represent doors, can you enter room 11 and exit from room 44 by passing through each room only once?

4. Professor Leo Moser, of the University of Alberta, always wins money in the following card game: He asks you to shuffle an ordinary deck of cards, and then turn the cards face up in pairs. If both cards of a pair are black, you take them. If both are red, he takes them. If one is red and one black, the pair is put aside. You pay him one dollar for the privilege of playing, but when the game is over, he pays you three dollars for every card that you have more than he. If your number of cards is less than or equal to his, then no one pays anything.

Why does Professor Moser always win? How much does he expect to win each time he plays?

5. Suppose you are in a party of 50 people captured by a ruthless villain, who states that he will execute 49 members of the party according to the following procedure: The 50 people are to sit down at a circular table with the seats numbered consecutively 1 through 50. He will then shoot every other person beginning with the person in chair number 2, continuing until only one person is left. Which seat would you choose in order to remain alive? Where would you sit if 100 people were in the party? 1,000? (Not easy.)

Mathematics, as a science, consists of theories built up by the deductive method. A deductive science is a body of knowledge organized in a special way. It begins with a *primitive frame,* consisting of a certain set of propositions which are assumed, and a certain set of terms which are not defined.

The assumptions are called *postulates* or *axioms*. All other propositions (theorems) in the science are proved by logical reasoning alone from the explicitly stated assumptions and previously proved propositions. All other terms are explained by means of the explicitly listed undefined terms (in the primitive frame) and previously defined terms. In Sec. 1.4, we shall return to a more complete discussion of deductive sciences.

Induction and deduction are methods of acquiring knowledge that might be termed first-hand methods. Among second-hand methods of acquiring knowledge, surely the most important is that of learning what other people have already learned. This implies taking cognizance of past, as well as recent and current scholarship. And this, in turn, requires a mastery of the arts of communication, especially in the native and foreign languages. Enormous quantities of first-rate scientific research papers are published regularly in French, German and Russian, with small likelihood that very many of these works will be translated.† Every creative mathematician—perhaps every creative scientist—feels the need for literacy in French, German, Russian, and English. In this connection, it should be realized that *mathematics itself is a language*, as well as a science. Nowadays, the literature of nearly every field of knowledge from physics and engineering to economics and psychology to linguistics is written in the language of mathematics.

As a language, mathematics has its rules of grammar and syntax; moreover, in a sense, it has its poetry. Just as aesthetics is a concern of those who read and write English, a sense of beauty is of major concern to mathematicians. Many mathematicians consider themselves artists as well as scientists; in fact, another definition of mathematics given by a leading figure in the field is: *The art of building logical structures.*

A deductive science (logical structure) is often the finished product of mathematics. *Mathematics in the making is an art.* In choosing the postulates, in deciding (or guessing) what theorems to prove, and in constructing definitions and proofs, a mathematician behaves much like a poet. He is usually guided by a desire for *elegance*, by his feeling for the beauty of the structure which he is building. Defining the idea of mathematical beauty is as difficult as defining musical beauty. But, just as one develops an appreciation for music by listening, playing, and composing, you will develop an appreciation for mathematics as an art by learning good mathematics, by expounding what you have learned, and by creating new mathematics. Our intent is to provide you with opportunities for first-hand mathematical experience that will enhance the cultivation of an aesthetic sense with regard to the art of mathematics.

† For the inherent limitations of machine translation, see the paper by Professor Y. Bar Hillel, "The Present Status of Automatic Translation of Languages," in *Advances in Computers*, Vol. 1, edited by Franz Alt (New York: Academic Press, Inc., 1960).

Listed below are leading books in several areas of scholarship. Choose one in a field of special interest to you. Then proceed with Exercises 1–3.

Art: Susanne K. Langer, *Feeling and Form: A Theory of Art* (New York: Charles Scribner's Sons, 1953).

Astronomy: R. H. Baker, *Astronomy* (6th ed.; Princeton, N.J.: D. Van Nostrand Co., Inc., 1955).

Botany: Harvey E. Stork, *Evolution of Plants* (Minneapolis: Burgess Publishing Co., 1953).

Chemistry: M. J. Sienko and R. A. Plane, *Chemistry* (2nd ed.; New York: McGraw-Hill Book Company, 1961).

Ecology: R. Pearl, *Biology of Population Growth* (New York: Alfred A. Knopf, Inc., 1925).

Economics: R. K. Davidson, R. Kirby, *et al.*, *Economics: An Analytical Approach* (rev. ed.; Homewood, Ill.: Richard D. Irwin, Inc., 1962).

History: P. A. Sorokin, *Social and Cultural Dynamics* (Totowa, N. J.: Bedminster Press, 1962).

Linguistics: Z. S. Harris, *Structural Linguistics* (Chicago: University of Chicago Press, 1960).

Music: G. Haydon, *Introduction to Musicology* (Chapel Hill, N.C.: University of North Carolina, 1941).

Physics: F. W. Sears and M. N. Zemansky, *College Physics* (3rd ed.; Reading, Mass.: Addison-Wesley Publishing Co., Inc., 1960).

Political Science: K. J. Arrow, *Social Choice and Individual Values* (2nd ed.; New York: John Wiley & Sons, Inc., 1963).

Psychology: L. L. Thurstone, *Vectors of the Mind: Multiple-factor Analysis for the Isolation of Primary Traits* (Chicago: University of Chicago Press, 1935).

R. R. Busch and C. F. Mosteller, *Stochastic Models for Learning* (New York: John Wiley & Sons, Inc., 1955).

Sociology: P. Lazarsfeld, ed., *Mathematical Methods in the Social Sciences:* 1959 Proceedings of Stanford University Symposium on Mathematical Models in the Social Sciences (Stanford, Calif.: Stanford University Press, 1959).

1. List some of the mathematical language of the text, including perhaps equations, inequalities, and the like.

2. Read the preface to determine the mathematical knowledge that is assumed.

3. Look at the author's references, noting (a) the mathematical references and (b) those in foreign languages.

1.2

Mathematics in Modern Society, Career Opportunities   There is certainly no doubt that we are living in the most rapidly changing society in history. Within our own lifetimes we have witnessed scientific progress that has revolutionized technology. And the process continues, under our very noses, bringing new problems in economics, psychology, and biology, to mention just three areas that command man's interest.

Today's college graduate will continually be faced with new problems and situations, for which he has neither been specifically prepared nor which can be predicted. As a student, you should consider that any field you enter is likely to be changing so rapidly that in order to practice a profession, you will have to learn new things every few years—even things which haven't, as yet, been discovered. In order to live in this kind of a society, you will have to continue learning for the rest of your life; and acquiring the tools for continued learning should therefore be a principal aim of your college career. Mathematics is one of the most important of these tools, by virtue of its power in specific fields and by virtue of the wide variety of subject matter to which it may be applied.

The economic demands of our changing society are forcing an increase in productivity per individual. This, in turn, is putting pressure on the economy to become increasingly scientific and technical, with the result that machine labor is replacing human labor whenever possible. That is, we are living in an era in which skilled manpower is scarce and manpower, in general, is expensive, while machines and the like are plentiful; hence anything that can be done by machine will be done by machine. Witness the rapid expansion of automation and the disappearance of many types of routine work in industry. The pace at which jobs for the unskilled are disappearing represents one of the major social and economic problems of our time.

In order to take your place as a productive member of society, you should find within yourself some essentially human ability—something requiring intelligence, judgment, or taste—and develop it to your utmost capacity. You are being faced with the exciting challenge of a future where work need no longer be irksome, where human beings will be employed in essentially human tasks, not as cogs in a machine. In order to succeed, you will have to exercise your creative imagination to its fullest extent.

The applications of mathematics to the physical sciences and engineering are well known. Fascinating fields such as atomic physics and electronics are highly mathematical. The design of a new airplane often requires as many as 100,000 hours of theoretical paperwork as well as extensive use of high-speed computers. However, it is less well known, but nonetheless true, that mathematics is successfully being employed in the biological sciences and is becoming increasingly fundamental to their study. The related fields of biochemistry, biophysics, and the applied fields of medicine and agriculture have all benefited from mathematical contributions. It is also not well known that the past 30 years have brought a number of fundamental breakthroughs in the social sciences, and that these are essentially mathematical. The work of mathematician John von Neumann and economist Oskar Morgenstern, first published in book form in *The Theory of Games and Economic Behavior* in 1944,[†] paved the way for the development of the new science of *economic decision making*. This field of study has applications in psychology and sociology, as well as in economics, and is being applied on a large scale by government and business. Another new field of mathematics that has been developed primarily to serve the needs of government and business is that of *operations research*.

The *Cowles Commission*, a nonprofit corporation, was founded in 1932 for the purpose of conducting and encouraging investigations into economic problems. This commission has sponsored and published a host of mathematical studies of problems in the social sciences. The work of men such as W. K. Estes, R. R. Bush, and F. Mosteller has opened new vistas in the application of mathematics to psychology. The relatively new fields of *information theory* and *mathematical linguistics* and the development of translation machines have transformed linguistics, also, into a mathematical science. Leaders in this area have been people such as Professors Claude Shannon of M.I.T. and Benoit Mandelbrot of Harvard University. Even problems in military strategy are being subjected to mathematical analyses, with the National Security Council employing professional mathematicians expressly for this purpose.

Mathematics, as an instrument for analysis and as a language, is being utilized in an ever-increasing number of fields. It is hardly an exaggeration to say that no matter what vocation you pursue, you will need to be literate in mathematics.

Even if you are not a "user" of mathematics and science, you must develop some literacy in these subjects in order to grasp what goes on about you. To illustrate this point, we remark that approximately 80 per cent of the bills before the Congress of the United States involve science. In order to take your place in such a society, it is imperative that you have some appreciation and understanding of science and mathematics.

If you have ability and interest in mathematics, you may wish to consider it as a career possibility. According to the best available estimates, there were, in 1962, approximately 38,000 mathematicians employed in the United States, about 18,500 in industry, 3,500 in government, and 16,000 in colleges and universities. In addition, there were over 100,000 secondary school mathematics teachers.

[†] J. von Neumann and O. Morgenstern, *Theory of Games and Economic Behavior* (Princeton, N.J.: Princeton University Press, 1944).

In recent years, the whole field of mathematics teaching, from kindergarten up, has been revolutionized. Outstanding research mathematicians, educators, school teachers, and psychologists have been working together on several very exciting projects in mathematics education. There is a tremendous shortage of adequately prepared teachers at all levels. College professors are often active in research, and many do consulting work for industry and government.

In industry and government many mathematicians work on the applications to the physical and engineering sciences. Besides these classical fields, there is now a growing demand for mathematicians in the applications to the biological and social sciences.

Mathematicians may work on the transmission of impulses in the nervous system, quality control for the production of a new vaccine, or design of agricultural experiments. They work on military strategy, economic decision making in business and government, theory of learning, analysis of syntax, and prediction of elections. The insurance industry employs many actuaries.

With the advent of electronic computers, there are many new jobs in programming, coding, numerical analysis, and the logical design of computers.

The training for these positions varies from the bachelor's degree to the Ph.D. In 1960, about 61.3 per cent of the mathematicians in industry and government had the bachelor's degree, about 25.7 per cent had the master's degree, and about 7.2 per cent had the Ph.D. It is expected that by 1970 we shall need about 39,000 mathematicians in nonacademic jobs.

In 1963 median salaries for new Ph.D.'s in mathematics were $7,200 (9 months) in college teaching, $6,800 (9 months) in academic research, $12,000 (12 months) in industry, $11,700 (12 months) in research institutes, and $11,155 (12 months) in government.

For added readings on the widespread applications of mathematics, career opportunities in these areas, and the general significance of science and mathematics in modern society, we present the list of references below. In addition to these readings, you may gain some insight by investigating the number of companies in your area that have arrangements for employees to continue studying. Such arrangements may take the form of company classes and release-time and/or financial assistance for employees to carry on graduate study.

V. Bush, *Endless Horizons* (Washington, D. C.: Public Affairs Press, 1946).

A. H. Dupree, *Science in the Federal Government* (New York: Harper & Row, Publishers, Inc.).

A. H. Dupree, *Science in the Federal Government: A History of Policies and Activities to 1940* (Cambridge, Mass.: Harvard University Press, 1957).

J. F. McCloskey and F. N. Trefethen, *Operations Research for Management* (Baltimore, Md.: The John Hopkins Press, 1954).

Careers in Mathematics (Washington, D.C.: National Council of Teachers of Mathematics, and National Academy of Sciences–National Research Council, 1961).

Meeting Manpower Needs in Science and Technology. Report No. 1: Graduate Training in Engineering, Mathematics, and Physical Sciences (Washington, D.C.: The President's Science Advisory Committee, 1962).

Professional Opportunities in Mathematics (6th ed.; Buffalo, N.Y.: The Mathematical Association of America, 1964).

1.3

Outline of the Course   In order to give you any meaningful idea of what *analysis* is about, we must first discuss the subject of *calculus*. In this relatively short section you will learn about the fundamental notions of calculus, and thereby obtain sufficient perspective to understand an outline of the principal ideas of our prelude.

To borrow (and paraphrase) an analogy used by Professor W. W. Sawyer,† we shall take you to a quiet country road for your first driving lesson. While you are learning the rudiments, we will not burden you with advice on how to drive in heavy traffic or under hazardous road conditions. However, the fundamentals you learn today are truly fundamental; they will stand you in good stead. Moreover, they will provide you with enough comprehension to appreciate the rationale for our program.

The central concept of calculus is that of a *rate of change*, or *derivative*. We will explain with an example.

Let x be the distance in feet traveled in the time t seconds by a falling body, which is at rest initially (i.e., when $t = 0$). Then, as Galileo discovered, x is related to t by the simple equation:

$$x = 16t^2.$$

We can make a table of values:

t	x
0	0
1	16
2	64
3	___
4	___
5	___

† W. W. Sawyer, *What is Calculus About?* (New York: Random House, 1961), p. 5.

(You fill in the rest: when $t = 2$, $x = 16t^2 = 16 \cdot (2)^2$ = $16 \cdot$ _____ = _____, and similarly when $t = 3$, $x =$ $16 \cdot ($_____$)^2 = 16 \cdot$ _____ = _____, etc.) We can also draw a graph, as shown in Fig. 1-2.

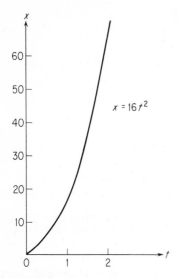

Figure 1-2

How far does the body fall during the first second? Of course, you get _____ − 0 feet, or _____ feet. You subtract the distance at the beginning of this time interval from the distance at the _____ of the interval. How far does the body fall during the second from $t = 1$ to $t = 2$? You subtract the value of x when $t = 1$ from the value of x when $t =$ _____:

$$\text{change in } x = \underline{\quad} - \underline{\quad} = \underline{\quad} \text{ feet.}$$

t	x	Change in x
0	0	
		16
1	16	
		48
2	64	
		80
3	_____	
		_____
4	_____	
		_____
5	_____	

The *average velocity* during any time interval is

$$\frac{\text{the distance traveled}}{\text{length of time interval}} = \frac{\text{change in } x}{\text{change in } t}.$$

The average velocity during the first second is

$$\frac{\text{change in } x}{\text{change in } t} = \frac{16}{1} = 16 \text{ feet per second.}$$

The average velocity during the time interval from $t = 2$ to $t = 3$ is

$$\frac{\text{change in } x}{\text{change in } t} = \frac{\rule{2em}{0.4pt}}{1} = \rule{2em}{0.4pt} \text{ feet per second.}$$

48, 48

   This will be only an approximation to the instantaneous velocity at $t = 2$, the velocity at the exact moment when $t = 2$. We will obtain a better approximation if we average the velocity over a shorter time interval, say from $t = 2$ to $t = 2.1$.
   The value of x when $t = 2.1$ is $16 \cdot (\rule{2em}{0.4pt})^2$. The distance fallen from $t = 2$ to $t = 2.1$ is the change in x, or $\rule{2em}{0.4pt} - 64 = \rule{2em}{0.4pt}$ feet. The length of the time interval is the change in t, or $2.1 - \rule{2em}{0.4pt} = \rule{2em}{0.4pt}$ sec. Therefore, the average velocity or distance traveled per unit time, or *change in x per unit change in t is*

2.1

70.56, 6.56
2, 0.1

$$\frac{\text{change in } x}{\text{change in } t} = \frac{\rule{2em}{0.4pt}}{0.1} = 65.6 \text{ feet per second.}$$

6.56

   We can obtain better and better approximations if we average over smaller and smaller time intervals, say from $t = 2$ to $t = 2.01$, or $t = 2.001$, and so on. We can make a table (you fill in the blanks):

Time interval from $t = 2$ to $t =$	Change in t	Change in x	Average velocity
3	1	80	80
2.1	0.1	_____	65.6
2.01	_____	0.6416	_____
2.001	_____	_____	_____
2.0001	_____	_____	_____
$2 + h$	h	_____	_____

   If you are shrewd, you will fill in the last line first! How will this help you?

Do you notice anything about the numbers in the last column? Do the average velocities seem to be approaching some definite number as the time interval becomes smaller and smaller? Can you make the average velocity over the interval from $t = 2$ to $t = 2 + h$ close to a certain number, simply by taking h to be very small? What is the instantaneous velocity when $t = 2$, i.e., at the end of 2 seconds?

We can calculate the instantaneous velocity at the end of 3 seconds in the same way. At $t = 3$, we know that $x = 16 \cdot 3^2$. After h seconds, $t = 3 + h$ and
$$x = 16(3 + h)^2.$$

The change in x is $16(3 + h)^2 - 16 \cdot 3^2$, in a time interval of h seconds. The average velocity is, then,

average velocity = change in x per unit change in t

$$= \frac{\text{change in } x}{\text{change in } t} = \frac{16(3 + h)^2 - 16 \cdot 3^2}{h} = \underline{} + 16h. \qquad \text{\textit{96}}$$

As h approaches 0, this average velocity approaches _____ feet per second. This is the instantaneous velocity at the time $t = 3$. $\qquad$ *96*

1.3.1
EXERCISES

1. Calculate the instantaneous velocity of the falling body at $t = 1$, $t = 4$, $t = 0$. (Assume that it falls from rest at $t = 0$.)

2. Make a table of the instantaneous velocity v at various times t:

t	v
0	—
1	—
2	—
3	—
4	—

The formula $v = $ _____ fits this table.

3. The distance x traveled by a body, starting from rest, rolling down an inclined plane is given by $x = 5t^2$. Calculate the velocity v at the times $t = 0, 1, 2, 3, 4$ and make a table. What formula for v fits this table?

4. The (instantaneous) velocity v of a body rolling down an inclined plane is $v = 3t$ at the time t. What is the (instantaneous) *acceleration* a, i.e., the rate of change of the velocity per unit time, at the time $t = 2$? At the time $t = 5$? At the time t?

5. The height y of a falling body at the time t is given by the formula

$$y = -16t^2 + 3t + 100.$$

(a) Find the velocity v at the time $t = 2$.

(b) Find the velocity at the times $t = 0, 1, 3, 4$, and make a table.

(c) Find a formula for the velocity v at the time t which fits the table.

If $x = 16t^2$, then we call the rate of change of x (in our physical interpretation, the velocity) *the derivative of x with respect to t.* We denote the value of this derivative at $t = 3$ by $x'(3)$ (read "x-prime of 3"). We found that $x'(3) = 96$. In Exercise 2 above you should have found that $x'(0) = 0$, $x'(1) = 32$, $x'(2) = 64$, $x'(3) = 96$, etc. In general, you should have found that $x'(t) =$ _____. At least this formula fits your table. | $32t$

Let us prove this formula. We wish to calculate the velocity at the time t. At the time t, we have $x = 16t^2$. At the time $t + h$, x is $16(t + h)^2$. So, if $h \neq 0$, we find that

$$\frac{\text{change in } x}{\text{change in } t} = \frac{16(t + h)^2 - 16t^2}{h} = \underline{} + 16h. \qquad 32t$$

As h approaches 0, this average rate of change approaches _____. This is the value of $x'(t)$, *the rate of change of x with respect to t.* Does this agree with your formula for v? | $32t$

Let us look at a geometrical problem. The volume V of a sphere of radius r is given by the formula

$$V = \frac{4\pi r^3}{3}.$$

What is the rate of change of V with respect to r? If you like, imagine an expanding spherical drop whose radius r is increasing at the rate of 1 inch per second. How fast is its volume increasing?

We use the same method as before. As the radius increases from r to $r + h$, V changes from $(4\pi/3)r^3$ to $(4\pi/3)(r + h)^3$. Therefore, we have

$$\frac{\text{change in } V}{\text{change in } t} = \frac{(4\pi/3)(r + h)^3 - (4\pi/3)r^3}{h}$$

$$= \frac{4\pi}{3}(\underline{} + 3rh + h^2). \qquad 3r^2$$

As h approaches 0, this average rate of change of V approaches _____. We find that the derivative of V with respect to r is given by | $4\pi r^2$

$$V'(r) = \underline{}. \qquad 4\pi r^2$$

In Exercise 4 above, we had $v = 3t$. What is the acceleration $a = v'(t)$? Again we apply the same reasoning. As the time changes from t to $t + h$, the velocity v changes from $3t$ to $3(t + h)$. Therefore we find

$$\frac{\text{change in } v}{\text{change in } t} = \frac{\rule{1cm}{0.4pt} - \rule{1cm}{0.4pt}}{h} = \rule{1cm}{0.4pt}.$$

$3(t + h),\ 3t,\ 3$

What does this ratio approach as h approaches 0? Amazing, isn't it? The average acceleration is already as close as any number can be to $v'(t)$! As h changes, it doesn't change at all!

1.3.2
EXERCISES

1. The acceleration of a falling body at the time t is $a = 32$ feet per second per second. What is $a'(t)$, the rate of change of the acceleration?

2. The total amount E ergs of energy radiated by a black body in an enclosure at absolute temperature T degrees is given by the formula

$$E = T^4 \qquad \text{(Stefan–Boltzmann law)}.$$

(The general formula is $E = aVT^4$, where V is the volume of the enclosure and $a = 7.6 \times 10^{-15}$ ergs per cc.) What is $E'(T)$, the rate of change of E with respect to T?

3. Work out $x'(t)$ when x and t are related by the equations $x = t^n$, $n = 0, 1, 2, 3, 4$, and tabulate your results:

x	$x'(t)$
1	——
t	——
t^2	——
t^3	——
t^4	——

Guess the formula for $x'(t)$ if $x = t^n$.

4. Find the derivative $x'(t)$ if
   (a) $x(t) = 5t^2$.
   (b) $x(t) = 7t^3$.
   (c) $x(t) = 5t^2 + 7t^3$.

5. The volume V of a perfect gas in a certain vessel at the pressure P and constant temperature is given by $V = 1/P$. Calculate $V'(P)$, the rate of change of volume with respect to pressure, and find a formula for the isothermal compressibility:

$$K = \frac{-V'(P)}{V},$$

which is the relative rate of change of volume with respect to pressure. As P increases (change in P positive), does V increase or decrease? Why is $V'(P)$ negative?

6. The volume V of a sphere of radius r is $V = \frac{4}{3}\pi r^3$. Find the volume of a spherical shell with inner radius r and outer radius $r + h$. Give a "good" approximate formula when h is small. How is this volume related to the surface area of the sphere? How is it related to $V'(r)$?

7. The area A of a circle of radius r is $A = \pi r^2$. Find $A'(r)$, the rate of change of A with respect to r. Lo and behold, $A'(r)$ is simply the _____ of the circle!

According to Newton's laws of motion, the force acting on a body is proportional to its acceleration:

$$F = ma,$$

where m is the mass of the body. For example, the gravitational force on a falling body of mass 1 kilogram is 9.8 newtons. So the acceleration a is

$$a = v'(t) = 9.8 \text{ meters/sec.}^2$$

We have reminded you that acceleration is the rate of change of velocity.

Here we have an equation involving a derivative. This is called a *differential equation.* The basic laws of physics, engineering, and most other branches of science are relations between rates of change, or derivatives, and so are expressed mathematically as differential equations. The fundamental problems in applied mathematics are problems of solving differential equations, finding what the quantities are when we know certain relations between their derivatives.

The finding of v from the differential equation

$$v'(t) = 9.8$$

is the simplest type of such problems. We have to find v at any time t, given the derivative $v'(t)$ in terms of t. The process of finding v is called *integration.* Differentiation and integration are the two main processes of calculus.

Do you know a quantity whose derivative is 9.8 for all t? Look at Exercises 3 and 4 in 1.3.2. If $v = at + b$, where a and b are constants, such as 3 or 7, what is $v'(t)$? For what values of a and b is $v'(t) = 9.8$ for all t? Do you have enough information to determine b?

Suppose that the initial velocity is 10 meters/sec., i.e., $v = 10$ when $t = 0$. Now can you determine b? Give the formula for v:

$$v = \underline{\quad\quad} t + \underline{\quad\quad}. \qquad\qquad\qquad 9.8, 10$$

What you have found is an *integral* of 9.8.

17

If x is the distance traveled by the falling body at time t, then $x'(t) = v$. Can you *integrate* your formula for v, and find x? At $t = 0$, the body has fallen 0 meters; so $x = 0$. Can you use this information to determine x in terms of t?

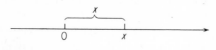

If we have a body moving along a line, and we let x be its distance from a fixed point at the time t, as shown in Fig. 1.3, then

Figure 1-3

$$x'(t) = v.$$

Similarly the acceleration a is the derivative of v:

$$v'(t) = a.$$

But, by Newton's law, $a = F/m$. We obtain a *system* of differential equations

$$x'(t) = v, \qquad v'(t) = \frac{F}{m}.$$

If the force F acting on the body at the time t is known, we can find the motion by solving this system of equations for x and v. For example, in simple harmonic motion, $F = -kx$, where k is a certain constant. In courses in calculus and differential equations, you learn how to solve equations like this.

1.3.3
EXERCISES

1. Find x if for all t
(a) $x'(t) = 1$.
(b) $x'(t) = 2t$.
(c) $x'(t) = 3t^2$.

(d) $x'(t) = 4t^3$.
(e) $x'(t) = t^3$.
(f) $x'(t) = t^n$.

2. Are the answers to Exercise 1 unique? In each case find solutions such that $x = 1$ when $t = 0$.

3. Solve the system of differential equations

$$x'(t) = v, \qquad v'(t) = 1,$$

given that $x = 0$ when $t = 0$ and when $t = 1$.

The equation $x = 16t^2$ defines a special type of *relation*. If $t = 3$, then $x = 16 \cdot 3^2 = 144$. No number other than 144 has this relation to the number 3; that is, if $t = 3$, then 144 is the only value of x for which $x = 16t^2$. In general, for each number t there is one and only one number x which is related to t in this way, namely $x = 16t^2$. We say that this equation defines x *as a function* of t. Note that if $x = 16$, then $t = \underline{\hspace{1.5em}}$ or $t = \underline{\hspace{1.5em}}$. For this value of x there are $\underline{\hspace{2em}}$ numbers t which have this relation to x. The given equation does *not* define t *as a function* of x.

1, −1

two

Differentiation and integration are processes which are applied to functions. When we differentiate the function defined by the equation $x = 16t^2$, we obtain the function defined by $v = x'(t) = 32t$. If we integrate the latter function, we obtain some function of the form $x = 16t^2 + C$, where C is a constant. To find out what C is, we must have more information.

We can represent relations between numbers graphically. Here we use a way of naming points by means of pairs of numbers. The graph of the relation $x = 16t^2$ is shown in Fig. 1-4. The points (3, 144), (0, 0) and ($\underline{\hspace{1.5em}}$, 16) lie on this graph. We can use this graphical representation to interpret algebraic problems

±1

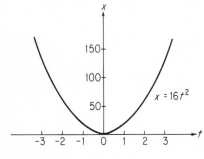

Figure 1-4

geometrically and geometrical problems algebraically. *Analytic geometry* is the branch of mathematics which deals with this relation between algebra and geometry.

Look back at the process of finding the derivative of the function defined by the equation $x = 16t^2$. At a crucial step, we calculated the average rate of change of x per unit change in t in the time interval from 3 to $3 + h$, and obtained

$$\frac{16(3 + h)^2 - 16 \cdot 3^2}{h} = 96 + 16h.$$

Then we asked, what number does this ratio approach as h approaches 0? We see that the difference between this number and 96 can be made as small as we please by taking h sufficiently small. Indeed, it differs from 96 by the amount $16h$. This difference will be numerically less than 0.001 if h is numerically less than $0.001/16 = 0.0000625$. You can make the difference less than 0.000001 by taking h numerically less than $\underline{\hspace{4em}}$.

0.0000000625

We express this fact by writing

$$\lim_{h \to 0} \frac{16(3 + h)^2 - 16 \cdot 3^2}{h} = 96.$$

(Read "the limit, as h approaches zero, of the quantity on the left is 96.")

19

We see that the concept of *limit* is basic to the process of differentiation. We can go pretty far in the study of the differentiation of elementary functions with only an intuitive idea of what a limit is; but if we wish to integrate even such a simple function as the one defined by the equation

$$x = \frac{1}{t},$$

we already run into more sophisticated problems. (Not all highways are quiet country roads.) For example, the solution of the problem of finding y such that

$$y'(t) = \frac{1}{t}, \qquad \text{and given that } y = 0 \text{ when } t = 1,$$

is

$$y = \lim_{n \to \infty} \left[\frac{t-1}{n+t-1} + \frac{t-1}{n+2(t-1)} + \cdots + \frac{t-1}{n+n(t-1)} \right].$$

This means that to calculate y for any given value of t, you must calculate this sum for larger and larger values of n, and find out what the numbers, computed in this way, approach. If t is greater than $\frac{1}{2}$, you can also calculate y by the somewhat simpler formula:

$$y = \lim_{n \to \infty} \left[\left(1 - \frac{1}{t}\right) + \frac{1}{2}\left(1 - \frac{1}{t}\right)^2 + \cdots + \frac{1}{n}\left(1 - \frac{1}{t}\right)^n \right].$$

It should be understood that solutions of such sophisticated problems are obtained by methods that are treated in a full-fledged calculus course. You are certainly not expected, at this stage, to see how they have been obtained.

In the theory of radioactive decay, we must solve the differential equation

$$x'(t) = -x, \qquad \text{given that } x = 1 \text{ when } t = 0.$$

The solution is given by the formula

$$x = \lim_{n \to \infty} \left[1 - t + \frac{t^2}{2} - \frac{t^3}{2 \cdot 3} + \cdots + \frac{(-1)^n t^n}{2 \cdot 3 \cdot 4 \cdot \ \cdots \ \cdot n} \right].$$

For example, when $t = -1$, you obtain x by calculating the sums

$$1, \quad 1 + 1, \quad 1 + 1 + \frac{1}{2}, \quad 1 + 1 + \frac{1}{2} + \frac{1}{2 \cdot 3}, \quad \text{etc.,}$$

and finding what number these sums approach as we take more and more terms. The answer is 2.71828182845904523536..., but, of course, we seldom need the value to twenty decimal places! (This number, usually designated by the letter "e," is one of the two most important special numbers in mathematics, the other being π.)

In our elementary example it was quite obvious that the numbers $96 + 16h$ do approach a limit as h approaches 0, and the limit was also obvious. In the other examples it is not obvious what the limit is, and it is not even clear that the numbers approach some definite value.

In most of the scientific problems that are solved on digital computers you need to calculate limits of sequences like those of the last two examples. In a problem like the last one, you would stop at a certain value of n, say $n = 10$ or $n = 100{,}000$ because your machine can't run forever. So you would commit an error, and you must estimate this error. You may want to estimate how the error depends on n, so that you can tell your electronic slave how large to choose n to make the error small enough for your particular purpose.

Therefore, it is important to master the concept of limit. Calculus is part of *analysis*, the branch of mathematics which deals with limit processes in general. Our prelude has as its aim to outfit you with the mathematical background necessary to launch into calculus. Thus, one of our principal goals is to give you an understanding of the notion of limit. However, you will discover that you can't really understand the limit concept without making a fundamental study of the number system.

In our work we use mostly the *real numbers*. A convenient way to picture the real numbers is to consider them as corresponding to points on a line in such a way that there is one real number for each point and one point for each real number, and equal differences between numbers correspond to equal distances between points (Fig. 1-5).

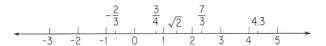

Figure 1-5

There are four basic *operations* on real numbers: addition $(+)$, subtraction $(-)$, multiplication $(\cdot)$, and division $(/)$.

These operations obey the following fundamental laws:

commutative laws:

$$a + b = b + a, \qquad a \cdot b = b \cdot a;$$

associative laws:

$$(a + b) + c = a + (b + c),$$
$$(a \cdot b) \cdot c = a \cdot (b \cdot c);$$

21

distributive laws:

$$a \cdot (b + c) = (a \cdot b) + (a \cdot c),$$

$$(b + c) \cdot a = (b \cdot a) + (c \cdot a);$$

laws of inverse operations:

$$a + (b - a) = b, \qquad a \cdot (b/a) = b \qquad \text{if } a \neq 0;$$

properties of 0 *and* 1 :

$$a + 0 = a, \qquad a \cdot 1 = a, \qquad a \cdot 0 = 0.$$

The real numbers have an *order*. We denote the relation "*a* is less than *b*" by "$a < b$." This order relation has the properties:
Trichotomy (or *linearity*):

$$\text{either } a = b \text{ or } a < b \text{ or } b < a;$$

irreflexitivity:

$$\text{it is false that } a < a;$$

transitivity:

$$\text{if } a < b \text{ and } b < c, \text{ then } a < c.$$

The basic operations are related to the ordering by the following:

if $a < b$, then $a + c < b + c$;

if $a < b$ and $0 < c$, then $a \cdot c < b \cdot c$.

Our main themes are, then,

1. the real numbers and their properties;
2. the relations between algebra and geometry;
3. the limit concept;
4. mathematics and the sciences.

You will see how important scientific problems lead to mathematical questions. You will study how mathematicians attack these questions. You will discover the power of fundamental theory by applying it, not only to the scientific problem you started with, but also to apparently unrelated problems.

We can't promise you an easy time with all this. On the contrary, we can promise you a strenuous life, and an exciting one! In fact, our subject is so fascinating that only the most extreme incompetence on our part can make it seem dull.

1.3.4

EXERCISES

1. Compute the real numbers, to three decimal places,

$$\left(1 - \frac{1}{t}\right) + \frac{1}{2}\left(1 - \frac{1}{t}\right)^2 + \frac{1}{3}\left(1 - \frac{1}{t}\right)^3 + \cdots + \frac{1}{n}\left(1 - \frac{1}{t}\right)^n$$

for $t = 10/11$, for $n = 1, 2, 3, 4$, and 5. Do these numbers appear to be approaching some definite number as n increases?

2. A convenient way to arrange your work for the computation of e is to write

$$1 + 1 = \qquad\qquad\qquad 2.0000000000,$$

$$1/2 = \qquad\qquad\qquad 0.5000000000,$$

$$1/(2 \cdot 3) = (1/3)(0.5) = \qquad\qquad 0.1666666667,$$

$$1/(2 \cdot 3) \cdot 4 = (1/4)(0.1666666667) = \underline{\qquad\qquad},$$

and so on. Continue the computation and add the successive terms. Do the sums appear to approach a definite number as you add more and more of these numbers?

3. Let $x_0 = 1$, and

$$x_{n+1} = \frac{1}{1 + x_n} \qquad \text{for } n = 0, 1, 2, 3, \ldots.$$

Then

$$x_1 = \frac{1}{1 + x_0} = \frac{1}{1 + 1} = \frac{1}{2} = 0.5,$$

$$x_2 = \frac{1}{1 + x_1} = \frac{1}{1 + \frac{1}{2}} = \frac{2}{3} = 0.6667, \quad \text{etc.}$$

Compute x_n for $n = 3, 4, 5$, and 6. Do the numbers x_n appear to be approaching a limit? Compute $x_n^2 + x_n$ for $n = 0, 1, 2, 3, 4, 5$, and 6. What do you notice? Guess the exact value of $x = \lim_{n \to \infty} x_n$.

4. Let $x_0 = 1$, and

$$x_{n+1} = 1 + \frac{1}{1 + x_n} \qquad \text{for } n = 0, 1, 2, 3, \ldots.$$

Compute x_n and x_n^2 for $n \leq 6$. Does x_n seem to be approaching a limit? Guess the value of this limit.

5. Choose any value you like for x_0, and compute x_n for $n \leq 6$, where

$$x_{n+1} = 1 - 0.1x_n, \qquad \text{for } n = 0, 1, 2, \ldots.$$

What do the numbers x_n seem to approach? How can you choose x_0 so that $x_1 = x_0$?

6. Choose x_0 and y_0 to be any numbers you like between -8 and 8. Define x_n and y_n by the equations

$$x_{n+1} = \frac{1 + y_n}{2}, \quad y_{n+1} = -1 - 0.1x_ny_n, \quad \text{for } n = 0, 1, 2, \ldots.$$

Compute x_n and y_n for $n \le 6$. Do these numbers appear to approach limits as n increases? Guess at the exact values of the limits.

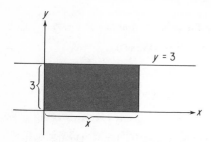

y = 3

Figure 1-6

7. (a) What is the area A of the shaded region in Fig. 1-6? What is the change in A if the change in x is 1? 0.1? 0.05?

(b) Find a formula for the rate of change of A with respect to x.

(c) Exhibit the relation between A and x on a graph, using the horizontal axis to denote x. (This graph would be *the graph of A as a function of x*.)

8. (a) What is the area of the shaded region in Fig. 1-7? How much does A change if x increases from 1 to 2? from 10 to 11? from 100 to 101?

(b) Find the change in A if x changes from:

1 to 1.5,

1 to 1.01,

1 to 1.000001.

(c) Exhibit the relation between A and x on a graph. That is, sketch the graph of A as a function of x.

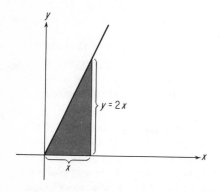

y = 2x

Figure 1-7

9. (a) Let y be a function of x. We are going to define a sequence of values of y:

$$y_0, y_1, y_2, \ldots,$$

in terms of a sequence of values of x:

$$x_0, x_1, x_2, \ldots.$$

Let $x_0 = 0$, $x_1 = 0.1$, $x_2 = 0.2, \ldots, x_n = n/10, \ldots.$ We take the average rate of change in y from x_0 to x_1 equal to 1, the average rate of change in y from x_1 to x_2 equal to 1, and so on. Then

$$\frac{y_1 - y_0}{x_1 - x_0} = 1,$$

$$\frac{y_2 - y_1}{x_2 - x_1} = 1, \quad \text{etc.}$$

Begin with $y_0 = 0$ and compute y_1, y_2, y_3, ... Then plot on graph paper $(0, y_0)$, $(0.1, y_1)$, $(0.2, y_2)$, etc. What do you notice about the graph? How does your result change if you start with $y_0 = 0.3$?

(b) Suppose, as in (a), that $y_0 = 0$ and $x_0 = 0$, $x_1 = 0.1$, $x_2 = 0.2$, ... Suppose, also, that the average change in y from x_n to x_{n+1} equals $2x_{n+1}$. Compute y_1, y_2, y_3, etc., and graph the points (x_0, y_0), (x_1, y_1), (x_2, y_2), etc. How does your result change if x increases by steps of 0.05?

(c) Compare the graphs of this exercise with the graph of A as a function of x in Exercise 8. What do you notice?

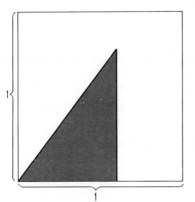

10. Consider the square in Fig. 1-8 as a target for dart throwing, and suppose you throw darts randomly, i.e., in such a way that you have equal chances of hitting any two parts of equal area. If you throw the dart 3000 times, what would you predict about the frequency of hitting the lower half of this square? Predict the frequency of the dart hitting the shaded area ($\frac{1}{3}$ sq. in.) in 3000 throws.

Figure 1-8

Exercise 10 suggests that the laws of chance (the theory of probability) may be viewed through a consideration of area. In relatively recent years scientists have reversed the picture by utilizing the laws of chance to determine areas! (The dart-throwing problem is an illustration of the application of the so-called *Monte Carlo* method.)

As you've probably discovered from some of the above exercises, the theory of area provides a geometric interpretation of integration. Now we see that probability theory also provides an interpretation of integration. (The relation between probability and integration is a product of the research of only the past half-century.) Thus, there is a strong interconnection between the theories of *area*, *integration*, and *probability*; any knowledge in one of these studies can be applied in the other two.

1.4

Examples of Deductive Sciences   Throughout the book we are going to use the idea of a scale on a line. That is, we shall think of the line as a *map* of the real number system. In this map we assume that each real number corresponds to one and only one point on the line. That is, to each real number there corresponds exactly one point, which we call its *image*; and each point is the image of exactly one number. A scale on a line is an example of a *one-to-one mapping* of the set of all real numbers onto the set of all points on the line.

Figure 1-9

A scale of the sort that is seen on an ordinary ruler is shown in Fig. 1-9. In this mapping, the order relation *"is less than"* between numbers corresponds to the order relation *"is to the left of"* between points. In other words, if a and b are numbers, and A and B are their respective images on the line, then

$$a < b \qquad (a \text{ is less than } b)$$

if and only if

$$A \text{ is to the left of } B.$$

You are probably so accustomed to using this kind of a scale that the mapping may seem trivial. It may even be difficult for you to see which properties of order are important because many of them are intuitively obvious. However, when we deal with a new situation we are often forced to rethink some of our most fundamental ideas. We take an example from social science, which is concerned with the notion of order. The problem is that of the meaning of *utility* in economics. While this is an old problem, it is still under investigation by leading economists and mathematicians. Similar problems also arise in psychology, political science, statistics, and military strategy.

Imagine that you are at a market. You have a certain set $\mathscr{C}$ of choices open to you—a dozen oranges, two dozen oranges, a pound of caviar, a shoeshine, a thousand shares of Uranium Unlimited, a freighter trip to Paris, France, a deluxe flight to Paris, Kentucky, a half dozen bagels, a pound of lox, a lox and bagel sandwich, a Rembrandt painting, an Irish Sweepstakes ticket, a pin-up photograph, and so on. If a and b are elements of $\mathscr{C}$, then you may *prefer b to a*. We shall denote this relation by

$$aRb.$$

If you do not prefer b to a, then we shall express this relation by

$$a\mathcal{R}b.$$

If aRb and bRa, then it is *indifferent* to you whether you get a or b. If a is a five-dollar bill, then presumably you would be willing to pay five dollars for b.

While we can make some fairly crude economic analysis working only with the preference relation *R*, we can make available the tremendous machinery of mathematical analysis if we can describe preferences in terms of *utility* (to you at that moment):

aRb if and only if a has less utility than b.

We should like to associate with each choice *a* in $\mathscr{C}$ a unique number $U(a)$, the utility of *a*, in such a way that

(1) aRb if and only if $U(a) < U(b)$.

In other words, we should like to map the set $\mathscr{C}$ of choices into the set of numbers in such a way that your preference relation corresponds to the "is less than" relation between numbers. (Since, as mentioned above, we have a one-to-one correspondence between numbers and points on a line, we can also think of the utilities as points on a line.) A mapping of this kind, of choices into numbers, is called a *utility function*.

We can find out what your preference relation is by offering to you all possible pairs of choices *a* and *b*, in the set $\mathscr{C}$, and seeing which you prefer. How can we tell whether it is possible to represent your preferences by numeral utilities?

Suppose that *aRb* and *bRa*, and that $U(a) = 5$. What can $U(b)$ be? Consider the possibilities:

If $5 = U(a) < U(b)$, then what conclusion can you draw from (1)? Can $U(b)$ be greater than 5?
If $U(b) < 5 = U(a)$, what conclusion can you draw?
What number is neither less than nor greater than 5? What must $U(b)$ be?

If *x* and *y* are any real numbers, what possibility is there other than

(2) $x < y,$ $x = y,$ or $x > y$?

How must the utilities of indifferent choices be related?

If *aRb*, can *bRa*? If *aRb*, then how must the utilities of *a* and *b* be related? If *x* and *y* are real numbers, is it possible that both $x < y$ and $y < x$? In fact, can more than one of the alternatives in (2) be true? Is it possible that *aRa*? What would this imply about $U(a)$?

If *aRb* and *bRc*, then what is your preference between *a* and *c*? Let us see what the hypotheses imply about the utilities $U(a)$, $U(b)$, and $U(c)$:

If *aRb*, then $U(a)$ _____ $U(b)$.	<
If *bRc*, then $U(b)$ _____ $U(c)$.	<
If *x*, *y*, and *z* are numbers such that $x < y$ and $y < z$, then $x(< / = / >)z$.	<

Therefore, if aRb and bRc, then $U(a)$ _____ $U(c)$. $\begin{matrix} < \\ R \end{matrix}$
But if this is so, then a _____ c.

By answering the above questions you have discovered some *necessary* conditions on your preferences that they may be described by numerical utilities. You have shown that *if* there is a utility function, *then* your preference relation R *must* satisfy certain conditions:

P_1. If a is in $\mathscr{C}$, then a _____ a. R
P_2. If aRb, then b _____ a. R
P_3. If aRb and bRc, then a _____ c. R

These conditions are not *sufficient*. That is, if a preference relation R among the choices in $\mathscr{C}$ satisfies the conditions P_1, P_2, and P_3 *we do not have sufficient* reason to conclude that the preferences may be described by numerical utilities. For let us suppose that your choices are represented by ordered pairs (t, p), where t is any nonnegative number and p is a nonnegative integer (whole number). The choice (t, p) means the combination of t hours alone with your sweetheart, together with p peanuts. Let us suppose that an extra moment with your sweetheart means more to you than any number of peanuts but that given equal times with your sweetheart, the more peanuts you have the better you like it. Then your preference relation is defined by

(3) $(t_1, p_1)R(t_2, p_2)$ if and only if $t_1 < t_2$ or $t_1 = t_2$ and $p_1 < p_2$.

Then it is impossible to define a utility function which satisfies (1)! Do you know why?

But our young sons feel the same way about tricycles as you do about time with your sweetheart. If their choices are represented by ordered pairs (t, p) of nonnegative integers (fractional parts of tricycles are meaningless), then their preference relation is also defined by (3). Our sons' preferences can be described by the utility function

(4) $U(t, p) = t - \dfrac{1}{p + 2}.$

Using this function we can map their preferences into a line in such a way that the relation of preference between choices corresponds to the relation "is to left of" between points, as in Fig. 1-10. The figure indicates some choices above the line, and the corresponding utilities on the scale below the line.

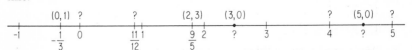

Figure 1-10

1. Calculate $U(0, 2)$, $U(0, 3)$, $U(0, 4)$, ..., $U(2, 0)$, $U(3, 0)$, $U(4, 0)$, ... from formula (4) above. Check that this utility function satisfies (1) in these cases. Mark the corresponding points on the above scale.

2. Show that the utility function $U(t, p) = 2t + p/(p + 1)$ also fits our sons' preferences. If a utility function exists, is it unique?

3. Suppose that your choices are represented by ordered pairs (t, p) of a nonnegative number t and a nonnegative integer p. Now (t, p) represents a package deal of t tons of chocolate-covered ants and p peanuts. We assume that your preference relation R is defined by

$$(t_1, p_1)R(t_2, p_2) \text{ if and only if } p_1 < p_2 \text{ or } p_1 = p_2 \text{ and } t_1 < t_2.$$

Define a utility function which satisfies (1).

4. A society $\mathcal{S}$ has a set of $\mathcal{C}$ choices before it. Each individual i in $\mathcal{S}$ has a preference relation R_i among the choices. We define the society's preference relation $R_{\mathcal{S}}$ by majority rule:

$$aR_{\mathcal{S}}b \text{ if and only if } aR_i b \text{ for a majority of individuals } i \text{ in } \mathcal{S}.$$

Consider the situation where $\mathcal{S}$ has five members, denoted by 1, 2, 3, 4, 5, and $\mathcal{C}$ has three members, denoted by A, B, and C. The individual preferences are defined by

$$1: \text{ABC},$$
$$2: \text{ABC},$$
$$3: \text{BCA},$$
$$4: \text{CAB},$$
$$5: \text{CAB}.$$

(The first line means that AR_1B, BR_1C, and, of course, that AR_1C.) In the following table check ($\times$) the square in the A-row, B-column, if and only if $AR_{\mathcal{S}}B$. Similarly work out the rest of the table.

$R_{\mathcal{S}}$	A	B	C
A			
B			
C			

Does the relation $R_{\mathcal{S}}$ satisfy the conditions P_1–P_3? The situation described in this problem is an example of the so-called *Voters' Paradox*. Can you explain the reason for this name?

5. A psychologist wishes to measure strength of preference for tail-fins on cars. He asks a series of ten questions, for each of which the answer "yes" indicates a favorable attitude toward tail-fins. The relation *aPb* (read "*b* prefers tail-fins more strongly than *a*") is defined by:

aPb if and only if *b* answers "yes" whenever *a* does, but not conversely.

Under what condition can one set up a numerical scale for strength of preferences [i.e., an assignment of a number $S(a)$ to each individual a, measuring how strongly a prefers tail-fins] so that

$$aPb \text{ if and only if } S(a) < S(b)?$$

In our preliminary study of utility, we have run into the following properties of the order of points on the line:

P_1. If a is in $\mathscr{S}$, then $a\mathcal{R}a$.

P_2. If a and b are in $\mathscr{S}$, and aRb, then $b\mathcal{R}a$.

P_3. If a, b, and c are in $\mathscr{S}$, and aRb and bRc, then aRc.

P_4. If a and b are in $\mathscr{S}$, then aRb or $a = b$ or bRa. [NOTE: "$a = b$" is taken to mean "a is the same element as b" i.e., "'a' and 'b' are names for the same element."]

These statements are true if $\mathscr{S}$ is the set of all points on a line, and "aRb" means "a is to the left of b." But they are also true if $\mathscr{S}$ is the set of all real numbers and "aRb" means "$a < b$." Which of these properties hold if $\mathscr{S}$ is the set of all choices before you, and "aRb" means "you prefer b to a"? Which of these hold if your preferences can be represented by a utility function?

We say that the set $\mathscr{S}$ is *linearly ordered* with respect to the relation R if P_1–P_4 are true. Thus the set of points on a line is linearly ordered with respect to the relation "is to the left of." The set of all real numbers is linearly ordered with respect to the relation "is less than ($<$)."

The theory of linear order is an example of a deductive science. We can take $\mathscr{S}$ and R to be *undefined*, and assume P_1–P_4 as postulates. This constitutes the primitive frame. We can prove various propositions, or theorems, by logical reasoning from postulates P_1–P_4 alone. Anything we prove in this way applies immediately to any particular example of a set $\mathscr{S}$ linearly ordered with respect to a relation R. Thus, in one fell swoop, we obtain results both for the order of points on a line and for order among numbers.

We don't need to know what $\mathscr{S}$ and R are in developing this theory. The concrete intepretations which we have in mind often suggest to us what theorems may be interesting or useful.

The two interpretations in which we are, at the moment, most interested, the points on a line and the real numbers, have the same abstract structure. That is, there is a one-to-one correspondence between these two sets (see p. 26) in such a way that the ordering is preserved:

If the number a corresponds to the point A and the number b to the point B, then $a < b$ if and only if A is to the left of B.

The set of positive integers, $\{1, 2, 3, \ldots\}$, is also linearly ordered with respect to the relation $<$. But it has quite a different structure from the set of points on a line and the set of real numbers. The easiest way to see this is to notice some other properties of these sets:

P_5. If a and b are in $\mathscr{S}$ and aRb, then there is a c in $\mathscr{S}$ such that aRc and cRb.

P_6. There is an a in $\mathscr{S}$ such that for any b in $\mathscr{S}$ other than a, we have aRb.

Which of these properties holds for the set of all real numbers? Which holds for the set of positive integers?

Just as in biology, for example, we cannot appreciate the functions of the lung or the liver properly until we compare these organs in different animals, so we cannot understand the significance of such properties as having a first element until we compare various ways of ordering sets. Before we go further we need to assemble a little collection of specimens—ordering relations and properties.

1.4.2
EXERCISES

Imagine that the following are paths to be traversed, in directions indicated by the arrows. For any of these paths, we define aRb, where a and b are points, to mean that the point b can be reached, starting from the point a and *moving* in permitted directions. [NOTE: "Moving" implies that bRb for every b in $\mathscr{S}$, in (a).]

(a) A straight line (extending indefinitely far in both directions).

(b) A closed line segment (endpoints included).

(c) An open line segment (endpoints excluded).

(d) A forked road.

(e) Two parallel lines.

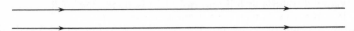

(f) A line with a loop.

(g) A path with branches.

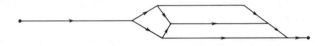

(h) A discrete finite set. (In discrete sets, a "path" means a "path of stepping stones.")

(i) A discrete infinite set.

(j) A half-open segment (initial point excluded, endpoint included).

(k) Another half-open segment.

(l) A line with gaps.

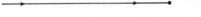

(m) A ray (endpoint included, extending indefinitely far to the left).

(n) A half-line [obtained from ray (m) by omitting the endpoint].

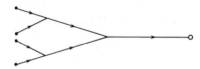

(o) Another path with branches.

Here is a list of properties:

P_1–P_6. As above.
P_7. There is an a in $\mathscr{S}$ such that bRa for any b in $\mathscr{S}$ other than a.

P_8. If a is in $\mathscr{S}$, then there is a b in $\mathscr{S}$ such that aRb.
P_9. If a is in $\mathscr{S}$, then there is a b in $\mathscr{S}$ such that bRa.
P_{10}. If a is in $\mathscr{S}$, then there is a b in $\mathscr{S}$ such that
    (i) aRb and
    (ii) bRc for any c in $\mathscr{S}$ such that aRc and $b \neq c$.
P_{11}. If a is in $\mathscr{S}$, then there is a b in $\mathscr{S}$ such that
    (i) bRa and
    (ii) cRb for any c in $\mathscr{S}$ such that cRa and $c \neq b$.
P_{12}. If a and b are in $\mathscr{S}$, then there is a c in $\mathscr{S}$ such that aRc and bRc.
P_{13}. If a and b are in $\mathscr{S}$, then there is a d in $\mathscr{S}$ such that dRa and dRb.
P_{14}. If a and b are in $\mathscr{S}$, then there is a c in $\mathscr{S}$ such that
    (i) aRc and bRc, and
    (ii) cRd for any d in $\mathscr{S}$ such that aRd, bRd, and $c \neq d$.
P_{15}. If a and b are in $\mathscr{S}$, then there is a c in $\mathscr{S}$ such that
    (i) cRa and cRb and
    (ii) dRc for any d in $\mathscr{S}$ such that dRa, dRb, and $d \neq c$.

1. Make a table showing which of properties P_1–P_{15} hold for the various examples (a)–(o):

	P_1	P_2	$\cdots$	P_{15}
(a)				
(b)				
.				
.				
.				
(o)				

Check off the properties which hold in these examples.

2. Show that the above properties are not *independent*. That is:
    (a) Prove P_1 from P_2.
    (b) Prove P_2 from P_1 and P_3. (What happens if aRb and bRa?)

3. Can a relation R have properties P_2, P_5, and P_{10}?

4. Prove that if the set $\mathscr{S}$ is linearly ordered with respect to the relation R, and $\mathscr{S}_1$ is a subset of $\mathscr{S}$ containing three elements, then $\mathscr{S}_1$ is also linearly ordered with respect to R, and satisfies P_6 as well.

Here are some other examples of relations:

    (p) $\mathscr{S}$ is the set of ordered pairs of nonnegative numbers (x, y), representing commodity packages such as x pounds of butter and y guns. We define

$$(x, y) \leq (x_1, y_1) \text{ if and only if } x \leq x_1 \text{ and } y \leq y_1.$$

(q) $\mathscr{S}$ is the set of all events occurring on a straight line, an event being represented by an ordered pair of numbers (x, t) indicating the place and time. In relativity theory, the event (x_1, t_1) is *simultaneous with* or in the *absolute future* of (x, t) if a light signal emitted at (x, t) reaches x_1 at a time before or equal to t_1. This is described by the relation

$$(x, t)R(x_1, t_1) \text{ if and only if } t \leq t_1 \text{ and } c^2(t_1 - t)^2 - (x_1 - x)^2 \geq 0,$$

where c is the speed of light.

(r) $\mathscr{S}$ is the set of all integral divisors of 30 (e.g., 1, 2, 3, 30). aRb if and only if a *divides* b, i.e., b/a is an integer.

(s) $\mathscr{S}$ is the set of all subsets of $\{1, 2, 3\}$. aRb means that a is included in b.

(t) $\mathscr{S}$ is the set of all integral divisors of 36. aRb if and only if a divides b.

5. Extend the table of Exercise 1 by checking which of properties P_1–P_{15} hold for the relations defined in examples (p)–(t).

6. In many important cases we deal with a *partially ordered* set. The set $\mathscr{S}$ is partially ordered with respect to the relation R if the following are true:

P_3 above, and
P_{16}. If a is in $\mathscr{S}$, then aRa. (Reflexivity.)

Notice that P_4 need not hold. You may think of the $\leq$ relation among numbers as typical.

Which of the above examples (a)–(t) are partially ordered with respect to the given relation?

7. In many partially ordered sets R has the additional property:

P_{17}. If a and b are in $\mathscr{S}$ and aRb and bRa, then $a = b$. (Antisymmetry.)

For which of the examples (a)–(t) does property P_{17} hold?

8. Prove that if $\mathscr{S}$ is linearly ordered with respect to R and if the relation R_1 is defined by

$$aR_1b \text{ if and only if } aRb \text{ or } a = b,$$

then $\mathscr{S}$ is partially ordered with respect to R_1.

9. Prove that if $\mathscr{S}$ is partially ordered with respect to R and properties P_4 and P_{17} hold, and if the relation R_2 is defined by

$$aR_2b \text{ if and only if } aRb \text{ and } a \neq b,$$

then $\mathscr{S}$ is linearly ordered with respect to R_2.

10. (a) Give an example of a partially ordered set that is not linearly ordered.
(b) Given an example of a partially ordered set that does not satisfy P_{17}.

Concluding Note on the Utility Problem

Recent contributions by mathematicians and economists have partially solved the problem of the existence of utility functions.

Professor Gerard Debreu discovered conditions under which there exists a mapping (utility function) of a linearly ordered set into the real numbers, preserving order:

$$aRb \text{ if and only if } U(a) < U(b).$$

While his conditions are quite simple, they involve concepts to be introduced later. Debreu has also found interesting conditions under which a numerical utility function does not exist!

The order-preserving mapping, whose existence was established by Debreu, is not unique. However, von Neumann and Morgenstern, in their earlier-mentioned classic work, investigating certain kinds of preference relations, found conditions under which these can be described by an essentially unique utility function. This result, to be understood, requires a knowledge of the theory of probability.

Chapter Two **The Real Number Line** *Relying somewhat on the reader's experience with real numbers and elementary geometry, the chapter begins a description of the real number system. The process of constructing a scale acts as a vehicle for assigning numbers (co-ordinates) to points. Integers are discussed in Sec. 2.2 and rational numbers in Sec. 2.3. In Sec. 2.4, the reader will learn how to prove that a host of numbers is irrational. Section 2.8 then introduces a geometric postulate that provides the basis for constructing a real number scale on a line. Section 2.6 returns to the notion of linear order of the real numbers and the associated geometric order on the real number line. In the course of the development to this point, the reader will encounter the concept of* absolute value, *which finds application to the notion of* distance. *The chapter closes with a short treatment of the change of coordinate systems on a given line. This treatment provides the first (*explicit*) return to the concept of* function; *it also applies the ideas of order and distance of earlier sections and introduces the new concept of directed distance.*

36

2.1

Descartes' Brainstorm   There is a story to the effect that the great French philosopher-mathematician, René Descartes (1596–1650), didn't like to get up in the morning. He would lie awake in bed for hours trying to stir up enough energy to get out of bed. But while lying awake, he didn't daydream idly; he usually thought to some purpose.

One morning, as he was staring at one corner of the room, a great idea suddenly came to him. "If I know how far my shoes are from the west wall and the south wall of the room, then I can locate the position of my shoes on the floor precisely. In fact, if I know how far a point is from the ceiling and each of the two walls, then I can locate the point exactly. To each point in the room there is a triple of numbers, and to each triple of numbers there is a point." Thus, Descartes realized that he could translate geometrical ideas into algebraic relations, which would enable him to solve geometrical problems algebraically. The story continues that he was so excited by the inspiration that he hopped out of bed and wrote it all down. And this was said to be the beginning of *analytic geometry*.

2.2

The Number Line; Integers   The basic step in the process of describing positions of points by number triples is that of setting up a scale on a line, i.e., a one-to-one correspondence between numbers and the points on a line. We discussed this briefly in Sec. 1.4, where you saw that there are many ways to set up a scale. A few examples are given in Fig. 2-1.

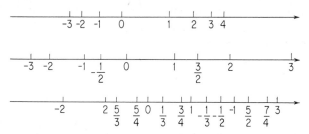

Figure 2-1

You may not like these scales, partly because you have been thoroughly indoctrinated with a certain special type of scale. The kind you have used since childhood is constructed according to the principle:

(1)   *equal distances correspond to equal differences.*

Since this type of scale is most useful (e.g., ruler, thermometer) we shall discuss it first, but be aware that it is not the only one which has practical value.

On the given line we choose some point, label it "0," and call it the *origin*. Then we choose another point on the line and label it "1." This serves two purposes: the distance between the two points gives us a *unit of length*, and the direction from "0" to "1," which we call the *positive direction*, gives an *orientation* of the line. The choice of points labeled "0" and "1" is arbitrary, but, once made, firmly fixes the *unit* and the *positive direction* on the number line. We are now prepared to make use of principle (1).

We lay off our unit distance successively, starting at "0," and in the positive direction (from "0" to "1"). We label these points "2," "3," and "4," etc., since $2 - 1 = 3 - 2 = \ldots = 1 - 0$. Similarly, starting at "0," we lay off our unit distance successively in the *negative direction*, from "1" to "0." We label these points "-1," "-2," "-3," etc., as shown in Fig. 2-2, since $0 - (-1) = (-1) - \underline{\hspace{1cm}} = \underline{\hspace{1cm}} - (-3) = \ldots = 1 - 0$ (fill in the blanks). So far we have marked on the scale only the points which correspond to the *integers*.

Figure 2-2

Note that in the preceding paragraph we said "the point '0'" when we meant "the point labeled '0'" and "starting at '0'" when we meant "starting at the point labeled '0'." These conveniences of language, while introducing some inaccuracy, make life simpler without serious sacrifice. If it is really necessary to distinguish between the point and its label, and if the context does not make it absolutely clear, we will exert the effort necessary to make the language precise.

2.2.1
EXERCISES

1. Explain how to perform addition and subtraction of integers geometrically, by using the scale above (Fig. 2-2) and a compass.

2. On the same sheet of paper draw two parallel lines. On each mark off a scale as we just did. Draw the lines joining

the point 0 on the first line to the point 0 on the second.
the point 1 on the first line to the point 2 on the second.
the point 2 on the first line to the point 4 on the second.
the point a on the first line to the point $2a$ on the second.

What do you notice about the intersection(s) of these lines (extended, if necessary)? How could you use this pair of scales to multiply by 2 geometrically?

3. Give a geometrical method for multiplying by m, where m is any integer (positive, negative, or 0).

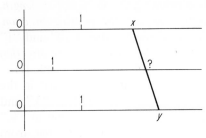

Figure 2-3

4. Draw three equally spaced parallel lines and a line perpendicular to them (see Fig. 2-3). Mark off scales on the three lines, taking as the 0 points the intersections with the perpendicular. Take equal units of length on the two outer lines, but take half this distance as the unit of length on the middle line. Take any two points x and y on the outer lines. Where (what is the label of the point?) does the line joining them intersect the middle line? How can you use these scales to perform addition and subtraction geometrically?

5. Let the symbol "$\square$" stand for some operation. For which of the interpretations of $\square$, as $+$, $-$, $\cdot$, or $\div$, is the following statement true for all a and b?

If a and b are integers, then $a \square b$ is an integer.

2.3
Rationals on the Number Line   So far we have shown how to identify the points on the line which are to correspond to the integers. To put it in another way, we are trying to set up a one-to-one correspondence between the points on a line and numbers, and we have carried this out for a certain *subset* of the points on the line.

Which point on the line should be labeled "$\frac{1}{2}$"? We can use our principle that *equal distances correspond to equal differences*. Since $\frac{1}{2} - 0 = 1 - \frac{1}{2}$, the point $\frac{1}{2}$ must be equidistant from the points 0 and 1. Which point on the line is equidistant from 0 and 1?

Mark off on your scale the points $\frac{1}{2}, \frac{3}{2}, \frac{5}{2}, \frac{7}{2}, \frac{1}{4}, \frac{1}{8}$.

Which point should be labeled $\frac{1}{3}$? We apply our basic principle, using the relation:

$$\tfrac{1}{3} - 0 = \tfrac{2}{3} - \tfrac{1}{3} = 1 - \tfrac{2}{3}.$$

We must divide the segment from 0 to 1 into three parts of equal length. How can we do it?

2.3.1
EXERCISES

1. Draw a line L and mark points 0 and 1 on it. Draw a second line M through 0, and choose another point A on M. Then lay off on M, in the direction from 0 to A, points B and C so that the distances from A to B and from B to C are the same as the distance from 0 to A. Draw the line joining C to 1. Draw lines through A and B parallel to this last line.

Recall a theorem from your high school geometry:

> *If three or more parallel lines cut off equal distances on one transversal, then they* ——————————————— *on any other transversal.* (*Fill in the blank*.)

Where do the parallels through A and B intersect the line L from 0 to 1? Mark these points with the appropriate numbers.

2. Describe straight-edge and compass constructions to locate the points $\frac{2}{5}$, $-\frac{3}{4}$, $\frac{5}{3}$, and 1.2 on L.

3. (a) Explain another method (construction) for locating the points $\frac{1}{4}$, $\frac{1}{8}$, and, in general, $1/2^n$, where n is any positive integer.

(b) How would you locate the points $m/2^n$, where m is any integer and n is any positive integer? What about the points $m/2^n$, where m is any integer and n a non-positive integer?

You can apply the methods of the last set of exercises to locate the point of L corresponding to any number which can be represented by a fraction m/n, where m and n are integers and n is not 0. These numbers are called *rational* numbers. The word "rational" refers to the fact that m/n is the *ratio* of m to n.

2.3.2
EXERCISES

1. Express the following rational numbers in the form m/n, where m and n are integers:

$$\frac{6}{5-4}, \quad \frac{7-10}{14-13}, \quad \frac{7-7}{65}, \quad \frac{1}{2}\left(\frac{3}{4}+\frac{7}{11}\right).$$

2. (a) Is 0 a rational number? If so, express 0 in the form m/n, where m and n are integers and $n \neq 0$.

(b) Is -2 a rational number? If so, express it in the form m/n, where m and n are integers.

(c) Are all integers rational numbers?

(d) Are all numbers rational?

3. Consider the statement:

> If a and b are rational numbers, then $a \square b$ is a rational number.

Replace "$\square$" by "$+$," "$-$," "$\cdot$," and "$\div$." For which of these interpretations of the symbol "$\square$" is the resulting statement *always* true?

4. Prove those statements of Exercise 3 that you decided were true. If you fill in the blanks in the paragraph below, you will have a model for the requested proofs.

If a and b are rational, then a + b is rational.

Proof: Let $a = m/n$ and $b = r/s$, where m, n, r, and s are integers, and _____ and _____ are different from 0.
Then

$$a + b = \frac{m}{n} + \underline{\hspace{1cm}}$$

$$= \frac{\overline{\hspace{1cm}}}{ns} + \frac{\overline{\hspace{1cm}}}{ns}$$

$$= \frac{\underline{\hspace{0.8cm}} + \underline{\hspace{0.8cm}}}{ns}.$$

But if m, n, r, and s are integers, then ns, ms, _____, and, therefore, the numerator _____ of this fraction, are integers. Also, since n and _____ are different from 0, so is the denominator _____ different from 0. Therefore, $a + b$ is a _____ number.

n, s
$\dfrac{r}{s}$
ms, nr
ms, nr
nr
$ms + nr$
s
ns, *rational*

Exercises 3 and 4 explain why these four operations are often called the *rational* operations.

5. Prove that if a and b are rational, then the midpoint of the segment joining a to b is also rational. Give a formula for this midpoint. (Note that we have identified the point with its label. Have you been confused?)

6. Prove that between two rational points, there is another rational point. (A *rational point* is a point labeled by a rational number.)

7. Is there any segment on L that contains no rational points? Is there any segment which contains less than a million rational points?

2.4

Irrationals on the Number Line   Real numbers that cannot be represented as the ratio of two integers are called *irrational*. Thus, the set of real numbers can be partitioned into two mutually exclusive subsets: the rationals and the irrationals (Fig. 2-4).

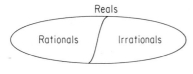

Figure 2-4

The fact that irrational numbers actually exist, that is that there are real numbers which are not the ratio of two whole numbers, was discovered about 500 B.C. by the school of Greek mathematicians called *Pythagoreans*. Since Greek mathematics was primarily concerned with geometry, it is no surprise that irrational numbers were first encountered in a geometric problem. The problem led to a consideration of square roots. Can you guess the problem?

It is quite likely that prior to the discovery of irrationals, people merely assumed that every number was the ratio of two integers. The Pythagoreans, then, very likely asked, "What is the ratio of integers that gives the length of the diagonal of a unit square?" Today, we represent this length by the symbol "$\sqrt{2}$."

By means of a rather simple and elegant chain of reasoning, the Pythagoreans discovered that $\sqrt{2}$ cannot be rational. Since the proof that $\sqrt{2}$ is irrational is now included in many high school textbooks, we shall lead you to construct a proof that $\sqrt{3}$ is irrational. If the length of the diagonal of a rectangle is 2 and the width is 1, then the length of the rectangle is $\sqrt{3}$.

According to our definition, a given number must be either rational or irrational; it cannot be both. (What definition do we have in mind?)

Suppose that $\sqrt{3}$ is rational. What does this mean in mathematical language? Referring to the definition, your answer should be equivalent to the following: there are integers m and n ($n \neq 0$) such that

(1)
$$\sqrt{3} = \frac{m}{n}.$$

Since a single rational number has many representations (e.g., $\frac{1}{2} = \frac{3}{6} = \frac{5}{10}$), we stipulate as part of our assumption that m/n *is a fraction in lowest terms; that is, m and n have no common factors other than the trivial factor* 1.

We square both members of (1), getting

$$3 = \frac{m^2}{n^2}.$$

Thus, $m^2 = 3n^2$, which states that m^2 is divisible by 3. Can you draw any conclusion about m itself? If you divide an integer by 3, what are the possible values of the remainder r? How would you check, that on division of m by 3, the quotient is q and the remainder is r?

The general rule is

dividend = (quotient · divisor) + _____, | *remainder*

that is,

____ = (____ · ____) + r. | *m, q, 3*

And the remainder r is 0, ____, or ____. | *1, 2*

But

$$(3q + 1)^2 = 3(\underline{\quad\quad}) + \underline{\quad\quad}$$

and

$$(3q + 2)^2 = 3(\underline{\quad} + \underline{\quad} + \underline{\quad}) + \underline{\quad}.$$

If $r \neq 0$, is $m^2 = (3q + r)^2$ divisible by 3?
_____ (Yes/No).

Therefore, if m^2 is divisible by 3, then $r =$ _____, that is, m is divisible by _____.

Since $m = 3q +$ _____, then $3n^2 = m^2 =$ _____, so that $n^2 =$ _____.

Since q^2 is an integer, n^2 is also divisible by _____.

By the same reasoning as before, it follows that n is divisible by _____.

We have now shown that m and n have the common factor _____, which contradicts our assumption that they have no common factor except _____.

What got you into this trouble? Your trouble began with the statement "Suppose that $\sqrt{3}$ is rational." Since you have deduced a contradiction from this statement, the statement must be false. In other words, $\sqrt{3}$ is an _____ number.

Answers (right margin):

$3q^2 + 2q, 1$

$3q^2, 4q, 1, 1$

No

0

3

0, 9q²

3q²

3

3

3

1

irrational

The argument above is an example that is typical of many proofs in mathematics. It involves several interesting features. First, all the possibilities (rational and irrational) were enumerated, and the proof relied on a process of elimination. The second, and more important, feature was that the proof was "indirect," which means that we started with a certain assumption (that $\sqrt{3}$ is rational), and showed that this led to a contradiction, or absurdity. We therefore discarded this assumption, making use of a fundamental proposition of logic that tells us *a true statement always implies a true statement;* so the only way we could have arrived at a false statement was to have begun with a false statement ($\sqrt{3}$ is rational). The method of *indirect proof* is sometimes referred to as the method of *reductio ad absurdum,* reduction to an absurdity. It is interesting to observe that such advanced logical reasoning was used by Greek mathematicians so early in the history of science. Furthermore, the use of *reductio ad absurdum* proofs by the Pythagoreans, and very likely by Euclid also, preceded the first formal development of the principles of logic by Aristotle (when did he live?).

1. Is $\sqrt[3]{2}$ irrational? Prove that you are right.

2. Recall from Exercise 4 of Sec. 1.4.2 that the statement "5 divides the integer b" means that there is an integer n such that $b = 5n$.

(a) Experiment, in order to complete the following sentence:

If 5 divides a^2, then _____ divides a.

(b) Assuming your answer in (a) is correct, prove that $\sqrt{5}$ is irrational.

3. Exhibit euclidean (straight-edge and compass) constructions of the lengths $\sqrt{2}$ and $\sqrt{5}$.

4. (a) What can be said of the sum of a rational and an irrational? Is it always, sometimes, or never rational? Prove your answer.

(b) What about the sum of two irrationals? Is it always, sometimes, or never irrational?

5. Do Exercise 4, replacing the word "sum" by "product."

6. Referring to the right triangle ABC in Fig. 2-5, solve for x in terms of m and n.

7. (a) How would you construct $\sqrt{7}$ by euclidean methods?

(b) How would you construct $\sqrt{257}$ by euclidean methods?

8. Let n represent a positive integer. How would you construct $\sqrt{n}$ by euclidean methods?

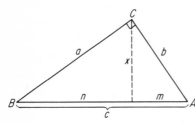

Figure 2-5

9. How would you construct $\sqrt[4]{5}$ by euclidean methods?

2.5

The Number Line Postulate In the previous three sections we have been concerned with constructing a one-to-one correspondence between numbers and points on a line, as though we were making a scale for a very long ruler or thermometer. After arbitrarily choosing positions for "0" and "1," we found that we could locate by means of a straight-edge and compass alone, positions for all the rational numbers. And in Exercises 2.4.1 you found positions for some irrational numbers—also by euclidean methods. In fact, the exercises were designed to show you that euclidean constructions enable you to find positions for "$\sqrt{n}$," where n is any positive integer.

Thus, you can construct lengths representing $2\sqrt{2}$, $3\sqrt{5}$, $\sqrt{5 + \sqrt{7}}$, and $\sqrt[4]{3}$. However, there are other irrationals that do not admit to construction by straight-edge and compass in only a finite number of steps! It is one of the triumphs of *modern algebra* that proves, for example, that given only a unit length *you cannot construct a segment of length* $\sqrt[3]{2}$ *by euclidean methods*. (You can read an elementary discussion on the impossibility of certain euclidean constructions in *What is Mathematics?* by R. Courant and H. Robbins.)†

If, in our search for positions that correspond to numbers, we don't insist on the exclusive use of the methods of high school geometry, then much more is possible. But, no matter how much freedom we permit ourselves, we cannot *prove* that it is possible to locate a point corresponding to each number unless we have some further information about the geometry of the line. In fact, we can't really prove anything, for we haven't yet specified a set of postulates from which to make deductions. Our work has been informal, using only an intuitive conception of the line that fits the scheme of high school geometry. This informal investigation has been pursued to give us an idea of how best to set up a primitive frame for the deductive system of *analytic geometry*.

Having been forced into the position of assuming some property or properties of the line, we begin with an existence postulate that paves the way for establishing the desired scale, i.e., the *real number line*.

Postulate G: *There is a one-to-one correspondence between the points of a line and the real numbers such that, if the points A and B correspond to the numbers a and b respectively, then the distance from A to B is*
    (i) $b - a$ if $a < b$,
    (ii) $a - b$ if $b < a$,
    (iii) 0 if $a = b$.

Pertaining to the scale on a line L, what are the distances from:

(a) the point marked 1 to the point marked 5?
(b) the point marked 5 to the point marked 1?
(c) the point marked 0 to the point marked 6?
(d) the point marked 0 to the point marked -6?
(e) the point marked 7 to the point marked 3?
(f) the point marked -1 to the point marked 3?
(g) Finally, what is the distance from the point marked a to the point marked b?

† R. Courant and H. Robbins, *What is Mathematics?* (Fair Lawn, N.J.: Oxford University Press, 1941).

In answering these questions on distance, you sometimes subtracted the first number from the second, and other times subtracted the second from the first. Why? Because you were obeying Postulate G, which agrees with convention that the distance between two distinct points is positive. For instance, we say the distance from Chicago to New York is 900 miles, and that the distance from New York to Chicago is also 900 miles. But what about a question like (g)? We could say, "it depends, ...," but that is rather clumsy. We would like a convenient symbolism so that we can give a single simple answer no matter what the relative positions of the points on the line. That is made possible by the

Definition of Absolute Value: (a) *If* $x \geq 0$, *the* absolute value *of* x *is taken to be equal to* x. (b) *If* $x < 0$, *the* absolute value *of* x *is taken to be equal to* $-x$.

The notation for the absolute value of x is $|x|$. Thus, in succinct form, the definition may be stated:

(a) *If* $x \geq 0$, *then* $|x| = x$.
(b) *If* $x < 0$, *then* $|x| = -x$.

Illustrations:

$$|2| = 2, \quad |-2| = 2, \quad |2 - 3| = |3 - 2| = 1, \quad |0| = 0.$$

The answer to question (g) is then $|a - b|$ or $|b - a|$, since $|a - b| = |b - a|$. From the definition of absolute value we see, therefore, that distance is always nonnegative. (Why don't we say distance is always positive?)

With the aid of absolute value we can now restate our basic assumption in more convenient form.

Postulate G: *There is a one-to-one correspondence between the points of a line and the real numbers such that, if A and B are points which correspond to real numbers a and b, respectively, then the distance between A and B equals* $|a - b|$.

Reflecting on Postulate G, the beginning of the deductive science, we ask: What are the undefined terms? What are the notions that the postulate rests on? A moment's thought should indicate to you that we have taken for granted the geometric terms *point* and *line*, while *distance* is, in a sense, defined by the postulate to conform to our previous notions. Furthermore, the *real number system*, the relations inherent in it, and the notion of *one-to-one correspondence* have also been assumed as part of the primitive frame.

We could remain content with this as a beginning, building upon Postulate G, but we can also choose to build more of a foundation under this assumption by propping up the undefined terms and ideas. We shall take the latter alternative. One of our primary concerns in this *Prelude to Analysis* is to impart a description of the real numbers and to have you develop a working knowledge with them, so we shall, ultimately, provide a set of postulates for the real number system.

Remark 1: When a scale is established on a line by means of Postulate G, the line may be referred to as *the real line, the number line,* or *the real number line.* You will find that these three terminologies are used interchangeably.

Remark 2: We reiterate: On the real line we may refer to a point by the number assigned to it, if we are certain that no confusion will result. This *ellipsis,* or convenience of language, enables us to say, e.g., "the distance from 3 to 2 is $|2 - 3|$" in place of "the distance from the point represented by '3' to the point represented by '2' is $|2 - 3|$."

Notation: The set of real numbers will hereafter be denoted by $\mathscr{R}$. Occasionally, when we want to distinguish between the (geometric) points on the real line and the real numbers, we will denote the set of points of the real line by $\mathscr{R}_1$.

The symbol "$\in$" will be used as shorthand for "is a member of" or "is an element of" or "belongs to" or, even simpler, "is in." Thus, we will write

"$3 \in \mathscr{R}$" for "3 is an element of the set of real numbers,"
"$A \in \mathscr{R}_1$" for "A is in $\mathscr{R}_1$,"
"$x \notin \mathscr{R}$" for "x is not in $\mathscr{R}$."

2.5.1
EXERCISES

1. If $\rho(X, Y)$ denotes the distance from point X to point Y, where $X, Y \in \mathscr{R}_1$,
(a) Prove the *symmetry property of distance:*

$$\text{For any pair } X, Y \in \mathscr{R}_1, \qquad \rho(X, Y) = \rho(Y, X).$$

(b) Prove that $\rho(X, Y) = 0$ if and only if $X = Y$. [Notice that you have two things to prove:

(i) If $\rho(X, Y) = 0$, then $X = Y$, and
(ii) If $X = Y$, then $\rho(X, Y) = 0$.]

2. Draw a real line to get a geometric meaning for each problem. Find all $x \in \mathcal{R}$ such that

(a) $|x| = 2$.

(b) $|x - 1| = 2$.

(c) $|x + 1| = 2$.

(d) $|x - 2| = 3$.

(e) $|x - (-2)| = 4$.

(f) $|x - 0| = 1$.

(g) $|x - a| = 1$.

(h) $|x| < 1$.

(i) $|x^2| = 4$.

(j) $|x - 2| < 1$.

3. (a) A geometric interpretation of the statement

$$|x - 2| = 1$$

is: The distance from x to _____ is _____.

(b) A geometric interpretation of the statement

$$|x + 2| = 1$$

is: The distance from x to _____ is _____.

(c) Give a geometric interpretation of the statement

$$|x - a| = b, \qquad b \geq 0.$$

4. (a) Find all the values of x such that

$$|x - 1| = |x + 2|.$$

(b) Let a, b be given real numbers. Give a geometric interpretation of the statement

$$|x - a| = |x - b|.$$

(c) How many real values of x satisfy the equation

$$|x - a| = |x - b|?$$

5. Find all real values of x that satisfy the relations below. Give an interpretation on $\mathcal{R}_1$ in each case.

(a) $|x - \frac{3}{4}| = \frac{3}{4}$.

(b) $|2x| = 3$.

(c) $|2x + 2| = 3$.

(d) $|2x - 3| = 3$.

(e) $|5 - 3x| = 7$.

(f) $|x^2 - 1| = 1$.

(g) $|x - 2| < 1$.

(h) $|x + 2| > 0$.

(i) $|1 - x| \geq 1$.

(j) $|x^2 - 3x + 2| = 0$.

2.6

Order   We have yet to establish the intuitive order properties of the number line (see Sec. 1-4) within the framework of our deductive system. The problem is to impart to the number line the order properties of $\mathcal{R}$. But what are these properties?

In Sec. 1.4 we summarized the order properties of $\mathcal{R}$ by saying that $\mathcal{R}$ is linearly ordered with respect to the relation $<$. For completeness, we restate this definition.

Definition: *A set $\mathcal{S}$ is said to be* linearly ordered *with respect to a relation R if:*

1. *aRa holds for no member of $\mathcal{S}$. (Irreflexive property.)*
2. *For a, b, and c in $\mathcal{S}$: if aRb and bRc, then aRc. (Transitive property.)*
3. *If a and b are any two elements in $\mathcal{S}$, then exactly one of the following three relations holds:*

   (i) *aRb,*   (ii) *a = b,*   (iii) *bRa.   (Law of trichotomy.)*

With this definition, we make our first formal assumption, in the form of an order postulate, regarding the real numbers.

Postulate O: *$\mathcal{R}$ is linearly ordered by the relation $<$.*

What we need to do now is to relate the number relation $<$ (less than) to a relation among points of $\mathcal{R}_1$. It is easy to recapture the "precedes" or "is to the left of" that we used in Sec. 1.4. All we need to do is make the "right" definition.

Definition: *Suppose there is a one-to-one correspondence satisfying Postulate G, such that*

$$\begin{array}{cc} \mathcal{R} & \mathcal{R}_1 \\ \hline a & \leftrightarrow & A \\ b & \leftrightarrow & B \end{array}$$

We will say that A precedes *B if and only if $a < b$.*

Thus the relation "less than" between numbers corresponds to the relation "precedes" between points. This tells us that *$\mathcal{R}_1$ is linearly ordered by the relation precedes.* That is, the linear ordering of $\mathcal{R}$ induces a linear ordering of $\mathcal{R}_1$.

In our informal construction of a scale on a line (Sec. 2.2) we talked about the *positive* and *negative* directions on a line. Now, we can bring these notions into the scheme of our logical treatment by stating:

If A and B are distinct points of a line on which a scale has been constructed, then the direction from A to B is called
  (i) *positive* if A precedes B, and
  (ii) *negative* if B precedes A.

So we see that learning about the order properties and studying inequalities in $\mathscr{R}$ will enable us to learn about corresponding geometric properties on lines. In the exercises below and in succeeding sections you will be given the opportunity to sharpen your skills in these directions.

First, we extend our vocabulary for handling order properties:

1. $a > b$, read "a is greater than b," means $b < a$.
2. $a \leq b$, read "a is less than or equal to b," means $a < b$ or $a = b$.
3. $a \geq b$, read "a is greater than or equal to b," means $a > b$ or $a = b$.

2.6.1
EXERCISES

1. Draw a conclusion from each of the following:
  (a) $a \geq 2$ and $a \leq 2$. (c) $a < x$ and $b > x$.
  (b) $a < 2$ and $b > 2$. (d) $x \leq y$ and $x \neq y$.

2. Prove your answer to each of the following questions.
  (a) Is $\mathscr{R}$ linearly ordered by the relation $>$?
  (b) Is $\mathscr{R}$ linearly ordered by the relation $\leq$?
  (c) Is $\mathscr{R}$ linearly ordered by the relation $=$?
  (d) Is the set of integers linearly ordered?
  (e) Is the set of rationals linearly ordered?
  (f) Is the set of irrationals linearly ordered?

3. Have we relied on any additional primitive (undefined) terms or relations in adding an order postulate?

4. Give three simply stated relations which provide linear orderings of the fingers of your left hand.

5. Define a relation by which the points of a circle are linearly ordered.

6. Name at least three order properties of $\mathscr{R}$ that are not provided for in Postulate O. [*Hint:* Refer to Sec. 1.4.]

7. (a) The rational numbers $x = m/n$, where the integers m and n have no common factor except $1, 0 \leq x \leq 1$, and $n \leq 4$, are

$$\frac{0}{1}, \quad \frac{1}{1}, \quad \frac{1}{2}, \quad \frac{1}{3}, \quad \frac{2}{3}, \quad \frac{1}{4}, \quad \text{and} \quad \frac{3}{4}.$$

Arrange these in increasing order (order them by the relation $<$). The resulting sequence is called a *Farey series* of order 4. Write the Farey series of orders 5 and 6.

(b) Find the difference between two consecutive terms of a Farey series. What general property does this difference seem to have?

8. (a) Which numbers are in the Farey series of order 5 but not in the Farey series of order 4?

(b) How is each of the new fractions related to its two neighbors in the Farey series of order 5?

(c) Does this relation also hold for the numbers in the Farey series of order 6 which are not in the series of order 5?

9. Predict, by some principle (which we hope you discovered in Exercise 8) the Farey series of order 7, and check.

10. Again we denote the distance between points X and Y by $\rho(X, Y)$.

(a) Let A, B, and C be three points in a plane. Give a geometric interpretation of the statement

$$\rho(A, C) \leq \rho(A, B) + \rho(B, C).$$

(b) Would the statement in (a) hold if A, B, and C were collinear (on one line)?

(c) Let $A, B, C \in \mathscr{R}_1$. State the *triangle inequality*, the statement in (a), in terms of absolute values.

(d) Let $X, Y, Z \in \mathscr{R}_1$. Give a geometric interpretation of the equation

$$\rho(X, Z) = \rho(X, Y) + \rho(Y, Z).$$

(e) Let A_1, A_2, A_3 be three collinear points. Using our two postulates, *prove* that there is always some way to choose the points so that the triangle inequality becomes an equation. That is, show that there is a way to choose i, j, k in order that

$$\rho(A_i, A_j) = \rho(A_i, A_k) + \rho(A_k, A_j).$$

2.7

Change of Coordinates   If a scale is set up on a given line in accordance with Postulate G, the number assigned to a point P is called the *coordinate* of P. The entire scale is referred to as a *coordinate* system on the line.

In setting up a coordinate system on a given line L, we make an arbitrary decision in choosing the *origin* (the point whose coordinate is 0) and the *unit point* (the point whose coordinate is 1). If someone else were to construct a scale on L, he would also be accorded the privilege of making arbitrary choices for the location of the origin and unit point. His scale—no better or worse than ours—might be quite different from the one we constructed. How can we determine the relationship between the two coordinate systems?

Consider the example in Fig. 2-6, which shows coordinates in the first (old) system below L and coordinates in the second (new) system above L.

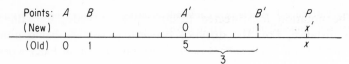

Figure 2-6

If a point P has an old coordinate of x and a new coordinate of x', we can make a table (fill in the blanks):

Points	x	x'	
A'	5	0	
B'	_____	1	8
C	_____	3	14
A	0	_____	$-\frac{5}{3}$
B	1	_____	$-\frac{4}{3}$
D	10	_____	$\frac{5}{3}$
E	_____	10	35

In describing the relationship between the two coordinate systems, we again encounter the notion of a *function*, first mentioned in Sec. 1.3. The new coordinate x' (of P) is a function of the old coordinate x, for to each x there corresponds a unique value x'. It is also true that the old coordinate x is a function of the new, x'. The table above gives a partial description of these functions. In the exercises below, we will lead you to complete algebraic descriptions that hold for all points, rather than just seven.

The first question on the table might be phrased: What is the old coordinate b of the new unit point B'? Figure 2-5 tells us that B' is at a distance of three old units from the old 5. Thus, $|b - 5| = 3$. How many values of b satisfy this equation? It is clear that we have not said enough to find b, for we left out the crucial fact that B' *is to the right of the old 5*. In other words, we have encountered a very elementary question that requires a statement of a distance in a specified direction, that is, a *directed distance*. In order to facilitate discussion we make the following

Definition: *The directed distance from A to B, which we denote by $\overline{AB}$, is:*

(a) *the distance between A and B if the direction from A to B is the positive direction;*

(b) *the negative of the distance between A and B if the direction from A to B is the negative direction.*

Remark 1:   Note that the concepts of *distance, direction,* and *directed distance* all depend on the particular scale.

Remark 2:   The notation for directed distance also provides us with a notation for distance. For, the distance between A and B, being non-negative, is

$$|\overline{AB}|.$$

(Provided we agree that $\overline{AA} = 0$, i.e., the directed distance between a point and itself is zero.)

Thus, if A and B are points with respective coordinates a and b, the directed distance from A to B is $b - a$, while the distance between A and B is $|b - a|$. In our new notation:

$$\overline{AB} = b - a,$$

$$|\overline{AB}| = |b - a|.$$

Using the concept of directed distance we continue the discussion of the change of coordinates in the exercises.

2.7.1
EXERCISES

Refer to the example of Fig. 2-6 in answering Exercises 1–6.

1. What is the directed distance $\overline{A'B'}$ in the old coordinate system? in the new coordinate system?

2. What is the directed distance $\overline{AB}$ in the old coordinate system? in the new coordinate system?

3. What is the directed distance $\overline{AP}$ in the old coordinate system? in the new coordinate system?

4. If Q and R are any two points of the line L, what is the ratio of directed distances

$$\frac{\overline{QR} \text{ in old system}}{\overline{QR} \text{ in new system}}.$$

5. Express the ratio $\overline{A'P}/\overline{A'B'}$ in terms of x (old coordinates) and in terms of x' (new coordinates).

6. Observe that x and x' are related by equations of the form

$$x = ux' + c \qquad \text{and} \qquad x' = Ux + C.$$

What are u, c, U, and C? Give geometric interpretations of u, c, U, and C.

7. No longer referring to the special situation in Fig. 2-6, answer the following questions:

(a) If the origin is changed, but not the size or the direction of the unit, is the directed distance $\overline{AB}$ changed, where A and B are any two given points?

(b) If the size of the unit is doubled, but its direction remains unchanged, then the directed distance $\overline{AB}$, where A and B are given points, is multiplied by _____.

If the size of the unit is multiplied by 12, but its direction is not changed, and A, B, and C are given points, then the directed distances $\overline{AC}$ and $\overline{BC}$ are multiplied by _____, and the ratio

$$\frac{\overline{AC}}{\overline{BC}}$$

is multiplied by _____.

(c) If A, B, and C are any given points on the line, how does the ratio

$$\frac{\overline{AC}}{\overline{BC}}$$

change when the coordinate system is changed as in (a) or (b)?

(d) Let A and B be the points 0 and 1 in the old coordinate system and let A' and B' be the points 0 and 1 in the new coordinate system. Let the point P have old coordinate x and the new coordinate x'. Calculate the ratio

$$\frac{\overline{A'P}}{\overline{A'B'}}$$

in both coordinate systems. Apply part (c). Let U be the directed distance $\overline{AB}$ calculated in the new coordinate system, and C be the new coordinate of the point A. Give a formula for x' in terms of x.

(e) Give a formula for x in terms of x'.

8. From Exercises 6 and 7 you have learned that a change or transformation of coordinates on a line can be described by an equation of the form

$$x' = Ux + C,$$

where x refers to the coordinate of a point P in one system, while x' refers to the co-ordinate of P in the second system.

(a) How are the origins related when $C = 0$?

(b) How are the origins and units related when $U = 1$?

(c) What happens when $U < 0$?

(d) Is it possible for U to be zero? (Recall the computation of U in Exercises 6 and 7.)

9. In Exercise 6 you discovered explicit formulas for the functions relating the old and new coordinates in Fig. 2-6. For example, x' is expressed as a function of x by the equation

$$x' = Ux + C.$$

If we want to denote this particular function by F, we write

$$x' = F(x), \qquad \text{where } F(x) = Ux + C.$$

Sometimes it is convenient to use the suggestive notation

$$F:x \to x' \qquad \text{(read "}F\text{ maps }x\text{ into }x'\text{"),}$$

or the equivalent

$$F:x \to Ux + C \qquad \text{(read "}F\text{ maps }x\text{ into }Ux + C\text{").}$$

(a) Describe, in geometric language, the effect of the function G, where

$$G:x \to -x.$$

(b) Describe, in geometric language, the effect of the function H, where

$$H:x \to x + 1.$$

(c) Let G and H be the functions in (a) and (b) that define changes in coordinates. If $G \circ H$ denotes the function obtained by applying H first and G second, find the effect of $G \circ H$. That is, find a formula for $(G \circ H)(x)$.

(d) Find a formula for $(H \circ G)(x)$.

10. Let F be a function defining a change of coordinates, i.e., $F:x \to y$. Suppose also that $F(0) = c$.

(a) Find a formula for $F(x)$ if you are given: $y \geq c$ if $x \geq 0$.
(b) Find a formula for $F(x)$ if you are given: $y \leq c$ if $x \leq 0$.
(c) Find a formula for $F(x)$ if you are given: $y \leq c$ if $x \geq 0$.

SUPPLEMENTARY EXERCISES

1. (a) Read the section on Descartes in an encyclopedia.
(b) Determine what was happening in France, England, America, Spain, Italy, and Russia during his lifetime. Can you name at least one important contemporary of Descartes in each of these countries?
(c) What was Descartes famous for besides mathematics?

2. (a) Read the chapter on Descartes in *Men of Mathematics* by E. T. Bell.†
(b) Would you say that Descartes died because of a woman or because of getting up too early in cold weather?

3. (a) Read the first chapter of Descartes' *La Geometrie*. (There is an inexpensive paperback edition, published by Dover Publications, Inc., New York, which has the English translation together with the original French.)
(b) How does this approach differ from ours?
(c) How did Descartes deal with negative numbers?

4. (a) Read the chapter on Fermat in *Men of Mathematics* by E. T. Bell.

† E. T. Bell, *Men of Mathematics* (New York: Simon and Schuster, Inc., 1937).

(b) To what extent did Fermat invent analytic geometry simultaneously with, and independently of, Descartes?

(c) What is *Fermat's Last Theorem*?

5. (a) Look up the dates of Archimedes, Aristotle, and Euclid.

(b) What is the approximate date that Aristotle first wrote his work on logic? Compare this with the probable date that Euclid wrote his *Elements*.

(c) What religious ideas did the Pythagoreans associate with the integers?†

(d) Why did the Pythagoreans try to keep secret the discovery of the existence of irrational numbers?

---

† See T. L. Heath, *History of Greek Mathematics* (2 vols.; Fair Lawn, N.J.: Oxford University Press, 1921).

Chapter Three **Algebraic Structures** *Special functions
are introduced to study the four basic operations of arithmetic in the
real number system. In Sec. 3.4, we present a set of postulates that
characterizes the arithmetic properties of real numbers in terms of the
functions. The concept of a* field, *which is an algebraic generalization
of the real number system, is also introduced (in terms of functions) in
Sec. 3.4. In Sec. 3.5, this system of field postulates is shown to be
equivalent to the more common postulates (that are given in terms of
operations rather than functions). Reflecting on those field properties
that deal with only one operation at a time leads to the concept of an*
abelian group, *which is the subject of Sec. 3.7. In Sec. 3.9, we unite
the concept of a field with the concept of linear order to obtain a new
structure called an* ordered field, *of which the real number is a prime
example. The study of ordered fields leads to a study of inequalities,
which is begun in Sec. 3.9 and continued more forcefully in Sec. 3.10.
The final section of the chapter is devoted to an analysis of the logical
principles that were used in constructing the arguments and solving
the problems of the preceding sections. Thus, the logical meaning of
"and," "or," and "implies" is made explicit.*

3.1

Introduction In this chapter we continue the process of propping up Postulate G, which assumed the real number system $\mathcal{R}$. We will look at $\mathcal{R}$ as we know it from earlier experience, searching for its essential algebraic properties. Our aim is to extract a relatively small number of such properties from which we can deduce the rest. In this way we hope to arrive at a relatively simple set of postulates for the algebraic structure of the real numbers.

3.2

Addition and Multiplication How many answers do you get if you add 3 to a given number?

If $x \in \mathcal{R}$, then $3 + x$ is uniquely determined. This fact is part of the experience of every school child. If we think of this operation as a correspondence

$$x \rightarrow 3 + x,$$

we encounter the idea of *function* once again: the sum $(3 + x)$ is a function of x (see Sec. 1.3 and Exercises 9 and 10 of Sec. 2.7.1). Let's call this function or operation A_3 so that

(1) $$A_3 : x \rightarrow 3 + x.$$

The result of operating with the function A_3 on x is called the *value of the function A_3 at x* and is denoted by $A_3(x)$. Therefore,

(2) $$A_3(x) = 3 + x.$$

Either (1) or (2) is sufficient as a definition of A_3.

Now suppose we add 3 and 4 successively to an arbitrary real number x. Let A_4 denote the operation of adding 4 to a real number so that we can study the situation by means of our *functional notation*. Since $A_3(x)$ is the result of adding 3 to x, the result of adding first 3 and then 4 is

$$A_4(A_3(x)).$$

Using the definitions of the functions involved, we get

$$A_4(A_3(x)) = A_4(3 + x) = 4 + (3 + x)$$

or

$$x \overset{A_3}{\rightarrow} (3 + x) \overset{A_4}{\rightarrow} 4 + (3 + x) \qquad \text{(Are the parentheses necessary?)}$$

It appears clear that the composition of these two operations on x is also a function, for to each $x \in \mathcal{R}$ there corresponds a *single* real number, namely $4 + (3 + x)$. We will denote the *composite* or *composition* of A_3 and A_4 by $A_4 \circ A_3$. Then

$$A_4 \circ A_3 : x \rightarrow 4 + (3 + x);$$

and in the function value notation,

$$(A_4 \circ A_3)(x) = A_4(A_3(x)).$$

More generally, if a is any real number in $\mathcal{R}$ we define the addition

function A_a such that
$$A_a : x \to a + x.$$

And if $b \in \mathscr{R}$, we have

$$(A_b \circ A_a)x = A_b(A_a(x)) = A_b(a + x) = b + (a + x).$$

We will soon give you a chance to explore the properties of the functions A_a, but first we will define functions M_a, $a \in \mathscr{R}$, which perform the operation of multiplication for us. Namely, if $a \in \mathscr{R}$

$$M_a : x \to a \cdot x.$$

The functions A_a and M_a are said to be defined on $\mathscr{R}$, for they operate on any member of $\mathscr{R}$. Are the function values always in $\mathscr{R}$?

3.2.1
EXERCISES

1. Practice with Functional Notation

(a) $M_3(2) = \underline{\hspace{1cm}}$.	6
(b) $M_{-1} : 2 \to \underline{\hspace{1cm}}$.	-2
(c) $A_2 : x \to \underline{\hspace{1cm}} + \underline{\hspace{1cm}}$.	$2, x$
(d) $A_0(-4) = \underline{\hspace{1cm}}$.	-4
(e) $M_0(-4) = \underline{\hspace{1cm}}$.	0
(f) $A_2(x) = \underline{\hspace{1cm}} + \underline{\hspace{1cm}}$.	$2, x$
(g) $M_{-1}(6) = \underline{\hspace{1cm}}$.	-6
(h) $M_{-1}(-6) = \underline{\hspace{1cm}}$.	6
(i) $A_2(1 + \sqrt{2}) = \underline{\hspace{1cm}}$.	$3 + \sqrt{2}$
(j) $M_3(1 + \sqrt{2}) = \underline{\hspace{1cm}}$.	$3 + 3\sqrt{2}$
(k) $M_{-1}(-\pi) = \underline{\hspace{1cm}}$.	π
(l) $A_2(M_3(x)) = A_2(\underline{\hspace{1cm}}) = \underline{\hspace{1cm}} + \underline{\hspace{1cm}}$.	$3x, 2, 3x$
(m) $M_3(A_2(x)) = M_3(\underline{\hspace{1cm}} + x) = \underline{\hspace{1cm}} + \underline{\hspace{1cm}}$.	$2, 6, 3x$
(n) $M_3(4x) = \underline{\hspace{1cm}} x$.	12
(o) $M_3 \circ M_4 : x \to \underline{\hspace{1cm}}$.	$12x$
(p) $(A_{-2} \circ M_1)(5) = \underline{\hspace{1cm}}$.	3
(q) $(A_{-2} \circ M_3)(5) = \underline{\hspace{1cm}}$.	13
(r) $(M_3 \circ A_{-2})(5) = \underline{\hspace{1cm}}$.	9
(s) $M_{-1}(A_2(M_{-1}(3))) = \underline{\hspace{1cm}}$.	1
(t) $A_2(x^3) = \underline{\hspace{1cm}} + x^3$.	2
(u) $M_2(x^3) = \underline{\hspace{1cm}}$.	$2x^3$
(v) $A_2(1 - 3x) = \underline{\hspace{1cm}} + (1 - 3x) = \underline{\hspace{1cm}} - \underline{\hspace{1cm}}$.	$2, 3, 3x$
(w) $A_2(2t) = \underline{\hspace{1cm}}(1 + t)$.	2
(x) $M_2(2t) = \underline{\hspace{1cm}}$.	$4t$
(y) $M_{\sqrt{2}}(\sqrt{2}) = \underline{\hspace{1cm}}$.	2
(z) $M_{1-\sqrt{2}}(1 + \sqrt{2}) = \underline{\hspace{1cm}}$.	-1

2. Equality. At an earlier stage (Sec. 1.4–9) we indicated what is meant by equality among numbers. Let's now agree on the general concept of equality: The *equals sign* "=" will be used to mean that the symbols on the two sides of it are names for the same thing.

(a) Referring to the table, if $x = y$, the blank in the x-row and y-column should be filled with "Y" indicating "yes, x is equal to y." Otherwise the symbol "N" should appear. We have given you some information about the integers $a, b, c,$ and d by filling three of the blanks. You deduce which letters should appear in the remainder of the table.

=	a	b	c	d
a		Y		N
b			Y	
c				
d				

(b) How would your answers in (a) differ if $a, b, c,$ and d were irrational numbers? arbitrary real numbers? functions?

(c) State the property of equality that enables you to fill the blanks in the diagonal from the upper left to the lower right of the table.

(d) State the property of equality that enables you to fill the blank in the second row and first column.

(e) How did you decide whether $a = c$? State the property of equality.

(f) Drawing from the names given to order properties (see Sec. 1.4), give names to the properties stated in (c)–(e).

3. Equality of Functions

(a) Let F and G be functions, and $F = G$.

$$\text{If } F:a \to y, \qquad \text{then } G:a \to \underline{\quad}. \qquad\qquad y$$

If there is only one b such that

$$F:b \to z, \qquad \text{then } G:\underline{\quad} \to z. \qquad\qquad b$$

In general, if x is any element for which $F(x)$ is defined, then $F(x) = G(\underline{\quad}).$ x

(b) $A_7(x) = \underline{\quad} + x,$ for any $x \in \mathscr{R}.$ 7

$$(A_3 \circ A_4)(x) - A_7(x) = \underline{\quad}. \qquad\qquad 0$$

$$(A_4 \circ A_3)(x) - A_7(x) = \underline{\quad}. \qquad\qquad 0$$

(c) From part (b), you get

$$A_3 \circ A_4 = A_{\_} \qquad \text{and} \qquad A_4 \circ A_3 = A_{\_}. \qquad\qquad 7,7$$

(d) Applying your answer in 2(e) to 3(c), you get

$$A_3 \circ A_{\_} = A_4 \circ A_{\_}. \qquad\qquad 4,3$$

4. (a) $A_{-3}(A_3(2)) = $ _____.

   (b) $(A_3 \circ A_{-3})(x) = $ _____.

   (c) $(A_{-3} \circ A_3)(x) = $ _____.

   (d) $A_{-3} \circ A_3 = A_{\_}$.

   (e) Generalize the result of (d).

5. (a) $M_4(M_1(x)) = $ _____.

   (b) $M_1(M_4(x)) = $ _____.

   (c) $M_1 \circ M_4 = M_{\_}$.

   (d) $M_4 \circ M_{-4} = M_{\_}$.

   (e) Generalize the result in (c).

   (f) $M_4 \circ M_{\_} = M_1$.

   (g) Generalize the result in (f).

2
x
x
0
4x
4x
4
−16
$\frac{1}{4}$

6. If $A_3(b) = A_3(c)$, then $A_{-3}(A_3(b)) = A_{-3}(A_3(c))$. What justifies operating on both sides with A_{-3}?

   (b) If $A_{-3}(A_3(b)) = A_{-3}(A_3(c))$, then

$$(A_{\_} \circ A_{\_})(b) = (A_{\_} \circ A_{\_})(c).$$

Find $b - c$.

   (c) Find $b - c$ if given $A_a(b) = A_a(c)$.

7. (a) $a + (b + x) = a + (A_{\_}(x)) = A_{\_}(A_{\_}(x)) = (A_{\_} \circ A_{\_})(x)$.

   (b) $a + (b + x) = A_{\_}(b + x) = (A_{\_} \circ A_{\_})(x)$.

   (c) $(a + b) + x = A_{\_}(x)$.

   (d) Solve for x: $(839 + 625) + 3047 = x + (625 + 3047)$.

   (e) What algebraic property of real numbers enables you to answer (d) by inspection? State it generally: If $a, b, c \in \mathscr{R}$, then

$$(a + b) + c = \text{_____}.$$

   (f) The property in (e) is called the *associative* property of real numbers with respect to addition. It is equivalent to a statement about functions, namely

$$A_{a+b} = A_{\_} \circ A_{\_}.$$

8. (a) Solve for x: $(839 \cdot 625) \cdot 3047 = x \cdot (625 \cdot 3047)$.

   (b) Solve for x: $(2 \cdot x) \cdot y = 2 \cdot (738 \cdot y)$, $(y \neq 0)$.

   (c) Solve for x: $(2 \cdot x) \cdot y = 6y$, $(y \neq 0)$.

   (d) State precisely the property that enabled you to solve for x in (a)–(c). [This is called the *associative* property of real numbers with respect to multiplication. Compare it with your answer to 7(e).]

   (e) State the associative property of real numbers with respect to multiplication in terms of functions.

9. (a) The following equations were designed with malice aforethought. Look for shortcuts in solving for x.

$$2 + 3 = 3 + x,$$

$$2 + (-3) = (-3) + x,$$

$$2 + (-y) = (-y) + x,$$

$$179 + 628 = 628 + x,$$

$$(372 + (-729)) + 927 = (927 + (-729)) + x,$$

$$473x = 1269 \cdot 473,$$

$$(-y) \cdot x = 52 \cdot (-y) \qquad (y \neq 0),$$

$$(7 \cdot x) \cdot z = (7 \cdot z) \cdot y \qquad (z \neq 0).$$

(b) Which equations in (a) required the use of an associative property for solution?

(c) What property of addition of real numbers enabled you to solve the first four problems by inspection? State it generally: If a and b are any numbers in $\mathcal{R}$, then

$$a + b = \underline{\qquad}.$$

This is called the *commutative* property of $\mathcal{R}$ with respect to addition.

(d) Does $\mathcal{R}$ possess a commutative property with respect to multiplication?

(e) If we are searching for a way to express the commutative property with respect to addition in terms of functions, we note first that we may write

$$(a + b) + x = a + b + x$$

(What property permits dropping parentheses?), and then

$$a + b + x = a + (A\_(x)) = (A\_ \circ A\_)(x) \qquad \text{(skipping steps)}.$$

Now finish the job of expressing the commutative property with respect to addition in terms of the A-functions.

(f) State the commutative property with respect to multiplication in terms of the M-functions.

10. In this exercise, f, g, and h are functions.
(a) $f : x \to f(\underline{\qquad})$, $g : x \to \underline{\qquad}$, $h : x \to \underline{\qquad}$.
(b) $f \circ g : t \to f(\underline{\qquad})$, $g \circ h : t \to g(\underline{\qquad})$.
(c) We will help you to investigate the triple composite $f \circ (g \circ h)$.

$$x \xrightarrow{g \circ h} g(\underline{\qquad}) \xrightarrow{f} f(\underline{\qquad}).$$

Thus, $f \circ (g \circ h) : x \to \underline{\qquad}$.

(d) Find $((f \circ g) \circ h)(x)$, the value of $(f \circ g) \circ h$ at x.

(e) Compare the functions $(f \circ g) \circ h$ and $f \circ (g \circ h)$. Your answer to this question can be described by saying: Functions satisfy the $\underline{\qquad}$ property with respect to $\underline{\qquad}$.

(f) Experiment with the A-functions and M-functions to investigate the question of commutativity; namely, are functions commutative with respect to composition?

3.3

Subtraction and Division The *binary operations* addition and multiplication were the primary concern of the previous section. Now we look at the other two of the four basic binary operations of arithmetic, namely subtraction and division. We speak of these as *binary operations* (or binary laws of composition) because they combine two elements to yield a third:

addition: $(a, b) \rightarrow a + b$,
multiplication: $(a, b) \rightarrow a \cdot b$,
subtraction: $(a, b) \rightarrow a - b$,
division: $(a, b) \rightarrow a \div b$ (or a/b).

Similarly, composition of functions ($\circ$) is a binary operation:

$$(F, G) \rightarrow G \circ F.$$

In order to explore the properties of subtraction and division we define two new sets of functions. For every $a \in \mathcal{R}$, we define functions S_a and D_a such that

$$S_a : x \rightarrow x - a$$

$$D_a : x \rightarrow x/a.$$

3.3.1
EXERCISES

1. (a) $S_3(4) = \underline{\hspace{1cm}} - 3.$ *4*
   (b) $S_3(2) = \underline{\hspace{1cm}}.$ *−1*
   (c) $S_3(0) = \underline{\hspace{1cm}}.$ *−3*
   (d) $S_3(3) = \underline{\hspace{1cm}}.$ *0*
   (e) $(S_3 \circ A_3)(4) = \underline{\hspace{1cm}}.$ *4*
   (f) $(A_3 \circ S_3)(4) = \underline{\hspace{1cm}}.$ *4*
   (g) $(A_3 \circ S_3)(x) = \underline{\hspace{1cm}}.$ *x*
   (h) $A_3 \circ S_3 = S_3 \circ \underline{\hspace{1cm}}.$ A_3
   (i) $A_3 \circ S_3 = A_{\underline{\hspace{0.3cm}}} = S_{\underline{\hspace{0.3cm}}}.$ *0,0*
   (j) $S_0 = A_{\underline{\hspace{0.3cm}}}.$ *0*
   (k) $A_{-1} = S_{\underline{\hspace{0.3cm}}}.$ *1*
   (l) $S_a = A_{\underline{\hspace{0.3cm}}}$, for every $a \in \mathcal{R}$.   *−a*

2. Are the S-functions commutative with respect to composition?
   (b) Is $\mathcal{R}$ commutative with respect to subtraction?
   (c) Is $S_a \circ A_b = A_b \circ S_a$ for every $a, b \in \mathcal{R}$?

3. Associativity with Respect to Subtraction
   (a) For what real values of x is the following true?
$$(2 - 1) - x = 2 - (1 - x).$$

   (b) For what values of x is the following true?

$$(2 - x) - 1 = 2 - (x - 1).$$

   (c) For what real values of x is the following true?

$$(x - 2) - 1 = x - (2 - 1).$$

   (d) Is $\mathcal{R}$ associative with respect to subtraction?

4. (a) Solve for n: $S_n = S_a \circ S_1$.
  (b) Solve for m: $A_m = S_a \circ S_1$.
  (c) Solve for n: $S_n = S_a \circ S_b$.

5. (a) $D_3(2) = 2/\underline{\hspace{1cm}}$. 3
  (b) $D_3(0) = \underline{\hspace{1cm}}$. 0
  (c) $D_3(3) = \underline{\hspace{1cm}}$. 1
  (d) $(D_3 \circ M_3)(2) = \underline{\hspace{1cm}}$. 2
  (e) $(M_3 \circ D_3)(2) = \underline{\hspace{1cm}}$. 2
  (f) $(D_{-3} \circ M_{-3})(2) = \underline{\hspace{1cm}}$. 2
  (g) $D_3 \circ M_3 = M_{\underline{\hspace{0.3cm}}} = D_{\underline{\hspace{0.3cm}}}$. $1, 1$
  (h) $D_3 \circ M_{\underline{\hspace{0.3cm}}} = A_0$. $\frac{1}{3}$
  (i) $M_3 \circ D_{\underline{\hspace{0.3cm}}} = S_0$. $\frac{1}{3}$
  (j) $D_{-3} = M_{\underline{\hspace{0.3cm}}}$. $-\frac{1}{3}$

6. (a) Are the D-functions commutative with respect to composition?
  (b) Is $\mathscr{R}$ commutative with respect to division?
  (c) Is $M_a \circ D_b = D_b \circ M_a$ for every $a, b \in \mathscr{R}$?

7. Is $\mathscr{R}$ associative with respect to division?

8. (a) Solve for n: $D_a \circ D_b = D_n$.
  (b) Solve for m: $D_a \circ D_b = M_m$.

Just a few computations with the S- and D-functions show them to be "undoers" of the effects of A- and M-functions, respectively. We say that subtraction is the *inverse* operation to addition, and division the inverse operation to multiplication. Stated in functional notation, this means

(1) $$(S_a \circ A_a)(x) = x,$$

and

(2) $$(D_a \circ M_a)(x) = x.$$

Let's look at (1) and (2), one at a time.

What is the A-function that has the effect of $S_a \circ A_a$? The important fact that you are relying on is

(3) $$0 + x = x \quad \text{for every } x \in \mathscr{R}.$$

The property of the number zero, expressed in (3), is the basis for calling zero the *identity with respect to addition*, or simply the *additive identity*. In terms of functions,

(3') $$A_0(x) = x.$$

The function that leaves every element fixed is called the *identity function* and is denoted by I. Thus,

$$I : x \to x \quad \text{for every } x \in \mathscr{R}.$$

Equations (3) and (3') tell us that

$$A_0 = I.$$

Our discussion of division as the inverse of multiplication will be continued in the exercises.

1. For what values of n are the following true?

(a) $D_n \circ M_2 = I.$

(b) $M_2 \circ D_n = I.$

(c) $D_n \circ M_{1/3} = I.$

(d) $D_n \circ M_1 = I.$

(e) $D_n \circ M_{-1} = I.$

(f) $M_{-3} \circ D_2 = M_n.$

(g) $M_2 \circ D_{-3} = D_n.$

(h) $D_{-5/3} \circ D_n = I.$

(i) $D_n \circ M_{-7} = M_1.$

(j) $D_n \circ M_0 = I.$

2. (a) The *multiplicative identity* of $\mathcal{R}$ is the number u such that $M_u = I$. What is the real number u?

(b) Find n such that $D_n \circ M_u = I$, where u is the multiplicative identity of $\mathcal{R}$.

3. (a) If $M_3 \circ M_n = I$, then $3n = n \cdot$ _____ = _____, and $n =$ _____.

(b) If $M_n \circ M_{-3} = I$, then $n \cdot (-3) =$ _____, and $n =$ _____.

(c) If $M_3 \circ D_n = I$, then $n =$ _____, and $D_n = M_-.$

(d) If $D_n \circ M_3 = I$, then $n =$ _____, and $D_n = M_-.$

4. (a) If $D_n \circ M_0 = I$, then

$$(D_n \circ M_0)(1) = \text{\_\_\_\_} \qquad \text{and} \qquad I(1) = \text{\_\_\_\_}.$$

Do you find this a shocking result?

(b) If $M_m \circ M_0 = I$, then

$$(M_m \circ M_0)(1) = \text{\_\_\_\_} \qquad \text{and} \qquad I(1) = \text{\_\_\_\_}.$$

(c) What is the trouble that leads to such disturbing results as $0 = 1$?

5. In Exercise 4, assumptions

$$D_n \circ M_0 = I \qquad \text{and} \qquad M_m \circ M_0 = I$$

led to the results that contradict our knowledge of $\mathcal{R}$.

(a) In terms of elements of $\mathcal{R}$, these assumptions are

$$\text{\_\_\_\_} \cdot 0 = 1 \qquad \text{and} \qquad \text{\_\_\_\_} \cdot 0 = 1.$$

Since these assumptions led us to absurdities, we reject them, stating *that there is no* $x \in \mathcal{R}$ such that

$$x \cdot 0 = 1.$$

How were you led to believe otherwise?

(b) The assumption $D_n \circ M_0 = I$ takes for granted the existence of an operation, D_n, that is inverse to multiplication by zero. Thus, we have to scrutinize the statement that functions D_a exist for every $a \in \mathcal{R}$. Which D_a shall we discard?

(c) If $k \neq 0$, then D_k is the inverse operation to M_-. If the function D_0 exists at all, it must be the inverse of M_0. This would imply

$$(M_0 \circ D_0)(1) = I(1)$$

or

$$0 \cdot (\underline{\quad}/\underline{\quad}) = \underline{\quad}.$$

Again you see that a contradiction follows from the assumption that D_0 exists.

7. Relations between the A-, S-, M-, and D-*functions*

   (a) For every $a \in \mathcal{R}$, $S_a = A_-$; and whenever D_a exists $D_a = M_-$.

The relations you gave in part (a) were "old stuff." We will now help you develop some new nontrivial relations.

   (b) In order to see how the A-functions and M-functions are related, expand $a \cdot (b + c)$, and express your result in the form

$$(M_- \circ A_-)(c) = (a \cdot b) + M(\underline{\quad}) = (A_- \circ M_-)(\underline{\quad}).$$

Since this holds for every $c \in \mathcal{R}$,

$$M_- \circ A_- = A_- \circ M_-.$$

   (c) From (b), or otherwise, find the relations

$$M_{1/a} \circ A_b \circ M_a = A_-,$$

$$M_{1/a} \circ A_{ab} \circ M_a = A_-,$$

$$M_a \circ A_b \circ M_{1/a} = A_-.$$

   (d) Find a formula, analogous to those in (c), relating the S-functions and D-functions. [NOTE: The expansions

$$a \cdot (b + c) = (a \cdot b) + (a \cdot c),$$

$$(a + b) \cdot c = (a \cdot c) + (b \cdot c)$$

are called *distributive laws* or, more explicitly, *the distributive laws of multiplication with respect to addition.* Thus your results of (b), (c), and (d) express the distributive laws in terms of functions.]

8. Prove that the additive identity is unique. That is, show that if $x + a = a$, for each $a \in \mathcal{R}$, then $x = 0$.

9. Prove that the multiplicative identity is unique.

10. (a) Prove that there is only one element x, such that

$$a + x = 0.$$

   (b) Prove that there is only one element x, such that

$$a \cdot x = 1 \qquad (a \neq 0).$$

3.4

Postulates for the Algebraic Structure of $\mathscr{R}$ With the information and experience accumulated by reflecting on the algebraic properties of $\mathscr{R}$, we are about ready to siphon off several as postulates, so that the remainder can be proved as consequences. But there is a danger of losing delicious mathematical fruits if we focus too narrow-mindedly on $\mathscr{R}$. The point is that the algebraic properties we will postulate may hold for other number systems (e.g., rational, complex) as well, in which case *we* shall be describing a class of number systems of which $\mathscr{R}$ is but one example. For this reason, we won't prejudice the discussion by calling the system $\mathscr{R}$. Instead, we call this abstract system a *field*. After developing the properties of abstract fields, you will see that several of your old friends are examples, and you may even discover some new number systems as fields.

Definition: *A field $\mathscr{F}$ is a set of elements, with two binary operations $+$ and $\cdot$, satisfying the following postulates.*

  I. *For every $a \in \mathscr{F}$, there are uniquely determined functions A_a and M_a that map $\mathscr{F}$ into $\mathscr{F}$ according to definitions:*

$$A_a : x \to (a + x) \qquad and \qquad M_a : x \to a \cdot x$$

  II. *There are two unequal elements 0 and 1 in $\mathscr{F}$. (That is, $0, 1 \in \mathscr{F}$ and $0 \neq 1$.)†*

  III. *For every $a, b \in \mathscr{F}$.*

  $(+)$ $\qquad\qquad\qquad A_a \circ A_b = A_{a+b}, \quad and$

  $(\cdot)$ $\qquad\qquad\qquad M_a \circ M_b = M_{a \cdot b}.$

  IV. *If I is the identity function then*

  $(+)$ $\qquad\qquad\qquad A_0 = I, \quad and$

  $(\cdot)$ $\qquad\qquad\qquad M_1 = I.$

  V. *For every $a \in \mathscr{F}$, there is a uniquely determined element $-a \in \mathscr{F}$; and if $a \neq 0$, there is also a uniquely determined element $a^{-1} \in \mathscr{F}$.*

  VI. *For every $a \in \mathscr{F}$,*

  $(+)$ $\qquad\qquad\qquad A_a \circ A_{-a} = I; \quad and$

  $(\cdot)$ $\qquad\qquad\qquad M_a \circ M_{a^{-1}} = I, \quad if \ a \neq 0.$

  VII. *For every $a, b \in \mathscr{F}$,*

  $(+)$ $\qquad\qquad\qquad A_a \circ A_b = A_b \circ A_a; \quad and$

  $(\cdot)$ $\qquad\qquad\qquad M_a \circ M_b = M_b \circ M_a.$

---

† The elements 0 and 1 are not to be construed as the real numbers zero and one, but rather as two abstract elements of $\mathscr{F}$ that satisfy the postulates.

VIII. *For every* $a \in \mathscr{F}$,

(+) $$A_a(0) = a, \quad and$$

(·) $$M_a(1) = a.$$

IX. *For every* $a, b \in \mathscr{F}$,

$$M_a \circ A_b = A_{a \cdot b} \circ M_a.$$

It is our hope to develop the algebraic properties of $\mathscr{R}$ from these postulates alone, being careful not to assume anything special regarding the familiar 0, 1, +, ·, $-a$, and a^{-1}. You might expect that when $\mathscr{F} = \mathscr{R}$, these symbols may represent precisely the zero, one, plus, etc., of $\mathscr{R}$; but this must now be proved. Remember: we may assume only what is given in the set of postulates.

What sort of theorems (properties) do we expect to prove? Certainly, the ones we named in the last two sections: associativity, commutativity, identity, and distributivity—but what else? Let's name a few to aim for:

(i) $a + (-a) = 0$.
(ii) $-1 \cdot (a) = -a$.
(iii) *If* $a + b = a + c$, *then* $b = c$.
(iv) The converse of (iii): *If* $b = c$, *then* $a + b = a + c$.
(v) *If* $a + b = 0$, *then* $b = -a$.
(vi) $-0 = 0$.
(vii) $-(-a) = a$.
(viii) $(a^{-1})^{-1} = a$, *if* $a \neq 0$.
(ix) *If* $a \cdot b = 0$, *then* $a = 0$ *or* $b = 0$.
(x) $(a + b) \cdot (c + d) = a \cdot c + a \cdot d + b \cdot c + b \cdot d$.

Before we launch into an effort to prove such statements, we call your attention to a subtle implication of Postulate I. The statement that "A_a and M_a map $\mathscr{F}$ into $\mathscr{F}$" is tantamount to saying that

$$a + x \quad and \quad a \cdot x$$

are both elements of $\mathscr{F}$, for every $x \in \mathscr{F}$. That is, $A_a(x) \in \mathscr{F}$ and $M_a(x) \in \mathscr{F}$. This property of $\mathscr{F}$ is described by saying that $\mathscr{F}$ is *closed with respect to* + and $\mathscr{F}$ is *closed with respect to* ·. Accordingly, Postulate I may be called a *closure* postulate.

Theorem 1: $(a + b) + c = a + (b + c)$, *for every* $a, b, c \in \mathscr{F}$.

Proof: Let's write the left member in terms of A-functions so that we can apply the postulates.

$$(a + b) + c = A_{\_+\_}(c), \qquad \text{by I} \qquad\qquad | \quad a, b$$
$$= (A_{\_} \circ A_{\_})(c), \qquad \text{by III}(+) \qquad | \quad a, b$$
$$= A_{\_}(A_{\_}(c)), \qquad \text{by definition of} \quad | \quad a, b$$
$$= A_{\_}(\underline{\quad} + c), \qquad \text{by I} \qquad\qquad | \quad a, b$$
$$= a + (b + c), \qquad \text{by} \underline{\quad}. \qquad\quad | \quad \text{I}$$

Therefore, we have proved that

$$(a + b) + c = a + (b + c) \qquad \text{for every } a, b, c \in \mathscr{F}.$$

The *quantifying* phrases "for every" and "there exists" occur so often that we give them symbols for shorthand purposes.

∀   read "for every" or "for all" or "all."
∃   read "there exists" or "there is" or "exists."

The notation for the *universal quantifier* is easy to remember as an upside-down "A," standing for *all*. The notation for the *existential quantifier* is remembered as a backwards "E," standing for *exists*. Using this symbolism, Theorem 1 is stated

$$(a + b) + c = a + (b + c), \qquad \forall \, a, b, c \in \mathscr{F},$$
or
$$\forall \, a, b, c \in \mathscr{F}, \qquad (a + b) + c = a + (b + c).$$

Theorem 2: $\forall \, a \in \mathscr{F}, \, a + 0 = a.$

Proof : Again we translate the left member into the language of functions.

$$a + 0 = A_a(\underline{\quad}) \qquad \text{(Why?)} \qquad | \quad 0$$
$$= a, \qquad\qquad \text{by} \underline{\quad}(+). \qquad | \quad \text{VIII}$$

Theorem 3: $a + (-a) = 0, \forall \, a \in \mathscr{F}.$

Proof : Attempting to use a strategy similar to that in the previous two proofs, we write the left member in a form that enables easy application of the *A*-functions.

$$a + (-a) = [a + (-a)] + 0 \qquad \text{by Theorem}\underline{\quad} \quad | \quad 2$$
$$= A\underline{\qquad}(0) \qquad\qquad \text{by I} \qquad\qquad | \quad a + (-a)$$
$$= (A_{\_} \circ A_{\_})(0) \qquad \text{by} \underline{\quad}(+) \qquad | \quad a, -a, \text{III}$$
$$= I(0) \qquad\qquad\quad \text{by} \underline{\quad}(+) \qquad | \quad \text{VI}$$
$$= \underline{\qquad}, \qquad\qquad\quad \text{by Definition I.} \quad | \quad 0$$

Therefore, $a + (-a) = 0$.

Theorem 4: $a + b = b + a, \forall\, a, b \in \mathcal{F}$.

Proof: Try the same strategy as in Theorem 3.

$a + b = (a + b) + \underline{\quad}$	by Theorem $\underline{\quad}$		$0, 2$
$\quad = A\underline{\quad}(\underline{\quad})$	(Justify!)		$a + b, 0$
$\quad = (A\_ \circ A\_)(\underline{\quad})$	(Justify!)		$a, b, 0$

Now using VII($+$), you ought to be able to finish by yourself.

If $b = c$, then it is easy to see that $a + b = a + c$. Explain why this is "easy to see." How would you quantify the statement? Is the converse true?

Perhaps we should state precisely what we mean by the converse of a given proposition. If a statement is of the form:

$$\text{if } p, \quad \text{then } q,$$

we call it an *implication*. For, it can be rephrased

$$p \text{ implies } q.$$

The converse of this statement is

$$q \text{ implies } p;$$

that is, we interchange the hypothesis and conclusion of a given implication in order to obtain its converse. In the standard mathematical shorthand:

given proposition: $\quad p \Rightarrow q \quad$ (read "p implies q")

its converse: $\quad\quad q \Rightarrow p.$

Returning to the question before us, we have the proposition

$$b = c \Rightarrow a + b = a + c.$$

The converse is then

$$a + b = a + c \Rightarrow b = c.$$

How would you quantify the converse (after you quantify the given proposition)?

Let's investigate using the notation for implication. Beginning with the hypothesis, we have

$a + b = a + c \Rightarrow A\_(b) = A\_(\underline{\quad})$	a, a, c
$\Rightarrow A_{-a}(A_a(b)) = A\_(A\_(c))$	$-a, a$

$$\Rightarrow (A_{-a} \circ A_a)(b) = (A_{\_} \circ A_{\_})(c) \qquad | \quad -a, a$$

$$\Rightarrow I(b) = \underline{\qquad}(c) \qquad\qquad\qquad | \quad I$$

$$\Rightarrow b = c.$$

Therefore, by a sequence of implications we have

(1) $$a + b = a + c \Rightarrow b = c.$$

Were there any restrictions on a at any stage of the argument? Is the statement (1) true for all or for only some $a \in \mathscr{F}$?

We will dignify the *cancellation property of* $+$, the result of the previous paragraph, by calling it

Theorem 5: $\forall\, a \in \mathscr{F},\ a + b = a + c \Rightarrow b = c.$

Exercise: Prove that
$$A_a(x) = A_a(y) \Rightarrow x = y.$$

[NOTE: The fact that A_a is a function together with this exercise shows that A_a defines a one-to-one (1-1) correspondence between the elements of $\mathscr{F}$ and the elements of $\mathscr{F}$. Thus, A_a is called a "1-1 *function*," or a "1-1 *mapping*," or is simply said to be 1-1.

Also, note that the universal quantifier $\forall_a$ is "understood." Mathematical language is often written without quantifiers, when the context makes the situation quite clear. This is analogous to using pronouns in prose; when there are dangers of misinterpretation, you return to the appropriate noun. When we think there is danger of confusion we will specify the quantifiers and other items necessary to remove ambiguities. Otherwise, we leave the statements as simple as possible.]

From the definition of A_a, we know that
$$A_a : x \to a + x.$$

But suppose you know that some A-function F operates so that
$$F : x \to a + x.$$

Must the function be A_a? Investigate the alternatives, before reading the next theorem.

Theorem 6: $A_a = A_b \Rightarrow a = b.$

Proof:

$$A_a(x) = A_b(x) \Rightarrow a + x = b + x$$

$$\Rightarrow x + a = x + b \qquad \text{by Theorem } \underline{\qquad} \qquad | \quad 4$$

$$\Rightarrow a = b \qquad\qquad\quad \text{by Theorem } \underline{\qquad}. \qquad | \quad 5$$

PROGRAMMED TEXT
FOLLOWS

This proves the theorem. How does it answer the question posed in the preceding paragraph?

3.4.1
EXERCISES

1. Prove: If $a + b = 0$, then $b = -a$ and $a = -b$. [*Hint:* Use one of the theorems to write 0 in an alternative form.]

2. Prove that $-0 = 0$. [*Hint:* Prove that $0 + 0 = 0$, and use this equation.]

3. Theorem 7: $a = -(-a), \forall\, a \in \mathscr{F}$. Prove this result.

4. Theorem 8: $a \cdot (b \cdot c) = (a \cdot b) \cdot c, \forall\, a, b, c \in \mathscr{F}$. Prove this result.

5. Theorem 9: $a \cdot b = b \cdot a, \forall\, a, b \in \mathscr{F}$. Fill the blanks and justify each equality in the argument.

$$a \cdot b = M\_(1) = (M\_ \circ M\_)(1) = (M_b \circ M\_)(1)$$
$$= M\_(1) = b \cdot a.$$

6. Prove: $x + x = x \Rightarrow x = 0$.

Thus far we have proved associative and commutative properties of $\mathscr{F}$ with respect to its two operations. That 0 is the identity with respect to $+$ is the content of Theorem _____. We now turn attention to the proof that 1 is the identity element with respect to $\cdot$.

| | 2 |

Theorem 10: $a \cdot 1 = 1 \cdot a = a, \forall\, a \in \mathscr{F}$.

Proof:

$a \cdot 1 = 1 \cdot a,$ by Theorem _____, | 9

and

$a \cdot 1 = M\_(\_\_\_\_\_) = a,$ by Postulate _____($\cdot$). | $a, 1,$ VIII

The identity with respect to $+$ has a very special multiplicative property as shown in

Theorem 11: $a \cdot 0 = 0, \forall\, a \in \mathscr{F}$.

Proof: $a \cdot 0 = M\_(0).$ | a

Since $0 = 0 + 0 = A_0(0)$, we have

$$a \cdot 0 = M\_(0) = M\_(A_0(0)) \qquad\qquad a, a$$

$$= (M\_ \circ A_0)(0) \qquad\qquad a$$

$$= (A_{a \cdot 0} \circ M\_)(0) \quad \text{by Postulate \_\_\_\_} \qquad a, \text{IX}$$

$$= A_{a \cdot 0}(M\_(0)) \qquad\qquad a$$

$$= a \cdot 0 + \text{\_\_\_\_} \cdot 0. \qquad\qquad a$$

But $x + x = x \Rightarrow x = \text{\_\_\_\_}$. Therefore, $\qquad\qquad 0$

$$a \cdot 0 = 0.$$

3.4.2
EXERCISES

1. Complete the following alternative proof of Theorem 11, justifying each step. You must show that $M\_(0) = 0$. To this end, write

$$A_a(0) = a = M\_(1) = M\_(A\_(0)) = (M\_ \circ A\_)(0)$$

$$= (A\_ \circ M\_)(0) = A\_(M\_(0)) = A\_(a \cdot 0).$$

Corollary: $\quad M_a(0) = \text{\_\_\_\_}, \forall\, a \in \mathscr{F}.$

2. Theorem 12: $\quad -1 \cdot a = -a, \forall\, a \in \mathscr{F}$. Prove this. [*Hint:* You can prove the theorem if you can show that $-1 \cdot a + a = 0$ or $a \cdot (-1) + a = 0$.]

3. Theorem 13: $\quad a \cdot a^{-1} = 1$. Note that you know a^{-1} exists only if you know that $a \neq 0$. Prove the theorem for all $a \neq 0$.

4. (a) Show that 0^{-1} does not exist in $\mathscr{F}$. [*Hint:* Construct a *reductio ad absurdum* proof by computing $(M_0 \circ M_{0^{-1}})(x)$.]
(b) What is 1^{-1}?

5. Prove: **Theorem 14:** $\quad (a^{-1})^{-1} = a$.

6. *Distribution laws.* Prove the following.
(a) **Theorem 15:** $\quad a \cdot (b + c) = (a \cdot b) + (a \cdot c)$.
(b) **Theorem 16:** $\quad (a + b) \cdot c = (a \cdot c) + (b \cdot c)$.
(c) $\quad (a + b) \cdot (c + d) = (a \cdot c) + (d \cdot a) + (c \cdot b) + (d \cdot b)$.

7. Theorem 17: $\quad$ If $a \cdot b = 0$, then $a = 0$ or $b = 0$ (*or both*). Prove this result, with or without the following hint: If $a \neq 0$, then a^{-1} exists; show that this assumption implies $b = 0$.

Simplification of Notation: In the foregoing exercises and discussion we have adhered strictly to the agreed-upon symbolism of fields, and have not taken the conventional shorthands of elementary algebra. Now that you see that much of the algebra of fields is like high school algebra, we agree on the following simplifications:

Simplified version	of
$a - b$	$a + (-b)$
ab	$a \cdot b$
$a + b + c$	$(a + b) + c$
$a + b + c + d$	$[(a + b) + c] + d$
$a + b - c$	$(a + b) + (-c)$
$a - b + c$	$[a + (-b)] + c$
$a - b - c$	$[a + (-b)] + (-c)$
$a - b - c - d$	$\{[a + (-b)] + (-c)\} + (-d)$
$a + bc$	$a + (bc)$

The last listing indicates that *operation · takes precedence over* +. Thus, if we mean $(a + b) \cdot c$, we may drop " $\cdot$ " but may not drop the parentheses.

8. (a) Write in abbreviated form: $[a - b - (c + d)] + [e - (f + g)]$.
   (b) Justifying each step by a field property, solve for x:

$$ax + b = 0, \qquad a \neq 0.$$

   (c) Justifying each step by a field property, solve for x:

$$(x - r_1)(x - r_2) = 0.$$

   (d) Justifying each step by a field property, solve for x:

$$(x \cdot x - a \cdot a)(x + b) = 0.$$

9. The Real Field. Our principal purpose in constructing the concept of field was to be able to treat $\mathscr{R}$ as a concrete example of this abstract algebraic structure. Do you agree that $\mathscr{R}$ is a field?

   (a) Here is a table of corresponding notions of an abstract field $\mathscr{F}$ and $\mathscr{R}$. Fill the blanks.

$\mathscr{F}$			0	=		a^{-1}		1				
$\mathscr{R}$	+	×		=	D_a		÷		S_a	−	$1/a$	a/b	a^3

   (b) Let $a, b, c, d \in \mathscr{R}$, with $b \neq 0$ and $d \neq 0$. Then

$$\frac{a}{b} + \frac{c}{d} = \frac{\rule{2cm}{0.4pt}}{\rule{2cm}{0.4pt}}.$$

Justify each step of this addition by a field property.

10. (a) Let $a, b \in \mathscr{R}$. Using the field properties of $\mathscr{R}$, justify the laws of signs for multiplication

$$a(-b) = (-a)b = -(ab)$$
$$(-a)(-b) = ab.$$

(b) If $a, b \in \mathcal{R}$ and $b \neq 0$, justify

$$\frac{a}{-b} = \frac{-a}{b} = -\left(\frac{a}{b}\right).$$

3.5

Field Properties (Second Version)

In this section we would like to look at the field properties directly in terms of the elements of the field, rather than through the A-functions and M-functions. The aim is to obtain an alternative definition for a field that is logically equivalent to the one given in Sec. 3.4. One obvious approach is to translate the existing definition into the language of elements, devoid of mention of A- and M-functions. This gives us the standard definition that is found in most textbooks.

Definition: *A field $\mathcal{F}$ is a set of (at least two distinct) elements, with two binary operations $+$ and $\cdot$, satisfying the following postulates.*

A_1. $\forall\, a,\, b \in \mathcal{F}$, $a + b$ *is a uniquely defined element of $\mathcal{F}$.* [*Closure.*]

A_2. $(a + b) + c = a + (b + c)$, $\forall\, a,\, b,\, c \in \mathcal{F}$. [*Associativity.*]

A_3. $\exists\, 0 \in \mathcal{F}$, *such that* $a + 0 = a$, $\forall\, a \in \mathcal{F}$. [*Identity.*]

A_4. $\forall\, a \in \mathcal{F}$, $\exists\, -a \in \mathcal{F}$, *such that* $a + (-a) = 0$. [*Inverse.*]

A_5. $\forall\, a,\, b \in \mathcal{F}$, $a + b = b + a$. [*Commutativity.*]

M_1. $\forall\, a,\, b \in \mathcal{F}$, $a \cdot b$ *is a uniquely defined element of $\mathcal{F}$.* [*Closure.*]

M_2. $(a \cdot b) \cdot c = a \cdot (b \cdot c)$, $\forall\, a,\, b,\, c \in \mathcal{F}$. [*Associativity.*]

M_3. $\exists\, 1 \in \mathcal{F}$ *such that*

$$a \cdot 1 = a, \quad \forall\, a \in \mathcal{F}. \qquad [\textit{Identity.}]$$

M_4. $\forall\, a \in \mathcal{F}$, *such that* $a \neq 0$, *there exists an element* $a^{-1} \in \mathcal{F}$ *satisfying the equation*

$$a \cdot a^{-1} = 1. \qquad [\textit{Inverse.}]$$

M_5. $\forall\, a,\, b \in \mathcal{F}$, $a \cdot b = b \cdot a$. [*Commutativity.*]

D. $\forall\, a,\, b,\, c \in \mathcal{F}$, $a \cdot (b + c) = a \cdot b + a \cdot c$. [*Distributivity (left).*]

[NOTE. As indicated in the footnote on p. 67, the elements 0 and 1 are not to be construed as the real numbers zero and one. 0 and 1 are the elements of $\mathcal{F}$ that play the roles of additive and multiplicative identities, respectively. Similarly, $+$ and $\cdot$ are not to be construed as ordinary addition and multiplication, but rather as abstract operations with respect to which $\mathcal{F}$ satisfies the given postulates. Finally, the symbols "$-$" and "$^{-1}$" used to express inverses should not connote *negative* and *fraction*. *Negative* and *positive*, while most important in the real field, are not inherent in the definition of fields in general. We shall say more about this in Sec. 3.9.]

It is certainly clear that the definition of field given in Sec. 3.4 implies the one given here; for the properties A_1–A_5, M_1–M_5, and D are consequences of the former definition. The logical equivalence of the two definitions will be shown if the converse can be proved. What needs to be done?

The first major question arises in proving Postulate II, namely that $0 \neq 1$. Let's see what has to be done in order to accomplish this.

Suppose $0 = 1$ and $a \neq 0$. (How do you know there is such an $a \in \mathscr{F}$?) Then

$$a \cdot 1 = a, \qquad \text{by } M_3.$$

Therefore

$$a \cdot 1 \neq 0, \qquad \text{since } a \neq 0.$$

If we knew that $a \cdot 0 = 0$ (as in Theorem 11 of Sec. 3.4), we would have the desired contradiction. Thus, our first target is

Theorem 1: $\quad x \cdot 0 = 0, \forall\, x \in \mathscr{F}.$

Proof: Justify each step.

$$x \cdot 0 = x \cdot (0 + 0)$$
$$= x \cdot 0 + x \cdot 0.$$

Therefore

$$x \cdot 0 + (-(x \cdot 0)) = (x \cdot 0 + x \cdot 0) + (-(x \cdot 0)).$$
$$x \cdot 0 + (-(x \cdot 0)) = x \cdot 0 + [x \cdot 0 + (-(x \cdot 0))],$$
$$0 = x \cdot 0 + 0.$$

Therefore

$$0 = x \cdot 0.$$

Now you can easily prove

Theorem 2: $\quad 0 \neq 1.$

3.5.1
EXERCISES

1. On the basis of the definition of this section, prove the following:
   (a) If $a = b$ and $c = d$, then $a + c = b + d$ and $ac = bd$.
   (b) $(a + b) \cdot c = a \cdot c + b \cdot c, \forall\, a, b, c \in \mathscr{F}.$

ALGEBRAIC STRUCTURES
SECTION 3.5

(c) $a + b = c \Rightarrow b = c + (-a)$.

(d) If $a \neq 0$ and $ab = c$, then $b = a^{-1} \cdot c$.

2. On the basis of the definition of this section, prove the cancellation laws:

(a) $a + b = a + c \Rightarrow b = c$.

(b) If $a \neq 0$, then $ab = ac \Rightarrow b = c$.

3. Prove:

(a) $\forall \, a \in \mathscr{F}, \ -(-a) = a$.

(b) If $a \neq 0$, $(a^{-1})^{-1} = a$.

4. (a) Prove that the additive identity 0 is unique. That is, show that if $a + x = a$, $\forall \, a \in \mathscr{F}$, then $x = 0$.

(b) Prove that the multiplicative identity 1 is unique.

(c) The element $-a$ is called the *additive inverse of a*. What result establishes a as the additive inverse of $-a$? Prove that additive inverses are unique. That is, prove that

$$a + x = 0 \Rightarrow x = -a.$$

(d) a^{-1} is called the *multiplicative inverse of a*. If $a \neq 0$, then a is the multiplicative inverse of a^{-1}. Prove the uniqueness of multiplicative inverses.

(e) Prove that $(-1) \cdot a = -a$.

5. Carry out the resolution of the two definitions of field. That is, define A_a and M_a for every $a \in \mathscr{F}$, and prove that Postulates I–VIII of Sec. 3.4 follow from the new definition.

6. (a) Define the functions S_a and D_a in terms of the A-functions and M-functions.

(b) Give a definition of field in terms of S-functions and D-functions, alone.

7. Definition: *A schmield $\mathscr{S}$ is a set of (at least two distinct) elements, with four binary operations $+$, $-$, $\cdot$, and $/$, satisfying the following postulates.*

I. *There are two special elements, 0 and 1, in $\mathscr{S}$.*

II. *If $a, b \in \mathscr{S}$, then $a + b, a - b, a \cdot b$ are uniquely determined elements of $\mathscr{S}$; a/b is a uniquely determined element of $\mathscr{S}$ if $b \neq 0$.*

III. $\forall \, a, b \in \mathscr{S}$,

$(+)$ $a + b = b + a$,

$(\cdot)$ $a \cdot b = b \cdot a$.

IV. $\forall \, a, b, c \in \mathscr{S}$,

$(+)$ $a + (b + c) = (a + b) + c$,

$(\cdot)$ $a \cdot (b \cdot c) = (a \cdot b) \cdot c$.

V. $\forall \, a, b, c \in \mathscr{S}, a \cdot (b + c) = (a \cdot b) + (a \cdot c)$.

VI. $\forall \, a, b \in \mathscr{S}, a + (b - a) = b$; *if, in addition $a \neq 0$, then $a \cdot (b/a) = b$.*

(a) Justify the following proposition for schmields: If a, b, c, and d are in a schmield, such that $a = b$ and $c = d$, then

$$a + c = b + d,$$

$$a - c = b - d,$$

$$a \cdot c = b \cdot d;$$

if, in addition, $c \neq 0$, then $a/c = b/d$.

(b) Assuming x, 3, and 4 are elements of a schmield and using only the properties of schmields, we shall solve for x in the equation $x - 3 = 4$. You supply the reasons.

$$x - 3 = 4 \Rightarrow 3 + (x - 3) = 3 + 4 \qquad \text{by} \underline{\hphantom{xxx}}.$$
$$\Rightarrow x = 3 + 4 \qquad \text{by} \underline{\hphantom{xxx}}.$$

(c) Assuming x, 4, and 7 are in a schmield, we attempt to solve for x in the equation $x + 4 = 7$. You help.

$$x + 4 = 7 \Rightarrow (x + 4) + (0 - 4) = 7 + (0 - 4) \qquad \text{by} \underline{\hphantom{xxx}}.$$
$$\Rightarrow x + (4 + (0 - 4)) = 7 + (0 - 4) \qquad \text{by} \underline{\hphantom{xxx}}.$$
$$\Rightarrow x + \underline{\hphantom{xxx}} = 7 + (0 - 4) \qquad \text{by} \underline{\hphantom{xxx}}.$$

Can we go farther in the usual way? That is, do you know whether $x + 0 = x$ is true in a schmield?

(d) Let's try and do better with the equation $2 \cdot x = 1$, assuming 2, x, and 1 are in a schmield.

$1/2$ is in the schmield, by $\underline{\hphantom{xxx}}$.

$$2 \cdot x = 1 \Rightarrow (1/2) \cdot (2 \cdot x) = (1/2) \cdot 1 \qquad \text{by} \underline{\hphantom{xxx}}.$$
$$\Rightarrow ((1/2) \cdot 2) \cdot x = (1/2) \cdot 1 \qquad \text{by} \underline{\hphantom{xxx}}.$$
$$\Rightarrow (2 \cdot (1/2)) \cdot x = (1/2) \cdot 1 \qquad \text{by} \underline{\hphantom{xxx}}.$$
$$\Rightarrow \underline{\hphantom{xxx}} \cdot x = (1/2) \cdot 1 \qquad \text{by VI}.$$

Can we go farther in the usual way? That is, do we know whether $1 \cdot x = x$ is true in a schmield?

8. (a) Prove the following theorems for schmields. Also, fill in the implicit quantifiers.

$T_1.\ (a + b) \cdot c = (a \cdot c) + (b \cdot c).$
$T_2.\ (b - a) + a = b.$
$T_3.\ \text{If } a \neq 0, (b/a) \cdot a = b.$

(b) We would hope to be able to prove that

$$b + a = c + a \Rightarrow b = c.$$

Try it before going farther, but be sure that you use only the schmield properties.

In order to be able to use the information at our disposal we proceed as follows:

$$b + a = c + a \Rightarrow (b + a) + (0 - a) = c + a + (\underline{\hphantom{xx}} - \underline{\hphantom{xx}}) \qquad \text{by} \underline{\hphantom{xxx}}.$$
$$\Rightarrow b + [a + (0 - a)] = c + [a + (\underline{\hphantom{xx}} - \underline{\hphantom{xx}})] \qquad \text{by} \underline{\hphantom{xxx}}.$$
$$\Rightarrow b + \underline{\hphantom{xx}} = c + \underline{\hphantom{xx}} \qquad \text{by} \underline{\hphantom{xxx}}.$$

Thus far, we do not have sufficient information to infer that $b = c$.

(c) Prove that: If $a \neq 0$ and $b \cdot a = c \cdot a$, then

$$b \cdot 1 = c \cdot 1.$$

(d) Prove that $b = (b - a) + a$.

ALGEBRAIC STRUCTURES
SECTION 3.5

9. Continuation of schmields.

    (a) Assist with the proof of the following theorem:

T_4. $b + (a - a) = b.$

Proof: Using 8(d) to rewrite the left member, we get

$$b + (a - a) = [(\underline{\hspace{1cm}} - \underline{\hspace{1cm}}) + \underline{\hspace{1cm}}] + (a - a)$$
$$= (\underline{\hspace{1cm}} - \underline{\hspace{1cm}}) + [\underline{\hspace{1cm}} + (a - a)] \qquad \text{by} \underline{\hspace{1cm}}$$
$$= (\underline{\hspace{1cm}} - \underline{\hspace{1cm}}) + a \qquad \text{by} \underline{\hspace{1cm}}$$
$$= b.$$

    (b) Similarly, for the following theorem:

T_5. $a - a = b - b.$

Proof: From T_4, we have

$$(\underline{\hspace{1cm}} - \underline{\hspace{1cm}}) + (a - a) = b - b,$$

and
$$(\underline{\hspace{1cm}} - \underline{\hspace{1cm}}) + (b - b) = a - a.$$

Complete the proof.

    (c) Since T_5 states that $x - x$ is independent of the element x in the schmield, we are then justified in ascribing a symbol for this unique element. We thus *define* the element $0: 0 = a - a$. Now you are ready to prove

T_6. $b + 0 = b.$

    (d) Prove the analogues of T_4 and T_5:

T_7. $b \cdot (a/a) = b$ if $a \neq 0.$

T_8. $a/a = b/b$ if $a \neq 0$ and $b \neq 0.$

    (e) Give an appropriate definition for 1 and prove

T_9. $a \cdot 1 = a.$

10. Continuation of schmields.

    (a) Prove the following:

T_{10}. $b + a = c + a \Rightarrow b = c.$

T_{11}. If $a \neq 0$ and $b \cdot a = c \cdot a$, then $b = c.$

    (b) Assist in the proof of

T_{12}. $x + a = b \Rightarrow x = b - a.$

Proof: Using 8(d) to rewrite the right member of $x + a = b$, we obtain

$$x + a = (\underline{\hspace{1cm}} - \underline{\hspace{1cm}}) + a.$$

Then

$$(x + a) + (0 - a) = [(\underline{\hspace{1cm}} - \underline{\hspace{1cm}}) + a] + (\underline{\hspace{1cm}} - \underline{\hspace{1cm}}) \qquad \text{by} \underline{\hspace{1cm}}.$$

Complete the proof on your own.

    (c) Prove: T_{13}. *If $a \neq 0$ and $a \cdot x = b$, then $x = b/a$.*

    (d) Prove that every schmield is a field, and conversely every field is a schmield. [*Hint*: Define: $-a = 0 - a$ and $a^{-1} = 1/a$ if $a \neq 0$.]

    Note that if you carry out this part you have still another definition for a field.

11. Proofs, as presented in textbooks, usually obscure the method by which they were discovered. We will discuss this matter with regard to some theorems of schmields (which you now know are simply fields). We shall use only the definition of schmield and theorems T_1–T_{13}.

    (a) T_{14}. $a \cdot (b - c) = (a \cdot b) - (a \cdot c)$.

One approach to discovering a proof is to think about the theorem as follows: $x = b - c$ is the solution to $c + x = b$, and $y = (a \cdot b) - (a \cdot c)$ is the solution to $(a \cdot c) + y = a \cdot b$. Explain.

Thus the problem is to prove that $a \cdot x = y$, i.e., $a \cdot x$ is the solution to the equation which defines y:

(1) $$(a \cdot c) + (a \cdot x) = a \cdot b.$$

But, from the equation defining x, we can obtain

(2) $$a \cdot (c + x) = a \cdot b. \quad \text{(How?)}$$

Now you write the polished proof as follows

$$c + (b - \underline{\quad\quad}) = b \qquad\qquad \text{by} \underline{\quad\quad},$$

$$a \cdot [c + (b - \underline{\quad\quad})] = \underline{\quad\quad} \cdot b \qquad \text{by} \underline{\quad\quad},$$

$$(a \cdot c) + \underline{\quad\quad\quad} = \underline{\quad\quad} \cdot b \qquad \text{by} \underline{\quad\quad},$$

$$\underline{\quad\quad\quad} = \underline{\quad\quad} \cdot b - a \cdot c \qquad \text{by} \underline{\quad\quad}.$$

And you appear to be ingenious!

    (b) T_{15}. $a + (b - c) = (a + b) - c$.

Reasoning the same way as in (a), we note that $x = (a + b) - c$ is the solution to the equation

(3) $$c + x = \underline{\quad\quad} + \underline{\quad\quad},$$

and $y = b - c$ is the solution to the equation

(4) $$c + y = \underline{\quad\quad}.$$

We want to prove that

(5) $$a + y = x.$$

Investigate to see whether $a + y$ satisfies (3), which defines x. That is, find out whether

$$c + (a + y) = a + b$$

is true for all a, b, and c in the schmield. [*Hint*: What do you know about y? And, how can you use it?]

After discovering a method of proof, you might choose to write it in the form:

$$c + [a + (b - c)] = (\underline{\hspace{1cm}} + \underline{\hspace{1cm}}) + (\underline{\hspace{1cm}} - \underline{\hspace{1cm}}) \qquad \text{by} \underline{\hspace{1cm}},$$
$$= (a + \underline{\hspace{1cm}}) + (\underline{\hspace{1cm}} - \underline{\hspace{1cm}}) \qquad \text{by} \underline{\hspace{1cm}},$$
$$= a + [\underline{\hspace{1cm}} + (\underline{\hspace{1cm}} - \underline{\hspace{1cm}})] \qquad \text{by} \underline{\hspace{1cm}},$$
$$= a + \underline{\hspace{1cm}} \qquad \text{by} \underline{\hspace{1cm}}.$$

Therefore

$$[a + (b - c)] = (a + b) - c \qquad \text{by} \underline{\hspace{1cm}}.$$

In this presentation, we have erased all traces of the work involved in thinking it up. The proof seems to flow effortlessly like a Beethoven symphony. The preliminary work is analogous to what appears in Beethoven's sketch books.

12. Taking hints from Exercise 11, find proofs for the following:

T_{16}. $a - (b + c) = (a - b) - c$.

T_{17}. $a - (b - c) = (a - b) + c$.

3.6

Examples of Fields   Our principal aim in introducing the abstract concept of field was to enable us to study the algebraic properties of the real numbers within a deductive system. The intent, as you remember, was to postulate a sufficient amount of the "right" properties, so that the rest would be derived as theorems. Thus, $\mathscr{R}$, as we know it from experience, should be a notable example of a field. In order to put this within a logical framework we introduce this fact as a postulate.

Postulate F: $\mathscr{R}$ *is a field with respect to its operations addition* $(+)$ *and multiplication* $(\cdot)$.

In studying $\mathscr{R}$ it is natural to wonder whether there is a set in $\mathscr{R}$, smaller than $\mathscr{R}$ itself, that is also a field with respect to real number addition and multiplication. That is: Is there a *subfield* within $\mathscr{R}$? If so, what is the smallest subfield within $\mathscr{R}$? We shall investigate.

Any field within $\mathscr{R}$ must contain the two elements 0 and 1. By additions alone, we see that

$$1 + 1 = 2, \qquad 2 + 1 = 3, \qquad 3 + 1 = 4, \qquad \text{etc.}$$

must be in any subfield of $\mathscr{R}$. Thus, any subfield of $\mathscr{R}$ must contain all the positive integers and 0. What field properties tell you that all the negative integers must also be in any subfield of $\mathscr{R}$?

So far, we have the set of integers in any subfield. Test to see which one of the field properties (in Sec. 3.5) is not satisfied by this set. What is missing?

The multiplicative inverse of the nonzero integer n is $1/n$, so the subfield must contain these fractions as well. Now it is an easy matter for you to show that every rational number must be in any subfield of $\mathscr{R}$.

Exercise: Verify that the rational numbers form a subfield of $\mathscr{R}$.

Hereafter, the set of rationals will be designated by $\mathscr{R}a$. Are there any other subfields of $\mathscr{R}$ besides $\mathscr{R}a$? If there are, we know that they must contain $\mathscr{R}a$. Why?

3.6.1
EXERCISES

In the following exercises use the field postulates A_1–A_5, M_1–M_5, and D, given in Sec. 3.5.

1. (a) Suppose a subfield of $\mathscr{R}$ has $\sqrt{2}$ in it. What field postulates guarantee that all numbers of the form

$$a + \sqrt{2}, \qquad a \in \mathscr{R}a$$

are in the subfield?

(b) What field postulates guarantee that all numbers of the form $b\sqrt{2}$, $b \in \mathscr{R}a$, belong to the subfield?

(c) What is the number x, such that

$$(3 + \sqrt{2})x = 1?$$

(d) If the product

$$(3 + \sqrt{2})(3 + a\sqrt{2})$$

is rational, then $a = $ _____.

(e) If $(3 - 2\sqrt{2})(3 + a\sqrt{2})$ is rational, then $a = $ _____.

(f) Write the multiplicative inverse of $3 + \sqrt{2}$ in the form $a + b\sqrt{2}$, where $a, b \in \mathscr{R}a$.

(g) The set of elements of the form

$$a + b\sqrt{2}, \qquad a, b \in \mathscr{R}a$$

is usually denoted by $\mathscr{R}a(\sqrt{2})$, and is called the *adjunction* of $\sqrt{2}$ to $\mathscr{R}a$, for we have adjoined $\sqrt{2}$ to the field of rationals. Verify that $\mathscr{R}a(\sqrt{2})$ is a field.

2. Prove that (a) $\mathscr{R}a(\sqrt{3})$ is a field, (b) $\mathscr{R}a(\sqrt{-1})$ is a field.

3. (a) In high school algebra you write

$$x^2 + x - 6 = (x + 3)(x - 2), \quad \forall\, x \in \mathscr{R}.$$

Justify this factorization on the basis of Postulate F.

(b) Solve for x: $2x^2 + 5x - 3 = 0$. Can you justify each step by the field properties?

(c) Solve for x: $x^2 + 2xy + y^2 = 0$.

(d) Solve for x: $x^2 - y^2 = 0$.

(e) Solve for x: $x^4 - 5x^2 - 6 = 0$.

4. Quadratic equations (in $\mathscr{R}$) of the form $x^2 = a^2$ are often solved by taking the square root of both members, arriving at the result $x = \pm a$. Justify this reasoning and solve the following for x.

(a) $9x^2 = 4$.

(b) $(x - 14)^2 = 2$.

(c) $\left(x + \dfrac{b}{2a}\right)^2 = \dfrac{b^2 - 4ac}{4a^2}$.

5. Let $\mathscr{F}$ be any field and $a, b \in \mathscr{F}$. Prove that

$$(a + b)^2 = a^2 + 2ab + b^2.$$

6. In each of (a)–(d), find real numbers r and s such that the equation is true for all $x \in \mathscr{R}$.

(a) $x^2 + 2x + r = (x + s)^2$.

(b) $x^2 + 4x + 4 = (x + s)^2$.

(c) $x^2 + Ax + r = (x + s)^2$.

(d) $x^2 + \dfrac{b}{a}x + r = (x + s)^2$.

(e) Formulate a general rule for "completing the square," if given an expression of the form

$$x^2 + Ax.$$

7. The general quadratic equation in x is written

$$ax^2 + bx + c = 0, \quad a \neq 0 \text{ and } a, b, c \in \mathscr{R}.$$

(a) Transform the general quadratic equation so that the left member is ready for completing the square as in Exercise 6.

(b) Complete the square on the left member, being sure to add the same number to the right member as you added to the left.

(c) Making use of Exercise 4, deduce the familiar *quadratic formula*

$$x = \frac{-b \pm \sqrt{b^2 - 4ac}}{2a}.$$

(d) Can you justify all of your steps in the derivation?

8. Solve for x:

   (a) $2x^2 + xy + 1 = 0$.

   (b) $2x^2y + xy + z = 0$.

   (c) $x^2 = 256y^4$.

9. (a) Let $x^2 - 126x - 165 = 0$. Then

$$x = y + k \Rightarrow y^2 + By + C = 0.$$

Find B and C in terms of k. Find k so that $B = 0$, and solve for y. How can you obtain a solution for x if you know y?

   (b) Apply the method of (a) to the general quadratic equation

$$x^2 + bx + c = 0.$$

   (c) If B and C are defined as in (a), and b and c as in (b), calculate $B^2 - 4C$ in terms of b and c.

   (d) Substitute $x = y + k$ into the cubic equation

$$x^3 + 6x^2 - 4x + 7 = 0.$$

Then find a value of k such that the equation in y takes the form

$$y^3 + py + q = 0,$$

where p and q are specific numbers.

10. Find b and c such that

$$(x - r)(x - s) = x^2 + bx + c$$

for all numbers x.

   (a) Calculate $b^2 - 4c$ in terms of r and s.

   (b) Let $Q_0 = 2, Q_1 = r + s, Q_2 = r^2 + s^2$. Calculate

$$Q_2 + bQ_1 + cQ_0.$$

If $Q_3 = r^3 + s^3$, calculate

$$Q_3 + bQ_2 + cQ_1.$$

Obtain formulas for Q_2 and Q_3 in terms of b and c.

   (c) Generalize part (b) to obtain a formula for $Q_4 = r^4 + s^4$ in terms of b and c.

   (d) Generalize this whole problem to the equation

$$(x - r)(x - s)(x - t) = x^3 + bx^2 + cx + d.$$

   Part (a) may be harder than parts (b) and (c).

11. (a) Find the general form for the elements of $\mathcal{R}a(\sqrt[3]{2})$, the smallest subfield of $\mathcal{R}$ containing $\sqrt[3]{2}$.

   (b) What is the smallest subfield of $\mathcal{R}$ that contains both $\sqrt{2}$ and $\sqrt{3}$?

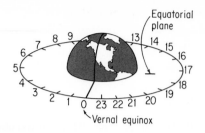

Equatorial plane

Vernal equinox

Figure 3-1

Although the real field is the most important one for our purpose, it will be instructive to discuss other fields as well. The remainder of this section will be devoted to this pursuit.

Analogous to longitude, which is used in locating a position on the surface of the earth, is the concept of *right ascension* used by astronomers and physicists in locating heavenly bodies.

Right ascension (R.A.) is measured eastward on the equatorial plane from a fixed point in the sky (which has been arbitrarily set as the vernal equinox). The unit of measurement is called the hour (h) with a complete circuit of the earth divided into 24 hours (24^h) (see Fig. 3.1).

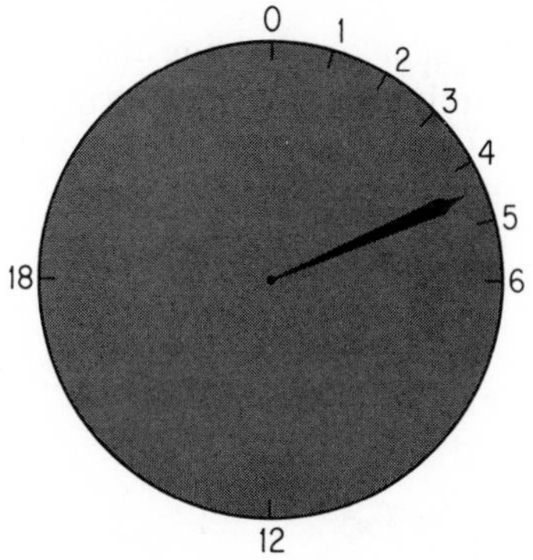

Suppose we are tracking a satellite that is moving eastward. For simplicity, we will assume that the satellite moves in the equatorial plane of the earth and that its starting position was at 0^h R.A. It will be simplest if we think of the R.A. of the satellite being indicated by a clock with a single hand (see Fig. 3.2).

After the satellite has traversed 17^h, its R.A. is 17^h so the indicator points to "17"; after the satellite has swept out 27^h, its R.A. is 3^h so the indicator points to "3."

Figure 3-2

We could make a table accumulating such data. A few entries in such a table appear below (fill in the blanks):

Hours traversed	R.A.	
17	17	
27	3	
48	0	
74	___	*2*
95	___	*23*
123	___	*3*
1000	___	*16*

If the hours traversed by the satellite are any integral multiple of 24, then its R.A. is ___h.

In filling in the last entry in the table, you divided 1000 by ___, obtaining a quotient of ___ and a

0,

24, 41

remainder of _____. This computation can be represented | *16*

$$\frac{1000}{24} = 41 + \frac{16}{24},$$

but we prefer to write the equivalent

$$1000 = 24 \cdot 41 + 16,$$

for this makes prominent display of the remainder (16), which is the important term for us. In general, we can determine the R.A. of the satellite after it has traversed n hours by dividing n by 24, obtaining a quotient q and a remainder r:

$$n = 24 \cdot ____ + ____.$$ | *q, r*

The R.A. of the satellite is then ____^{h}. | *r*

If $\rho(n, 24)$ is used to designate the remainder on dividing the integer n by 24, the table above can be written in purely mathematical terms.

n	$\rho(n, 24)$
17	17
27	3
48	0
74	2
95	23
123	3
1000	16

By this method every nonnegative integer n is reduced to its R.A. $= \rho(n, 24)$, which is one of the integers

$$0, 1, 2, \ldots, 23.$$

What about negative integers, which correspond to a position westward from the vernal equinox? Think of the clock in Fig. 3-2. If you go 2^h in the counterclockwise direction, the indicator points to "____"; if you go 31^h in the counterclockwise direction, the indicator points to "____." Fill in the blanks. If we make the simple agreement that $\rho(n, 24)$ be nonnegative, we can always find q and $\rho(n, 24)$, so that

22
17

$$n = 24 \cdot q + \rho(n, 24)$$

even if n is a negative integer.

We will invent a bit of algebra that fits the computation with the remainders $\rho(n, 24)$, which, in turn, have interpretations as right ascensions.

Since we are working with *integers,* and reducing them to their remainders upon division, we shall find it useful to establish some notation which will be retained hereafter:

$\mathscr{Z}$ – the set of integers.

$\mathscr{Z}^+$ – the set of positive integers.

$\mathscr{Z}^-$ – the set of negative integers.

$\mathscr{Z}_{24}$ – the set of remainders $\rho(n, 24)$.

For our new algebra of remainders $\rho(n, 24)$, we define the operations $+_{24}$ and $\cdot_{24}$ as follows:

$$a +_{24} b = \rho(a + b, 24), \qquad \forall\, a, b \in \mathscr{Z}_{24},$$

$$a \cdot_{24} b = \rho(a \cdot b, 24), \qquad \forall\, a, b \in \mathscr{Z}_{24}.$$

Thus,

$17 +_{24} 16 = (\underline{\qquad}, 24) = \underline{\qquad},$	*33, 9*
$17 \cdot_{24} 2 = (\underline{\qquad}, 24) = \underline{\qquad},$	*34, 10*
$12 +_{24} (-37) = (\underline{\qquad}, 24) = \underline{\qquad},$	*− 25, 23*
$-3 \cdot_{24} 13 = (\underline{\qquad}, 24) = \underline{\qquad}.$	*− 39, 9*

Thus for the set of all $\rho(n, 24)$, i.e., for the integers

$$0, 1, 2, 3, \ldots, 23,$$

we have defined two operations that are analogous to addition and multiplication.

We could easily do this more generally: Let $\rho(n, m)$ denote the remainder on dividing the integer n by the integer $m, m \neq 0$. Then

$$n = m \cdot q + \rho(n, m), \qquad \rho(n, m) \geq 0.$$

We let $\mathscr{Z}_m$ represent the set of m nonnegative integers

$$0, 1, \ldots, m - 1,$$

and define operations on $\mathscr{Z}_m$ as follows:

$$a +_m b = \rho(a + b, m), \qquad \forall\, a, b \in \mathscr{Z}_m.$$

$$a \cdot_m b = \rho(a \cdot b, m) \qquad \forall\, a, b \in \mathscr{Z}_m.$$

3.6.2
EXERCISES

1. (a) Complete the addition and multiplication tables of $\mathscr{Z}_3$.

$+_3$	0	1	2
0			
1			
2			

$\cdot_3$	0	1	2
0			
1			
2			

(b) How can you tell, by a quick inspection of the tables, that $\mathscr{Z}_3$ obeys the commutative laws with respect to $+_3$ and $\cdot_3$?

(c) Can you tell whether $\mathscr{Z}_3$ obeys the associative laws with respect to $+_3$ and $\cdot_3$ without trying all possible triples?

(d) It should be clear that 0 is the additive identity and 1 is the multiplicative identity. Using this information, find the additive and multiplicative inverses of 2, if they exist.

(e) Solve for $x \in \mathscr{Z}_3$:

$$1 +_3 x = 0.$$

(f) Carry out the complete verification that $\mathscr{Z}_3$ is a field (with respect to $+_3$ and $\cdot_3$).

2. Investigate $\mathscr{Z}_2$, $\mathscr{Z}_4$, and $\mathscr{Z}_5$, and determine which are fields.

3. Do you have to make complete tables to determine whether $\mathscr{Z}_{24}$ is a field? Is $\mathscr{Z}_{24}$ a field?

[NOTE: Those of $\mathscr{Z}_m$ that are fields are examples of *finite fields*. In particular $\mathscr{Z}_2$ is the smallest possible field.]

4. In this problem we consider the set of all ordered pairs (a, b) of reals. The ordered pairs will be the numbers of a system which we denote by $\mathscr{C}$. We define the operations $+$ and $\cdot$, and the relation E in $\mathscr{C}$.

(i) $(a, b) + (c, d) = (a + c, b + d)$.

(ii) $(a, b) \cdot (c, d) = (ac - bd, bc + ad)$.

(iii) $(a, b) E (c, d) \Leftrightarrow (a = c \text{ and } b = d)$.

(a) Prove that the relation E satisfies the three properties of equality. (Use the definitions!)

(b) Is $\mathscr{C}$ closed with respect to $+$ and $\cdot$?

(c) Prove that $\mathscr{C}$ satisfies both associative laws.

(d) Solve for x and y:

$$(1, 1) + (x, y) E (1, 1).$$

$$(a, b) + (x, y) E (a, b).$$

$$(1, 1) \cdot (x, y) E (1, 1).$$

$$(1, 2) \cdot (x, y) E (1, 2).$$

(e) What are the additive and multiplicative identities of $\mathscr{C}$?

(f) If (a, b) is not the additive identity, find the multiplicative inverse of (a, b).

(g) Complete the verification of $\mathscr{C}$ as a field with respect to the defined operations.

5. Let $i = \sqrt{-1}$. The numbers of the form

$$bi, \qquad \text{where } b \in \mathscr{R},$$

are called (*pure*) *imaginary numbers*. We rely on your experience in computing with these numbers.

(a) Is the set of pure imaginaries closed with respect to addition? multiplication?

(b) Do the pure imaginaries form a field?

(c) The set of all numbers of the form

$$a + bi, \qquad \text{where } a, b \in \mathscr{R},$$

is called *complex number system*. Show that this number system is a field.

(d) Look back at Exercise 4, and note that: If (a, b) corresponds to $a + bi$, then the rules for $+$ and $\cdot$ in $\mathscr{C}$ correspond to those of complex numbers. Verify this statement. (In consequence of this exercise, we shall hereafter denote the complex field by $\mathscr{C}$.)

(e) What is the smallest subfield of $\mathscr{C}$ that contains i?

(f) What is the smallest subfield of $\mathscr{C}$ that contains all the irrationals? (Booby.)

In Exercises 6–8 our numbers will be ordered pairs (a, b) of *positive rationals*. We shall denote the set of all such pairs by $\mathscr{R}'$. We define $+, \cdot$, and E in $\mathscr{R}'$.

(i) $(a, b) + (c, d) = (a + c, b + d)$.

(ii) $(a, b) \cdot (c, d) = (ac + bd, ad + bc)$.

(iii) $(a, b) \, E \, (c, d)$ if and only if $a + d = b + c$.

6. (a) Does E satisfy the properties of equality?

(b) Prove that if $(a, b), (c, d), (A, B)$, and (C, D) are in $\mathscr{R}'$, and if $(a, b) \, E \, (A, B)$ and $(c, d) \, E \, (C, D)$, then

$$(a, b) + (c, d) \, E \, (A, B) + (C, D) \qquad \text{and} \qquad (a, b) \cdot (c, d) \, E \, (A, B) \cdot (C, D).$$

What does this result have to do with field properties?

(c) Does $\mathscr{R}$ satisfy the associative, commutative, and distributive postulates? If not, give particular ordered pairs for which one of these postulates fails.

(d) Find a number (x, y) in $\mathscr{R}'$ such that

$$(a, b) + (x, y) \, E \, (c, d),$$

where (a, b) and (c, d) are any given elements of $\mathscr{R}'$. Does this "equation" (note that we have "E" instead of "$=$") have any other solutions? If (X, Y) is any other solution, is it true that $(x, y) \, E \, (X, Y)$?

(e) Give a "good" definition of $(c, d) - (a, b)$ in $\mathscr{R}'$.

7. (a) Find a number (x, y) in $\mathscr{R}'$ such that

$$(5, 3) \cdot (x, y) \, E \, (11, 7).$$

(b) Find a number (x, y) in $\mathscr{R}'$ such that

$$(3, 3) \cdot (x, y) \, E \, (11, 7).$$

(c) Find a number (x, y) in $\mathscr{R}'$ such that

$$(1, 3) \cdot (x, y) \, E \, (11, 7).$$

(d) Find all numbers (x, y) in $\mathscr{R}'$ such that

$$(3, 3) \cdot (x, y) \, E \, (7, 7).$$

(e) If any of the above parts (a)–(d) have other solutions (X, Y) besides the ones you found, does the relation

$$(x, y) \, E \, (X, Y)$$

hold?

(f) Give a "good" definition of $(c, d)/(a, b)$ in $\mathscr{R}'$, and test schmield Postulate VI (see Exercise 7 in set 3.5.1).

(g) Are there 0- and 1-elements in $\mathscr{R}'$? Is $\mathscr{R}'$ a field? Justify your answer.

8. Continuing the discussion of $\mathscr{R}'$, we make the following definitions:

$$^{+}a = (a + 1, 1), \qquad ^{-}a = (1, a + 1).$$

(a) Prove that if $^{+}a \, E \, ^{+}b$, then $a = b$.

(b) Prove that $^{+}(ab) \, E \, (^{+}a) \cdot (^{+}b)$ and $^{+}(a + b) \, E \, (^{+}a) + (^{+}b)$.

(c) If (a, b) is a given element of $\mathscr{R}'$, when is there an x such that $(a, b) \, E \, ^{+}x$? When does there exist a y such that $(a, b) \, E \, ^{-}y$?

(d) For which elements (a, b) in $\mathscr{R}'$ does neither part of (c) have a solution?

In Exercises 9 and 10 our numbers are ordered pairs (a, b) of rationals. Let $\mathscr{R}''$ be the set of all such pairs. Note that now we are permitting a or b to be negative. We define operations in $\mathscr{R}''$ as follows:

$$(a, b) + (c, d) = (a + c, b + d),$$

$$(a, b) \cdot (c, d) = (ac - 2bd, ad + bc).$$

9. (a) Does $\mathscr{R}''$ satisfy the associative, commutative, and distributive postulates with respect to the operations $+$ and $\cdot$?

(b) If (a, b) and (c, d) are given elements of $\mathscr{R}''$, find elements (x, y) and (u, v) such that

$$(a, b) + (x, y) = (c, d)$$

and

$$(a, b) \cdot (u, v) = (c, d).$$

(c) Do solutions of these equations always exist? Are the solutions uniquely determined?

(d) Give "good" definitions for $(c, d) - (a, b)$ and $(c, d)/(a, b)$ and test the schmield postulates in Exercises 3.5.1. Which ones, if any, fail?

(e) Give "good" definitions of 0 and 1 in $\mathscr{R}''$. Test to see if they satisfy all the field requirements.

10. If a is any rational number, define $T(a) = (a, 0)$.

(a) Prove that

$$T(a + b) = T(a) + T(b),$$

$$T(ab) = T(a) \cdot T(b),$$

$$T(a - b) = T(a) - T(b),$$

$$T(a/b) = T(a)/T(b) \qquad \text{if } b \neq 0,$$

(b) Is there a rational x such that $x^2 = 2$?
Is there a rational x such that $(T(x))^2 = T(2)$?
Is there a number (x, y) in $\mathscr{R}''$ such that $(x, y)^2 = T(2)$?
Is there a number (x, y) in $\mathscr{R}''$ such that $(x, y)^2 = T(3)$?

(c) Let (a, b) be any number in $\mathscr{R}''$, and let $\xi = (a, b)$. Calculate $\xi^2 + T(-2a) \cdot \xi$.
Find a rational number c such that ξ satisfies the equation

$$\xi^2 + T(-2a) \cdot \xi + T(c) = 0.$$

11. If $\mathscr{R}'''$ is the set of all ordered pairs of *real* numbers, and we define the operations in $\mathscr{R}'''$ by the same formulas as in $\mathscr{R}''$, which of the field postulates fail? Why?

12. Define addition and multiplication on $\mathscr{R}''$ in such a way that the equation $\xi^2 = T(-3)$ has a solution.

13. (a) Suppose ξ is a solution of the equation $\xi^3 = 2$. If a, b, c, d, e, and f are rational numbers, find rational numbers A, B, and C such that

$$(a + b\xi + c\xi^2)(d + e\xi + f\xi^2) = A + B\xi + C\xi^2.$$

(b) Let $\mathscr{R}^{\mathrm{iv}}$ be the set of all ordered *triples* (a, b, c) of rational numbers. Define operations of addition and multiplication on $\mathscr{R}^{\mathrm{iv}}$ by the equations

$$(a, b, c) + (d, e, f) = (a + d, b + e, c + f),$$

$$(a, b, c) \cdot (d, e, f) = (A, B, C),$$

where A, B, and C are given by the formulas you found in part (a).

(c) Give "good" definitions of subtraction and division in $\mathscr{R}^{\mathrm{iv}}$. Define $U(a) = (a, 0, 0)$ for all $a \in \mathscr{R}a$. Find a solution in $\mathscr{R}^{\mathrm{iv}}$ of the equation $\xi^3 = U(2)$. Find a solution in $\mathscr{R}^{\mathrm{iv}}$ of the equation $\eta^3 = U(4)$.

14. Invent a field in which the equation $\xi^4 = 1 + \xi$ has a solution.

15. If a and b are real numbers, define the operations

$$a \oplus b = a + b + 3$$

and

$$a \odot b = \frac{(a + 3)(b + 3)}{5} - 3.$$

(a) Compute $b \oplus a$, $b \odot a$, $(a \oplus b) \oplus c$, $a \oplus (b \oplus c)$, $(a \odot b) \odot c$, $a \odot (b \odot c)$, $a \odot (b \oplus c)$, and $(a \odot b) \oplus (a \odot c)$.

(b) Find numbers x and y such that

$$a \oplus x = b \quad \text{and} \quad a \odot y = b.$$

Do these equations always have solutions? Are the solutions unique? If not, what are the exceptional cases?

(c) Give "good" definitions for $b \ominus a$ and $b \oslash a$. Which ones, if any, fail to satisfy the schmield postulates? Which numbers now play the roles of 0 and 1?

3.7

Abelian Groups   For easy reference we repeat the standard definition of field given in Sec. 3.5.

Definition: *A field $\mathscr{F}$ is a set of (at least two distinct) elements, with two binary operations $+$ and $\cdot$, satisfying the following postulates.*

A_1. $\forall\, a, b \in \mathscr{F}$, $a + b$ *is a uniquely defined element of $\mathscr{F}$.* [*Closure.*]

A_2. $(a + b) + c = a + (b + c)$, $\forall\, a, b, c \in \mathscr{F}$. [*Associativity.*]

A_3. $\exists\, 0 \in \mathscr{F}$, *such that* $a + 0 = a$, $\forall\, a \in \mathscr{F}$. [*Identity.*]

A_4. $\forall\, a \in \mathscr{F}$, $\exists\, -a \in \mathscr{F}$, *such that* $a + (-a) = 0$. [*Inverse.*]

A_5. $\forall\, a, b \in \mathscr{F}$, $a + b = b + a$. [*Commutativity.*]

M_1. $\forall\, a, b \in \mathscr{F}$, $a \cdot b$ *is a uniquely defined element of $\mathscr{F}$.* [*Closure.*]

M_2. $(a \cdot b) \cdot c = a \cdot (b \cdot c)$, $\forall\, a, b, c \in \mathscr{F}$. [*Associativity.*]

M_3. $\exists\, 1 \in \mathscr{F}$, *such that*

$$a \cdot 1 = a, \qquad \forall\, a \in \mathscr{F}. \quad [Identity.]$$

M_4. $\forall\, a \in \mathscr{F}$, *such that* $a \neq 0$, *there exists an element* $a^{-1} \in \mathscr{F}$ *satisfying the equation*

$$a \cdot a^{-1} = 1. \quad [Inverse.]$$

M_5. $\forall\, a, b \in \mathscr{F}$, $a \cdot b = b \cdot a$. [*Commutativity.*]

D. $\forall\, a, b, c \in \mathscr{F}$, $a \cdot (b + c) = a \cdot b + a \cdot c$. [*Distributivity (left).*]

3.7.1
EXERCISES

1. Rewrite A_1, replacing "$+$" by "$\cdot$." What do you notice?

2. Rewrite A_2, replacing "$+$" by "$\cdot$." Is the resulting statement true in $\mathscr{F}$?

3. What simple replacement of symbols in A_3 will give you M_3?

4. Rewrite A_4, replacing "$+$" by "$\cdot$," "0" by "1," and "$-a$" by "a^{-1}." Do you obtain M_4?

5. What replacement of symbols in A_5 results in M_5?

Since the set of postulates A_1–A_5 are in such close analogy with postulates M_1–M_5, we can achieve an economy of effort by studying the consequence of one set of postulates (say A_1–A_5), thereby obtaining results about both in one fell swoop. And, as a bonus, we obtain results about any system at all which satisfies the same set of postulates. Such systems will be called *abelian groups*, after the great Norwegian mathematician, Niels Henrik Abel (1802–1829), of whom we shall say more in Sec. 7.8. We will discuss abelian groups formally, below.

Let us not prejudice the following discussion by using the symbols " $+$ " and " $\cdot$," which we have been using to denote field operations. Also, we shall refrain from using " $-$ " and " $^{-1}$ " for inverses. (However, we will retain $=$ as the symbol for equality.)

Definition: *The set $\mathscr{G}$ is called an* abelian group *with respect to the operation $*$ if and only if the following propositions are true:*

G_1. $\forall\, a, b \in \mathscr{G}, a * b$ *is a uniquely defined element of $\mathscr{G}$. [Closure.]*

G_2. $(a * b) * c = a * (b * c), \forall\, a, b, c \in \mathscr{G}$. *[Associativity.]*

G_3. $\exists\, e \in \mathscr{G}$, *such that* $a * e = a, \forall\, a \in \mathscr{G}$. *[Identity.]*

G_4. $\forall\, a \in \mathscr{G}, \exists\, a' \in \mathscr{G}$, *such that* $a * a' = e$. *[Inverse.]*

G_5. $\forall\, a, b \in \mathscr{G}, a * b = b * a$. *[Commutativity.]*

It is clear that field $\mathscr{F}$ is an abelian group with respect to $+$, but your discoveries in Exercises 3.7.1 show that the statement

(1) $\qquad\qquad \mathscr{F}$ is an abelian group with respect to $*$

is false. However, you can modify (1) slightly so that you obtain a true statement: The set $\mathscr{F}^*$ of all elements $x \in \mathscr{F}$ such that x_____ is an abelian group with respect to $*$.

Now, let's make use of the economy by proving theorems that simultaneously hold for $\mathscr{F}$ with respect to $+$, $\mathscr{F}^*$ with respect to $\cdot$ and, moreover, in any set satisfying the properties G_1–G_5.

3.7.2
EXERCISES

In this set of exercises, $\mathscr{G}$ refers to an abelian group with respect to $*$. All theorems refer to this system.

1. Prove: Theorem 1: $\quad a * b = a * c \Rightarrow b = c$. (Notice that this establishes both parts of Exercise 2 of Sec. 3.5.1.)

2. Prove: Theorem 2: $\quad (a')' = a, \forall\, a \in \mathscr{G}$. (Notice that this proves both parts of Exercise 3 of Sec. 3.5.1.)

3. Prove: Theorem 3: *There is exactly one element $e \in \mathcal{G}$ that satisfies* G_3. (If you can establish this theorem, you may then refer to e as THE *identity element* of $\mathcal{G}$.)

4. Prove: Theorem 4: *If $a \in \mathcal{G}$, then there is exactly one element $a' \in \mathcal{G}$ that satisfies* G_4. (If you succeed in proving this result you may then refer to a' as THE *inverse* of a.)

5. The American mathematician E. H. Moore (1862–1932) enunciated the principle:

The existence of analogies between central features of various theories implies the existence of a general theory which underlies the particular theories and unifies them with respect to those central features.

(a) Explain how the theory of abelian groups illustrates Moore's principle.

(b) A Neanderthal man named Utnapishtim put a set of 2 stones together with a set of 3 stones, and counted the *union* of the sets. Then he led 2 sheep into a pen which contained 3 sheep, and counted all the sheep in the pen. When he came home to his cave he lined up his 2 daughters and 3 sons and counted his children. His friend Gilgamesh, who was a Neanderthal genius, showed him how to save work by applying an anticipation of Moore's principle. What did Gilgamesh tell Utnapishtim?

6. (a) Let $\mathcal{S}$ consist of the two real numbers 1 and -1. Show that $\mathcal{S}$ is an abelian group with respect to the operation multiplication of real numbers.

(b) What is the least number of elements that a group may have?

7. Let $\mathcal{S}$ be the set of all ordered pairs (a, b) of real numbers such that $a^2 + b^2 = 1$. Define the operation $\times$ by $(a, b) \times (c, d) = (ac - bd, ad + bc)$.

(a) Show that $\mathcal{S}$ satisfies the closure property with respect to $\times$.

(b) Verify that $\mathcal{S}$ with respect to $\times$ is an abelian group.

(c) What is the identity element?

(d) What are the inverses of $(0, 1)$, $(-1, 0)$, $(0, -1)$ in $\mathcal{S}$?

(e) What is the inverse of (a, b) in $\mathcal{S}$?

8. Referring to $\mathcal{G}$ with respect to $*$.

(a) Solve $a * x = e$ for x.

(b) Solve for x and y in the system of equations

$$a * x = e, \qquad x * y = e.$$

(c) Solve for $x : a * x = b$.

(d) Can e' be different from e?

9. (a) Is $\mathcal{R}$ an abelian group with respect to $\cdot$?

(b) Is $\mathcal{R}a$ an abelian group with respect to $+$? with respect to $\cdot$?

(c) What is the smallest abelian group contained in $\mathcal{R}$ with respect to the operation $+$? (Booby.)

(d) What is the smallest abelian group in $\mathcal{R}$, with respect to $+$, that contains 5?

(e) What is the smallest abelian group in $\mathcal{R}$, with respect to $+$, that contains -1?

(f) What is the smallest abelian group in $\mathcal{R}$, with respect to $\cdot$?

10. Criticize the following definition: A field $\mathcal{F}$ is a set of elements, with two binary operations $+$ and $\cdot$, satisfying the following properties:

(i) $\mathscr{F}$ is an abelian group with respect to $+$.

(ii) If 0 is the identity with respect to $+$, and $\mathscr{F}^*$ is the set of all $x \in \mathscr{F}$ such that $x \neq 0$, then $\mathscr{F}^*$ is an abelian group with respect to $\cdot$.

Armed with the concept of an abelian group, we should be able to give a (verbally) more economical definition of field. Exercise 10 in Sec. 3.7.2 was a step in this direction, but you discovered that it fell short. Actually, we are looking for a simply stated theorem of the form

$$\mathscr{F} \text{ is a field if and only if } \ldots,$$

for we already have given a definition; the aim is to find a proposition, in terms of abelian groups, that is logically equivalent to the given definition.

Several recently written textbooks give the following *Well-known Proposition*: Set $\mathscr{F}$, with binary operation $+$ and $\cdot$, is a field if and only if

(i) $\mathscr{F}$ is an abelian group with respect to $+$,

(ii) $\mathscr{F}^*$ (i.e., $\mathscr{F}$ with the additive identity excluded) is an abelian group with respect to $\cdot$, and

(iii) $\forall a, b, c \in \mathscr{F}, a \cdot (b + c) = a \cdot b + a \cdot c$.

Is *Well-known Proposition* true? Is it logically equivalent to the definition of field at the beginning of this section? Let's see.

First, it is clear that properties A_1–A_5 of the definition are equivalent to (i) in *Well-known Proposition*, and property D is the same as (iii). But M_1, M_2, and M_5 present some difficulty, for (ii) in *Well-known Proposition* doesn't tell us anything about the additive identity 0. We could attempt to proceed further with a general proof, but it might pay to experiment a bit by testing *Well-known Proposition* on some examples.

We will test on the simplest candidate for a field, the set of remainders $\rho(n, 2)$ (see Sec. 3.6). This set consists only of 0 and 1. In order to satisfy (i) we take the familiar definition of $+$ according to the table

(2)

$+$	0	1
0	0	1
1	1	0 .

But (ii) merely states that the element 1 constitutes an abelian group, so all we know about the multiplication table is a single entry:

(3)

$\cdot$	0	1
0	—	—
1	—	1

and it appears that we have some freedom in filling the remaining blanks of the table. Let's see.

We know that if we take the usual multiplication of remainders, namely

·	0	1
0	0	0
1	0	1

(3′)

we get a field (see Exercise 2 in Sec. 3.6.2). But the question before us is: Are there other possibilities for the multiplication table that leave us with a system satisfying *Well-known Proposition*? What about the following?

·	0	1
0	0	1
1	0	1

(3″)

Using (2) and (3″) to define the operations gives us a system satisfying *Well-known Proposition*, but is the system a field according to the definition?

M_1 (closure) is satisfied by the very existence of a table like (3″). The next easy property to test is M_5, but we see that

$$0 \cdot 1 = 1 \quad \text{and} \quad 1 \cdot 0 = 0,$$

which is impossible for a field! Therefore, *Well-known Proposition* is false! So you see that even leading textbooks may have errors that can be found by careful reading and checking.†

3.7.3
EXERCISES

1. (a) Using (2) and (3) as definitions for $+$ and $\cdot$ for the set of $\rho(n, 2)$, establish the left distributive law **D**:

$$a \cdot (b + c) = a \cdot b + a \cdot c.$$

(b) Show, by example, that the right distributive property

$$(a + b) \cdot c = a \cdot c + b \cdot c$$

does not follow.

2. A careful look at *Well-known Proposition* indicates that M_1 presents the first difficult—or impossible—thing to prove, because we don't even know that

$$0 \cdot x \quad \text{and} \quad x \cdot 0$$

† For an interesting elementary article pertinent to the above discussion, see A. H. Lightstone, "A Remark Concerning the Definition of a Field," *Mathematics Magazine*, Vol. 37, No. 1 (January 1964), pp. 12–13.

are uniquely defined elements of the set. On the other hand, even adding condition M_1 isn't sufficient, for the counterexample we gave satisfied M_1, but not M_5; and in the previous exercise you proved that the left distributive property was violated. So we try *Modification of Well-known Proposition.* Set $\mathcal{F}$, with binary operations $+$ and $\cdot$, is a field if and only if

(i) $\mathcal{F}$ is an abelian group with respect to $+$.

(ii) $\mathcal{F}$ is closed with respect to $\cdot$. [Closure law M_1.]

(iii) $\mathcal{F}^*$ is an abelian group with respect to $\cdot$.

(iv) The two distributive properties,

$$a \cdot (b + c) = a \cdot b + a \cdot c$$

and

$$(a + b) \cdot c = a \cdot c + b \cdot c,$$

hold for all $a, b, c \in \mathcal{F}$.

All parts of this question refer to this modification. You may use only the conditions set forth in the proposition and, of course, their consequences.

(a) What is $0 \cdot 0$? [*Hint:* $0 \cdot 0 = 0 \cdot (0 + 0)$.]

(b) Prove that $x \cdot 0 = 0$, and $0 \cdot x = 0$, $\forall x \in \mathcal{F}$.

(c) Prove that the *Modification* is true. [*Hint:* All that you have left to prove are M_2, M_3, and M_5 for cases that involve 0.]

3. We define a binary operation $*$ in $\mathcal{R}$ by

$$a * b = (a^3 + b^3)^{1/3} \qquad \text{for } a, b \in \mathcal{R}.$$

(a) Show that $\mathcal{R}$ is an abelian group with respect to $*$.

(b) What is the identity element?

(c) What is the inverse of 1? of 0?

4. Let $\mathcal{G}$ be the set of all nonnegative integers. We define the binary operation $\square$ by

$$m \square n = \begin{cases} m + n, & \text{if } m \text{ and } n \text{ are both even,} \\ m + n + 1, & \text{if } m \text{ and } n \text{ are both odd,} \\ |m - n| - 1, & \text{if one is even, the other odd, and the even number is greater than the odd,} \\ |m - n|, & \text{if one is even, the other odd, and the odd number is the greater.} \end{cases}$$

(a) Calculate $2 \square 2$, $4 \square 2$, $6 \square 2$, $2 \square 1$, $1 \square 1$, $3 \square 1$, $5 \square 1$.

(b) Solve the equation $2 \square x = 12$.

(c) Solve the equation $2 \square y = 11$.

(d) Is $\mathcal{G}$ an abelian group with respect to $\square$?

5. Let $\mathcal{T}$ be the set of four ordered pairs

$$(1, 0), \qquad (-1, 0), \qquad (0, 1) \quad \text{and} \quad (0, -1).$$

As in Exercise 7 of Sec. 3.7.2, we define the operation $\times$ by

$$(a, b) \times (c, d) = (ac - bd, ad + bc).$$

Is $\mathscr{T}$ an abelian group with respect to $\times$?

6. Let $\mathscr{U}$ be the set of all ordered pairs (a, b) where a and b may be either 1 or -1. We define the operation $\triangle$ by

$$(a, b) \triangle (c, d) = (ac, bd).$$

(a) Is $\mathscr{U}$ closed with respect to $\triangle$?
(b) Is $\mathscr{U}$ an abelian group?
(c) How many elements does $\mathscr{U}$ have?
(d) If $\zeta \in \mathscr{U}$, compute $\zeta \triangle \zeta$.

7. Let $\mathscr{V}$ be the set of all ordered triples (a, b, c), where each element is either 1 or -1. We define the operation $\triangle$ by

$$(a, b, c) \triangle (d, e, f) = (ad, be, cf).$$

Is $\mathscr{V}$ an abelian group with respect to $\triangle$?

8. Consider the set $\mathscr{W}$ of all the rotations of a wheel about its axle.

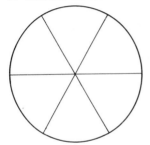

Let R_α be the rotation counterclockwise through the angle $\alpha°$. We define $\cdot$ in $\mathscr{W}$ by

$R_\alpha \cdot R_\beta$ is the single rotation equivalent to R_β followed by R_α.

For instance, if we rotate the wheel through $40°$, then through $70°$, then this is equivalent to rotating the wheel through _____. Therefore $R_{70} \cdot R_{40} = R_?$.

We define equality in $\mathscr{W}$ by saying: $R_\alpha = R_\beta$ if and only if R_α and R_β both bring the wheel from a given position to the same final position. Thus R_{390} is the same as R_β, where β is a certain angle between $0°$ and $360°$. Which one?

(a) Find the rotation R_α such that

$$R_{50} \cdot R_\alpha = R_{30}.$$

(b) Find a rotation R_α such that
$$R_\alpha \cdot R_\alpha = R_0.$$

How many solutions does this equation have?

(c) Does the set $\mathscr{W}$ form an abelian group with respect to $\cdot$?

9. Place a square with its center at the origin and vertices on the coordinate axes as in Fig. 3-3. Let $\mathscr{Y}$ be the set of all rotations of the square about its center which leaves its vertices on the coordinate axes, and define equality and the operation $\cdot$ as in the preceding exercise.

(a) How many rotations are there in $\mathscr{Y}$?

(b) Denote the elements of $\mathscr{Y}$ by the letters A, B, C, etc., and make a table for the operation $\cdot$:

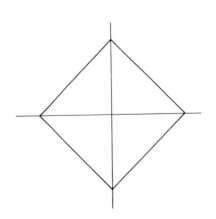

Figure 3-3

·	A	B	C	...
A				
B				
C				
⋮				

How can you read off $A \cdot B$ from this table?

(c) Prove that $\mathscr{Y}$ is an abelian group with respect to $\cdot$.

10. As in Sec. 3.6, we let $\mathscr{Z}_m$ represent the set of nonnegative integers

$$0, 1, \ldots, m - 1$$

$$a +_m b = \rho(a + b, m), \qquad \forall\, a, b \in \mathscr{Z}_m$$

$$a \cdot_m b = \rho(a \cdot b, m), \qquad \forall\, a, b \in \mathscr{Z}_m.$$

Call $\mathscr{Z}_m^*$ the set of all nonzero elements of $\mathscr{Z}_m$.

(a) Which, of $\mathscr{Z}_3^*$, $\mathscr{Z}_4^*$, $\mathscr{Z}_5^*$, are abelian groups with respect to $\cdot_m$?

(b) Referring to part (a), in each case where $\mathscr{Z}_m^*$ is a group with respect to $\cdot$, identify the identity element and make a table of inverses.

(c) Is $\mathscr{Z}_{12}^*$ an abelian group with respect to $\cdot_{12}$?

(d) Is the subset of $\mathscr{Z}_{12}$, consisting of

$$1, 5, 7, 11,$$

an abelian group with respect to $\cdot_{12}$?

(e) Is the subset of $\mathscr{Z}_{20}$, consisting of

$$1, 3, 7, 9, 11, 13, 17, 19,$$

an abelian group with respect to $\cdot_{20}$?

(f) Which of $\mathscr{Z}_m$ $(m = 2, 3, 4, 5, 6)$ are fields with respect to $+_m$ and $\cdot_m$?

11. In $\mathscr{Z}_5$ make a table for the function C, defined by

$$C(a) = (a \cdot_5 a) \cdot_5 a, \qquad a \in \mathscr{Z}_5$$

and a table for the function F, where

$$F(a) = C(a) \cdot_5 a.$$

What do you notice? What is the analogue for $\mathscr{Z}_7$?

3.8

(Optional†) The Affine Line and Its Group The number line (the set of all points on a line together with the kind of one-to-one correspondence between points and numbers assumed in Postulate G) is both a geometrical and an

† Although much may be learned from a careful study of this section, it is optional in the sense that none of the results of this section are required for—or referred to in—the remaining portion of the book.

algebraic object. The geometry of the line is independent of the choice of 0-point and the choice of unit. Changes in the latter merely change the description but do not change the geometry.

The directed distance from the point a to the point b is $b - a$. This does not change if you change the 0-point. If c is any other point, then the ratio of the directed distances

$$\frac{c - a}{b - a}$$

is independent of the choice of unit. Hence if A, B, and C are any points ($A \neq B$), then the ratio of the directed distances

$$\overline{AC}/\overline{AB}$$

is independent of the choice of 0-point and unit.

A one-to-one mapping T of the line onto itself which leaves ratios of directed distances unchanged, or *invariant*, is called an *affine transformation*. In other words, if whenever

$$T : A \to A', \qquad T : B \to B', \qquad T : C \to C'$$

we have

$$\overline{A'C'}/\overline{A'B'} = \overline{AC}/\overline{AB},$$

then T is an affine transformation. The study of the properties which are left invariant by affine transformations is called *affine geometry*.

Let us see how affine transformations are described in terms of coordinates. As usual, we shall denote points by their corresponding numbers. Suppose that T is an affine transformation, and

$$T(a) = a_1, \qquad T(b) = b_1, \qquad T(x) = y, \qquad \text{where } a \neq b.$$

Then, according to the definition of an affine transformation

$$\frac{y - a_1}{b_1 - a_1} = \frac{x - a}{b - a}.$$

Solve for y:

(1) $$y = mx + k,$$

where

$$m = \underline{\qquad} \qquad \text{and} \qquad k = \underline{\qquad}.$$

Conversely, if the transformation $T : x \to y$ is defined by (1), where $m \neq 0$, then

$$T(a) = a_1 = m\underline{\qquad} + k \qquad \text{and} \qquad T(b) = b_1 = \underline{\qquad} + \underline{\qquad}.$$

Compute

$$\frac{y - a_1}{b_1 - a_1}.$$

Is T an affine transformation?

3.8.1
EXERCISES

1. Given a, b, a_1, and b_1, with $a \neq b$ and $a_1 \neq b_1$, is there an affine transformation T such that $T(a) = a_1$, $T(b) = b_1$? Is there more than one such transformation? Give formulas for m and k.

2. If T is an affine transformation defined by (1), compute $T(0)$ and $T(1) - T(0)$.

3. Let $T_{m,k}$ be the transformation defined by (1). Compute

$$(T_{m,k} \circ T_{m_1,k_1})(x)$$

where m_1 and k_1 are any numbers and $m_1 \neq 0$. Can this composite transformation be expressed in the form T_{m_2,k_2}? If so, give formulas for m_2 and k_2.

4. What is the necessary and sufficient condition on m_1 and k_1 that

$$T_{m,k} \circ T_{m_1,k_1} = T_{m_1,k_1} \circ T_{m,k}$$

for all admissible values of m and k?

5. If $T_{m,k} = I$, then $m = $ _____ and $k = $ _____.

6. Given m and k, with $m \neq 0$, find m_1 and k_1 such that

$$T_{m,k} \circ T_{m_1,k_1} = I.$$

With this choice of m_1 and k_1, compute $T_{m_1,k_1} \circ T_{m,k}$.

7. What are the fixed points of $T_{m,k}$; that is, for which values of x is

$$T_{m,k}(x) = x?$$

For which values of m and k does $T_{m,k}$ have no fixed points? For which values of m and k does $T_{m,k}$ have more than one fixed point?

8. Given a and m, find k so that a is a fixed point of $T_{m,k}$. If $m \neq 0$, how many such k's are there?

9. Let $G(a)$ be the set of affine transformations $T_{m,k}$ such that

$$T_{m,k}(a) = a.$$

If T_{m_1,k_1} and T_{m_2,k_2} are in $G(a)$, compute

$$T_{m_1,k_1} \circ T_{m_2,k_2} \quad \text{and} \quad T_{m_2,k_2} \circ T_{m_1,k_1}$$

What do you notice?

10. If T and U are in $G(a)$, is $T \circ U$ in $G(a)$? Is T^{-1} in $G(a)$?

11. Find all affine transformations T which are *involutions*. T is an involution if

$$T \circ T = I, \qquad T \neq I.$$

12. Given a, how many involutions are there in $G(a)$?

13. If T, U, and V are involutions, is $T \circ U$ an involution? Is $T \circ U \circ V$ an involution?

We can summarize the properties of affine transformations of the line as follows:

Let G be the set of all affine transformations of the line L.
  I. L is a set with at least three elements.
  II. G is a group of one-to-one transformations of L onto itself.
  III. If $a \neq b$ and $a_1 \neq b_1$ and $a, b, a_1, b_1 \in L$, then there is a unique $T \in G$ such that

$$T(a) = a_1, \qquad T(b) = b_1.$$

  IV. If $a \in L$, then the set, $G(a)$, of all T in G such that $T(a) = a$, is an abelian subgroup of G.
  V. For $a \in L$, the group $G(a)$ contains a unique involution.
  VI. Every involution in G has a unique fixed point.
  VII. The product of three involutions in G is an involution.

Conversely, if G is a set of one-to-one mappings of a set L onto itself which satisfies the above conditions, then we can define operations $+$, $-$, $\cdot$, and $/$ with respect to which L is a field and G is the set of transformations represented by (1). If two elements P_0 and P_1 in L are chosen as 0 and 1, then the operations are uniquely determined.

The following exercises lead you to establish this converse.

3.8.2
EXERCISES

In the following we assume that G and L satisfy I–VII above. Choose two distinct elements of L and call them 0 and 1. If $a \neq 0$, let M_a be the unique element of G such that

$$M_a(0) = 0, \qquad M_a(1) = a.$$

If $a = 0$, we define

$$M_0(x) = 0 \qquad \text{for all } x \text{ in } L.$$

If $a \neq 0$, let J_a be the unique element of G such that

$$J_a(0) = a, \qquad J_a(a) = 0.$$

If $a = 0$, we define J_0 as the unique involution in $G(0)$. We define

$$a \cdot x = M_a(x),$$
$$a - x = J_a(x),$$
$$-x = J_0(x),$$
$$a + x = a - (-x).$$

You will show that L is a field with respect to these operations.

1. If T is in $G(0)$ and $T(1) = a$, can T be represented in the form M_b? What is b?

2. If $a, b \in L$, $a \neq 0$, $b \neq 0$, is $M_a \circ M_b$ in $G(0)$? If so, find c such that

$$M_a \circ M_b = M_c.$$

Compute

$$(M_a \circ M_b)(x) \qquad \text{and} \qquad M_c(x).$$

Which field property follows?

3. Now use the assumption that $G(0)$ is abelian. Which field property follows?

4. In Exercises 2 and 3, check that your conclusions are also valid when a or b is equal to 0.

Where does the statement

$$\forall\, x \in L, \qquad 0 \cdot x = 0$$

come from?

Where does the statement

$$\forall\, a \in L, \qquad a \cdot 0 = 0$$

come from?

5. Is the identity transformation I in G? Is it in $G(0)$? If it is, find a such that $I = M_a$.

6. Let $a \in L$, $a \neq 0$. Let T be the transformation in G such that $T(0) = 0$, $T(a) = 1$. Is T in $G(0)$?

Compute

$$(M_a \circ T)(0) \qquad \text{and} \qquad (M_a \circ T)(1).$$

What is $M_a \circ T$? What about $T \circ M_a$?

Let $T(1) = b$. Compute $a \cdot b$ and $b \cdot a$.

7. Let $a \neq 0$. Compute

$$(J_a \circ J_a)(0) \qquad \text{and} \qquad (J_a \circ J_a)(a).$$

What is $J_a \circ J_a$? Is $J_a(0) = 0$? Is $J_a = I$? For any $x \in L$, compute

$$a - (a - x).$$

8. Since J_0 is in $G(0)$, find a such that $J_0 = M_a$. Compute $a \cdot a$.

9. Let $b \neq 0, b \in L$. Compute

$$(M_a \circ J_b)(0), \qquad (M_a \circ J_b)(b).$$

Find c in L such that

$$(J_c \circ M_a) = (M_a \circ J_b)(0)$$

and

$$(J_c \circ M_a)(b) = (M_a \circ J_b)(b).$$

Can there be more than one transformation in G which maps 0 and b into two given elements of L?

What do you conclude about

$$(J_c \circ M_a)(x) \qquad \text{and} \qquad (M_a \circ J_b)(x)$$

for any $x \in L$? Is the resulting equation also true for $b = 0$?

10. Let $a, b, c \in L$, and let

$$T = J_a \circ J_b \circ J_c, \qquad U = J_c \circ J_b \circ J_a.$$

Compute $T \circ T, T \circ U, U \circ T.$
Compute

$$(T \circ T) \circ U = T \circ (T \circ U).$$

Compute $T(0)$ and $U(0)$. Can these elements be different?

11. In the conclusion of Exercises 10, set $b = 0$. What field property follows?

12. In the conclusion of Exercise 10, set $c = 0$. What follows?

13. Supply the reasons for the following steps:

$$
\begin{aligned}
(a + b) - c &= -(c - (a + b)) \\
&= -(c - (b + a)) \\
&= -(c - (b - (-a))) \\
&= -((-a) - (b - c)) \\
&= (b - c) - (-a) \\
&= (b - c) + a \\
&= a + (b - c).
\end{aligned}
$$

14. In the conclusion of Exercise 13, set $c = -x$. Which field property follows?

15. Compute $a + (b - a)$, using the results of Exercises 12 and 10.

16. Complete the proof that L is a field with respect to $+$ and $\cdot$.

The above reasoning can be reversed for almost any field. If L is a field in which $1 + 1 \neq 0$, and if G is the set of transformations defined by (1), then L and G satisfy conditions I–VII. You have essentially proved this in the first set of exercises.

17. Do you know a field L, containing at least three elements, in which $1 + 1 = 0$? How should I–VII be modified if L is such a field?

18. Suppose L is an ordered field (See Sec. 3.9). We say that the transformation T is *order preserving* if

$$\forall\, a, b \in L, \qquad a < b \Rightarrow T(a) < T(b).$$

We say that T is *order reversing* if

$$\forall\, a, b \in L, \qquad a < b \Rightarrow T(b) < T(a).$$

What are the necessary and sufficient conditions on m and k that $T_{m,k}$ be order preserving? That $T_{m,k}$ be order reversing?

Is there any transformation in G, the set of transformations of the form (1), which is neither order preserving nor order reversing?

Suppose L is a linearly ordered set containing at least three elements and that L and G satisfy I–VII and

VIII. Every transformation in G is either order preserving or order reversing.

We should like to define the operations on L so that it becomes an *ordered field* (see Sec. 3.9). Is there any restriction on which elements of L may be chosen as 0 and 1? If these elements are chosen properly, is L an ordered field with respect to the operations as defined above?

3.9

Ordered Fields   Thus far, our postulates concerning the real number system $\mathscr{R}$ tell us

1. $\mathscr{R}$ is a linearly ordered set, and
2. $\mathscr{R}$ is a field.

We now concern ourselves with the question of uniting the order properties implied by (1) with the algebraic properties implied by (2); for example, is there an association between the linear ordering of $\mathscr{R}$ and addition in $\mathscr{R}$? More generally, since we have been studying $\mathscr{R}$ as an example of a field, we will consider the more general problem of introducing (linear) order into a field. If this can be done in a desirable way, the end product will be called an *ordered field*, and—once again—$\mathscr{R}$ will constitute a particular example.

What is a "desirable way?" What would you think desirable for the relationship between the order properties and the algebraic properties of the field? Let's explore these and related questions by working some exercises in the familiar territory of the real number system.

3.9.1
EXERCISES

1. Answer "true" or "false." If "false," give a counterexample.
   (a) If $x < y$, then $x + 2 < y + 2$.

(b) If $x < y$, then $x - 2 > y - 2$.
(c) If $x < y$ and $a > 0$, then $x + a < y + a$,
(d) If $x < y$ and $a < 0$, then $x + a > y + a$.

2. Answer "true" or "false." If "false," give a counterexample.
(a) $x < y \Rightarrow ax < ay$.
(b) $x < y \Rightarrow (-1)x < (-1)y$.
(c) $[x < y \text{ and } y < 0] \Rightarrow 2x < 2y$.
(d) $[x < y \text{ and } a > 0] \Rightarrow ax < ay$.
(e) $[x < y \text{ and } a < 0] \Rightarrow ax < ay$.

3. If $x < y$, then $1/x < 1/y$. Is this statement true always, sometimes, or never?

4. From your answers to Exercise 1, formulate a desirable postulate for the relation between ordering and addition.

5. From your answers to Exercise 2, formulate a desirable postulate for the relation between ordering and multiplication.

6. Using your answer to Exercise 5, show how to change the statement in Exercise 3 so as to obtain a true statement.

From the above exercises you learned at least one desirable way that linear order may be associated with algebraic field properties. Using this as a basis (since $\mathscr{R}$ is to be a particular example) we establish the following

Definition: A set $\mathscr{F}$ is called an *ordered field* if and only if $\mathscr{F}$ is a field satisfying the following addition postulates relative to the undefined binary relation $<$:

O_1. $\mathscr{F}$ is linearly ordered with respect to $<$.

O_2. $\forall\, a, b, c \in \mathscr{F}$:

$$a < b \Rightarrow a + c < b + c.$$

O_3. $\forall\, a, b, c \in \mathscr{F}$:

$$[a < b \text{ and } 0 < c] \Rightarrow ac < bc.$$

Now we supersede Postulates O and F by

Postulate OF: $\mathscr{R}$ is an ordered field.

In addition, we make another simple

Definition: $a > b$ means $b < a$.

In searching for theorems that are true in ordered fields, we look at $\mathscr{R}$ for hints. For example, in $\mathscr{R}$ we know that

$$3 + 1 < 4 + 2$$

and in general:

(3) $$[a < b \text{ and } c < d] \Rightarrow a + c < b + d.$$

High school students are often taught to write

$$a < b$$

$$\text{and} \quad \underline{c < d}$$
$$a + c < b + d.$$

Can (3) be proved from the ordered field postulates?

If we are given $a < b$, we can certainly add the same element to both members of this inequality by Postulate _____. Thus

$$\quad O_2$$

$$a + c < b + c.$$

We see that we could finish our proof if we knew that

(4) $$c < d \Rightarrow b + c < b + d.$$

Let us establish this "stepping-stone proposition," or *lemma*† Remember that we must justify each step by referring to a postulate or a previously proved theorem.

$$c < d \Rightarrow c + b < \underline{\quad\quad}, \quad \text{by Postulate } \underline{\quad}.$$ $$\quad d + b, O_2$$

But $c + b = b + \underline{\quad}$ and $d + b = \underline{\quad\quad}$, by Postulate _____. Therefore, $$\quad c, b + d,$$
$$\quad A_5$$

$$b + c < b + d.$$

(Note the power of the commutative property A_5, which tells you that $c + b$ is the same number as $b + c$. This means that you may replace "$c + b$" by "$b + c$" in any statement without changing its truth.)

Now, using O_1, you can complete the proof of (3) which we state as:

Theorem 1: $$[a < b \text{ and } c < d] \Rightarrow a + c < b + d.$$

Another familiar result from $\mathscr{R}$ that we can prove for any ordered field is

Theorem 2: $$a < b \Rightarrow c - b < c - a.$$

This appears somewhat similar to O_2, except that subtraction is now replacing the addition in the postulate. Is O_2 a possible key to the proof? What else may we use? The question is always—at least partially—answered

† *Lemma* is the name given to a preliminary proposition, one particularly used to assist in the proof of a theorem.

107

by: The hypothesis, of course! So we state

$$a < b.$$

If we could only prove that $-b < -a$ [Exercise 2(b) above suggests that this is true in $\mathscr{R}$], then we could add c to both members O_2. How can we achieve $-b < -a$ on the basis of our postulates?

To prove that $a < b \Rightarrow -b < -a$, we begin with $a < b$. We want a conclusion with "$-b$" on left of "$<$." Try using O_2:

If $a < b$, then $a + x < b + x$.
Try to choose x such that $a + x = -b$.
We find that $x = -a - b$.
Therefore $b + x = -a$. Amazing!

Can this process be generalized to prove Theorem 2? If you succeed in constructing this proof, you will also have the

Corollary: *If $a < b$ then $-a > -b$.*

3.9.2
EXERCISES

1. Review Exercise. Using the field postulates of $\mathscr{R}$, prove the familiar statements

(a) $$a \neq 0 \Rightarrow \frac{b + c}{a} = \frac{b}{a} + \frac{c}{a}.$$

(b) $$a \neq 0 \Rightarrow \frac{b - c}{a} = \frac{b}{a} - \frac{c}{a}.$$

(c) $$bd \neq 0 \Rightarrow \frac{a}{b} + \frac{c}{d} = \frac{ad + bc}{bd}.$$

(d) $$\frac{a}{b} = \frac{-a}{-b}, \; b \neq 0.$$

(e) $$\frac{-a}{b} = \frac{a}{-b} = -\frac{a}{b}, \; b \neq 0.$$

2. If $\mathscr{F}$ is an ordered field and $a \in \mathscr{F}$, prove:
(a) $a > 0 \Rightarrow -a < 0$.
(b) $a < 0 \Rightarrow a^2 > 0$.
(c) $a > 0 \Rightarrow a^{-1} > 0$. [*Hint:* If you can't produce a direct proof, try for an indirect proof.]

3. For $a, b, c \in \mathscr{R}$ and $c \neq 0$, prove:

$$[a < b \text{ and } c > 0] \Rightarrow \frac{a}{c} < \frac{b}{c}.$$

4. If $\mathscr{F}$ is an ordered field and $a, b, c \in \mathscr{F}$, prove:
(a) $[a > 0 \text{ and } a < b] \Rightarrow b^{-1} < a^{-1}$.

(b) $[c > 0$ and $ac > bc] \Rightarrow a > b$.

(c) $a + c < b + c \Rightarrow a < b$.

5. If $\mathscr{F}$ is an ordered field and $a, b \in \mathscr{F}$, prove:

(a) $a \neq 0 \Rightarrow a^2 > 0$.

(b) $a^2 + b^2 = 0 \Rightarrow a = b = 0$.

(c) $0 < a < b \Rightarrow a^2 < b^2$. (If you have only that $a < b$, does it follow that $a^2 < b^2$? Justify your answer.)

6. (a) Concerning $\mathscr{R}$: If $0 < a < b$, replace the question mark with "$<$," "$>$," or "$=$" in:

$$1 + \cfrac{1}{1 + \cfrac{1}{a}} \quad ? \quad 1 + \cfrac{1}{1 + \cfrac{1}{b}}.$$

and prove the resulting conclusion.

(b) Generalize part (a) to a result in any ordered field.

7. Let $\mathscr{R}^+$ be the set of positive real numbers. Prove:

(a) If $a \in \mathscr{R}$, then exactly one of the following is true:

    (i) $a \in \mathscr{R}^+$.

    (ii) $-a \in \mathscr{R}^+$.

    (iii) $a = 0$.

(b) If $a, b \in \mathscr{R}^+$, then $a + b \in \mathscr{R}^+$ and $ab \in \mathscr{R}^+$.

(c) $a < b$ if and only if $(b - a) \in \mathscr{R}^+$.

[NOTE: One of the best ways of proving an inequality such as "$a < b$" is expressed in 7(c); that is, the strategy is to try to prove that $b - a$ is positive.]

8. We generalize Exercise 7. Let $\mathscr{F}$ be a field and $\mathscr{P}$ a set of elements in $\mathscr{F}$ such that:

(a) If $a \in \mathscr{F}$, then exactly one of the following statements is true: (i) $a \in \mathscr{P}$, (ii) $-a \in \mathscr{P}$, (iii) $a = 0$.

(b) If $a, b \in \mathscr{P}$, then $a + b \in \mathscr{P}$ and $ab \in \mathscr{P}$.

Drawing upon 7(c), we make the definition of "$a < b$" by stating that: $a < b$ if and only if $(b - a) \in \mathscr{P}$.

Now prove that $\mathscr{F}$ is then an ordered field with respect to $<$.

[NOTE: The set $\mathscr{P}$ in $\mathscr{F}$ is, very naturally, called the set of *positive* elements of $\mathscr{F}$. Thus, the question of whether a field can be ordered becomes a question of finding a subset $\mathscr{P}$ of $\mathscr{F}$ which satisfies 8(a) and 8(b), rather a simple set of axioms to check. It is conceivable that a field may appear to be unordered, but on closer examination you discover a subset which satisfies 8(a) and 8(b). You can thereby define "$a < b$" and thus have an ordering. For this reason, some mathematicians prefer speaking about "*orderable*" fields. Furthermore, it is also conceivable that a field might have two different subsets which satisfy 8(a) and 8(b), thus permitting it to be ordered in more than one way. We shall return to this interesting subject in later sections.]

9. Prove: if $\mathscr{F}$ is an ordered field, then $0 < 1$.

10. Research Problem. Is there any other way of ordering the field of rational numbers besides the usual one?

What you have now learned about fields equips you with a basis for justifying all the manipulative rules for handling fractions and equations via the methods of high school algebra. And the work with ordered fields provides you with a logical basis for handling inequalities. We will, therefore, feel free to ask you to call upon your previous algebraic knowledge in future discussions and exercises.

3.10

Gaining Algebraic Experience   Although the discussion of the previous section pertains to general *ordered fields*, this section will focus on the particular ordered field of real numbers. Unless explicitly stated otherwise, you are to understand that all statements and problems pertain to $\mathscr{R}$.

3.10.1
EXERCISES

Since manipulating inequalities may be new to you, we begin with several exercises that you can work by filling the gaps in the usual manner.

1. Consider the inequality

(1)
$$\frac{2ab}{a + b} < \frac{a + b}{2}.$$

Do you think that it is always, sometimes, or never true?

Let's try some real numbers as substitutions for a and b.

Let $a = 1$ and $b = 2$. The left member equals ____. The right member equals ____. In this case, the inequality (1) is (true/false).

$\frac{4}{3}$	
$\frac{3}{2}$, *true*	

The left member is meaningless if $a + b =$ ____. Thus, if $a = 1$ and $b = -1$, the left member is _____. In general, the left member is meaningless if $a =$ ____. It is therefore clear that (1) is (always/sometimes/never) true.

0
meaningless
$-b$
sometimes

Merely presenting cases, even a million cases, in which (1) is true and in which it is false may not—and usually doesn't—give a *complete* answer to the question: Under what conditions is (1) true?

We begin with the (questionable) statement

$$\frac{2ab}{a + b} \overset{?}{<} \frac{a + b}{2}$$

and ask ourselves how we can prove it. It would follow, if we could show that

(2)
$$\frac{4ab}{a + b} < a + b,$$

for we could go from (2) to (1) by multiplying both members of (2) by _____, which is legitimate by order postulate _____. And (2) could be proved if we knew that

$\frac{1}{2}, O_3$

(3) $4ab < (a + b)^2$ and $a + b >$ _____,

0

for we could divide both members of (3) by $a + b$. Now (3) is true if

(4) $(a + b)^2 - 4ab$ is $(> 0/ = 0/ < 0)$.

> 0

(See the definition of $>$ in Exercise 8 of Sec. 3.9.2.) Expanding and simplifying the left member of (4) yields _____ > 0. The last inequality can then be rewritten as

$a^2 - 2ab + b^2$

(5)   (_____$)^2 > 0$.

$a - b$

But $x^2 > 0$, as long as $x \neq$ _____. [See Exercise 5(a) of Sec. 3.9.2.] Therefore, (5) holds as long as _____ $\neq$ _____.
   Finally, (1) is true if

0
a, b

$a + b >$ _____ and $a \neq$ _____.

$0, b$

2. Investigate

(6) $a^2 + \dfrac{1}{a^2} > 2$,

to determine conditions under which it is true. This is true if _____ > 0. (Compare with definition of $>$ in Exercise 8 of Sec. 3.9.2.) But the left member equals $(a -$ _____$)^2$. This is positive if $a \neq$ _____. And this is true if $a^2 \neq$ _____; in other words, if $a \neq$ _____. But $1/a^2$ is meaningless if $a =$ _____. There-fore, the inequality (6) is true if $a \neq$ _____ and if $a \neq$ _____.

$a^2 + \dfrac{1}{a^2} - 2$
$1/a$
$1/a, 1,$
$\pm 1, 0$

$\pm 1, 0$

3. We do the same for

(7) $\dfrac{x}{y^2} + \dfrac{y}{x^2} > \dfrac{1}{x} + \dfrac{1}{y}$,

attempting to find conditions on x and y, if any exist, which would guarantee the truth of (7).
   We could prove (7) by dividing, by x^2y^2, both members of the inequality

$x^2y^2(\underline{\quad} + \underline{\quad}) > x^2y^2(\underline{\quad} + \underline{\quad})$,

$\dfrac{x}{y^2}, \dfrac{y}{x^2}, \dfrac{1}{x}, \dfrac{1}{y}$

which could be simplified to read

(8) $x^3 +$ _____ $>$ _____ $+$ _____.

y^3, xy^2, x^2y

This operation is legitimate if $x \neq$ _____ and $y \neq$ _____, since then x^2y^2 is always (positive/negative).

$0, 0$
positive

Now

$$x^3 + y^3 = (x + y)(\underline{\hspace{2cm}}),$$ $x^2 - xy + y^2$

and

$$xy^2 + x^2y = \underline{\hspace{1cm}}(y + \underline{\hspace{1cm}}).$$ xy, x

Therefore, (8) can be rewritten

(9) $(x + y)(\underline{\hspace{2cm}}) > \underline{\hspace{1cm}}(y + \underline{\hspace{1cm}}),$ $x^2 - xy + y^2,$
                                                                            xy, x

which we could prove by multiplying by $x + y$, both members of inequality

(10) $x^2 - \underline{\hspace{1cm}} + \underline{\hspace{1cm}} > xy,$ provided $x + y \neq \underline{\hspace{1cm}}.$ $xy, y^2, 0$

But (10) is true if $\underline{\hspace{3cm}} > 0$; in other words, if $x^2 - 2xy + y^2$

$$(\underline{\hspace{1cm}} - \underline{\hspace{1cm}})^2 > 0.$$ x, y

This last inequality holds as long as $x \neq \underline{\hspace{1cm}}$. Therefore, (7) is y
true if $x \neq \underline{\hspace{1cm}}$ and $x + y > \underline{\hspace{1cm}}.$ $y, 0$

Corollary: If x and y are positive and if $x \neq \underline{\hspace{1cm}}$, then y

$$\frac{x}{y^2} + \frac{y}{x^2} > \frac{1}{x} + \frac{1}{y}.$$

In Exercises 4–8, determine conditions under which the inequalities hold.

4. $2x < 1 + x^2.$

5. $x + \dfrac{1}{x} > 2.$

6. $x^3 - y^3 > (x - y)^3.$

7. $\dfrac{x - y}{x + y} < \dfrac{x^2 - y^2}{x^2 + y^2}.$

8. $(a + b + c)^3 > a^3 + b^3 + c^3.$

9. The *arithmetic mean* (average) of two numbers a and b is

$$A = \frac{a + b}{2}.$$

The *harmonic mean* H of a and b is the number whose reciprocal is the arithmetic mean of the reciprocals of a and b. That is,

$$\frac{1}{H} = \frac{\dfrac{1}{a} + \dfrac{1}{b}}{2}.$$

If $a > 0$ and $b > 0$ and $a \neq b$, prove that $A > H$.

10. Suppose you drive from Philadelphia to New York averaging 25 mph, but on the return trip you average 50 mph. What is your average speed for the entire trip? What relation does this have to harmonic means?

11. State and prove a general result which would give the average speed for a trip, one way traveled at r_1 mph and the return trip traveled at r_2 mph.

12. Suppose you have traveled from Philadelphia to New York at an average speed of 30 mph for the entire trip. How fast must you travel on the return to have an average speed of 40 mph for the entire trip?

3.11

Some Points of Logic and Language In the preceding exercises with inequalities, there was a great deal of thinking of the form

(1) $\qquad\qquad\qquad$ q is true if p is true,

or, in the more usual form,

(1′) $\qquad\qquad\qquad$ if p, $\quad$ then q.

This was certainly not the first time you encountered such statements. We discussed these *implications* briefly in Sec. 3.4, and we introduced the notation

(1″) $\qquad\qquad\qquad$ $p \Rightarrow q.$

Implications pervade all of mathematics. In fact, all theorems are implications, even though some may not seem to be. Theorems are statements of the form.

$\qquad\qquad$ *hypothesis* implies *conclusion.*

Thus, in (1), (1′) and (1″), p is referred to as the hypothesis and q is called the conclusion.

Try your hand at phrasing the four familiar theorems below as implications, making sure that you know exactly what the hypothesis is and what the conclusion is:

Pythagorean theorem.
The diagonals of a parallelogram bisect each other.
The s.a.s. condition for the congruence of triangles.
A square has a circumscribed circle.

In the last two of these theorems, it may not be immediately obvious that they are implications because they are not in the easily recognized form where the hypothesis follows "if" and the conclusion follows "then." In addition to theorems stated in this manner, scientists use several other standard phrasings of implications. We give these below. All six of these statements are equivalent; i.e., from the point of view of logic, they all say the same thing.

(i) If p, then q.
(ii) p implies q.
(iii) q if p.
(iv) p only if q.
(v) q is (a) necessary (condition) for p.
(vi) p is (a) sufficient (condition) for q.

The last three of these often confuse readers of mathematical literature. Some hints for keeping them straight follow.

Think of (iv) as saying

$$p \text{ holds only if } q \text{ follows (from } p).$$

Of course, what "follows" must be the conclusion. Similarly, think of (v) as stating

$$q \text{ necessarily follows from } p.$$

Thus, q "follows" again, which clearly indicates q as the conclusion. Finally, you may think of (vi) as saying

$$p \text{ is sufficient to conclude } q.$$

Again, what follows?

Our shorthand notation allows us to write any of the statements (i)–(vi) as:

$$p \Rightarrow q.$$

If the implication "$p \Rightarrow q$" is true, then is it also true that "$q \Rightarrow p$"? Try your answer on the four theorems above. Consider also the case:

p is the statement that Nero is a dog,
q is the statement that Nero has four legs.

Recall from Sec. 3.4 that the implication "$q \Rightarrow p$" is the *converse of* "$p \Rightarrow q$." If we write the fourth theorem as an implication in the form

$[A, B, C, \text{ and } D \text{ are vertices of a square}] \Rightarrow [A, B, C, \text{ and } D \text{ lie on a circle}]$,

the converse is then

$[A, B, C, \text{ and } D \text{ lie on a circle} \Rightarrow [A, B, C, \text{ and } D \text{ are vertices of a square}]$.

Since it is clear that the converse of a theorem is sometimes true and sometimes not true, we shall single out for special attention those cases in which a theorem and its converse are both true, and use a symbolism for expressing this fact: The statements $p \Rightarrow q$ and $q \Rightarrow p$ are coupled as follows:

(2)   "$p \Leftrightarrow q$" means "both $p \Rightarrow q$ and $q \Rightarrow p$."

The statement $p \Leftrightarrow q$ may be read "p is (logically) equivalent to q," "p if and only if q," "p is necessary and sufficient for q," or even "A necessary and sufficient condition for q is p."

Let's review the solution to the inequality in Exercise 1 of Sec. 3.10.1 making use of our new symbolism. As you worked through the exercise, you reasoned

$$p \text{ if } q, \text{ and } q \text{ if } r, \text{ and } r \text{ if } s, \text{ etc.}$$

In symbols, this would be

$$q \Rightarrow p, r \Rightarrow q, s \Rightarrow r, \text{etc.,}$$

which we can abbreviate by

$$p \Leftarrow q \Leftarrow r \Leftarrow s \Leftarrow \ldots.$$

Consequently, you may think that a summary of the work might more naturally begin with the last line of your proof, in which case it would read

$$[a + b > 0 \text{ and } a \neq b] \Rightarrow 0 < (a - b)^2,$$

$$0 < (a - b)^2 \Rightarrow 0 < a^2 - 2ab + b^2,$$

$$0 < a^2 - 2ab + b^2 \Rightarrow 4ab < a^2 + 2ab + b^2,$$

$$4ab < a^2 + 2ab + b^2 \Rightarrow 4ab < (a + b)^2,$$

$$4ab < (a + b)^2 \Rightarrow \frac{4ab}{a + b} < a + b \qquad (\text{using } a + b > 0),$$

$$\frac{4ab}{a + b} < a + b \Rightarrow \frac{2ab}{a + b} < \frac{a + b}{2}.$$

We would have saved a great deal of writing by not repeating the conclusion each time.

$$a + b > 0 \text{ and } a \neq b \Rightarrow 0 < (a - b)^2$$

$$\Rightarrow 0 < a^2 - 2ab + b^2$$

$$\Rightarrow 4ab < a^2 + 2ab + b^2$$

$$\Rightarrow 4ab < (a + b)^2$$

$$\Rightarrow \frac{4ab}{a + b} < a + b$$

$$\Rightarrow \frac{2ab}{a + b} < \frac{a + b}{2}.$$

Is the reasoning reversible? That is, is the converse true? This question is generally one of mathematical interest, but the technique of pursuing a sequence of reversible steps may be quite useful in itself—for example, in proving certain inequalities. To illustrate this point, we attempt the above exercise by beginning with the desired inequality and reasoning through some reversible steps:

$$\frac{2ab}{a+b} < \frac{a+b}{2} \Leftrightarrow 4ab < (a+b)^2 \qquad \text{(At this point we see the need for including } a + b > 0 \text{ as part of the hypothesis.)}$$

$$\Leftrightarrow 4ab < a^2 + 2ab + b^2$$
$$\Leftrightarrow 0 < a^2 - 2ab + b^2$$
$$\Leftrightarrow 0 < (a - b)^2$$
$$\Leftrightarrow a \neq b.$$

So we see that reasoning from top to bottom and the converse reasoning depends on $a + b > 0$. This could be summarized by stating:

If $a + b > 0$, then:

$$a \neq b \Leftrightarrow \frac{2ab}{a+b} < \frac{a+b}{2}$$

Written entirely in our new symbols, we have

$$(a + b > 0) \Rightarrow \left[a \neq b \Leftrightarrow \frac{2ab}{a+b} < \frac{a+b}{2} \right].$$

In this formulation the hypothesis $a + b > 0$ applies to the reasoning in both directions of the logical equivalence in brackets.

3.11.1
EXERCISES

1. Review the proofs of the inequalities in Exercises 2–7 of Sec. 3.10.1, formulating them as implications.

2. Modify the statements of the inequalities in Exercises 2–7 of Sec. 3.10.1, as we did with Exercise 1, so that your reasoning yields a logical equivalence in each exercise.

3. Check back to see the meaning of *reflexive, symmetric,* and *transitive.* Is the *implication* relation reflexive? Symmetric? Transitive? Which property did you find most useful in the above exercises?

You are already acquainted with the convenient notation for "is less than or equal to." We can define it formally by stating:

(3) $$x \leq y \Leftrightarrow [x < y \text{ or } x = y].$$

Thus, with this notation we are able to assert that

$$a \in \mathcal{R} \Rightarrow 0 \leq a^2.$$

Of course, we use "$x \geq y$" to mean the same as "$y \leq x$." (Read "x is greater than or equal to y.")

In (3) the use of the word *or* may have been clear to you, but occasionally this word is ambiguous. We will, therefore, digress briefly to discuss the mathematical usage of *or*.

Compare the use of *or* in the following statements:

Defense Attorney: My client was at home or at school at the time of the bank robbery.

District Attorney: Your client either knew that the robbery was taking place or he was committing the robbery himself.

Make the comparison in the following two questions, seeing whether you can answer "yes" or "no" sensibly.

Are you married or single?
Does your name begin with A or B?

What would you have answered to the last question if your name is Abraham? Does it make sense to say "Yes?"

The defense attorney used "or" to mean that his client was at home or at school, but *not both*. This usage is sometimes referred to as the *exclusive* form of "or," while the district attorney's usage is termed the *inclusive* form, for the district attorney was asserting one possibility or the other, *possibly both*. And, the meaning of "or" in "Does your name begin with A or B?" is not at all made clear by the language. If we desire our scientific language to be clear and precise, so that no ambiguities occur, we must make some agreement, or establish a convention, to which we will adhere in the future. *We therefore stipulate that our mathematical use of "or" will always be the inclusive form, unless we explicitly state otherwise.* That is, if we say

"p or q is true,"

then we shall mean that one of the following holds:
(a) p alone is true,
(b) q alone is true,
(c) both p and q are true;
or simply, *at least one* of the two statements (p, q) is true. A common notation for "p or q" is

$$p \lor q.$$

Since "or" combines two statements to form still another statement it is referred to as a logical *connective*. The word "implies" is a connective that we considered earlier. Still another connective is "and," with

$$p \text{ and } q$$

true if and only if *both* p and q are true. A common notation for "p and q" is

$$p \wedge q.$$

Illustrations of the Use of Connectives: Postulate O_1 for an ordered field $\mathscr{F}$ states that $\mathscr{F}$ is linearly ordered. We will give the postulates of linear order in terms of our new notation.

$\mathscr{F}$ is linearly ordered with respect to $< \Leftrightarrow$:

1. $a \in \mathscr{F} \Rightarrow a \not< a$. (What is the understood quantifier?)
2. $\forall\, a, b, c \in \mathscr{F}$:

$$[a < b \wedge b < c] \Rightarrow a < c.$$

3. $[a \in \mathscr{F} \wedge b \in \mathscr{F}] \Rightarrow [(a = b) \vee (a < b) \vee (b < a)]$.

The additional postulates for an ordered field are:

O_2. $[a, b, c \in \mathscr{F} \wedge a < b] \Rightarrow [a + c < b + c]$.
O_3. $[a, b, c \in \mathscr{F} \wedge a < b \wedge 0 < c] \Rightarrow ac < bc$.

You should be aware that a *definition is actually a statement of logical equivalence.* For example, our definition of $a > b$ could be written

$$a > b \Leftrightarrow b < a.$$

3.11.2
EXERCISES

1. Each part of this exercise is a statement concerning $\mathscr{R}$; i.e., $x, y \in \mathscr{R}$. Fill the blanks with logical connectives so that each statement becomes a true proposition.
   (a) $xy = 0 \Rightarrow [x = 0 \underline{\hspace{1cm}} y = 0]$.
   (b) $x^2 = 4 \Rightarrow [x = 2 \underline{\hspace{1cm}} x = -2]$.
   (c) $xy > 0 \Rightarrow [(x < 0 \underline{\hspace{1cm}} y < 0) \underline{\hspace{1cm}} (x > 0 \underline{\hspace{1cm}} y > 0)]$.
   (d) $x > 0 \Rightarrow [x > 0 \underline{\hspace{1cm}} x < 0)]$.
   (e) $|x| = |y| \underline{\hspace{1cm}} x^2 = y^2$. (Two answers are possible. Which asserts more?)

2. The solution to $x^2 = 9$ is often written as $x = \pm 3$. What does "$\pm$" mean?

3. Justify the statement concerning $\mathscr{R}$: $a^2 = b^2 \Leftrightarrow a = \pm b$.

4. Fill in the appropriate logical connective:

$$\forall\, a \in \mathscr{R}, \qquad a^2 > 0 \underline{\hspace{1cm}} a^2 = 0.$$

5. A statement like

$$x < y < z$$

is shorthand for

$$x < y \wedge y < z.$$

Prove the following statements concerning $\mathscr{R}$, and give a geometric interpretation in each case.

(a) $|x| < 3 \Leftrightarrow [-3 < x < 3]$.
(b) $|x - 3| < 1 \Leftrightarrow [2 < x < 4]$.
(c) $|x| > 3 \Leftrightarrow [(x < -3) \vee x > 3]$.
(d) $|x - a| < b \Leftrightarrow [a - b < x < a + b]$.
(e) $|x| > b \Leftrightarrow [(x < -|b|) \vee (x > |b|)]$.

The remaining problems of this section are devoted to *some properties of absolute value* that are essential to much of the work that follows.

6. (a) Justify the proposition:

$$\forall \, a \in \mathscr{R}, \qquad -|a| \le a \le |a|.$$

Under what conditions does equality hold?

(b) Using part (a), establish the inequality

(4) $$|x + y| \le |x| + |y|, \qquad \forall \, x, y, z \in \mathscr{R}.$$

[*Hint:* Substitute x and y for a, obtaining two sets of inequalities.] Under what conditions does equality hold?

(c) Prove that

$$|x + y + z| \le |x| + |y| + |z|, \qquad \forall \, x, y, z \in \mathscr{R}.$$

7. (a) Fill the blanks and justify each step in the following argument.

$$\forall \, x, y \in \mathscr{R}, \qquad |x| = |(x - y) + (\underline{\hspace{1cm}})| \Rightarrow |x| \le |x - y| + |\underline{\hspace{1cm}}|$$

$$\Rightarrow |x| - |\underline{\hspace{1cm}}| \le |x - y|.$$

Similarly,

$$|y| - |x| \le |\underline{\hspace{1cm}}|.$$

Therefore,

$$-K \le |x| - |y| \le K, \qquad \text{where } K = \underline{\hspace{1cm}}.$$

Finally, this implies

(5) $$\|x| - |y\| \le \underline{\hspace{1cm}}, \qquad \forall \, x, y \in \mathscr{R}.$$

(b) Under what conditions does equality hold in (5)?

8. Prove that

(6) $$|y - x| \ge \|x| - |y\|, \qquad \forall \, x, y \in \mathscr{R}$$

and

(7) $$|xy| = |x\|y|, \qquad \forall \, x, y \in \mathscr{R}.$$

9. (a) Let $p \in \mathcal{R}^+$ and $a, b, c \in \mathcal{R}$. Prove the following implication:

$$[|a - c| \leq p \wedge |b - c| \leq p] \Rightarrow |a - b| \leq 2p.$$

(b) Give a geometric interpretation of part (a).

(c) When does equality hold in the conclusion of the implication in part (a)?

10. (a) State the *triangle inequality* (see Exercises 2.6.1) in terms of absolute value.

(b) Using (4) and the fact that $a - c = (a - b) + (b - c)$, prove the triangle inequality.

(c) Assuming the triangle inequality, prove (1).

[NOTE: Parts (b) and (c) of this exercise show that the triangle inequality, as given in Sec. 2.6, is logically equivalent to

(4) $$|x + y| \leq |x| + |y|.$$

This is part of the reason why (1), itself, is often called the triangle inequality; another good reason will appear later.]

Chapter Four **Coordinates in the Plane** *Section 4.1 indicates the advantages of a geometric method for describing numerical data. The notions of the real number line are used to introduce rectangular coordinate systems in the plane. Section 4.2 carries on the study of rectangular coordinate systems and introduces polar coordinate systems, as well. The analytic geometry of straight lines is the principal topic of Secs. 4.3 through 4.5. Much of the development and many of the exercises foreshadow the work of differential calculus.*

4.1

Points and Number Pairs Suppose we should like to study the diffusion of molecules in a long thin tube containing a solution of sugar with a certain initial distribution of concentration, measured in grams per unit volume. It is convenient to use a simple model and to focus attention on a single sugar molecule. Therefore, we shall assume that the tube is so thin that the position of the molecule can be described by means of a single coordinate; in other words, the thin tube is assumed to be a segment.

As a first approximation, we divide the tube into ten equal parts (intervals) and assume that the molecule can only occupy the interval

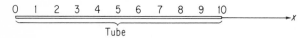

Tube

Figure 4-1

endpoints, which we label with integer coordinates as in Fig. 4-1. Thus, the only admissible positions for the molecule are at

$$x = 0, 1, 2, 3, 4, 5, 6, 7, 8, 9, 10.$$

To represent the diffusion in the simple model, we suppose that the molecule moves one unit in each second, with equal chance of moving left or right, except that if it is at an endpoint of the tube, it must bounce back one unit during the next second (totally reflective barriers).

We can carry out a simple experiment to represent this diffusion process. Start the molecule at one of the admissible positions, say $x = 7$. Toss a coin repeatedly, and move the molecule one step to the right every time the coin comes up heads and one step to the left for each tail. Of course, whenever it reaches an endpoint it must go back one step. Suppose we perform the experiment many times, say a million times. The number of times we choose to begin at the point x is taken to be proportional to the initial concentration at the point, and the initial concentration is a datum obtained by measurement at some fixed time, which we take as $t = 0$. We record the relative frequency with which we find the molecule at any given point y at the time t. This yields a good approximation to the concentration at the point y at the time t. We can improve the approximation by subdividing more finely the interval representing the tube and using an appropriate small number as the time for each step.

What we have described is another example of the Monte Carlo method. We have set up a probability problem which has the same abstract mathematical solution as the given physical problem. Further, the coin tossing experiments can be simulated on a high-speed computer. With the aid of such a computer, a million "tosses" can readily be accomplished, yielding a very accurate solution to the physical problem.

Here is the record of four sequences of tosses, showing the position of the molecule after t steps.

t	x		t	x		t	x		t	x
0	9		0	7		0	2		0	1
1	8		1	8		1	3		1	0
2	7		2	9		2	2		2	1
3	6		3	8		3	3		3	2
4	7		4	7		4	4		4	3
5	8		5	6		5	5		5	4
6	7		6	7		6	4		6	3
7	6		7	6		7	5		7	2
8	5		8	7		8	4		8	1
9	4		9	8		9	3		9	2
10	5		10	9		10	4		10	1

It is a little hard to extract meaning from a table of data. A geometric picture conveys much more to the imagination. We can graph our data, using a rectangular coordinate system as in high school mathematics. To set up a rectangular coordinate system, we choose a pair of perpendicular lines in the plane and call one the t-axis and the other the x-axis. Then we set up scales on both axes, taking their intersection as the 0-point for both. This point is called the *origin* of the coordinate system. We use the same unit of length on both axes.

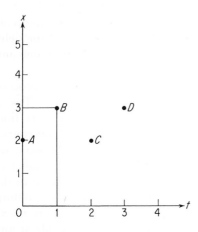

Figure 4-2

We can describe the position of the point B in Fig. 4-2 by dropping perpendiculars to the axes and finding the numbers associated with the feet of these perpendiculars on the given scales. Thus B is assigned the ordered pair $(1, 3)$ of numbers. We have adopted the convention of giving the t-coordinate first and then the x-coordinate. To locate the point $(3, 1)$, draw perpendiculars to the t-axis at 3 and to the x-axis at 1, and find the intersection of these lines.

4.1.1
EXERCISES

1. In Fig. 4-2 we have plotted some data from the third table above. The point A represents the pair $(0, 2)$, indicating that the molecule is at $x = 2$ at the time $t = 0$. The point B represents the next observation.

PROGRAMMED TEXT
FOLLOWS

(a) What are the coordinates of C? Do they agree with the next observation in the table?

(b) Finish graphing the data from the third table.

(c) What do you notice about the four consecutive points beginning with C?

2. (a) Graph the data from each of the other tables.

(b) How can you identify the heads and tails in each sequence of tosses?

In the above examples the value of x for a given t is, in general, a matter of chance. Also, the only values which make sense are nonnegative integers. If x represents the temperatures in degrees centigrade of the air at the time t hours after I began observing it, then x could be any real number > -273 (absolute zero!), and t could be any real number in a certain interval. Our data would then represent certain observations. Presumably the graph of the variation of x with time is a continuous curve, on which we have found several points.

We have set up a 1-1 correspondence between points in the plane and ordered pairs of real numbers. Such a correspondence is called a *rectangular coordinate system*, or a *cartesian coordinate system*, after René Descartes (see Sec. 2.1).

Of course, we can call the coordinates x and y instead of t and x. The letters we use are often suggested by the concrete interpretation of the coordinates.

4.1.2

EXERCISES

Exercises 1–8 refer to a coordinate system like that in Fig. 4-2.

1. (a) The origin O has coordinates (____, ____). If $B = (1, 3)$, $E = (4, 1)$, and $F = (5, ____)$, then $OBFE$ is a parallelogram.

    (b) O, B, and E are vertices of ____ (no/one/two) other parallelogram(s).

    (c) The fourth vertices of these other parallelograms are (____, ____) and (____, ____).

2. The foot of the perpendicular from the point $P = (3, 4)$ to the t-axis is at $Q = (3, ____)$. From the triangle OQP we see that the distance $|\overline{OP}| = ____$.

3. Locate the point $R = (4, 7)$ on the graph paper. The perpendicular from R to the t-axis intersects the perpendicular from $B = (1, 3)$ to the x-axis at the point $S = (____, ____)$. The (directed) distances $\overline{BS}$ and $\overline{SR}$ are ____ and ____, respectively.

(0, 0)
4
two
3, −2, −3, 2
0
5
4, 3
3, 4

Therefore, the distance $\overline{BR}$ is _____. (What have you taken as the positive direction for a line parallel to an axis?)

4. The midpoint of the segment BF, where $B = (1, 3)$ and $F = (5, 1)$ is $M = ($ _____ , _____ $)$.

5. The line joining O to $B = (1, 3)$ goes through the points $(2,$ _____ $)$, $($ _____ $, 9)$, $(10,$ _____ $)$, and $(-1,$ _____ $)$.

6. The line joining the points $(0, 1)$ and $(1, 4)$ goes through the points $(2,$ _____ $)$, $($ _____ $, 10)$, $(10,$ _____ $)$, and $(-1,$ _____ $)$.

7. The line in Exercise 5 goes through the point (t, x), where $x =$ _____ t.

8. The line in Exercise 6 goes through the point (t, x), where $x =$ _____ $t +$ _____ .

5

3, 2

6, 3, 30, −3

7, 3, 31, −2

3

3, 1

9. In the electrical circuit diagrammed in Fig. 4-3, a source of electromotive force of variable voltage V causes current I to flow through an unknown resistance R. The voltage V is measured with a voltmeter ⓥ, as indicated, and the current I is measured in amperes with an ammeter Ⓐ. Here is a set of observations of I corresponding to several values of V:

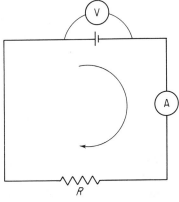

I	V
2.6	4.2
3.1	6.3
3.7	8.4
4.3	10.5
5.7	12.6
7.5	14.7
7.9	16.8
9.3	18.9
10.4	21.0
11.2	23.1

Figure 4-3

Set up a certain coordinate system, labeling the axes with I and V. Graph these data. Draw a simple curve which fits these points with a good approximation. Estimate the value of I when $V = 10$.

10. A marble is rolled down an inclined plane and the distance s traveled is measured at various times t:

t	s	t	s
0	0	6	10.7
1	0.2	7	14.8
2	1.1	8	19.1
3	2.8	9	24.2
4	4.9	10	29.9
5	7.6		

Graph these data in a cartesian coordinate system, labeling the axes t and s. Draw a smooth curve which fits the points approximately. Estimate the value of s when $t = 4.5$.

Of course, we can use any letters we please for labeling the axes. We often say that in Exercise 9 above we are graphing the data in the (I, V)-plane and, similarly, that we are using the (t, s)-plane in Exercise 10. A customary choice of letters is x and y, with the x-axis drawn horizontally and the y-axis vertically, as in Fig. 4-4. We have used arrows to indicate the positive directions of the axes.

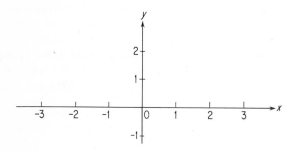

Figure 4-4

4.2

Some Practical Problems in Graphing Other Coordinate Systems   Some practical problems that often arise in the graphical representation of data can be seen by studying the following example. A high school class of 20 students took an intelligence test in September and a mathematics achievement test the following May. Here are the test results for the class:

IQ	Achievement score	IQ	Achievement score
109	590	113	612
115	616	125	731
112	615	117	630
114	619	116	619
111	610	132	794
123	711	121	708
113	605	116	624
118	700	110	601
119	690	120	681
128	781	117	675

We would like to use these data to make the best possible prediction of achievement for a student of given IQ. Then we can tell roughly whether or not a student is doing as well as might be expected.

Since it is hard to see through such a mass (or mess) of data, we try to represent the data graphically. If we use an ordinary sheet of graph paper and try to plot these points (109, 590), (115, 616), and so forth, we won't be able to get all these points on the paper unless we use a very small unit of length. Then the points will be crowded together at one small spot of the paper, and we won't be able to make much sense of them.

We notice that the IQ's vary from 109 to 132, and the achievement scores from 590 to 794. We might plot the excess of IQ over 109 versus the excess of achievement score over 590. Then the ranges will be from 0 to 23 and from 0 to 204, respectively. If we use $\frac{1}{4}$-inch graph paper and place the origin at the lower left-hand corner, then we will need $5\frac{3}{4}$ inches in one direction but 51 inches in the other. This is still too much for $8\frac{1}{2}$ by 11 inch paper! So we let $\frac{1}{4}$ inch (one unit on our paper) represent 20 units of achievement score, and now we need only 10.2 inches in that direction. This amounts to taking

$$x = \text{IQ} - 109$$

and

$$y = \frac{\text{achievement score} - 590}{20}.$$

We can then plot the points (x, y) corresponding to the data from the students in the class, according to the table:

x	y
0	0
6	1.3
3	1.25
5	1.45
2	1.00
14	6.05
4	0.75
.	.
.	.
.	.

Now we can make a reasonable graph on an ordinary sheet of graph paper. For clarity, we should indicate on our graph what x and y represent.

We could instead take x to be the deviation of the IQ from the average, which is 117.45, and y to be 1/20 of the deviation of the achievement from the average, which is 660.6. In this problem we would then have a lot of decimals, which might be unpleasant to plot. In other problems such choices of x and y would be preferable.

If we were presenting our graph to people who are not very literate mathematically, we might not even mention definitions of x and y, but simply label the axes "IQ" and "achievement," and label points to indicate our scales as in Fig. 4-5.

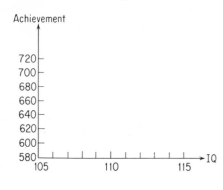

Figure 4-5

Plotting the given data, we see that it can be fitted fairly well by a straight line. Later in your mathematics courses you will study the problem of finding the straight line which fits the data *best*. A student whose point is far from this line is achieving much better or much worse than his intelligence would indicate, and in this way we can identify a student who needs special attention.

The exercises below are intended to broaden your experience with coordinate systems. Be sure to do them all!

EXERCISES

1. (a) For each integer x, let y be the number of ways that you can obtain a total of x on tossing a pair of dice. For instance, if $x = 11$, then you can get x only if one die comes up 6 and the other 5, or vice versa. Thus $y = 2$ if $x = 11$. Tabulate corresponding values of x and y.

(b) Plot the corresponding points (x, y). (We also speak of "plotting y against x" or "plotting y versus x.")

(c) Which has a greater likelihood of occurring in the toss of a pair of dice: 5 or 10?

(d) Which value of x is most likely to occur?

This simple example illustrates the most elementary use of plotting points (graphing) in determining probabilities of events. Can you see any tie-up between this problem and Exercise 10 of Sec. 1.3.4?

2. Suppose one die is colored red and the other white, and that when they are tossed you subtract the number on the white die from the number on the red one. That is, let $r =$ the number on the face of the red die,

$w =$ the number on the face of the white die,

$n = r - w$,

$N =$ the number of different ways of obtaining n from a cast of the dice.

(a) Plot N versus n [see Exercise 1(b)].

(b) What n is most likely to occur?

(c) What n is least likely?

3. Let r and w be defined as in Exercise 2. Call $s = r^2 - w$ and let $S =$ the number of ways in which s can occur.

(a) Plot S versus s.

(b) What is the maximum s that can occur?

(c) What is the minimum s that can occur?

4. (a) Plot the points $(1, 0)$, $(1, 1)$, $(1, 2)$, $(1, -3)$.

(b) Where are all the points (x, y) such that $x = 1$? Graph this set.

(c) Where are all the points such that $x > 1$?

(d) Where are all the points such that $y < 2$?

(e) Where are all the points such that $0 < y < 2$?

5. (a) Shade the set of points in the xy-plane that have $3 - \frac{1}{2} < x < 3 + \frac{1}{2}$.

(b) On the same graph paper, shade the set of points that have

$$-1 - \tfrac{1}{2} < y < -1 + \tfrac{1}{2}.$$

(c) Shade the set of points for which both

$$(3 - \tfrac{1}{2} < x < 3 + \tfrac{1}{2}) \quad \text{and} \quad (-1 - \tfrac{1}{2} < y < -1 + \tfrac{1}{2}).$$

6. Shade the set of points (x, y) such that

(a) $|x + 2| < \frac{1}{4} \wedge |y - 1| < \frac{1}{4}$.

(b) $|2x - 1| < 1 \wedge |y + 1| = 0$.

(c) $|2x + 1| > 4 \wedge y^2 - 1 = 0$.

7. Suppose you are navigating and plotting your position on a cartesian coordinate system, measuring distance in miles. You calculate your position to be at $(7, 3)$, but realize that your measurements may have led to an error as much as two miles in calculating each of the coordinates. On graph paper, shade in the set of all points where you might actually be. How far from $(7, 3)$ is it possible for you to be?

In Exercises 8–16 we develop another kind of coordinate system by means of which we can name the points in the plane.

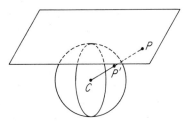

Figure 4-6

8. We set up a coordinate system in a plane by imagining the plane to be tangent to the earth at the North Pole. To obtain an ordered pair of numbers associated with the point P in the plane, join P to the center C of the earth, and let P' be the intersection of the segment PC with the surface of the earth, as shown in Fig. 4-6. The coordinates (ρ, θ) of P are the latitude north and the longitude east, respectively, in degrees of P'. By means of this *projection*, we obtain on the plane a *polar map* of the Northern Hemisphere.

On the more usual polar map of the Northern Hemisphere shown in Fig. 4-7:

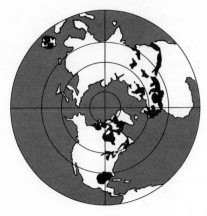

Polar map of Northern Hemisphere

Figure 4-7

The parallels of latitude appear as (lines/circles).	*circles*
The lines of longitude appear as (lines/circles).	*lines*
A point on the surface of the earth is located by (one/two/three) numbers.	*two*
New York has a longitude of approximately ____°W, which	*75*
is equivalent to ____°E.	*285*
The latitude of New York is approximately ____°N.	*40*
The large city located 30°E longitude and 60°N latitude	
is _____.	*Leningrad*
The latitude of the North Pole is ____.	*90°N*
The point with latitude 90°N and longitude 30°E is _____.	*the North Pole*
The point with latitude 90°N and longitude 60°E is _____.	*the North Pole*

Exercises 9–17 assume a slight familiarity with trigonometry.

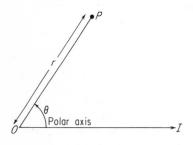

Figure 4-8

9. We can impose a *polar coordinate* system on a plane by selecting a point O for the *origin* or *pole* and a half-line OI emanating from O which we call the *polar axis*. (The point O plays the role of the North Pole, and the polar axis plays the role of the Greenwich Meridian, which is 0° longitude.) Now you can name any point P in the plane by two numbers: one tells how far P is from the pole and the other states the angle that OP makes with OI. We adopt the convention that a positive angle is to be measured counterclockwise (see Fig. 4-8).

The letter r is used to designate the distance $|\overline{OP}|$ and the Greek letter θ (theta) is used to designate the angle IOP. Thus, P may be named by the polar coordinates (r, θ), i.e., $P = (r, \theta)$.

COORDINATES IN THE PLANE
SECTION 4.2

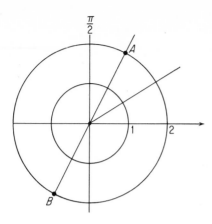

π/2

A

1 2

B

Figure 4-9

(a) Since r is a distance, r is always (rational/positive/nonnegative).

(b) Give the coordinates of A and B in Fig. 4-9. Mark the point C = (4, 2π/3).

(c) Let A and B be one pair of opposite vertices of a parallelogram ACBD. Find the polar coordinates of D.

10. On polar coordinate paper locate the points (a) (1, 30°), (b) (2, 5π/2), (c) (0, π/6), (d) (1, 2π), (e) (1, 376π), (f) (1, 1), (g) ($\frac{2}{5}$, $\frac{5}{2}$).

11. From Exercise 10, you see that the correspondence

$$P \leftrightarrow (r, \theta)$$

is not one-to-one.

(a) How many points correspond to each ordered pair (r, θ)?

(b) How many ordered pairs correspond to each point P?

(c) If one set of coordinates for P is (r, θ), name three other sets of coordinates.

12. For each of the following equations graph the set of all points (r, θ) which satisfy it.

$$r = 0, \qquad r = 1, \qquad r = 2, \qquad r = 3, \qquad r = 4,$$

$$\theta = 0, \qquad \theta = \frac{\pi}{4}, \qquad \theta = \frac{\pi}{2}, \qquad \theta = \frac{3\pi}{4}, \qquad \theta = \pi,$$

$$\theta = \frac{5\pi}{4}, \qquad \theta = \frac{3\pi}{2}, \qquad \theta = \frac{7\pi}{4}.$$

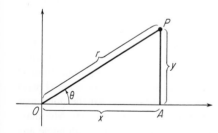

P

r

y

θ

O x A

Figure 4-10

13. Suppose we set up in a plane both a cartesian and a polar coordinate system. We choose the same origin for both, and we take the polar axis to be the positive x-axis. Now every point has two names. If P is (1, $\sqrt{3}$) in the cartesian coordinate system, then its alias in the polar coordinate system is (2, π/3). In many problems some aspects are easier to treat in rectangular coordinates, whereas others are better adapted to polar coordinates. It is useful, then, to be able to shift back and forth from one coordinate system to the other.

From the right triangle OAP in Fig. 4-10, it is clear that

$$\cos \theta = \underline{\qquad} \qquad\qquad \bigg| \quad x/r$$

and

$$\sin \theta = \underline{\qquad}. \qquad\qquad \bigg| \quad y/r$$

Therefore,

$$x = r\underline{\qquad},$$

cos θ

and

$$y = r\underline{\qquad}.$$

sin θ

By the Pythagorean theorem,

$$r^2 = \underline{\qquad} + \underline{\qquad}.$$

x^2, y^2

But since $r \geq 0$, we can equate the positive square roots and get

$$r = \sqrt{\underline{\qquad}}.$$

$x^2 + y^2$

The right triangle OAP also yields

$$\tan \theta = \underline{\qquad}$$

y/x

which is undefined when $\underline{\qquad}$.

$x = 0$

If $x = 0$, P must be on the $\underline{\qquad}$-axis, in which case

y

$$\theta = \underline{\qquad} \lor \theta = \underline{\qquad}.$$

$\pi/2, 3\pi/2$

Thus, the equations

$$x = r \cos \theta,$$

$$y = r \sin \theta,$$

determine well-defined values of x *and* y for each ordered pair (r, θ), and the equations

$$r = \sqrt{x^2 + y^2},$$

$$\tan \theta = y/x,$$

tell us how to obtain r and θ for any given point (x, y) except when $\underline{\qquad} = 0$.

x

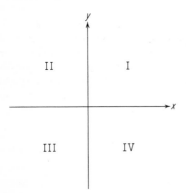

Figure 4-11

14. Relative to a cartesian coordinate system, the plane is divided into four *quadrants*, which are numbered counterclockwise as shown in Fig. 4-11. Your derivation of the equations of transformation was based on reasoning about a right triangle with P in the first quadrant. What modifications, if any, of your results in Exercise 13 are necessary if P happens to be in quadrants II, III, or IV?

15. The left column of the table gives the rectangular coordinates of a point; the corresponding polar coordinates are given on the right. Fill the blanks.

Cartesian	Polar
$(3, 4)$	_____
$(5\sqrt{3}, 5)$	_____
$(-12, 5)$	_____
$(-6, 6)$	_____
$(0, \pi)$	_____
_____	$(16, 7\pi/6)$
_____	$(10, 330°)$
_____	$(8, 3\pi/4)$
_____	$(0, -\pi/2)$
_____	$(12, 49\pi/4)$

16. (a) Shade the region in which

$$|r - 2| < \frac{1}{2} \wedge \left|\theta - \frac{\pi}{3}\right| < \frac{\pi}{6}.$$

(b) For given $(x, y) \neq (0, 0)$, how many θ's are there such that $\tan \theta = y/x$ and $0 \le \theta < 2\pi$? How can you tell which one is a polar coordinate of (x, y)?

If the polar coordinates of (x, y) are $(5, \pi/3)$, describe the set of all θ such that $x = r \cos \theta$ and $y = r \sin \theta$.

(c) An important (and perhaps obvious) characteristic of the cartesian correspondence of points with ordered pairs is that "*nearby points*" correspond to "*nearby pairs.*" This is certainly a desirable property, but is by no means true for all correspondences that give us coordinate systems. Referring to polar coordinates with the restriction $0 \le \theta < 2\pi$, can you say that "nearby points" correspond to "nearby ordered pairs?" Explain.

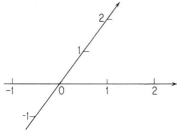

Figure 4-12

17. A cartesian coordinate system can be built up from a pair of intersecting axes, *even if the axes are not perpendicular*. This type of coordinate system is referred to as *oblique*—in contrast to rectangular—since the axes are said to be oblique. An example is shown in Fig. 4-12.

(a) What does the grid system look like?

(b) Locate the points $(2, 3)$, $(2, -3)$, $(-2, 3)$, $(-2, -3)$ on an oblique coordinate system in which the positive x- and y-axes meet at a 45° angle.

Frequent use of oblique coordinate systems is made by physicists and chemists who study the molecular structure of compounds (in crystal form) by means of X-ray crystallography. Just as a judicious choice of the position of a coordinate system may simplify a problem, so also does a judicious choice of the *type* of coordinate system sometimes simplify the problem. In X-ray crystallography, the mathematical analysis is simplified by selecting an oblique coordinate system that is suggested by the type of symmetry possessed by the crystal under analysis.

Important Summary Remark: The various coordinate systems in the plane that we have discussed are of the following general type: The position of a point is described by means of a pair of numbers, u and v. The set of all points where u is a given number is a curve. If we choose different values for this number, we obtain a family of curves, and we can label each curve by the number associated with it. Similarly, the set of all points where v is a given number is a curve in another family.

In general, a point in the plane lies on one curve in each family, and its coordinates are simply the labels of these two curves.

Thus in a rectangular coordinate system, the curves defined by equations such as $x = 3$ are the lines parallel to the ____-axis, and those defined by equations such as $y = 2$ are the lines _____ to the x-axis. Each point lies on one curve in each family.

y

parallel

In a polar coordinate system, the curves defined by equations such as $r = 3$ are the circles with center at _____, and the curves defined by equations such as $\theta = \pi/4$ are the rays emanating from _____.

the origin

the origin

4.3

Graph of $y = x + a$ In the previous section, we observed that the set of points in the (x, y)-plane for which $x = 3$ is a line parallel to the y-axis, and the set defined by the equation $y = 2$ is a line parallel to the x-axis. We will now look a bit beyond these simple examples.

Let's examine the statement

(1) $y = x,$

where it is understood that $x, y \in \mathscr{R}$. This statement is true for (some/all/no) ordered pairs (x, y). If we substitute in this equation a for x and b for y, i.e., we set $x = a$ and $y = b$, then we obtain the equation

some

(2)   ____ = ____.

a, b

If (2) is true, then (a, b) is said to *satisfy* the equation $y = x$. We will now look for some other ordered pairs that satisfy (1):

if $x = 0$,   then $y =$ ____;

0

if $x = -1$,   then $y =$ ____;

−1

if $y = 321$,   then $x =$ ____.

321

In general, if $x = a$, then $y =$ _____. For each value
of x there is (more than/exactly) one corresponding value
of y.

Complete the table for $y = x$, and draw the graph.

x	y
2	____
____	-2
π	____
$2b + 3$	____
____	x

The graph of $y = x$ intersects the x-axis at $x =$ _____
and the y-axis at $y =$ _____. The points at which a graph
intersects the axes are called the *intercepts* of the graph.
We refer to these intersections as the *x-intercept* and
y-intercept. In this special case the x-intercept and
y-intercept are both the point (_____, _____).

How would you describe the graph of (1) geometrically? Can you prove it?

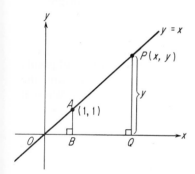

Figure 4-13

In Fig. 4-13, we show graph of $y = x$, which we know passes through
$O = (0, 0)$ and $A = (1, 1)$. If the graph is a line—as we suspect—the general
point $P = (x, y)$ of the graph must be on line OA. Let's try to prove this.

We call B and Q the feet of the perpendiculars from
A and P, respectively, to the x-axis. Thus,

$$B = (\underline{\quad}, 0) \quad \text{and} \quad Q = (\underline{\quad}, 0).$$

Comparing corresponding sides in the right triangles
OBA and OQP, we have

$$\frac{\overline{BA}}{\overline{OB}} = \frac{\overline{QP}}{\overline{OQ}}.$$

Therefore, these right triangles are _____, *similar*
which means that their corresponding angles are _____. *equal*
Thus,

$$\sphericalangle\, BOA = \sphericalangle\,\text{_____}.$$ *QOP*

But this tells us that points O, A, and P are on one line!

Question. We have shown that every point P of the graph is on line OA. Is every point on line OA on the graph of $y = x$? Prove it.

In summary, we may say that the *relation* $y = x$ is true for all ordered pairs in which the first and second elements are equal; furthermore, these are the only ordered pairs which satisfy $y = x$. The graph of the relation $y = x$ is the set of points (x, y) such that $y = x$. *Assuming some facts of euclidean geometry*, we have shown that the graph, or locus, described by $y = x$ is a line with an x-intercept equal to zero and a y-intercept equal to zero.

4.3.1

EXERCISES

1. (a) Sketch the graph of $y = x + 1$, and prove that it is a line.
(b) What is the acute angle made by this line and the x-axis?
(c) Find the x-intercept of the graph of $y = x + 1$.
(d) Find the y-intercept.
(e) Find the intersection of this line with the line $y = x$.

2. Same as Exercise 1 for $y = x + 9$.

3. Same as Exercise 1 for $y = x - 1$.

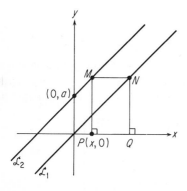

Figure 4-14

4. Refer to Fig. 4-14, in which $\mathcal{L}_1$ is the graph of $y = x$.
(a) If $\mathcal{L}_2$ is a line parallel to $\mathcal{L}_1$, and if the y-intercept of $\mathcal{L}_2$ is equal to a, find the equation of $\mathcal{L}_2$ in the form $y =$ _____.
(b) Find the coordinates of M.
(c) If MN is parallel to the x-axis, find the coordinates of N.
(d) Finally, find the coordinates of Q.

5. From Exercise 4, we see that the correspondence $P \to Q$ between points is essentially a correspondence $x \to x + a$ between real numbers. In effect, we have a geometric procedure for adding a to any real number.

(a) On one set of axes, show geometrically the additions $0 + 1$, $1 + 1$, $2 + 1$, $-3 + 1$ by the method of Exercise 4.

(b) Do the same for $0 - 1$, $1 - 1$, $2 - 1$, $-3 - 1$.

6. Examine Fig. 4-15, which exhibits geometric constructions for $a + b$ and $b + a$. According to the figure, $a + b \neq b + a$, which violates one of our field postulates for $\mathcal{R}$. Using your knowledge of euclidean geometry learned in high school, find the flaw in the figure.

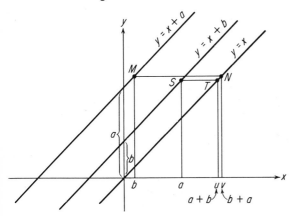

Figure 4-15

7. Exhibit constructions for $a - b$ and $-b + a$.

8. Prove the associative law for addition by means of our construction and your high school euclidean geometry.

9. In Exercises 4 and 5 we have introduced a geometric construction for a correspondence $x \rightarrow x + a$. We refer to this correspondence as a *mapping*, and denote it by $\bar{a}$. We shall write

$$\bar{a} : x \rightarrow x + a \qquad \text{or} \qquad x \xrightarrow{\bar{a}} x + a.$$

$\bar{a}$ maps each real number into exactly one real number. The number $x + a$ is called the *image of x under the mapping $\bar{a}$*. Find the image under

(a) $\bar{a}$ of $x - a$,

(b) $\bar{a}$ of $x + a$,

(c) $\bar{b}$ of a,

(d) $\bar{b}$ of $x + a$,

(e) $\overline{a + b}$ of $x + a$,

(f) $\bar{c}$ of the answer to (d),

(g) $\overline{b + c}$ of $x + a$,

(h) $\overline{-a}$ of $x + a$,

(i) $\bar{a}$ of $x + b$,

(j) $\bar{0}$ of x.

10. For every real number we have a mapping of the sort described in Exercise 9. Calling $\mathcal{T}$ the set of all these mappings, we define an algebraic operation $\circ$ in $\mathcal{T}$.

Definition: $\bar{a} \circ \bar{b}$ is defined to be $\bar{b}$ followed by the mapping $\bar{a}$. That is,

$$x \xrightarrow{\bar{b}} (x + b) \xrightarrow{\bar{a}} (x + b) + a = x + (b + a),$$

137

so

$$x \xrightarrow{\bar{a} \circ \bar{b}} x + (b + a).$$

(a) Prove that $\mathscr{T}$ is an abelian group with respect to the operation ∘.

(b) How do the mappings in $\mathscr{T}$ compare with the A-functions in Sec. 3.2?

(c) What name did we give to the operation ∘ in Sec. 3.2?

11. In this exercise, let us denote by $\bar{\alpha}$ the mapping which operates on the point (r, θ) to produce the point $(r, \theta + \alpha)$.

$$(r, \theta) \xrightarrow{\bar{\alpha}} (r, \theta + \alpha),$$

where points are described by polar coordinates.

(a) Describe what happens under the mapping $\overline{\pi/6}$.

(b) Draw a figure and show what happens to the points of a line through the origin under $\overline{\pi/6}$.

(c) What point does the origin map into under $\overline{\pi/6}$?

(d) What does the origin map into under any mapping of the type $\bar{\alpha}$?

12. We designate the set of all mappings of the type $\bar{\alpha}$ (as given in Exercise 11) by $\mathscr{U}$. Introduce algebraic operations into the set $\mathscr{U}$ so that $\mathscr{U}$ is an abelian group with respect to these operations.

A Word on Dimension. In the various coordinate systems that were used to name the points of the plane, we always required *two numbers* for naming a point. Two numbers were necessary and sufficient. Thus we established a correspondence between points of the plane and ordered *pairs* of numbers. This is one meaning of the statement that the plane is *two-dimensional*. Similarly, the physical space we live in is called *three-dimensional*, since the location of *a point in physical space requires three numbers*.

13. State the dimension of the following geometric sets:

(a) The surface of the earth.

(b) A circle (by a "circle" we always mean the boundary).

(c) A circle together with its interior.

(d) The interior of a square (excluding the square itself).

(e) A helix (the mathematical name for a curve which looks like the spiral binder of a notebook).

(f) The geometry of Einstein, which is used to locate an event (point) in time as well as in space.

(g) The surface of a cube.

(h) One quadrant of the cartesian plane.

(i) The surface of a torus (a doughnut or bagel-shaped surface).

Application of Dimension. The concept of dimension as discussed in the last exercise may be used in a great variety of applications apart from pure geometry. The physicist who may be working with a particle that is free to move in the plane speaks of the particle as having *two degrees of freedom*. The mathematician describes this situation by stating that "*the configuration-space of the mechanical system is two-dimensional.*"

The astronomer who is analyzing the two-body mechanical system consisting of the earth and the sun refers to his mechanical system as having six degrees of freedom since the position of the earth (considered as a point mass) is given by three numbers and the position of the sun (considered as a point mass) is given by three additional numbers. The mathematician would describe this situation by saying that "the configuration-space is six-dimensional."

14. State the number of degrees of freedom (or the dimension of the configuration-space) in each of the following cases:

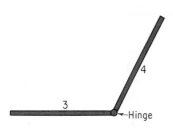

Figure 4-16

(a) A satellite moving in orbit.
(b) A bead moving on a circular wire.
(c) The population of the state of Minnesota.
(d) A ship at sea.
(e) A needle lying on the floor.
(f) The inventory of a tobacco company that markets one expensive and one inexpensive product in each of the following categories: cigarettes (both regular and king-size), pipe tobacco, and cigars.
(g) Two linked, rigid rods moving freely in the plane and rotating freely about the hinge, as shown in Fig. 4-16.

4.4

The Graph of $y = ax$ A particle is moving along a line at the velocity of 3 centimeters per second. We take the 0-point of the coordinate system on the line to be at the position of the particle at the time $t = 0$. Let x be its position at the time t. Where is the particle at the time $t = 1$, at the

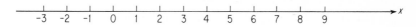

time $t = 2$, at the time $t = 5$? Where was it at the time $t = -4$ (four seconds before $t = 0$)? Make a table of corresponding times and positions.

t	x
0	0
1	3
2	___
5	___
-4	___
___	12
___	9
___	36

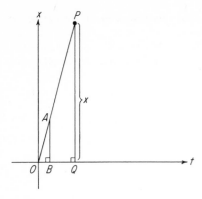

Figure 4-17

Graph these points in the (t, x)-plane. Do these points seem to form a simple geometrical figure? Where does the line $t = 5$ intersect this figure? Where does the line $x = 6$ intersect this figure?

Let A be the point $(1, 3)$, O be the origin $(0, 0)$, B the point $(1, 0)$, P the point $(5, x)$ on the line OA, and Q the point $(5, 0)$, as shown in Fig. 4-17. Since AB and PQ are both perpendicular to the t-axis, the triangles OBA and OPQ are similar. Therefore, we have $\overline{PQ}/\overline{OQ} = \overline{AB}/\overline{OB}$.

In this equation you know that $|\overline{OB}| = $ _____,	*1*
$|\overline{AB}| = $ _____, and $|\overline{OQ}| = $ _____.	*3, 5*
Solving for $\overline{PQ}$, you find that $x = $ _____.	*15*
More generally, if $P = (t, x)$ is any point on the line OA, then $\overline{PQ} = $ _____ and $\overline{OQ} = $ _____. The triangles OBA and OQP are similar. Therefore, the ratios in the above equation are equal. Substituting the values t for	*x, t*
$\overline{OQ}$, _____ for $\overline{PQ}$, _____ for $\overline{OB}$, and _____ for $\overline{AB}$, we obtain	*x, 1, 3*
$x = $ _____t.	*3*

Every point on the line satisfies this equation, and, therefore, represents an event in the motion of the particle. Does every point whose coordinates satisfy this equation lie on the line?

Let $R = (t, 3t)$ be a point which satisfies this equation. Let $Q = (t, 0)$ be the foot of the perpendicular from R to the t-axis, and let this perpendicular intersect the line OA at $P = (t, x)$. We have already shown that P satisfies the above equation. Therefore, we know that $x = 3t$, so that P and R are the same point. Therefore, R does lie on the line OA.

4.4.1
EXERCISES

1. Check that the above reasoning also works for $t = -5$. At $t = -5$, the particle is at $x = $ _____.

2. In the above problem, the particle was moving at the rate of 3 cm/sec to the _____ (left/right). If we set up the coordinate system on the line as above, then a velocity of -3 cm/sec would denote a motion to the _____ (left/right), and the equation of the motion would be $x = $ _____t. Graph this equation in the (t, x)-plane.

3. If the velocity of the particle is v cm/sec, then the equation of the motion is $x =$ _____ t.

(a) If v is positive, then (reading from left to right) the graph of this equation slopes _____ (upward/downward). If v is negative, then the graph slopes _____ .

(b) The graph of this equation is the _____ (what kind of curve?) through the points $(0,$ ____ $)$ and $(1,$ ____ $)$.

(c) Along this graph, when t increases by 1, then x increases by ____ . If t increases by 2, then x increases by ____ .

4. (a) If the velocity of the particle is 5 cm/sec, then the equation of the motion is $x =$ ____ t.

(b) When $t = 3$, $x =$ ____ . When $t = 3 + h$, then $x =$ ____ $+$ ____ . The change in x during this time interval from $t = 3$ to $t = 3 + h$, the length of which is ____ seconds, is ____ cm, and

$$\frac{\text{change in } x}{\text{change in } t} = \frac{\underline{\hspace{1cm}}}{h} = \underline{\hspace{1cm}}.$$

5. (a) Prove that if P is any point on the line joining $O = (0, 0)$ to the point $A = (1, 5)$, then P satisfies the equation $x =$ ____ . (Imitate the above proof.)

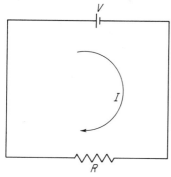

(b) Prove that if $P = (t, x)$ and P satisfies this equation, then P lies on the line OA.

6. In the electrical circuit with voltage V and resistance R, the current I satisfies the equation (Ohm's law)

$$V = IR.$$

(What are the units of V, R, and I?)

(a) Let $R = 6$ ohms. Graph this equation in the (I, V)-plane.

(b) If you want to increase the current by 7 amperes, how much do you have to increase the voltage?

7. Look again at the line OA joining the origin to the point $A = (1, 3)$ (Fig. 4-17). Let θ be the angle which OA makes with the positive t-axis. Then $\tan \theta =$ ____ .

8. We wish to find the equation of the set of points $P = (x, y)$ which are equidistant from the points $C = (3, 4)$ and $D = (0, 5)$: $\overline{PC} = \overline{PD}$.

(a) What geometrical figure is formed by this set?

(b) Referring to Fig. 4-18, find the distances

Figure 4-18

$$\overline{OE} = \underline{\hspace{1cm}}, \qquad \overline{EC} = \underline{\hspace{1cm}},$$

3, 4

$$\overline{OQ} = \underline{\hspace{1cm}}, \qquad \overline{QP} = \underline{\hspace{1cm}}.$$

x, y

The line CR is parallel to the x-axis. Therefore,

$$\overline{CR} = \overline{EQ} = \underline{\hspace{1cm}} - \underline{\hspace{1cm}}.$$

x, 3

Since $\overline{RQ} = \overline{C\underline{\hspace{1cm}}}$, we also have

E

$$\overline{PR} = \overline{PQ} - \overline{RQ} = \underline{\hspace{1cm}} - \underline{\hspace{1cm}}.$$

y, 4

The triangle CRP is a right triangle, with hypotenuse _____.

PC

Therefore,

$$\overline{PC}^2 = \overline{CR}^2 + \underline{\hspace{1cm}}^2$$

RP

$$= (\underline{\hspace{1cm}} - \underline{\hspace{1cm}})^2 + (\underline{\hspace{1cm}} - \underline{\hspace{1cm}})^2.$$

x, 3, y, 4

Similarly, we find that

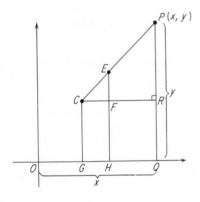

$$\overline{PD}^2 = (\underline{\hspace{1cm}})^2 + (\underline{\hspace{1cm}})^2.$$

x, y − 5

(c) Substitute your results into the equation

$$\overline{PC}^2 = \overline{PD}^2.$$

Multiply out the terms, and solve for y in terms of x:

$$y = \underline{\hspace{1cm}}x.$$

3

9. We wish to find the equation of the line joining the points $C = (3, 4)$ and $E = (5, 6)$. In Fig. 4-19, CG, EH, and PQ are perpendicular to the x-axis and CR is parallel to the x-axis. We find the distances

Figure 4-19

$$\overline{OG} = \underline{\hspace{1cm}}, \quad \overline{OH} = \underline{\hspace{1cm}} \quad \text{and} \quad \overline{OQ} = \underline{\hspace{1cm}},$$

3, 5, x

$$\overline{GC} = \underline{\hspace{1cm}}, \quad \overline{HE} = \underline{\hspace{1cm}} \quad \text{and} \quad \overline{QP} = \underline{\hspace{1cm}}.$$

4, 6, y

The triangles CFE and CRP are similar. Therefore,

$$\frac{\overline{PR}}{\overline{RC}} = \frac{\underline{\hspace{1cm}}}{\underline{\hspace{1cm}}}.$$

EF
FC

But

$$\overline{EF} = \overline{EH} - \overline{HF} = \overline{EH} - \overline{G\underline{\hspace{1cm}}} = \underline{\hspace{1cm}} - \underline{\hspace{1cm}},$$

C, 6, 4

and

$$\overline{FC} = \overline{H\_\_\_} = \overline{OH} - \overline{OG} = \_\_\_ - \_\_\_,$$

G, 5, 3

and

$$\overline{RP} = \overline{QP} - \overline{Q\_\_\_} = \_\_\_ - \_\_\_,$$

R, y, 4

and

$$\overline{CR} = \overline{G\_\_\_} = \overline{OQ} - \overline{OG} = \_\_\_ - \_\_\_.$$

Q, x, 3

Substituting for $\overline{EF}$, $\overline{FC}$, $\overline{RP}$, and $\overline{CR}$ in the above equation, we obtain

$$\frac{\underline{\qquad}}{\underline{\qquad}} = \frac{\underline{\qquad}}{\underline{\qquad}}.$$

y − 4, 2
x − 3, 2

Solving for y, we obtain

$$y = \_\_\_ + \_\_\_.$$

x, 1

10. Find the equation of the line DC in Exercise 8.

11. Find the equation of the perpendicular bisector of the segment $\overline{CE}$ in Exercise 9.

We frequently find that two quantities are so related that their quotient is a constant. Some examples that we have already seen are: the distance x traveled in time t by a particle moving at uniform velocity, the voltage V and the current I in the circuit of Exercise 6 above. Another example is *Hooke's law*, which says that if y is the force required to make a spring (or any other elastic solid) stretch x cm, then y/x is a constant.

If y and x are so related that y/x is a constant, then we say that y is *proportional* to x. The constant value of the quotient y/x is called the *constant of proportionality*. The relation may be expressed by means of an equation

$$y/x = a,$$

where a is the constant of proportionality, or

$$y = ax.$$

As we have seen, the graph of this equation in the (x, y)-plane is a line through the origin. Conversely, every line through the origin except the y-axis can be represented by such an equation. For if $A = (1, a)$ is the intersection of the given line with the line $x = 1$, and $P = (x, y)$ is any other point on the line, and B and Q are the feet of the perpendiculars from A and P, respectively, to the x-axis, then the triangles OBA and OQP are _____.

similar

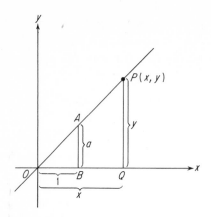

Figure 4-20

Therefore, we see that ratios of the lengths of corresponding sides of these triangles are equal:

$$\frac{\overline{BA}}{\overline{OB}} = \frac{\overline{Q\underline{}}}{\overline{O\underline{}}}.$$

P
Q

But we know that these distances are

$$\overline{BA} = \underline{}, \quad \overline{OB} = \underline{}, \quad \overline{QP} = \underline{}, \quad \overline{OQ} = \underline{}.$$

$a, 1, y, x$

Therefore, we obtain the equation

$$\frac{\overline{}}{\underline{}} = \frac{\overline{}}{\underline{}},$$

a, y
$1, x$

from which we deduce that $y = \underline{}$.

ax

Therefore, every point on the line OA satisfies this equation. Conversely, we wish to show that if $P = (x, y)$ satisfies this equation, i.e., if $y = \underline{}$, then P lies on the line. Let $R = (x, z)$ be the point on the line OA with the same x-coordinate as P. Since, by our above reasoning, R must satisfy the equation, we find that $z = \underline{} = y$, so that R is the same as P, and P lies on the line OA.

ax

ax

In many problems we assume such a relation (proportionality) between two quantities, at least as a first approximation.

If $\theta = \sphericalangle BOA = \sphericalangle QOP$, as in Fig. 4-20,

$$\tan \theta = y/x = \underline{}.$$

a

Thus we see that the constant of proportionality a has a simple geometric interpretation:

a is the tangent of the angle made by the line OA with the positive x-axis.

For this reason a is called the *slope* of the line OA.

4.4.2
EXERCISES

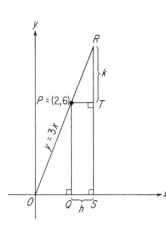

Figure 4-21

1. Start at the point $P = (2, 6)$ on the line $y = 3x$. Let x increase by h units, starting at 2, and let the corresponding change in y be k units (see Fig. 4-21). Let R be the point at which you arrive on the line $y = 3x$. Let Q and S be the feet of the perpendiculars from P and R, respectively, to the x-axis, and T be the foot of the perpendicular from P to RS. We see that

$\overline{OQ} = \underline{\quad}$, $\overline{QS} = \underline{\quad}$,	$2, h$
$\overline{OS} = \overline{OQ} + \overline{QS} = \underline{\quad}$,	$2 + h$
$\overline{ST} = \overline{QP} = \underline{\quad}$,	6
$\overline{TR} = \underline{\quad}$, $\overline{SR} = \underline{\quad}$.	$k, 6 + k$

Therefore,
$$R = (\underline{\quad}, \underline{\quad}).$$

$2 + h, 6 + k$

Since R is on the line $y = 3x$, its coordinates must satisfy this equation:
$$\underline{\quad} = 3(\underline{\quad}).$$

$6 + k, 2 + h$

We solve for k, and obtain
$$k = \underline{\quad};$$

$3h$

and we find that
$$\frac{\text{change in } y}{\text{change in } x} = \frac{k}{h} = \underline{\quad}.$$

3

How is this number related to the slope of this line?

2. A particle moves on the line $y = ax$ from the point (x, y) to the point $(x + h, y + k)$. Find a formula for k in terms of h. How is the ratio

$$\frac{\text{change in } y}{\text{change in } x} = \frac{k}{h}$$

related to the slope of the line?

3. (a) A particle moves along the x-axis at the constant velocity of v units of length per second, starting at $x = 0$ when $t = 0$. We represent the motion on the (t, x)-plane by the graph of the equation

$$x = \underline{\quad\quad} t.$$

What is the slope of this line? What is its physical meaning?

(b) In Exercise 6(a) of Sec. 4.4.1, what is the slope of the line? What is the physical meaning of the slope?

(c) In Exercise 1 of this set, what is $\tan \sphericalangle TPR$? How is $\sphericalangle TPR$ related to $\sphericalangle QOP$?

4. Draw the line $y = x$ and the line $\mathscr{L}$ joining the origin to the point $(1, 3)$. Take any number x. Start at the point $(x, 0)$ on the x-axis, go vertically until you reach the line $\mathscr{L}$, then horizontally until you reach the line $y = x$, and then vertically again until you reach the x-axis. What are the coordinates of the final point?

5. (a) Give a geometrical construction, as suggested in the last exercise, for the operation of multiplying by 5.

(b) Use the construction in part (a) to prove geometrically that

$$5(x + h) = 5x + 5h.$$

(c) Show how to use the constructions in Exercises 4 and 5(a) to prove that $3(5x) = (3 \cdot 5)x$.

(d) How can you see from the construction in part (a) that $5x$ is negative whenever x is negative?

(e) Give a geometrical construction, as in part (a), for the operation of multiplying by -5. How can you see from this construction the sign of the number $(-5)x$ when x is negative?

4.5

The Graph of $ax + by + c = 0$ You already know a good deal about the graphs of some special cases of *the general linear equation*

(1) $\qquad\qquad ax + by + c = 0 \qquad (a \neq 0 \lor b \neq 0).$

For example, Sec. 4.4 treated the special case in which $c = 0$ and $b \neq 0$. How would you give an algebraic description of the special case that was the subject of Sec. 4.3? What other special cases of (1) do you know about? Can you formulate a conjecture concerning the graph of (1), based on your knowledge of the several special cases?

The following exercises will assist you in understanding the general linear equation. You should do all of them!

4.5.1
EXERCISES

1. The height y, in centimeters, of a column of mercury in a thin tube (a thermometer) is related to the temperature x, in degrees centigrade, of the bulb at the bottom by the equation

$$y = 10 + (0.08)x.$$

Graph this equation in the (x, y)-plane.

(a) How high is the mercury column at 0°C?

(b) How much does the column rise for each degree increase in temperature? For each h degrees increase in temperature?

(c) According to the above relation, at which temperature is $y = 0$? Is this physically possible? Why not? What restriction is there on the set of numbers x for which this relation is valid?

(d) What geometrical figure is formed by this graph? Prove it.

(e) If θ is the angle which this graph makes with the positive x-axis, what is the value of $\tan \theta$?

2. Graph the equations:

(a) $y = 3x$.   (c) $y = 3x + 2$.

(b) $y = 3x + 1$.   (d) $y = 3x - 4$.

(e) Prove that the graphs in (a)–(d) are lines. Where do these lines intersect?

(f) For each of these lines, what is the *slope*, i.e., the tangent of the angle made with the positive x-axis?

(g) On each of these lines, if x increases by h units, what is the change k produced in y? Calculate k/h.

(h) Where does each of these lines intersect the y-axis?

3. Graph the equations:

(a) $y = \frac{1}{2}x + 1$.   (c) $y = 2x + 1$.

(b) $y = x + 1$.   (d) $y = (-3x) + 1$.

Answer questions (e)–(h) from Exercise 2 for this set of lines.

4. (a) Show how to use the graph in Exercise 2(b) to construct geometrically the value of $3x + 1$ for any given number x.

(b) Give a geometrical construction of the value of x, given the value of $3x + 1$, using the graph in Exercise 2(b).

5. Graph the lines $\mathscr{L}_1 : y = x$, $\mathscr{L}_2 : y = x + 1$, and $\mathscr{L}_3 : y = 3x$ on the same sheet of graph paper.

(a) Take any number x. Start at the point $(x, 0)$. Go vertically up to the line $\mathscr{L}_3$, then horizontally to the line $\mathscr{L}_1$, then vertically to the point Q on the x-axis. What are the coordinates of the point Q?

(b) As before, start at the point $(x, 0)$. Go vertically up to the line $\mathscr{L}_2$, then horizontally to the line $\mathscr{L}_1$, then vertically to the line $\mathscr{L}_3$, then horizontally to the line $\mathscr{L}_1$ again, then vertically to the point R on the x-axis. What are the coordinates of the point R?

(c) Adding 1 to a number x and then multiplying by 3 gives the same result as first multiplying by 3 and then adding _____.

(d) Adding 2 to a number x and then multiplying by 5 gives the same result as first multiplying by _____ and then adding _____.

6. (a) Write the equation of the line through the point $(0, 4)$ with slope 7.

(b) Write the equation of the line through the origin with slope 3.

(c) Write the equation of the line through the origin with slope $-\frac{1}{3}$.

(d) Graph the lines in parts (b) and (c) on the same sheet of graph paper. What is the angle between these lines?

7. (a) What is the slope of the line joining the origin $(0, 0)$ to the point $(3, 5)$?

(b) What is the slope of the line joining the point $(0, 1)$ to the point $(3, 5)$?

(c) What is the slope of the line joining the point $(4, 1)$ to the point $(7, 5)$?

(d) Draw the line joining the point $P = (4, 1)$ to the point $R = (7, 5)$. Drop the perpendiculars from P and R to the x-axis, the feet being Q and S, respectively. Let T be the foot of the perpendicular from P to RS. As a point moves along the line PR from P to R, the y-coordinate changes from _____ to _____, and the x-coordinate changes from _____ to _____. Therefore, we find that the

$$\text{slope} = \frac{\text{change in } y}{\text{change in } x} = \frac{\rule{1cm}{0.4pt}}{\rule{1cm}{0.4pt}}.$$

8. (a) The slope of the line $y = 3x + 2$ is _____. For each unit increase in x, the change in y is _____ units. As x increases, y _____ (increases/decreases).

(b) The slope of the line $y = -3x + 2$ is _____. For each unit increase in x, the change in y is _____ units. As x increases, y _____ (increases/decreases).

9. If the slope of a line is positive, then as x increases, y _____. If the slope of a line is zero, then the line is _____ to the x-axis, and as x increases, y _____ (increases/decreases/remains constant).

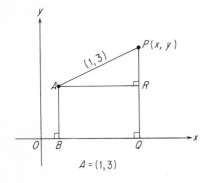

$A = (1, 3)$

Figure 4-22

10. (a) In Exercise 8 of Sec. 4.4.1, the slope of the line DC is _____. The slope of the perpendicular bisector of the segment DC is _____. The product of the slopes of these lines is _____.

(b) In Exercise 9 of Sec. 4.4.1, the slope of the line CE is _____. The slope of the perpendicular bisector of the segment CE is _____. (Remember Exercise 11 of the same section!) The product of these slopes is _____.

11. Let $A = (1, 3)$ and $P = (x, y)$ be any other point. Let B and Q be the feet of the perpendiculars from A and P, respectively, to the x-axis, and let R be the foot of the perpendicular from A to PQ.

Since $\overline{OB} =$ _____ and $\overline{OQ} =$ _____, then $\overline{BQ} = \overline{AR} =$ _____. | $1, x, x - 1$

Since $\overline{BA} = \overline{QR} =$ _____ and $\overline{QP} =$ _____, then $\overline{RP} =$ _____. | $3, y, y - 3$

Therefore, we have

$$\text{slope of } AP = \tan \underline{\quad} = \frac{\overline{RP}}{A\underline{\quad}} = \underline{\quad}.$$ | $\sphericalangle\ RAP, R, \dfrac{y - 3}{x - 1}$

12. (a) The slope of the line joining (a, b) to (x, y) is _____.

(b) Write the equation of the line through $A = (1, 3)$ with slope 5. [*Hint:* If $P = (x, y)$ is on the line, then the slope of AP is _____.]

13. What is the slope of each of the following lines:

(a) $y = 3x + 1$.

(b) $3x - y = 2$.

(c) $3x - 4y = 5$.

(d) $3x + 4y = 7$.

(e) $3x + 4y = 0$.

(f) $y = mx + b$, where m and b are constants.

(g) $Ax + By + C = 0$, where A, B, and C are constants and $B \neq 0$.

14. (a) Graph the equation $x + 1 = 0$. Prove that the graph is a line (using your high school geometry, if necessary).

(b) Graph the equation $2x - 3 = 0$.

(c) Do the lines in parts (a) and (b) have slopes? Why not?

15. (a) Using the method of Exercise 8 of Sec. 4.4.1, find the equation of the perpendicular bisector of the segment joining (a, b) to (c, d).

(b) What is the slope of this perpendicular bisector?

(c) The product of the slope of this perpendicular bisector with the slope of the line joining (a, b) to (c, d) is _____. (Remember Exercise 12 above!)

16. (a) How can you tell from the slopes of two lines whether they are parallel?

(b) How can you tell from the slopes of two lines whether they are perpendicular?

We can summarize the results of these problems as follows:

The set of points (x, y) which satisfy an equation of the form $y = mx + b$ is a straight line. This line intersects the y-axis ($x = 0$) at the point $(0, b)$, which is called the *y-intercept* of the line. If $P = (x, y)$ and $R = (x + h, y + k)$ lie on the line, then

$$y + k = m(x + h) + b.$$

Using the fact that $y = mx + b$ (since P is on the line), when we solve for k, we obtain

$$k = mh,$$

or

$$\frac{k}{h} = \frac{\text{change in } y}{\text{change in } x} = m,$$

which is the same for any two points on the line.

In other words, the rate of change of y with respect to x along the line, that is, the change in y per unit change in x, is equal to the constant m.

We can interpret this constant rate of change geometrically (see Fig. 4-23):

$$\tan \theta = \tan \sphericalangle TPR = \frac{k}{h} = m.$$

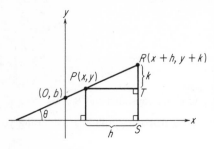

Thus m is the *slope* of the line, the tangent of the angle made by the line with the positive x-axis.

If m is positive, then y increases when x increases. If m is negative, then y decreases when x increases. If $m = 0$, then y is constant, and the line is parallel to the x-axis.

If $P_1 = (x_1, y_1)$ and $P_2 = (x_2, y_2)$ are any two points such that $x_1 \neq x_2$, then the slope of the line $P_1 P_2$ is

Figure 4-23

$$\text{slope} = \frac{\text{change in } y}{\text{change in } x} = \frac{y_2 - y_1}{x_2 - x_1}.$$

Thus the equation of the line through the point $A = (a, b)$ with the slope m is obtained by setting the slope of the line AP, where $P = (x, y)$, equal to m:

$$\frac{y - b}{x - a} = m,$$

which can be solved for y:

$$y = b + m(x - a).$$

The distance r from the point (x_1, y_1) to the point (x_2, y_2) is

$$r = \sqrt{(x_2 - x_1)^2 + (y_2 - y_1)^2}.$$

The perpendicular bisector of the segment joining (a, b) to (c, d) is the set of points (x, y) equidistant from these two points. Thus,

$$\sqrt{(x - a)^2 + (y - b)^2} = \sqrt{(x - c)^2 + (y - d)^2}.$$

If we square both sides of this equation and solve for y, we obtain

$$y = -\left(\frac{c - a}{d - b}\right)x + k \qquad \text{(provided } b \neq d\text{)},$$

where k is a certain constant. Since the slope of the line joining (a, b) to (c, d) is $(d - b)/(c - a)$, we see that the product of the slopes of these two lines is -1. This result is true generally: if m_1 and m_2 are the slopes of two perpendicular lines, then $m_1 m_2 = -1$.

If A, B, and C are constants and $B \neq 0$, then the equation

(1) $$Ax + By + C = 0$$

can be solved for y in terms of x. We recognize the resulting equation as having the form

$$y = mx + b.$$

(What are the geometric interpretations of m and b?) Hence, equation (1) represents a straight line.

If $B = 0$ but $A \neq 0$, then we find that x is a constant, so that the equation represents a line parallel to the y-axis.

Every line can be represented by an equation of the form (1), with A and B not both equal to zero.

4.5.2
EXERCISES

1. (a) The statement

> A and B are not both zero

can be put in symbolic form

$$(A \neq 0) \underline{\hspace{2em}} (B \neq 0).$$

(Fill in the connective.)

(b) Justify the following logical equivalence for $A, B \in \mathcal{R}$:

$$A \text{ and } B \text{ are not both zero} \Leftrightarrow A^2 + B^2 \neq 0.$$

2. Plot on one sheet of graph paper the lines $y = mx + 2$ for $m = 0, 1, 2, 3, -1, -2, -3$.

3. Plot on one sheet of graph paper the lines $y = 2x + b$ for $b = 0, 1, 2, 3, -1, -2, -3$.

4. Write the equation of each of the following lines:
(a) Through $(0, 2)$ with slope 3.
(b) Through $(1, 3)$ with slope 2.
(c) Through $(2, 5)$ with slope 2.
(d) Through $(1, 3)$ with slope 0.
(e) Through $(0, 0)$ and $(2, 3)$.
(f) Through $(1, 3)$ and $(2, 5)$.
(g) Through $(3, 0)$ and $(0, 4)$.
(h) The perpendicular bisector of the segment joining $(0, 3)$ to $(2, 7)$.
(i) Through $(0, 3)$ and $(2, 7)$.

5. (a) Find a point on the line $y = 5$ whose distance from the origin is 13.
(b) Find a point on the line $y = 3x - 5$ whose distance from the origin is 5.
(c) Are the answers to parts (a) and (b) unique?

6. (a) Find a point on the line $x = 4$ which is equidistant from the points $(0, -1)$ and $(0, 3)$.

(b) Where does the perpendicular bisector of the segment joining $(0, 3)$ to $(2, 7)$ intersect the y-axis?

7. (a) What is the set of all points (x, y) which satisfy the equation $0x + 0y - 1 = 0$?

(b) What is the set of all points (x, y) which satisfy the equation $0x + 0y + 0 = 0$?

8. (a) The line $y = 3x + 4$ can also be represented by the equation $Ax + By + C = 0$, where $A = $ _____, $B = -1$, and $C = $ _____.

(b) The line $x = 5$ can also be represented by the equation $Ax + By + C = 0$, where $A = 1$, $B = $ _____, and $C = $ _____.

9. (a) Graph the lines

$$3x + 4y - 5 = 0 \quad \text{and} \quad 6x + 8y - 10 = 0$$

on the same sheet of graph paper.

(b) The line $y = 3x + 4$ can also be represented by the equation $Ax + By + C = 0$, where $A = $ _____, $B = 2$, and $C = $ _____.

10. (a) Graph on one sheet of graph paper the lines

$$x + y - 2 + \lambda(y - 3x) = 0$$

for $\lambda = 0, 1, 2, 3, -1, -2, -3$.

(b) As λ takes on all possible values, we obtain the set of all lines through the intersection of the lines

$$x + y - 2 = \underline{\hspace{1cm}} \quad \text{and} \quad y - 3x = \underline{\hspace{1cm}}$$

except for which line?

(c) Find the line in this family through the origin.

(d) Find the line in this family with slope 4.

(e) Find the line in this family parallel to the line $3x + 4y - 5 = 0$.

(f) Find the line in this family perpendicular to the line $3x + 4y - 5 = 0$.

(g) Do you need to know the point of intersection of the two lines in (b) in order to solve parts (c)–(f)?

(h) Find the line in the family parallel to the x-axis.

(i) Find the line in the family parallel to the y-axis.

11. (a) What geometrical figure is formed by the set of all points (x, y) whose distance from $(3, 4)$ is 5?

(b) Write an equation satisfied by these points and no others.

12. (a) How can you tell from the values of A, B, and C whether the line

$$Ax + By + C = 0 \quad (A^2 + B^2 \neq 0)$$

goes through the origin?

(b) How can you tell whether the point $(1, 2)$ lies on this line?

(c) How can you tell whether this line is parallel to the line $3x + 4y - 5 = 0$?

13. (a) The position of a particle at the time t is given by the equations

$$x = 1 + 2t, \qquad y = 3 - 4t.$$

Make a table of the values of x and y for $t = 0, 1, 2, -1, -2$, and plot the path of the particle in the (x, y)-plane.

(b) Find an equation of the form (1) above satisfied by all points on this path and no others.

Remark on Language: We have continued to use elliptical statements that identify a geometric entity with its name (see Remark 2 in Sec. 2.5). For example, we have said "the point $(1, 3)$" and "the line $3x - 4y + 1 = 0$," in preference to the longer-winded "the point whose rectangular coordinate representation is $(1, 3)$" and "the line defined by the equation

$$3x - 4y + 1 = 0.\text{"}$$

Remark on Logic: In setting up a cartesian coordinate system, we *assumed* that the coordinate axes are lines. Moreover, we *assumed* that the graphs of the equations

$$x = \text{constant} \qquad \text{and} \qquad y = \text{constant}$$

are also lines. In order to prove that the graph of any linear equation is a line we had to be able to recognize a line when we saw one. In other words, we needed some characteristics of a line in order to have a basis for mathematical proof. For this purpose, we *assumed* that the plane described by the cartesian coordinate system satisfied the properties of high school geometry —that is euclidean geometry. Thus, we arrived at a distance formula,

$$(*) \qquad d = \sqrt{(x_2 - x_1)^2 - (y_2 - y_1)^2},$$

for the distance d between points (x_1, y_1) and (x_2, y_2), which is consistent with the *Pythagorean theorem*. On the other hand, we could begin with the distance formula $(*)$ and prove that the Pythagorean theorem follows! From there, we could then prove that the cartesian plane does, indeed, obey the postulates of euclidean geometry.

Chapter Five Functions *The reader has encountered the idea of a function in Chapter 1, and has used particular examples ever since. A more formal and complete discussion of functions and related notions has been reserved as the main topic of this chapter. The reader will see a great variety of functions and various methods of defining functions. He will also see that many other basic mathematical notions can be defined in terms of functions.*

5.1

Introduction   At several earlier points we made brief mention of the important idea of *function*. In fact, we made good use of this concept in Secs. 3.2–3.4, in developing the field properties via the A-functions and M-functions. Now we find it advisable to give a more complete treatment of the subject of functions, which is perhaps the most fundamental idea in all of modern mathematics. First, let us review.

Functions arise when you accumulate and record data in the simplest experiments. For example, suppose you were to try to repeat Galileo's experiment with the inclined plane in an effort to rediscover some of the laws of motion. What kind of data would you get and how would you organize them? The essential instruments for the experiment are an inclined plane (grooved if possible) marked with a scale, a marble to roll down the (groove of the) plane, and a stop-watch. Without getting too involved, we could say that your activity would consist mainly of clocking the marble as it rolled down the plane. In order to systematize these data, you would try to determine the distance s traveled t seconds after the marble was set in motion. At $t = 0$, you'd call the distance $s = 0$. You might find that the marble traveled 2 inches in 1 second and 8 inches in 2 seconds. This would be the beginning of an accumulation of data that takes the form of associating a distance s with each member of a set of time values:

t = time in seconds:	0	1	2	3	4	5
s = distance in inches:	0	2	8	18	32	50

Thus, we have a correspondence, which can be symbolized

$$t \to s,$$

indicating that each value t gives rise to a value s. Then s is said to be *a function* of t.

Another example of this type is seen in the expression of data given by the Census Bureau in its population reports. With a specific time there is associated a population figure. Thus, *population is a function of time.* Still another illustration is found in any weekly *Cost of Living Index*, published by the Bureau of Labor Statistics, which associates with each week a value for the cost of living.

The examples that should be most familiar are the A-functions and M-functions. In the context of Sec. 3.2, we considered these functions as *operations*, but they could just as well have been considered from the point of view of correspondences: with each number x, the function A_a associates the number $x + a$, and the function M_a associates the number ax.

We have attempted to give you a gradual introduction to functions by means of specific examples, for we do not intend to give a formal definition of function. For us, function shall be an undefined term, part of our primitive frame. However, we want to describe it sufficiently and to provide further examples so that the concept will be easy to grasp and work with.

We think of a *function f on set A to set B* as an operation which, acting on any element of *A*, yields an element (a unique element) of *B*. This is symbolized by

$$f: A \to B \qquad \text{or} \qquad A \xrightarrow{f} B.$$

In order to show what the operation does to the *elements* of *A*, we write

$$f: x \to f(x), \qquad x \in A.$$

That is, the function *f* operates on $x \in A$ to produce an element $f(x) \in B$. The element $f(x)$ is called the *value of the function f at x*; and since $f(x) \in B$, we often speak of *f* as being a *B-valued function* defined on *A*. *A* is referred to as the *domain of definition* of *f*, or, briefly, the *domain* of *f*. The symbol "$f(x)$" denotes the result of performing the operation *f* on *x*.

For example, let *f* be the operation of multiplying a real number by 3 (i.e., $f = M_3$). We can indicate this operation by showing what it does to any $x \in \mathcal{R}$:

$$f: x \to 3x.$$

Then $f(2)$ is the result of performing this operation on the number 2:

$$f(2) = 3 \cdot 2 = 6.$$

The sets *A* and *B* are the same, namely, the set of real numbers. As in Sec. 3.2, we sometimes define a function like this:

$$f(x) = 3x, \qquad \forall\, x \in \mathcal{R}.$$

Here we have simply shown what is obtained when we perform the operation *f* on *x*.

Similarly, if *g* is the operation of taking the negative of *x*, we may define *g* by either

$$g: x \to -x$$

or

$$g(x) = \underline{\qquad}, \qquad \forall\, x \in \mathcal{R}. \hspace{3cm} -x$$

If *h* is the operation of adding 2 to any real number (i.e., $h = A_2$), we may define it by either

$$h: x \to x + \underline{\qquad} \hspace{4cm} 2$$

or

$$h(x) = \underline{\qquad} + \underline{\qquad}, \qquad \forall\, x \in \mathcal{R}. \hspace{2cm} x, 2$$

If *j* is the operation of taking the absolute value, then $j: x \to |x|$, that is, $j(x) = \underline{\qquad}, \forall x \in \mathcal{R}$. $\hspace{2cm} |x|$

Using these definitions, we find that

$g(6) = \underline{\hspace{1cm}}$, $h(6) = \underline{\hspace{1cm}}$, $j(6) = \underline{\hspace{1cm}}$, $j(-6) = \underline{\hspace{1cm}}$, | $-6, 8, 6, 6$

We can apply these definitions to any element in the domain (here the set $\mathscr{R}$) of the function:

$$f(1 + \sqrt{2}) = 3(1 + \sqrt{2}), \quad g(-\pi) = -(-\pi) = \underline{\hspace{1cm}},$$ | π

$$j(-\pi) = |-\pi| = \underline{\hspace{1cm}},$$ | π

and if $x \in \mathscr{R}$, then

$$f(x + 2) = 3(x + 2) = \underline{\hspace{1cm}} + 6,$$ | $3x$

$$h(3x) = \underline{\hspace{1cm}} + 2,$$ | $3x$

$$j(3x) = |\underline{\hspace{1cm}}| = |3||\underline{\hspace{1cm}}| = \underline{\hspace{1cm}}|x|,$$ | $3x, x, 3$

and

$$g(3x) = -(\underline{\hspace{1cm}}) = (\underline{\hspace{1cm}})x.$$ | $3x, -3$

Let us get more practice in reading this *functional notation*. What is $f(g(2))$? This is the result of performing f on the number $g(2)$, and $g(2)$ is the result of performing the operation g on the number 2;

(1) $\qquad g(2) = -2 \quad$ and $\quad f(g(2)) = f(-2) = 3 \cdot (-2) = -6.$

In the other symbolism, the order of operation can be seen quite readily

$$2 \overset{g}{\rightarrow} g(2) \overset{f}{\rightarrow} f(g(2)).$$

Now you practice with the functions f, g, h, and j defined above.

(2) $\qquad f(g(5)) = f(\underline{\hspace{1cm}}) = \underline{\hspace{1cm}}.$ | $-5, -15$

$\qquad\qquad g(f(5)) = g(\underline{\hspace{1cm}}) = \underline{\hspace{1cm}}.$ | $15, -15$

$\qquad\qquad f(h(5)) = \underline{\hspace{1cm}}.$ | 21

$\qquad\qquad h(f(5)) = \underline{\hspace{1cm}}.$ | 17

$\qquad\qquad g(j(5)) = \underline{\hspace{1cm}}.$ | -5

$\qquad\qquad j(g(5)) = \underline{\hspace{1cm}}.$ | 5

$\qquad\qquad h(-2a) = \underline{\hspace{1cm}}.$ | $-2a + 2$

$\qquad\qquad -h(2a) = \underline{\hspace{1cm}}.$ | $-2a - 2$

Continuing with our review, recall that we can combine functions to obtain new functions. For example, we can combine the operations f and g

to obtain a new operation, consisting of first performing g on x and then performing f on the result:

$$x \xrightarrow{g} g(x) \xrightarrow{f} f(g(x)).$$

As in Sec. 3.2, we denote this new operation by $f \circ g$:

$$f \circ g : x \rightarrow f(g(x)) \quad \text{or} \quad (f \circ g)(x) = f(g(x)).$$

For example, in (1) we showed you that

$$(f \circ g)(2) = -6,$$

and in (2) you found that

$$(f \circ g)(5) = -15.$$

In this particular case, we see that

$$x \xrightarrow{g} -x \xrightarrow{f} 3(-x) = -3x,$$

so that

$$(f \circ g)(x) = -3 \quad \text{or} \quad f \circ g : x \rightarrow -3x.$$

The function $f \circ g$ is called the *composite* of f with g, and this method of combining functions is called *composition*.

Similarly, we find that

$$(g \circ f)(x) = g(f(x)) = g(\_\_\_\_) = \_\_\_\_\_. \qquad \textit{3x, } -3x$$

In this case, how do $(f \circ g)(x)$ and $(g \circ f)(x)$ compare? For any real number, x, they are _____. But, above, you calculated   *equal*

$$(f \circ h)(5) = \_\_\_\_\_ \quad \text{and} \quad (h \circ f)\ (5) = \_\_\_\_\_. \qquad \textit{21, 17}$$

In the composition of functions, does the order of the functions make any difference? In general, the answer is _____ (yes/no).   *yes*

5.1.1
EXERCISES

In the exercises below we are using the functions f, g, h, and j as defined above.

1. $h(3 + 4) - (h(3) + h(4)) = ?$.

2. $j(3 - 4) - (j(3) - j(4)) = ?$.

3. $f(h(x)) - h(f(x)) = ?$, $(f \circ h)(x) - (h \circ f)(x) = ?$.

4. $f(g(h(x))) = ?$, $(f \circ (g \circ h))(x) = ?$.

5. $f(g(h(j(x)))) = ?, (f \circ (g \circ (h \circ j)))(x) = ?.$

6. $f(-x) = ?.$

7. $g(h(-x)) = ?.$

8. $g(|x|) - |g(x)| = ?, (g \circ j)(x) - (j \circ g)(x) = ?.$

9. $h(g(1 - \sqrt{2})) = ?, (h \circ g)(1 - \sqrt{2}) = ?.$

10. $f(g(x^3)) = ?, (f \circ g)(x^3) = ?.$

We restate the meaning of equality for functions: If F and G are any functions, we say that $F = G$ if F and G have the same domain, and $F(x) = G(x)$ for all x in this common domain. In other words, F and G are equal if they are defined on the same set, and always yield the same result when they operate on any member of this set.

In our examples above we found that

$$f \circ g = g \circ f \quad \text{but} \quad f \circ h \neq h \circ f.$$

11. Which of the following equations hold?
   (a) $g \circ h = h \circ g,$
   (b) $g \circ j = j \circ g,$
   (c) $f \circ (g \circ h) = (f \circ g) \circ h,$
   (d) $(f \circ j) \circ h = f \circ (j \circ h).$
   Does the commutative law hold for the composition of functions?

12. The *product function* $f \cdot g$ is defined by $f \cdot g : x \to f(x) \cdot g(x)$. The function value $f(x) \cdot g(x)$ is also written $(f \cdot g)(x)$. Give formulas for the product functions $f \cdot g$ and $f \cdot h$, where f, g, and h are as defined above.

13. The *sum function* $f + g$ is defined by $f + g : x \to f(x) + g(x)$, or equivalently, $(f + g)(x) = f(x) + g(x)$.
   (a) Is it true that $f + g = g + f$? Justify your answer.
   (b) Find the value of the function $g + h$ at -1.2, and x, where g and h are as defined above.

14. Define the *difference function* $f - g$, and find $(f - g)(-1)$ and $j((f - g)(x))$.

15. Define the *quotient function* f/g.
   (a) If the set of real numbers is taken as the domain for f and g, find the domain of f/g for the given functions f and g.
   (b) Is $(f/g) \cdot g = f$? Explain.

16. Let I be the *identity function* on the set of real numbers defined by

$$I : x \to x \quad \text{or} \quad I(x) = x, \quad \forall x \in \mathcal{R}.$$

(a) What is the domain of the function j/I?
(b) Calculate

$$\left(\frac{j}{I}\right)(3), \quad \left(\frac{j}{I}\right)(-4), \quad \left(\frac{j}{I}\right)(0).$$

17. Let $I^2, I^3, \ldots$ be defined by

$$I^2 = I \cdot I, \quad I^3 = I \cdot I^2, \quad I^4 = I \cdot I^3, \ \ldots.$$

(a) Calculate $I^2(5)$, $I^3(5)$, $I^4(5)$. What is $I^n(x)$?
(b) Calculate $(I \circ I)(5)$, $(I \circ I \circ I)(5)$.
(c) Is $I \circ I = I \cdot I$?

5.2

Defining Functions Sometimes the definition of a function is not (and cannot be) given by means of a simple formula as in the examples of Sec. 5.1. For example, we define the function δ (small Greek letter "delta") on the set $\mathscr{R}$ to $\mathscr{R}$ by specifying

$$\delta(x) = \begin{cases} 0 \text{ if } x \neq 0, \\ 1 \text{ if } x = 0. \end{cases}$$

In order to determine $\delta(3)$, ask yourself: "Is $3 = 0$ or is $3 \neq 0$?" According to your answer, you will obtain $\delta(3) = 1$ or $\delta(3) = 0$. To recall the logical symbolism used earlier, we define the function δ as follows:

$$x = 0 \Rightarrow \delta(x) = 1,$$
$$x \neq 0 \Rightarrow \delta(x) = 0.$$

For another example, suppose you are completing an application form for a driver's license. When you are confronted with the blank for your age, what do you do if your precise age is

18 years, 25 days?
18 years, 2 months?
18 years, 6 months?
18 years, 300 days?

In the United States, at least, you are legally 18 years of age if you have reached your eighteenth birthday but have not yet reached your nineteenth birthday. Even if you will be 19 tomorrow, you are still 18 today! Another fact that brings out this point is that you cannot vote until your twenty-first birthday. Mathematically, we can describe this rule by stating that your legal age equals the integral number of years less than or equal to your precise chronological age.

Chronological age	Legal age
21 days $(= \frac{21}{365}$ years$)$	0
10 years, 2 months $(= 10\frac{1}{6}$ years$)$	10
18.5 years	18
21 years, 364 days $(= 21\frac{364}{365}$ years$)$	21

We therefore have a function defined by the correspondence

chronological age → legal age.

The function is integral-valued; in fact, the function values can only be nonnegative integers. The function operates on any nonnegative real number to produce a nonnegative integer.

An extension of this function (to a domain of all the real numbers) is called *the greatest integer function*. Instead of a letter, we use a bracket around a number to denote the value of the function. That is, the function is given by the correspondence $x \rightarrow [x]$, where

$$[x] = y \Leftrightarrow y \text{ is an integer} \quad \text{and} \quad y \leq x < y + 1,$$

for example, $[2.1] = 2$, $[\pi] = 3$, $[0] = 0$, $[-1.1] = -2$, $[-0.3] = -1$. In other words,

$$[x] = (\text{greatest integer} \leq x).$$

The function considered above,

chronological age → legal age,

may be defined as

$$\text{legal age} = [x],$$

where x is the chronological age in years, and x is a nonnegative real number. The legal age, as a function of the chronological age, is obtained from the greatest integer function by *restricting the domain* to the set of nonnegative real numbers.

We now give an example of a very simple function, a *constant function*, defined by

$$K : x \rightarrow 1,$$

which produces the same number 1, no matter which number it operates on. The word "constant" is chosen because the function value $K(x)$ is "constantly" equal to 1. Expressed in still other terms, you might say, "You can operate with the function K on different numbers of its domain, but the function value remains constant."

Another simple function is the *identity* function, defined by

$$I : x \rightarrow x, \qquad \forall x \in \mathcal{R}$$

which leaves every number of its domain unchanged.

Although we often use letters such as "f," "g," "F," "ϕ," and "p" as names of functions, there are some common functions such as $x \rightarrow [x]$ and $x \rightarrow |x|$ which have standard symbols but no standard letters to represent them. Recently, several authors have taken to using the special name "Abs" to represent the absolute value function:

$$\text{Abs}: x \to |x|.$$

In some contexts "Abs" may be a bit clumsy, so we will take the liberty to introduce, temporarily, a special letter (as "j" in Sec. 5.1) to represent the absolute value function.

5.2.1
EXERCISES

1. If $f(x) = -3x + 1$, find

(a) $f(1)$,

(b) $f([2])$,

(c) $[f(2)]$,

(d) $f([\pi])$,

(e) $f(-[\pi])$,

(f) $f([-\pi])$,

(g) $f(I(x))$,

(h) $I(f(x))$,

(i) $\delta(f(1))$,

(j) $f(\delta(1))$,

(k) $\delta(f(0))$,

(l) $f(\delta(0))$.

2. Let g be given by $g: z \to 1/z$ for any real number $z \neq 0$.

(a) Find $g(2)$, $g(\frac{1}{2})$, and evaluate $g(2 + \frac{1}{2}) - (g(2) + g(\frac{1}{2}))$.

(b) Find $g(a)$ and $g(2a)$, and determine whether (and if so, when) it is possible that $g(a) = g(2a)$.

(c) Under what condition(s) is it true that $g(|z|) = g(z)$?

(d) Find $g(\sqrt{5})$, $g([\sqrt{5}])$, $[g(\sqrt{5})]$.

(e) Find $I(g(x))$ and $g(I(x))$.

(f) Find $\delta(g(0))$, $g(\delta(0))$, $g(\delta([\sqrt{\frac{2}{2}}]))$.

(g) Using "Abs" to stand for the absolute value function and "[]" to stand for the greatest integer function, fill in the blanks:

$$-\frac{\pi}{3} \xrightarrow{\text{Abs}} \underline{\qquad} \xrightarrow{[]} \underline{\qquad} \xrightarrow{\delta} \underline{\qquad}.$$

3. Earlier we introduced you to the constant function

$$K: x \to 1, \qquad \forall\, x \in \mathscr{R},$$

which we will now denote by "K_1" because we would like to use constant functions K_a, defined on domain $\mathscr{R}$ by

$$K_a: x \to a,$$

for every real number a. That is, $K_2: x \to 2$, $K_{-3}: x \to -3$, and $K_{\sqrt{3}}: x \to \sqrt{3}$, $\forall\, x \in \mathscr{R}$.

(a) Find $K_2(K_1(x))$ and $K_1(K_2(x))$.

(b) Give a definition of the function $K_a \cdot K_b$.

(c) Describe the function $K_a \cdot I$ and the function $I \cdot K_a$.

(d) Describe the functions whose function values are

$$[K_a(x)], \qquad K_a([x]).$$

(e) In general, if F is any function, then the function value $K_a(F(x)) =$ _____.

(f) The product function $K_a \cdot I$ is given by

$$K_a \cdot I : x \to \text{_____}.$$

(g) The function $I \cdot I$ operates on x to produce _____.

(h) If g is defined as in Exercise 2, is it true that $g = K_1/I$? Explain.

4. (a) If F is any function, what is $(F \circ I)(x)$?

(b) If F is any function, what is $(I \circ F)(x)$?

(c) Is there an identity with respect to the operation of composition of functions, i.e., is there a function G such that

$$F \circ G = G \circ F = F$$

for all functions F on $\mathscr{R}$.

(d) If F is any function, what are $(K_1 \cdot F)(x)$ and $(F \cdot K_1)(x)$? Is there an identity with respect to multiplication of functions?

(e) Is there an a such that $K_2 \cdot K_3 = K_a$? Is there a b such that $K_2 \circ K_3 = K_b$?

(f) Find an a such that $K_2 \circ f = K_a$, where f is defined as in Exercise 1 above.

(g) Find a b such that $f \circ K_2 = K_b$, where f is defined as in Exercise 1.

(h) Find a c such that $K_0 \circ F = K_c$ for all functions F on $\mathscr{R}$.

(i) Find a function G such that

$$F + G = G + F = F$$

for all functions F on $\mathscr{R}$.

(j) Calculate $(\delta \cdot \delta) - \delta$. Can this function be represented in the form K_a?

5. (a) If $F = K_2 - (K_3 \cdot I)$, find $F(x)$.

(b) If $F = -K_2 - (I \cdot K_3)$, find $F(x)$.

(c) If $F = K_2 - (K_3 \cdot I \cdot I)$, find $F(x)$.

(d) If $\phi(x) = 2 - 3x$, find $\phi(\phi(0))$, $\phi(\phi(1))$, $\phi(\phi(x))$. Check your first two answers with your third.

(e) Find numbers a and b such that $\phi \circ \phi = K_a + (K_b \cdot I)$.

6. We call a function of the form

$$P_n : x \to a_0 + a_1 x + a_2 x^2 + \cdots + a_n x^n, \qquad (a_n \neq 0),$$

a *real polynomial of degree n*, if the *coefficients* $a_0, a_1, \ldots, a_n$ are real numbers.

(a) Which of the following are polynomials: $x \to \dfrac{1}{x}$, K_2, K_0, I, $x \to |x|, x \to [x]$?

(b) Calculate $((K_3 + K_2 \cdot I) + (K_{-4} \cdot I \cdot I))(x)$.

(c) Find a, b, and c such that the polynomial

$$P : x \to 3 + 2x - 5x^2$$

is represented in the form

$$P = K_a + (K_b \cdot I) + (K_c \cdot I \cdot I).$$

163

Sometimes we speak of an expression such as

$$3 - 2x + 5x^2$$

as a *polynomial in* x. In this situation we are talking in abbreviated language, about the polynomial

$$P: x \to 3 - 2x + 5x^2,$$

which can also be represented in the form

$$P: K_3 + (K_{-2} \cdot I) + (K_5 \cdot I^2).$$

(Remember Exercise 17 of Sec. 5.1.1!)

(d) Let P and Q be polynomials in x, defined by

$$P(x) = 1 + 2x + 3x^2, \quad Q(x) = 1 - 2x + x^2, \qquad \forall\, x \in \mathscr{R}.$$

Calculate $(P + Q)(x)$ and $(P \cdot Q)(x)$. Are $P + Q$ and $P \cdot Q$ polynomials? If so, what are their degrees?

(e) If P and Q are defined as in (d), what are the degrees of the polynomials $K_{-3} \cdot Q$ and $P + (K_{-3} \cdot Q)$?

[NOTE: Sometimes it is convenient to consider the degree of the polynomial

$$K_0: x \to 0 \qquad \text{(all the coefficients are zero!)}$$

as -1, whereas in other cases it is more convenient to consider the degree of this polynomial as undefined.]

7. (a) If $P(x)$ represents a polynomial in x, then the *roots* of $P(x)$ are the solutions (not necessarily real) to the equation $P(x) = 0$. The roots are also referred to as the *zeros* of the function P. That is the roots are the numbers which are transformed into zero by the function P. Find the roots of the following:

$$P(x) = 3x - 4,$$
$$P(x) = x,$$
$$P(x) = 2,$$
$$P(x) = 2x^2 - 3x - 1.$$

Give a *geometric* interpretation of real roots.

(b) Which of the following are polynomials in $x: x^{3/2} - 2, (x^{1/2} - 2)^2, 2x/x, x/2,$ $x^2/2, (x^{1/2} - 2)^2 + (-x^{1/2} - 2)^2$?

(c) Are the sum, difference, product, and quotient of two polynomials also polynomials? Prove your answer.

8. Degree. In high school algebra you encountered the lower-degree polynomials and you probably had names for them:

constant	a_0
linear	$a_0 + a_1x, \qquad a_1 \neq 0$
quadratic	$a_0 + a_1x + a_2x^2, \qquad a_2 \neq 0$
cubic	$a_0 + a_1x + a_2x^2 + a_3x^3, \qquad a_3 \neq 0$
quartic (or biquadratic)	$a_0 + a_1x + a_2x^2 + a_3x^3 + a_4x^4, \qquad a_4 \neq 0$
quintic	$a_0 + a_1x + a_2x^2 + a_3x^3 + a_4x^4 + a_5x^5, \qquad a_5 \neq 0$

(a) What is the degree of the product of a quadratic and a cubic?

(b) Show by examples that the sum of two quadratics can be a quadratic, linear, or even a zeroth-degree polynomial.

(c) If P_n and P_m represent polynomials of degree n and m, respectively, what is the degree of the product polynomial $P_n \cdot P_m$?

9. Let $P_2: x \to x^2$, $P_3: x \to x^3$, $P_4: x \to x^4$, ...

(a) What are $P_2 \circ P_3$ and $P_3 \circ P_2$? Are they the same?

(b) For what values of x is $P_2(x) > I(x)$? $P_3(x) > I(x)$?

(c) For what values of x is $P_3(x) > P_2(x)$? $P_4(x) > P_2(x)$?

10. The function on the rational numbers, $\mathcal{R}a$, to the nonnegative reals, defined by $E_2: x \to 2^x$, is referred to as an *exponential* function.

(a) Find $E_2(2)$, $E_2(-2)$, $E_2(\frac{1}{2})$, $E_2(5)$.

(b) Which is larger, $P_2(3)$ or $E_2(3)$? $P_2(5)$ or $E_2(5)$?

(c) Can you formulate a general conjecture on the relative sizes of $P_2(x)$ and $E_2(x)$ for $x \geq 0$ and $x \in \mathcal{R}a$?

(d) Compute $E_2(x + 3)/E_2(x)$.

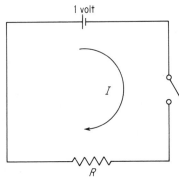

1 volt

I

R

Figure 5-1

11. The function δ was an example of a function that operated "differently" on different parts of its domain. We now give another such example, the so-called *Heaveside impulse function*. It was introduced by Heaviside to describe such phenomena as the voltage V at the time t in the circuit described by Fig. 5-1, in which there is a source of 1 volt and the switch is pressed at the time $t = 0$. Then $V = \eta(t)$, where

$$\eta(t) = \begin{cases} 0 \text{ if } t < 0, \\ 1 \text{ if } t \geq 0. \end{cases}$$

(a) Find $\eta(-2)$, $\eta(\eta(2))$, $\eta(\eta(\eta(-1)))$, $\delta(\eta(1))$.

(b) Give explicit descriptions of the functions $\delta \circ \eta$, $\eta \circ \delta$, $K_1 \circ \eta$, $\eta \circ K_1$, $I^2 \circ \eta$.

(c) Calculate the function $(I^2 - I) \circ \eta$ for at least five values of t, positive, negative, and zero. Give a simple expression for this function.

(d) For which values of x does $\eta(|x|) = \eta(x)$?

This function is important in the study of transients in electrical circuits.

12. Fill in the blanks:

(a) $\text{Abs}(3x) = 3\,\text{Abs}(\underline{\hspace{1cm}})$,

(b) $\text{Abs}(xy) = \text{Abs}(\underline{\hspace{1cm}})\,\text{Abs}(\underline{\hspace{1cm}})$,

(c) $\text{Abs}(-3x) = \underline{\hspace{1cm}}\,\text{Abs}(x)$.

13. Justify the following:

(a) $\text{Abs}(x^2) = (\text{Abs}(x))^2$,

(b) $\text{Abs}(x + y) \leq \text{Abs}(x) + \text{Abs}(y)$,

(c) $\text{Abs}(x - y) \geq \text{Abs}(\text{Abs}(x) - \text{Abs}(y))$.

165

14. Prove that

$$[\text{Abs}\,(x - y) \leq 1 \,\wedge\, \text{Abs}\,(z - y) \leq 1] \Rightarrow \text{Abs}\,(x - z) \leq 2.$$

15. Let $p \in \mathscr{R}^+$. Prove that

(a) $\text{Abs}\,(x) > p \Leftrightarrow [x > p \,\vee\, x < -p]$,

(b) $\text{Abs}\,(x) < p \Leftrightarrow [x < p \,\wedge\, x > -p]$.

5.3
Defining Functions (Continued)
Functions may be defined on all sorts of sets and to all sorts of sets. For example, $\bar{a}$ in Exercise 9 of Sec. 4.3.1 may be thought of as either a function on a line (considered as a set $\mathscr{R}_1$ of points) to itself, or a function on $\mathscr{R}$ to $\mathscr{R}$; $\bar{a}$ in Exercise 11 of Sec. 4.3.1 may be thought of as a function on the plane (as a set of points) to itself. In fact, the scale, or coordinate system, which we set up on a line, may be considered as a function on the line to the set of real numbers; this function operates on a point to produce a definite real number. Similarly, our cartesian coordinate system in the plane may be regarded as a function on the plane to the set of all ordered pairs of real numbers.

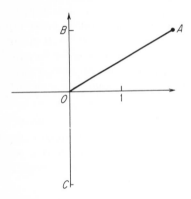

Figure 5-2

Let's consider a function on the set of all ordered pairs of numbers (r, θ), with $r \geq 0$, to the plane (as a set of points). We specify that $(r, \theta) \to P$, where P is the point whose polar coordinates are (r, θ) relative to a fixed origin and polar axis. Does each (r, θ) produce a point? In Fig. 5-2 we show the points A, B, C, O, such that: $(0, 0) \to O$, $(2, \pi/6) \to A$, $(1, \pi/2) \to B$, $(3/2, 3\pi/2) \to C$, $(1, 5\pi/2) \to B$, $(0, 1) \to O$.

Suppose we turn the picture around and ask if the correspondence of points of the plane to polar coordinates is a function. Each point of the plane can be identified by an ordered pair, but a single point possesses an infinite number of ordered pairs. We rule out such correspondences as functions! A function operating on an element of its domain must yield a unique result. Thus, the correspondence of points of the plane to their polar coordinates is not a function.

Exercise: Consider the correspondence of points of the plane to polar coordinates (r, θ) where the following restrictions are made: $r \geq 0$ and $0 \leq \theta < 2\pi$. Is this a function?

As we saw at the very beginning of the section, functions may arise in experiments or observations, but these functions needn't be on real numbers to real numbers. A geneticist may be accumulating data in a study of eye colors in a family line. He would get a function on a set of people to a set of colors:

$$x \rightarrow \text{color of } x\text{'s eyes.}$$

A gambler, tossing a penny, is constructing a function on the positive integers to $\{H, T\}$:

$$n \rightarrow \text{outcome (heads or tails) of } n\text{th toss.}$$

An engineer, working on the heat-transfer problems of a furnace, is concerned with the temperature u at the time t at the point P. He is dealing with a function on the set of ordered pairs (t, P), where t is a real number and P is a point in space, to the set of real numbers

$$(t, P) \rightarrow u(t, P) = \text{temperature at time } t, \text{ at point } P.$$

Since the position of a point in space can be described by three numbers, for example, as in a cartesian coordinate system, we may also regard the temperature as a function on the set of ordered quadruples (t, x, y, z) of real numbers.

An aeronautical engineer who wishes to calculate the flow of air around a wing whose cross section (*Joukowsky profile*) is shown in Fig. 5-3 can solve the problem if he can find a certain function on the set of points in the plane exterior to this curve to the set of points exterior to a circle

Figure 5-3

(Fig. 5-4). This function operates on points, such as Q, to produce points like P. The function which is needed must transform any pair of curves in the original plane into a pair of curves in the plane of the circle which intersect at the same angle. (The

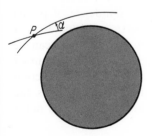
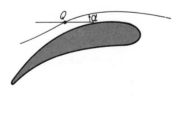

Figure 5-4

angle between two curves is the angle between their tangent lines at the point of intersection.) Such a function will transform the stream lines around the given wing into the stream lines produced in flow around an obstacle with a circular cross section. Thus, this aerodynamic problem is reduced to that of finding a special type of function on a given domain, whose values form another given set.

Other common terms for function are *"transformation"* and *"mapping."* (Of course, we have also used the word "operation.") We can think of a function as *transforming* each element of a set A, its domain, into a definite element of a certain set B. We also say that the function *maps* the set A into the set B. If f maps x into the element y $(y = f(x))$, then we call y the *image* of x under the mapping f. For example, an ordinary map of the earth is a function which operates on each point on the surface of the earth to produce a definite point, its image, in a plane. Here we have a function whose domain is the surface of the earth and which maps this set into a plane.

A scale on a line is a mapping of the set of points on a line into the set of real numbers.

In the following set of exercises you will work with some of these functions, and we shall introduce you to others that will be useful in your mathematical future.

5.3.1
EXERCISES

1. We define a function ρ_3 on the nonnegative integers to nonnegative integers by

$$\rho_3 : n \rightarrow \text{remainder on dividing } n \text{ by 3},$$

e.g.,

$$7 \rightarrow 1 \text{ because } 7 = (3 \cdot 2) + 1,$$
$$27 \rightarrow 0 \text{ because } 27 = (3 \cdot 9) + 0.$$

(a) Find the values of $\rho_3(n)$ for these values of n: 0, 37, 371, 1111, 33,339, and 3,692,763.

(b) Evaluate:

$$\rho_3(4 + 5) - (\rho_3(4) + \rho_3(5)),$$
$$\rho_3(1 + 17) - (\rho_3(1) + \rho_3(17)),$$
$$\rho_3(3k + r) - \rho_3(r),$$

for any nonnegative integers k and r.

(c) Evaluate:

$$\rho_3(4) \cdot \rho_3(5) - \rho_3(4 \cdot 5),$$
$$\rho_3(7) \cdot \rho_3(11) - \rho_3(7 \cdot 11).$$

(d) Evaluate:

$$\rho_3(3k + r),$$

where k and r are nonnegative integers and $0 \le r < 3$.

$$\rho_3((3m + r) + (3k + s)),$$

where m, r, k, and s are nonnegative integers and $0 \le r < 3, 0 \le s < 3$.

$$\rho_3(\rho_3(a + b) - (\rho_3(a) + \rho_3(b))),$$

where a and b are nonnegative integers.

$$\rho_3((3m + r)(3k + s)),$$

where m, r, k, and s are nonnegative integers, $0 \le r < 3$ and $0 \le s < 3$.

$$\rho_3(\rho_3(ab) - \rho_3(a)\rho_3(b)),$$

where a and b are nonnegative integers.

$$\rho_3(n) - (n - 3[n/3]),$$

where n is any nonnegative integer.

2. Given the mapping $(r, \theta) \to (x, y)$ of the polar coordinates of a point to the rectangular coordinates of the same point, where the origins of the coordinate systems coincide and the polar axis coincides with the positive x-axis.

(a) Find the images: $(0, \pi) \to$?, $(2, 7\pi/3) \to$?, $(\sqrt{3}, -5\pi/2) \to$?, $(2, \pi/3) \to$?, $(0, 2) \to$?, $(3, 5\pi/6) \to$?.

(b) Find all the ordered pairs (r, θ) that map into the origin.

(c) Find all the ordered pairs that map into $(7, 7)$.

3. Let's return to the function $\bar{\alpha}: (r, \theta) \to (r, \theta + \alpha)$, considered as a mapping of the plane into itself.

(a) Are there any fixed points—points which do not "move" when operated on by $\bar{\alpha}$?

(b) What happens to the other points? Give a geometric description.

(c) If $\alpha = 2\pi$, describe what happens.

(d) Suppose you know that for one point P, other than the origin, you have

$$\bar{\alpha}(P) = P;$$

then how many fixed points do you have?

(e) Suppose you know that there is one point P, other than the origin, for which

$$\bar{\alpha}(\bar{\alpha}(P)) = P \quad \text{but} \quad \bar{\alpha}(P) \ne P.$$

What deduction(s) can you make? Can you determine α?

4. Let (x, y) represent rectangular coordinates of points in this problem.

(a) What is the distance of $(3, 4)$ from $(0, 0)$?

(b) What is the distance of $(1, 1)$ from $(0, 0)$?

(c) What is the distance of $(-2, 3)$ from $(0, 0)$?

(d) What geometric theorem did you use to determine the answers to (a)–(c)?

(e) What is the distance of (x, y) from $(0, 0)$?

If O represents the origin and P a point of the plane, we define function
$$d : P \to \text{distance from } O \text{ to } P = |\overline{OP}|.$$
(f) The function d is defined on points to _____.
(g) The set of all points P such that $d(P) = 2$ is a _____.
(h) The set of points P such that $d(P) = 0$ contains only _____.

Ordered pairs in Exercises 5–7 are rectangular coordinates of points of the plane.

5. The mapping $T : (x, y) \to (x + 1, y)$ is a function of the plane into itself.
   (a) What is the image of $(0, 0)$ under T? That is, $T : (0, 0) \to$?.
   (b) What point (x, y) maps into the origin?
   (c) Let $P = (x, y)$ and $O = (0, 0)$. Suppose $T(P) = P'$ and $T(O) = O'$.
Find the distance $|\overline{OP}|$ and the distance $|\overline{O'P'}|$.
   (d) If $T(P) = P'$ and $T(Q) = Q'$, prove that $|\overline{PQ}| = |\overline{P'Q'}|$.
   (e) Let PQR be a triangle, with $T(P) = P'$, $T(Q) = Q'$, and $T(R) = R'$. Is triangle $P'Q'R'$ similar to triangle PQR? Can you deduce any more information?
   (f) Is every point (u, v) the image of some point (x, y) under the mapping T? Is any point (u, v) the image of more than one point under T?

6. Let $T : (x, y) \to (x + 1, y + 2)$.
   (a) What point does T map into $(0, 0)$?
   (b) What are the images under T of $(0, 0)$, $(1, 3)$, $(-5, 2)$, $(3, -5)$?
   (c) If $T(P) = P'$ and $T(Q) = Q'$, prove that $|\overline{PQ}| = |\overline{P'Q'}|$.
   (d) Is every point (u, v) the image of some point (x, y) under this mapping?

7. Let $T : (x, y) \to (x + h, y + k)$, where h and k are fixed real numbers.
   (a) What is the image of $(0, 0)$? And what point maps into $(0, 0)$?
   (b) In Exercises 5 and 6 you proved that "distance was preserved," that is, that the distance between two points was equal to the distance between their images. Do the same for the general function T of this problem.

Remark: The function $\bar{\alpha}$ of Exercise 3 is called a *rotation about the origin* and the functions T of Exercises 5–7 are called *translations*, with the general translation appearing in Exercise 7. We shall have much more to say about these transformations of the plane (functions of the plane onto itself) as we go on. In particular, Chapter 6 will bring us back to the subject of translations.

8. Consider $Q : (x, y) \to (x + y, xy)$, which is a mapping of the plane onto itself.
   (a) Find the images of the following points: $(1, 2)$, $(2, 1)$, $(1, 1)$, $(2, 2)$.
   (b) For each of the following, find all points which are mapped into it: $(3, 2)$, $(4, 3)$, $(4, 4)$, $(4, 5)$.
   (c) Find the set of all points (u, v) such that Q maps only one point, (x, y), into (u, v).
   (d) How can you tell whether the point (u, v) is the image of some point (x, y) under Q?

9. Consider the mapping $f : x \to 2x - 3$, $x \in \mathscr{R}$.
   (a) Given any $y \in \mathscr{R}$, is there an x such that $f(x) = y$? How many numbers x are mapped into y?

(b) Is the mapping f one-to-one? Is every real number y the image of some number x?

(c) What is the image of the *interval* $[0, 1]$, i.e., the set of numbers x such that $0 \le x \le 1$?

(d) What set is mapped onto the interval $[0, 1]$?

10. Find the numbers a and b such that the mapping $f : x \to ax + b$ maps the interval $[-3, 7]$ onto the interval $[0, 1]$. What choices are there for $f(-3)$?

11. Consider the mapping $f : x \to \dfrac{3x}{x + 1}$, where x is any real number except -1. (Why must we exclude -1?) Answer questions (a)–(d) of Exercise 9.

12. Find numbers a, b, c, and d such that the mapping $f : x \to \dfrac{ax + b}{cx + d}$, $x \in \mathcal{R}$, maps 0 into 1, no point into 0, and is undefined for $x = 1$. What does this mapping do to the interval $[0, 2]$?

13. For the function f in Exercise 9, find a function g such that $f \circ g = I$. Then find a function h such that $g \circ h = I$.

14. (a) The function Abs maps $\mathcal{R}$ onto _____.

(b) Enumerate the elements of the set of all x such that Abs $(x) = 2$.

(c) Describe the set of y such that Abs $(y - 3) = 2$.

(d) Describe the set of z such that Abs $(4 - z) = 4$.

(e) Describe the set of a such that Abs $(a + 1) = -1$.

15. Describe the largest possible subset $\mathcal{S}$ of $\mathcal{R}$ such that:

(a) Abs $(x + y) \le$ Abs $(x) +$ Abs (y), $\forall\, x$, $y \in \mathcal{S}$,

(b) Abs $(x + y) \ge$ Abs $(x - y)$, $\forall\, x$, $y \in \mathcal{S}$.

5.4

Properties The idea of an object's having some *property* is certainly a familiar one. We make use of it all the time; we identify and classify things by means of their *properties*. Two very obvious examples of this are biological and geological classification, in which specimens are placed in *sets* and *subsets* according to certain properties.

We begin our mathematical study of properties by specifying some examples to serve as a basis for discussion:

Example 1: The property of being a right triangle.

Example 2: The property of being greater than zero.

Example 3: The property of being a distance of one inch from a fixed point F.

Example 4: The property of immortality.

It is certainly clear from an intuitive point of view what is meant by a property. However, a precise logical formulation of the notion can be obtained from the concept of a function:

A *property* is a function on a set (sometimes called the *universe of discourse*) to the set of all *truth values* {truth, falsity}.

This definition is somewhat subtle so we return to the examples to clarify the idea.

Example 1: We designate the property (function) by "*r*." Then

$$r: x \rightarrow \text{truth value of "} x \text{ is a right triangle."}$$

If *a* is a square, then

$$r: a \rightarrow \text{falsity.}$$

If *b* is a triangle with sides equal to 3, 4, and 5 units, then

$$r: b \rightarrow \text{truth.}$$

One way of retrieving the old viewpoint is to observe that the elements that possess the property are all those, and only those, which map into *truth*.

What is the "universe of discourse"? Sometimes it is specified explicitly and sometimes not. In this case we could have specified it as the set of all plane polygons—or another possibility would be the set of all triangles, in which case *a* would not have come up as a candidate for consideration.

Example 2: We call the property *p*. Then,

$$p: x \rightarrow \text{truth value of "} x > 0 \text{."}$$

Let's specify the domain of *p* (the universe of discourse) to be $\mathcal{R}$. Then $p(0) = $ falsity, but $p(\pi) = $ truth. Thus, 0 does not possess the property, but π does.

Example 3: Designate the property by "*β*" and complete the discussion.

$$\beta: X \rightarrow \text{truth value of "} |\overline{F}| = \underline{}\text{."} \qquad X, I$$

If the universe of discourse is the set of points of a plane, then the points which possess property *β* form a _____. If the *circle* universe of discourse is the set of points in ordinary space, then the points possessing property *β* form a _____. *sphere*

Example 4: Designate the property by *γ* and let the universe of discourse be the set of all animals on earth.

$$\gamma: x \rightarrow \text{truth value of "} \underline{}\text{."} \qquad x \text{ is immortal}$$

How many animals possess property γ? _____. | *Zero*

The set with property γ is then empty. It is, therefore, called the *empty set* (other names are the *null set* or *void set*) and will be denoted by "ø."

    Sets are often defined by *properties*. Sometimes a set is defined by enumerating its elements inside a set of braces. For example, $A = \{1, 2, 3, 4\}$. But sometimes this type of definition is inconvenient or even impossible. For example, suppose you wished to specify the set of all positive real numbers, as in Example 2 above. Then you will admit an element to a set if and only if: (1) it is a real number, and (2) it is greater than zero. In order to specify this set we use the shorthand

$$\{x \mid x \text{ is a real number, } x > 0\},$$

which is read "the set of all x such that x is a real number and $x > 0$." Note that the defining properties of the set (elements) are listed to the right of the vertical line with a comma separating them. We omit "and," for that is understood as part of the notation; that is, *all* of the properties to the right of the vertical line must be satisfied.

    This notation is referred to as the "set-builder" notation. To see how it can be based on the concept of function, you may think of it as $\mathscr{S} = \{x \mid P(x)\}$, the set of all x having property P, i.e., the set of x such that $P(x) = $ truth. Or, we could write it in our older notation:

$$x \in \mathscr{S} \Leftrightarrow P(x) = \text{truth}.$$

    For ease in dealing with sets we shall use the special letters introduced earlier to represent some of the more frequently used sets:

$\mathscr{Z} = $ the set of all integers,

$\mathscr{Z}^+ = $ the set of all positive integers,

$\mathscr{Z}^- = $ the set of all negative integers,

$\mathscr{R} = $ the set of all real numbers,

$\mathscr{R}^* = \mathscr{R}$ with 0 excluded,

$\mathscr{R}a = $ the set of rational numbers.

We shall give a few more examples using set-builder notation and then give you some practice.

Example: $A = \{x \mid x \in \mathscr{Z}, 0 < x < 5\}$.

    The statement "$x \in \mathscr{Z}$" may be considered a specification of the universe of discourse and confines our attention to integers. The property $0 < x < 5$ limits the set to the first four positive integers. Therefore, we could also characterize A by enumerating its elements: $A = \{1, 2, 3, 4\}$. This latter notation is often referred to as "roster notation." Other ways of writing A are:

$$A = \{y \mid y \in \mathscr{Z}^+, y < 5\} = \{z \mid z \in \mathscr{Z}^+, z \leq 4\} = \{n \mid n \in \mathscr{Z}, 1 \leq n \leq 4\}.$$

Note that the letter used, such as "x," "y," "z," or "n," is a *dummy symbol*. It makes no difference which letter we use in this set-builder notation.

Occasionally, the universe of discourse may be displayed explicitly before the vertical line. For example,

$$A = \{n \in \mathscr{Z} \mid 1 \le n < 5\}.$$

Example: We could define $\emptyset$ by $\emptyset = \{x \mid x \in \mathscr{R}, x \ne x\}$.

Example: $L = \{(x, y) \mid y = 3x, x \in \mathscr{R}\}$. This is the set of all real ordered pairs (x, y) which satisfy the condition $y = 3x$. Geometrically, this is the line whose equation is $y = 3x$. Another simple way of describing L is

$$L = \{(x, 3x) \mid x \in \mathscr{R}\}.$$

This means the set of all ordered pairs of the form $(x, 3x)$, where x is a real number.

Let E be the set of even integers. Then

$$E = \{2n \mid n \in \underline{\qquad}\} = \{x \mid x = 2n, n \in \underline{\qquad}\} = \left\{ y \left| \frac{y}{2} \in \underline{\qquad} \right. \right\}. \qquad \mathscr{Z}, \mathscr{Z}, \mathscr{Z}$$

The nonnegative real numbers B can be written

$$B = \{x \mid x \in \underline{\qquad}, x \underline{\qquad} 0\}. \qquad \mathscr{R}, \ge$$

Let $M = \{0, 1, 2\}$ and $N = \{5\}$. Then

$$C = \{(m, n) \mid m \in M, n \in N\} = \{(0, 5), (1, \underline{\qquad}), (\underline{\qquad}, \underline{\qquad})\}. \qquad 5, 2, 5$$

$$\mathscr{R}a = \left\{ x \left| x = \frac{a}{b}, a \in \underline{\qquad}, b \in \underline{\qquad}, b \underline{\qquad} 0 \right. \right\}, \qquad \mathscr{Z}, \mathscr{Z}, \ne$$

$$= \left\{ \frac{a}{b} \left| a, b \in \underline{\qquad}, b \underline{\qquad} \right. \right\}. \qquad \mathscr{Z}, \ne 0$$

Just as the concept of property was explained in terms of that of *function*, so can the concept of ordered pair be based on *function*. The *ordered pair* (a, b) may be defined as the function f on $\{1, 2\}$ to $\{a, b\}$ defined by $f(1) = a$ and $f(2) = b$. Thus, the first element of the ordered pair is defined as the image of $\underline{\qquad}$, and the second element is the image of $\underline{\qquad}$. (Notice how the notation for an ordered pair differs from the notation for a set with two elements; e.g., $\{3, 4\} = \{4, 3\}$, but $(3, 4) \ne (4, 3)$.)

5.4.1
EXERCISES

1. What is the function f that defines the ordered pair $(3, 4)$? Why is it nonsense, in this case, to speak of $f(f(1))$? If f denotes the ordered pair (a, b), under what conditions is $f(f(1))$ defined?

2. Define *ordered triple*, and then define the generalization called an *ordered n-tuple*.

3. Let $L_1 = 3x + 4y - 5$ and $L_2 = x - y + 1$.

(a) Describe geometrically the sets

$$A = \{(x, y) \mid L_1 = 0\},$$

$$B = \{(x, y) \mid L_2 = 0\},$$

$$C = \{(x, y) \mid L_1 \cdot L_2 = 0\},$$

$$D = \{(x, y) \mid L_1^2 + L_2^2 = 0\}.$$

(b) How is the set D related to the sets

$$E_\lambda = \{(x, y) \mid L_1 + \lambda L_2 = 0\}$$

for

$$\lambda = 0, 1, 2, -1, -2?$$

(c) Graph the sets A, B, C, D, and E_λ in parts (a) and (b).

4. How many members does each of the following sets have?

(a) $\{x \mid x \in \mathscr{R}, x^2 \le 0\}$,

(b) $\{x \mid x \in \mathscr{R}, x^2 < 0\}$,

(c) $\{x \mid x \in \mathscr{R}a, x^2 = 2\}$,

(d) $\{x \mid x \in \mathscr{R}a, x^2 = 4\}$,

(e) $\{x \mid x \in \mathscr{R}, x^2 = 4\}$,

(f) $\{x \mid x \in \mathscr{R}, x(x - 1)(x + 2) = 0\}$,

(g) $\{(x, y) \mid x, y \in \mathscr{R}, x^2 + y^2 = 0\}$,

(h) $\{(x, y) \mid x, y \in \mathscr{R}, x^2 + y^2 = 1, y = 0\}$,

(i) $\{(x, y) \mid x, y \in \mathscr{R}, x^2 + y^2 = 1, y = 0.999999\}$,

(j) $\{(x, y) \mid x, y \in \mathscr{R}, x^2 + y^2 = 1, y = 1\}$,

(k) $\{(x, y) \mid x, y \in \mathscr{R}, x^2 + y^2 = 1, y = 1.000001\}$.

5. In the medieval town of Occam, there was a barber who was very particular about whom he shaved. The barber of Occam shaved all those and only those men of Occam who did not shave themselves. Did the barber of Occam shave himself?

In our fancy symbols, the clientele of the barber is defined by the property $P(x)$: x is a man of Occam and x does not shave x.

In some modern systems of logic you cannot get into this kind of trouble because there are restrictions on the kinds of property P for which there is a set $\{x \mid P(x)\}$.

5.5

Sequences A very useful concept in mathematics is that of *sequence*. You are familiar with sequences, such as

$$2, 4, 6, 8, \ldots,$$

$$1, \tfrac{1}{2}, \tfrac{1}{3}, \tfrac{1}{4}, \ldots,$$

$$1, 2, 0, 1, 2, 0, \ldots,$$

where the three dots indicate that the sequence goes on and on. Because the order of the elements—first, second, third, ... —is essential, the notion of *sequence* is actually a generalization of that of *ordered n-tuple*. Therefore, we are led to the definition:

A *sequence* is a function f on the set $\mathscr{Z}^+$.

If $n \in \mathscr{Z}^+$ and $f(n) = a_n$, we sometimes use the notation $\{a_n\}$ to denote the sequence $a_1, a_2, a_3, \ldots$. Here are some examples.

Example 1: $f(n) = 1/2^n$ or $\{1/2^n\}$. The first four terms of this sequence are: $\frac{1}{2}, \frac{1}{4}, \frac{1}{8}, \frac{1}{16}$. What is the tenth term?

Example 2:

$$g(n) = (1/2^n) + (n - 4)(n - 3)(n - 2)(n - 1).$$

$$g(1) = (1/2^1) + (-3)(-2)(-1)(0) = 1/2.$$

$$g(2) = \underline{\hspace{3cm}}.$$

$$g(3) = \underline{\hspace{3cm}}.$$

$$g(4) = \underline{\hspace{3cm}}.$$

Is this sequence the same as that of Example 1? This example should convince you that specifying the first few terms of a sequence *is not* sufficient to define the sequence! To define a sequence, one must tell what operation to perform on *any* positive integer n in order to obtain the nth term.

Example 3:

$$h(n) = \begin{cases} 1 \text{ if } n \text{ is even,} \\ 0 \text{ if } n \text{ is odd.} \end{cases}$$

The sequence proceeds $0, 1, 0, 1, \ldots$, alternating 0's and 1's. An alternative definition is given for $n \in \mathscr{Z}^+$ by

$$h(2n) = \underline{\hspace{2cm}},$$

$$h(2n - 1) = \underline{\hspace{2cm}}.$$

Example 4: $K_1(n) = 1$. Thus the sequence is $1, 1, 1, \ldots$, in which every term is equal to 1.

Notice the difference between a sequence and a set. The set of elements in the sequence of Example 3 is $\{0, 1\}$. You can form many other sequences whose terms belong to this set, e.g., $1, 1, 0, 1, 1, 0, \ldots$, which can be defined by the function $n \to 1 - \delta(\rho_3(n))$. (For the definition of δ, see Sec. 5.2; for the definition of ρ_3, see Exercise 1 of Sec. 5.3.1.)

1. Write the first four terms of each of the sequences:

$$\left\{\frac{1}{n^2}\right\}, \quad \left\{\frac{n-1}{n}\right\}, \quad \left\{\frac{n(n+1)}{2}\right\}, \quad \{n^n\}, \quad \left\{\frac{n\pi}{2}\right\}, \quad \{\rho_3(n)\},$$

when $n \in \mathscr{Z}^+$.

2. Find the sixth term of each of the following sequences:
(a) $f(n) = 2 + 1/10^n$ (write as a decimal).
(b) $f(n) = \begin{cases} 1 \text{ if } n \text{ is even,} \\ -1 \text{ if } n \text{ is odd.} \end{cases}$
(c) $f(n) = -n$.
(d) $f(n) = (n-6)/n$.
(e) $f(n) = (-1)^n/n$.

3. Let f be a function on $\{0, 1, 2\}$ defined by $f(0) = 1, f(1) = 0, f(2) = 0$. Let ρ_3 be defined as in Exercise 1 of Sec. 5.3.1:

$$\rho_3 : n \to \text{remainder on dividing } n \text{ by } 3 \ (n \in \mathscr{Z}^+).$$

Then the composite function $y = f \circ \rho_3$ defines a sequence.
(a) Exhibit the first five terms of the sequence.
(b) What is the 27th term of the sequence? the 52nd term? the 1000th term?
(c) The function g defining this sequence can also be described by:

$$g(n) = \begin{cases} \underline{\hspace{2cm}} \text{ if } n = 3k, \\ \underline{\hspace{2cm}} \text{ if } n = 3k + 1, \\ \underline{\hspace{2cm}} \text{ if } n = 3k + 2, \end{cases}$$

where $n \in \mathscr{Z}^+, k \in \mathscr{Z}$.

4. Some sequences are most easily defined *recursively*, by telling how to compute the nth term from its predecessors. An example of such a sequence is the famous Fibonacci sequence of numbers, which has application in geometry, botony (phyllotaxis), art, and architecture.†

$$f(1) = 0, \quad f(2) = 1, \quad f(n) = f(n-1) + f(n-2), \qquad n \in \mathscr{Z}^+ \land n > 2.$$

(a) Write the first six Fibonacci numbers.
(b) Define the sequence $\{1/3n\}$ recursively.

5. (a) The sequence $g(n) = ar^{n-1} (r \neq 0)$ is called a *geometric sequence* (or *progression*) with *ratio* r. Evaluate $g(n+1)/g(n)$ and $g(1)$. Give interpretations of a and r.
(b) Give a recursive definition for the *geometric sequence* whose first term is a and whose ratio is r.
(c) Identify the geometric sequences among the following, and give their ratios:
$\{1/2n\}, \{1/n^2\}, \{n/3^n\}, \{\sqrt[n]{2}\}, \{n^n\}$.

† See H. S. M. Coxeter, *Introduction to Geometry* (New York: John Wiley & Sons, Inc., 1961).

(d) Find all values of r such that the geometric sequence $f: n \to r^{n-1}$ satisfies the recursion equation for the Fibonacci numbers

$$f(n) = f(n-1) + f(n-2) \qquad \text{for } n \in \mathscr{Z} \land n > 2.$$

6. (a) An *arithmetic sequence* (or *progression*) with the first term a and the difference d is defined recursively by $h(1) = a$, $h(n+1) = h(n) + d$. Give a definition for h that is not recursive.

(b) Write the first four terms of the arithmetic sequence whose first term is $a = 1$ and whose difference is $d = -2$. Do the same for $a = -1$ and $d = \frac{1}{2}$.

(c) Let h define an arithmetic sequence as in (a). Evaluate

$$\frac{h(n-1) + h(n+1)}{2} \qquad \text{for } n > 1.$$

7. Define the sequence g by the equations

$$g(1) = 0, \quad g(n+1) = \frac{1}{1 + g(n)}, \qquad n \in \mathscr{Z}^+.$$

(a) Compute $g(n)$ for $1 \le n \le 7$.

(b) Does there seem to be a relation between this sequence and the Fibonacci numbers?

(c) Compute $x^2 + x - 1$ for $x = g(n)$, $1 \le n \le 7$. State a conjecture about the behavior of the quantity $(g(n))^2 + g(n) - 1$ as n increases. What is the relation between $g(n)$ and the roots of the equation $x^2 + x - 1 = 0$?

8. We can define two sequences simultaneously by the equations

$$f(1) = 1, \qquad g(1) = 25, \qquad f(n+1) = \sqrt{f(n)g(n)},$$

$$g(n+1) = \frac{(f(n) + g(n))}{2}, \qquad n \in \mathscr{Z}^+.$$

(a) Calculate $f(5)$ and $g(5)$ correctly to two decimal places.

(b) Do the same thing starting with $f(1) = 1$, $g(1) = 100$, and using the same recursion relations.

(c) If you start with $f(1) = a$ and $g(1) = b$, where $0 < a < b$, will you ever have $f(n) \ge g(n)$ for any value of $n \in \mathscr{Z}^+$? Is there a reason?

9. (a) Let

$$\gamma(x, y) = \frac{(x + y - 2)(x + y - 1)}{2} + x.$$

Then γ is a function on the set of ordered pairs (x, y) of positive integers to the set $\mathscr{Z}^+$. Compute $\gamma(1, 1)$, $\gamma(1, 2)$, $\gamma(2, 1)$, $\gamma(1, 3)$, $\gamma(2, 2)$, $\gamma(3, 1)$.

Find all pairs (x, y) such that $\gamma(x, y) = 30$. How many such pairs are there?

(b) Define the function s recursively, as follows:

$$s(1) = 2,$$

$$s(n+1) = s(n) + \delta(s(n)(s(n) - 1) - 2n),$$

where δ is the function introduced in Sec. 5.2.

Now define

$$\xi(n) = n - \frac{(s(n) - 2)(s(n) - 1)}{2},$$

$$\eta(n) = s(n) - \xi(n),$$

for $n \in \mathscr{Z}^+$. Compute $s(n)$, $\xi(n)$, and $\eta(n)$ for $1 \le n \le 6$.
  (c) What is $\gamma(\xi(n), \eta(n))$ for $n \in \mathscr{Z}^+$?
  (d) What are $\xi(\gamma(x, y))$ and $\eta(\gamma(x, y))$ for $x, y \in \mathscr{Z}^+$?

5.6

Relations   Ever since Chapter 1, when we spoke of order relations such as "is less than" and "is greater than," we have tacitly assumed that you know what a *relation* is. That is, we used the term "relation" as an *undefined term*—which was probably not shocking because you have so often used relations in propositions such as:

Gene *is the father of* Eric;
Eric *is the cousin of* Paul;
3 *is greater than* 2;
a is equal to b;
$\triangle ABC$ *is congruent to* $\triangle A'B'C'$.

We shall now show how the concept *relation* can be derived from the notion of *function*. (First, it would be a good idea to test yourself by recalling how the concepts of *property*, *sequence*, and *ordered pair* are all derived from the notion of *function*.) We may think of the process of finding out whether Gene has the relation *is the father of* to Eric as consisting of an operation on Gene and Eric to produce the proposition

Gene is the father of Eric

and finding the truth value of this proposition. Since it makes a difference whether we operate on Gene and Eric in that order or on Eric and Gene, we see that we are operating on *ordered pairs*. Thus we may regard a relation as a function on a set of ordered pairs to the set {truth, falsity}.

Definition: A *relation* R *is a function on a set of ordered pairs to the set of truth values* {*truth, falsity*}. *We often write "xRy" to mean "x has the relation R to y."*

Example: Let "R" stand for "is the cousin of." Then "Joe R Mary" means "Joe is the cousin of Mary." If this statement is true and if we regard it in terms of the definition, then

$$(\text{Joe, Mary}) \overset{R}{\to} \text{truth}.$$

179

Example: Let R stand for "is greater than" among real numbers. Then $xRy \Leftrightarrow x > y \Leftrightarrow (x, y) \overset{R}{\to}$ true. We see that we already have the symbol ">" for this relation. For example,

$$(3, 2) \overset{\to}{} \text{true},$$

$$(2, 3) \overset{\to}{} \text{false},$$

$$(\pi, 2\sqrt{2}) \overset{\to}{} \text{false},$$

$$(x, |x|) \overset{\to}{} \text{false}, \qquad \forall\, x \in \mathscr{R}$$

$$(|-3|, -3) \overset{\to}{} \text{true}.$$

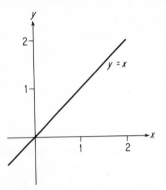

Figure 5-5

A relation R is associated with the set of all ordered pairs (x, y) for which it is true that xRy. In terms of the set-builder notation we have:

$$\text{set associated with } R = \{(x, y) \mid xRy\}.$$

As a matter of fact, some authors prefer to regard the set itself as the relation! Since we have already associated ordered pairs (x, y) of real numbers to points of the plane, we can regard the set associated with R as the *graph* of the relation.

Example 1: Let $xRy \Leftrightarrow x = y (x, y \in \mathscr{R})$. Then the graph of the relation (Fig. 5-5) is the set of points represented by

$$\{(x, y) \mid x = y, x \in \mathscr{R}\}.$$

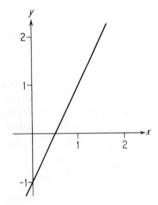

Figure 5-6

Example 2: $xRy \Leftrightarrow y = 2x - 1 (x, y \in \mathscr{R})$. Then the graph of the relation (Fig. 5-6) is the set of points represented by

$$\{(x, y \mid y = 2x - 1, x \in \mathscr{R}\}.$$

Example 3: $xRy \Leftrightarrow x \leq y$ $(x, y \in \mathscr{R})$. Then the graph (Fig. 5-7) is the shaded region including the boundary line.

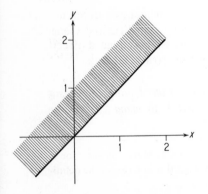

Figure 5-7

Let's trim down our language a bit. Instead of writing "the set of points represented by $\{(x, y) \mid \ldots \}$," we'll simply say "the set of points

$\{(x, y) \mid \ldots\}$." We shall also speak of the "the relation $y = 2x - 1$" or the "relation $x \le y$" when we mean

$$(x, y) \rightarrow \text{the truth value of "} y = 2x - 1 \text{,"}$$

and

$$(x, y) \rightarrow \text{the truth value of "} x \le y \text{,"}$$

respectively.

Now we shall give you some practice.

Let the relation R be defined by the equation $y^2 = x^2$ where $x, y \in \mathcal{R}$. That is, $xRy \Leftrightarrow y^2 = x^2$. Then $(1, \underline{\hspace{1cm}})$ and $(1, \underline{\hspace{1cm}})$ are on the graph of the relation. The set of ordered pairs $(x, 0)$ that satisfy the relation consists of $\underline{\hspace{1cm}}$.

1
-1
$(0, 0)$

The relation $|y| = |x|$ (is/is not) equivalent to the relation $y^2 = x^2$. Sketch the graph of $y^2 = x^2$. It consists of the lines $y = \underline{\hspace{1cm}}$ and $y = \underline{\hspace{1cm}}$.

is
$x, -x$

We define a relation C to mean $xCy \Leftrightarrow (x, y)$ is on the circle of radius 1 centered at $(0, 0)$ (Fig. 5-8). Then $(1, \underline{\hspace{1cm}})$, $(-1, \underline{\hspace{1cm}})$, and $(0, \underline{\hspace{1cm}})$ are on the graph of the relation. If $P = (x, y)$ is any point of the graph, the distance from P to the origin is equal to $\underline{\hspace{1cm}}$. Thus,

$0, 0, \pm 1$
1

$$\sqrt{(x - \underline{\hspace{1cm}})^2 + (y - \underline{\hspace{1cm}})^2} = 1.$$

$0, 0$

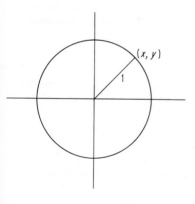

Figure 5-8

Squaring both members yields $(\underline{\hspace{1cm}})^2 + (\underline{\hspace{1cm}})^2 = 1$, which gives another equation defining the relation C. The

x, y

set of points associated with the relation can be specified in the equivalent forms:

$$\{(x, y) \mid x^2 + \underline{\quad\quad} = 1, x, y \in \mathcal{R}\}, \qquad\qquad y^2$$

$$\{(x, y) \mid y = \pm \sqrt{\underline{\quad\quad}}, x \in \mathcal{R}, |x| \leq 1\}, \qquad\qquad 1 - x^2$$

$$\{(x, y) \mid x = \pm \sqrt{\underline{\quad\quad}}, y \in \mathcal{R}, |y| \leq 1\}, \qquad\qquad 1 - y^2$$

$$\{(x, \pm \sqrt{1^2 - x^2}) \mid x \in \mathcal{R}, \underline{\quad\quad} \leq x \leq \underline{\quad\quad}\}. \qquad\qquad -1, 1$$

If a set $\overline{R}$ of ordered pairs is regarded as specifying the ordered pairs that map into Truth, then the set $\overline{R}$ actually specifies the relation R for it tells exactly how the function R operates on the ordered pair

$$[(a, b) \xrightarrow{R} \text{Truth}] \Leftrightarrow (a, b) \in \overline{R},$$

so we can talk about the relation (defined by)

$$\{(1, 2), (-2, 1), (3, 4)\},$$

or the relation defined by

$$\{(x, y) \mid [y] = [x], x, y \in \mathcal{R}\},$$

or even the relation defined by the points of a circle with center (h, k) and radius r in the (x, y)-plane.

Let "$\parallel$" denote the relation *is parallel to* for lines in the plane and let L_1, L_2, L_3 designate distinct lines.

$\parallel$ (is/is not) a symmetric relation.   *is*

If $L_1 \parallel L_2$, then

$$\parallel : (L_1, L_2) \to \underline{\quad\quad}. \qquad\qquad Truth$$

$$(L_1 \parallel L_2 \text{ and } \underline{\quad\quad} \parallel L_2) \Rightarrow L_1 \parallel L_3. \qquad\qquad L_3$$

Let lines be associated with equations as follows:

$$\begin{array}{ll} L_1: y = x + 1, & L_6: 2x - 3y = 0, \\ L_2: y = 0, & L_7: y = \tfrac{2}{3}(x + 1), \\ L_3: x = 0, & L_8: y = -2, \\ L_4: x + y = 2, & L_9: x = -2, \\ L_5: 3x - 2y = 1, & L_{10}: x + 3y = 0. \end{array}$$

Then, the following are ordered pairs of distinct lines associated with the relation $\parallel$.

$$(L_2, \underline{\quad\quad}), \; (L_7, \underline{\quad\quad}), \; (L_9, \underline{\quad\quad}), \; (\underline{\quad\quad}, L_2) \qquad\qquad L_8, L_6, L_3, L_8$$

The subset of $\{L_2,\ L_3,\ L_4,\ L_5,\ L_6,\ L_7,\ L_8,\ L_9,\ L_{10}\}$ defined by $\{L \mid L \parallel L_1\}$ is _____. (Booby!)

$\emptyset$ (*the empty set*)

The function f is associated with the relation defined by the equation $y = f(x)$. If f is a function on the set A to the set B, then f is also associated with the set of all ordered pairs $(x, f(x))$, where $x \in A$, which can also be defined as

$$\{(x, y) \mid y = f(x), x \in A\}.$$

Suppose f is a function, and R is the associated relation, so that

$$xRy \Rightarrow y = f(x).$$

Then we have

xRy and $xRz \Leftrightarrow$ _____ $=$ _____ and _____ $=$ _____,

$\Rightarrow y$ _____ $z.$

$y, f(x), z, f(x)$

$=$

In other words, if R is a relation associated with a function in this way, then R has the special property that there is, for any x, at most one element y such that xRy. In fact, for any $x \in A$, where A is the domain of the function, there is one and only one y such that xRy.

Conversely, if R has this property, then it is associated with the function f defined by

$$f : x \to \text{the unique } y \text{ such that } xRy, \forall\, x \in A.$$

We say that R is a *functional relation* if it has the property that

$$xRy \text{ and } xRz \Rightarrow y = z.$$

The domain A of the associated function is the set

$$A = \{x \mid \exists\, y,\ xRy\}.$$

Examples:
(a) The set $\{(x, y) \mid y = 2x, x \in \mathscr{Z}\}$ designates a function since each integer x is associated with a unique integer $2x$. The associated function $f : x \to 2x$ maps $\mathscr{Z}$ onto the set of all even integers.

(b) $\{(x, y) \mid y = |x|, x \in \mathscr{Z}\}$. This set is associated with the absolute value function on $\mathscr{Z}$ to the nonnegative integers.

(c) $\{(x, y) \mid |y| = x, x \in \mathscr{Z}\}$. This set is associated with a relation *but not* a function, since some x's may have two distinct y's corresponding to them. For example $(1, -1)$ and $(1, 1)$ are in this set. However, the relation S defined by

$$ySx \Leftrightarrow |y| = x, \qquad x \in \mathscr{Z}$$

is a functional relation. It is, in fact, the same relation as that associated with Example (b). We may express this situation briefly by saying that the sentence

$$|y| = x \qquad \text{and} \qquad x \in \mathscr{Z}$$

defines a functional relation between y and x, but not between x and y.

(d) The set $\{(0,0),(1,0),(2,1),(3,1)\}$ defines a function

$$\begin{cases} 0 \to 0, \\ 1 \to 0, \\ 2 \to 1, \\ 3 \to 1, \end{cases}$$

for each first element corresponds to a single second element.

5.6.1
EXERCISES

1. Which of the following sets are associated with functions?

(a) $\{(x, y) \mid x = 3y, y \in \mathcal{R}\}$.

(b) $\{(x, [x]) \mid x \in \mathcal{Z}\}$.

(c) $\{(y, [y]) \mid y \in \mathcal{R}\}$.

(d) $\{([y], y) \mid y \in \mathcal{R}\}$.

(e) $\{(x, y) \mid y^2 = 3x, x \in \mathcal{R}\}$.

(f) $\{(x, y) \mid |y| = [x], x \in \mathcal{R}\}$.

(g) The set of all ordered pairs (p, n), where p is a person and n is the legal name of p.

(h) $\{(P, (r, \theta)) \mid P$ is a point in the plane, (r, θ) the polar coordinates of $P\}$.

(i) $\{(r, \theta)R(x, y) \Leftrightarrow (r, \theta)$ is a polar representation of the point whose rectangular coordinates are (x, y), the polar axis being the positive x-axis.$\}$

(j) $\{(x, y) \mid y^2 = x^2$ if $x \geq 0$, $y^2 = -x^2$ if $x \leq 0\}$.

2. Graph the relations $y = x^2$ and $y^2 = x$. Which of these is a functional relation between x and y? How many intersections does a line perpendicular to the x-axis have with the graph of $y = x^2$? For each x, how many numbers y are there to which x has this relation? Answer the same questions for the relation $y^2 = x$.

(When a function f, whose domain is a set of real numbers, is graphed on a cartesian coordinate system, it is customary to represent the domain on the horizontal axis, and unless stated otherwise, we will follow this custom.)

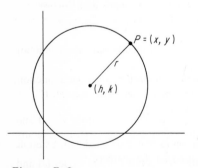

Figure 5-9

3. Let $C = (h, k)$ be a point in the plane. Let $P = (x, y)$ be any point on a circle of radius r and center C (Fig. 5-9). Find an equation which defines the circle by simplifying

$$\sqrt{(x - \underline{\quad})^2 + (y - \underline{\quad})^2} = r,$$

getting $(x - \underline{\quad})^2 + (y - \underline{\quad})^2 = r^2$. Does this equation define a functional relation between x and y?

4. The equation $x^2 + y^2 + 2x + 3y + 1 = 0$ can be written in a form $(x - \underline{\quad})^2 + (y - \underline{\quad})^2 = r^2$ by "completing the square" as follows.

Writing the equation in the equivalent form

$$(x^2 + 2x) + (y^2 + 3y) = -1,$$

we see that the quantity in the first set of parentheses can be made a perfect square by adding _____, and the quantity inside the second set of parentheses can be rendered a perfect square by adding _____. Therefore, we must likewise add _____ and _____ to the right member. This gives

$$(x + \underline{\quad})^2 + (y + \underline{\quad})^2 = \tfrac{9}{4},$$

the graph of which is a circle with center (_____, _____) and radius _____.
Does the sentence

$$x^2 + y^2 + 2x + 3y + 1 = 0 \qquad \text{and} \qquad y \geq -\tfrac{3}{2}$$

define a functional relation between x and y?

5. The following relations define circles. Find the center and radius of each.
(a) $x^2 + y^2 - 3x + 4y + 1 = 0$,
(b) $2x^2 + 2y^2 + 4x + 10y - 3 = 0$,
(c) $x + y - x^2 - y^2 + 9 = 0$,
(d) $\dfrac{x^2}{4} + \dfrac{y^2}{4} - x + \dfrac{3}{2}y = 3$,
(e) $x^2 + 2x + y^2 = 0$.

6. (a) Find an algebraic condition on A, B, and C that the graph of the equation $x^2 + y^2 + Ax + By + C = 0$ be a circle.
(b) Under this condition, find the center and the radius of the circle.
(c) When does the graph of the equation degenerate to a point?

7. Prove that the set of points $P = (x, y)$ such that

$$\overline{PA}^2 + \overline{PB}^2 + \overline{PC}^2 = 49,$$

where $A = (-1, 0)$, $B = (0, 2)$, $C = (7, 1)$, is a circle. Find the center and the radius.

8. Let $F = x^2 + y^2 - 1$ and $G = x^2 - 4x + y^2 - \tfrac{9}{4}$.
(a) What are the graphs of the four equations?

$$F = 0, \qquad G - F = 0,$$
$$G = 0, \qquad 3F - 2G = 0.$$

(b) Find all points in the intersection of the graphs of the equations $F = 0$ and $G = 0$. Is there any such point which is not on the graph of $G - F = 0$? Is there any such point which is not on the graph of $3F - 2G = 0$?
(c) Find the equation of the line through the intersections of the circles (a) and (e) in Exercise 5 above.

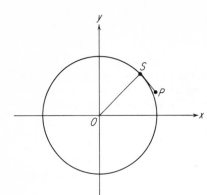

Figure 5-10

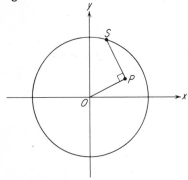

Figure 5-11

9. (a) Let the point $P = (a, b)$ be exterior to the circle with center at $(0, 0)$ and radius r (Fig. 5-10). Let S be on the circle and PS be tangent to the circle. Find a formula for $\overline{PS}^2$.

(b) Let the point $P = (a, b)$ be interior to the circle with center at $(0, 0)$ and radius r (Fig. 5-11). Let S be on the circle and let PS be perpendicular to OP. Find a formula for $\overline{PS}^2$.

10. In Sec. 5.5 we defined some sequences *recursively*. In the light of the current discussion, we note that the equation relating the nth term of a sequence to its predecessor is a *relation*. This equation is very naturally called a *recursion relation*.

(a) Write the first five terms of the sequence whose elements satisfy the recursion relation

$$a_{n+1} = (n + 1)a_n, \qquad n \in \mathcal{Z}^+,$$

together with $a_1 = 1$.

(b) For which values of n is

$$\frac{a_{n+1}}{10^{n+1}} > \frac{a_n}{10^n}?$$

11. Graph the relations:
(a) $y = |x|$,
(b) $y = |x - 1|$,
(c) $y = |x + 1|$,
(d) $y = |2x + 3|$,
(e) $|y| = x - 1$.

12. Graph the relations:
(a) $|y| = |x|$,
(b) $y \le |x|$,
(c) $|x + y| \le 1$,
(d) $x^2 + y^2 \ge 0$,
(e) $x^2 + y^2 = 0$.

13. Graph the relations:
(a) $x \ge 0$,
(b) $|x| \ge 0$,
(c) $|x + y| \ge 0$,
(d) $|x + y| \le |x| + |y|$,
(e) $|x + y| \ge |x - y|$.

14. Graph the following sets
(a) $\{(x, y) \mid |1 + 2x| \le 1 \land |y| \le 1\}$,
(b) $\{(x, y) \mid |4 - 3x| \le 4 \land y = 1\}$,
(c) $\{(x, y) \mid x = 0 \land |3x - 4| \le 3\}$,
(d) $\{(x, y) \mid ||x| - |y|| \le |x - y|\}$.

5.7

Inverse Functions   Consider the function

$$F: x \to 3x, \qquad x \in \mathcal{R}.$$

Suppose we know that $F(x) = 4$; what is x? We find only one value of x such that $F(x) = 4$, namely $x = \rule{1cm}{0.4pt}$.

On the other hand, if we consider the function

$$G: x \to x^2, \qquad x \in \mathcal{R},$$

we find that there are $\rule{1cm}{0.4pt}$ (how many?) numbers x such that $G(x) = 4$, namely $x = \rule{1cm}{0.4pt}$ and $x = \rule{1cm}{0.4pt}$.

A third example is $K_1: x \to 1$, $x \in \mathcal{R}$. Is there any value of x such that $K_1(x) = 4$?

We see that if f is a function on the domain A to the set B, there may be exactly one, more than one, or no value of x in A such that $f(x) = y$. For a given f, the situation may vary from one value of y (in B) to another. Consider the following, referring to the above examples F, G, and K_1:

Problem	Number of solutions
$F(x) = y$, any $y \in \mathcal{R}$	$\rule{1cm}{0.4pt}$
$G(x) = 0$	$\rule{1cm}{0.4pt}$
$G(x) = -1$	$\rule{1cm}{0.4pt}$
$K_1(x) = 1$	$\rule{1cm}{0.4pt}$

In the first example, we see that there is a unique $x \in \mathcal{R}$ for any $y \in \mathcal{R}$, such that $F(x) = y$. In other words, the equation $y = F(x)$ defines a *functional relation* between y and x. For any $y \in \mathcal{R}$, there is a unique x, namely $x = \rule{1cm}{0.4pt}$, such that $F(x) = y$. The operation which, acting on the number y, produces this unique x is called the *inverse function* to F. We denote it by F^{-1}.

In the above case, we find that

$$F^{-1}: y \to \frac{y}{3}, \quad \text{or} \quad F^{-1}(y) = \frac{y}{3}, \qquad \text{for } y \in \mathcal{R}.$$

Let us calculate $F \circ F^{-1}$:

$$(F \circ F^{-1})(y) = F(F^{-1}(y)) = F(\rule{1cm}{0.4pt}) = \rule{1cm}{0.4pt},$$

so that

$$F \circ F^{-1} = \rule{1cm}{0.4pt}.$$

Also, we can calculate $F^{-1} \circ F$:

$$(F^{-1} \circ F)(x) = F^{-1}(F(x)) = F^{-1}(\rule{1cm}{0.4pt}) = \rule{1cm}{0.4pt}.$$

Answers (right margin):

$\frac{4}{3}$

two

$2, -2$

one

one

zero

all $x \in \mathcal{R}$

$\dfrac{y}{3}$

$\dfrac{y}{3}, y$

I

$3x, x$

We see, then, that
$$F^{-1} \circ F = \underline{\qquad}.$$

I

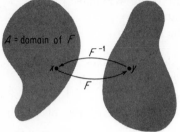

Figure 5-12

In general, the equations $y = f(x)$ and $x = f^{-1}(y)$ are equivalent, so that if x and y are related by these equations, then
$$(f \circ f^{-1})(y) = f(\underline{\qquad}(y)) = f(\underline{\qquad}) = \underline{\qquad},$$
and

f^{-1}, x, y

$$(f^{-1} \circ f)(x) = \underline{\qquad}(\underline{\qquad}(x)) = \underline{\quad}(\underline{\quad}) = \underline{\qquad}.$$

f^{-1}, f, f^{-1}, y, x

Thus if f has an inverse f^{-1}, then
$$f \circ f^{-1} = f^{-1} \circ f = \underline{\qquad}.$$

I

If f is a function on the set A to the set B, then f^{-1} exists and is a function on B to A provided that for every y in B, there is one and only one x in A such that $f(x) = y$. Then B is the domain of f^{-1}.

Sometimes f is a one-to-one mapping of the set A into a part of B, but not all of B. In that case, there will be elements $y \in B$ which are not the image of any x in A. Then f^{-1} is not defined for these elements y.

Now let's return to another example to see how we go about finding the inverse of a given function (that possesses an inverse). Let $f(x) = 3x + 2$.

If $f(x) = 0$,	then $x = \underline{\qquad}$.	$-\frac{2}{3}$
If $f(x) = 2$,	then $x = \underline{\qquad}$.	0
If $f(x) = y$,	then $x = \underline{\qquad}$.	$\dfrac{y-2}{3}$

This tells you that for every $y \in \mathscr{R}$ there is one and only one $x \in \mathscr{R}$ such that $f(x) = y$. And this is precisely what we need to know in order to be sure that f^{-1} exists! Moreover, the simple algebra you've done tells you that
$$f^{-1}(y) = \underline{\qquad}.$$

$\dfrac{y-2}{3}$

If you wish to sketch graphs of a function and its inverse on one set of axes, then it is appropriate to express the function values using the same letter to represent the domain elements. In the example we are working on we have

$$f(x) = 3x + 2 \quad \text{and} \quad f^{-1}(x) = \underline{\hspace{1cm}}.$$

$\dfrac{x - 2}{3}$

Sketch the graphs of f and f^{-1} on the same set of axes.

Let's review the procedure used to find f^{-1}. First, we write

$$y = 3x + 2.$$

Since the inverse function (if it exists) is to take us back, from y to x, we solve for x:

$$x = \frac{y - 2}{3}.$$

This solution confirms the existence of f^{-1}, since it shows that f is one-to-one. It also gives us the value of f^{-1} at y, namely $f^{-1}(y) = (y - 2)/3$. If it is desirable to have the x-axis represent the domain of f^{-1} (as well as of f), we simply interchange the letters "y" and "x" so that f^{-1} will operate on x. That is,

$$f^{-1}(x) = \frac{x - 2}{3}.$$

Now we should check our work. Compute:

$$f^{-1}(f(x)) = \underline{\hspace{1cm}} \quad \text{and} \quad f(f^{-1}(x)) = \underline{\hspace{1cm}}.$$

x, x

This shows that

$$f^{-1} \circ f = f \circ f^{-1} = \underline{\hspace{1cm}}.$$

I

What function, if any, is the inverse of f^{-1}? That is, does $(f^{-1})^{-1}$ exist? If so, give a defining formula for it.

Now let's look at the inverse function through the notion of ordered pairs. The set of ordered pairs that arises from the function F is given by

$$\{(x, y) \mid y = F(x)\}.$$

If you wish to go back from y to x, just consider the set of ordered pairs

$$\{(y, x) \mid y = F(x)\},$$

and ask whether this set (relation) defines a function. It defines a function if and only if to each first element (y this time) there corresponds a single x. This is why $G(x) = x^2$ and $K_1(x) = 1$ could not have inverse functions.

Suppose F does have an inverse function F^{-1} that we wish to graph on an (x, y)-plane following the custom that the domain (of F^{-1}) is taken on the x-axis. Then we merely interchange the letters x and y, getting

$$T = \{(x, y) \mid x = F(y)\}.$$

But this representation is still in terms of F rather than F^{-1}, so we make the final revision by noting

$$F^{-1}(x) = F^{-1}(F(y)) = y,$$

and writing this as the defining property of the set:

$$T = \{(x, y) \mid y = F^{-1}(x)\}.$$

5.7.1
EXERCISES

1. The graph of a function has the property that a vertical line can meet it _____ (how many times?).

2. Therefore, a function possesses an inverse if the graph of the function possesses the property that a horizontal line meets it _____.

3. Let the points $(2, 3)$, $(3, -1)$, $(1, 1)$, and $(0, 0)$ be on the graph of f. Determine four points of the graph of f^{-1} (assuming f^{-1} exists).

4. If (x, y) is the general point on the graph of f, then name the general point of the graph of f^{-1}. See if you can give a geometric interpretation of this fact. [*Hint:* There is symmetry involved!]

5. If $y = x$ defines a function g, find the inverse function.

6. In (a)–(h) we have defined various functions. Which of these functions possess inverses? Find the inverses when they exist. (All functions except the last one are defined on $\mathscr{R}$.)

(a) $f(x) = [x]$.

(b) $P_3(x) = x^3$.

(c) $P_4(x) = x^4$.

(d) $g(x) = -x - 1$.

(e) $h(x) = \begin{cases} x^2 & \text{if } x \geq 0, \\ -x^2 & \text{if } x \leq 0. \end{cases}$

(f) $F(x) = x - [x]$.

(g) $G(x) = |x - 1|$.

(h) $H(x) = \sqrt{x}, \; x \geq 0$.

Since the domain of an inverse function f^{-1} is the set of function values $f(x)$ (and for other reasons as well), it becomes necessary to have a name for the set of values of a function. This set is called the *range* (of values) of the function f. That is, if D is the domain of f, then

$$\text{range of } f = \{y \mid y = f(x), \; x \in D\}.$$

Sometimes it is an easy matter to determine the range of f; other times it is quite difficult, if an inverse function f^{-1} is to be defined, it is essential to determine the range of f, for this is precisely the domain of f^{-1}.

Find the ranges of the functions defined in Exercises 7–15. The domain in each case is in $\mathscr{R}$.

7. $f(x) = x^2 - 1$.

8. $g(x) = x^2 - x$.

9. $F(x) = [x - 1]$.

10. $H(x) = |x - 1|$.

11. $h(x) = -3x + 1$.

12. $K_2(x) = 2$.

13. $f - g$, where f is defined in Exercise 7 and g in Exercise 8.

14. $\delta(x) = \begin{cases} 1 \text{ if } x = 0, \\ 0 \text{ if } x \neq 0. \end{cases}$

15. $P_{100}(x) = x^{100}$.

A Logical Note: We have been dealing with three basic concepts: *set, relation,* and *function*. Intuitively, each is as fundamental as the other two. It has been discovered that any two of these concepts can be defined in terms of the other.

In constructing a formal deductive system, we may take all three as undefined if we wish. This probably agrees best with our intuitive ideas.

Alternatively, we may take one of these concepts as undefined and define the other two in terms of it. Each of these three alternatives has been worked out in considerable detail by some mathematical logician.

All four procedures are perfectly sound mathematically, which is preferred is essentially a matter of personal taste.

Many textbooks take the concept of *set* as basic, and then define a *relation* as a set of ordered pairs. A *function* is then a special kind of relation, satisfying the condition on page 183. (Of course, to carry out this procedure completely, one must define *ordered pair* in terms of set, which can be done.)

Since you may have been exposed to this procedure before, we thought that it might be fun for you to see another approach. This helps us emphasize that the choice among the four alternatives is arbitrary.

Chapter Six Vectors *Vectors, which are well known for their use in physical science, are introduced as another instrument for handling geometric problems. Section 6.2 unites the vector concept with the previous work on coordinate systems, and Secs. 6.3 and 6.4 develop the algebra of vectors. Sections 6.5 and 6.6 should help the reader develop facility in solving geometry problems with the aid of vectors. Since, in the course of Secs. 6.1 through 6.6, the reader encounters physical, geometric, and economic interpretations of vectors, Sec. 6.7 is devoted to an abstraction of the algebra of vectors* to the idea of a vector space, *which includes all the previous interpretations as special cases. Sections 6.8 and 6.9 show one useful way of introducing a multiplication among vectors; again, there are applications to physics, geometry, and economics.*

6.1

Translations and Vectors By a *translation* we mean a motion in which all points move the same distance in the same direction. If you shift this book

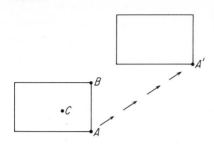

as illustrated in Fig. 6-1, then you are performing a translation. In this translation the point A is moved to the position A'. To what position is B moved? Call B' the new position of B.

What kind of figure is formed by $AA'B'B$? What is the relation between the lines

Figure 6-1

AA' and BB'?

AB and $A'B'$?

Which of the directed segments $\overline{AA'}$ and $\overline{BB'}$ is longer? Which of $\overline{AB}$ and $\overline{A'B'}$ is longer?

Construct the point C' into which the point C is moved. Now what kind of a figure is formed by $AA'C'C$? What is the relation between the lines

AA' and CC'?

AC and $A'C'$?

Which is longer?

$\overline{AC}$ or $\overline{A'C'}$?

$\overline{BC}$ or $\overline{B'C'}$?

$\overline{AA'}$ or $\overline{CC'}$?

What is the relation between $\triangle ABC$ and $\triangle A'B'C'$?

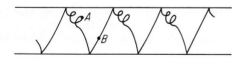

Figure 6-2

What shifts of the figure in 6-2 leave it invariant, i.e., bring it into coincidence with itself? Find all points which correspond to A and to B. A figure like this is called a *strip ornament*, since it lies in the region between two parallel lines. It can be obtained from a part contained in a rectangle by applying a certain set of transformations which leave the strip invariant.

193

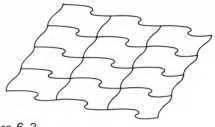

Figure 6-3

Figure 6-3 shows a *lattice ornament*. Which translations leave this lattice ornament invariant? Describe it in terms of translations.

Suppose a given translation moves A to A'. Referring to Fig. 6-4, where does the translation move the point B? Let B be moved to the position B'. Construct B'. Is B' uniquely determined? Is there more than one possible point B'? Let C be on the line AA'. Find the point C' into which C is moved by the translation. How much information do you need to determine a translation of the plane?

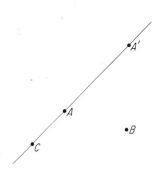

Figure 6-4

You surely recognize by now that a translation (of the plane) is actually a function (on the plane) to itself. (Does it have an inverse?) We shall denote the above translation by τ (small Greek letter "tau"). Then

$$\tau : A \to A' \quad \text{and} \quad \tau(A) = A'.$$

The translation τ is an operation which, acting on any point P, produces a uniquely determined point $P' = \tau(P)$.

Recalling that two functions on the same domain D are equal if they yield the same result when acting on any element of D, or in the function value language;

$$f_1 = f_2 \Leftrightarrow f_1(x) = f_2(x) \quad \text{for all } x \in D,$$

we say: *The translations τ_1 and τ_2 are equal if and only if $\tau_1(A) = \tau_2(A)$ for all points A in the plane.*

For the present we will be working only in the plane. You may think of a translation as a motion of the entire plane, where all points "shift" the same distance in the same direction in the plane. Accordingly, to test whether τ_1 and τ_2 are the same translation you must apply τ_1 and τ_2 to each point A in the plane and see whether

$$\tau_1(A) = \tau_2(A).$$

This sounds like a great deal of work, but from your answers to the questions in the above paragraphs, you should have discovered the following remarkable fact: It is enough to apply τ_1 and τ_2 to a *single* point. If $\tau_1(A) = \tau_2(A)$ for one point A, then $\tau_1(B) = \tau_2(B)$ for every other point B! That is, one (ordered) pair (A, A') of corresponding points is sufficient to determine the translation τ. We shall denote the unique translation τ

which moves A to A' by $\overrightarrow{AA'}$, and we shall write

$$\overrightarrow{AA'} = \tau \Leftrightarrow \tau(A) = A'.$$

Therefore, the special type of function, namely a translation, can be denoted in this special way, which serves to define it completely. Furthermore, as the symbolism emphasizes, a translation exists for any pair $\{A, A'\}$ of distinct points. Actually, physical motion is quite superfluous in the definition of translation. It is sufficient to know the correspondence of points, i.e., the function. Some people prefer to think of a translation as the physical motion of points; others find that viewing the concept as a correspondence (function) of points serves them best. In either case, a single point and its image are sufficient for a complete description of the translation.

The essential facts required to describe a translation τ are: (1) the length $|AA'|$ of the directed segment $\overline{AA'}$, where $A' = \tau(A)$, and (2) the direction from A to $\tau(A)$. That is, a description of a translation is by means of a *length* and a *direction*. Physicists, especially, study quantities (e.g., wind, velocity, force) that are described by a *magnitude* (length) and *direction*; they call such quantities *vectors*. An ordinary number is often called a *scalar*. A vector may be represented by a translation, or simply identified with a translation, and vice versa. You will soon find that an enormous harvest is reaped with the aid of vectors, both in and out of the world of physics.

Note that our use of the word "direction" carries with it more than the notion of the slope of a line. Is the direction from A to A' the same as the direction from A' to A? Is the translation $\overrightarrow{AA'}$ equal to the translation $\overrightarrow{A'A}$? It might be said that our use of the word "direction" carries with it the notion of *sense*. That is, every line L has two possible senses which are opposite to one another; e.g., we refer to the x-axis as having a positive and a negative direction (sense).

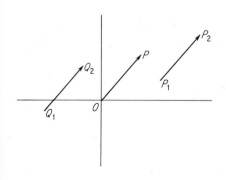

Figure 6-5

Example 1: Suppose the *wind velocity* is given as 5 mph in a northeasterly direction. It is described completely by its magnitude (5 mph) and direction (NE). Thus, wind velocity is a *vector* quantity. Geometrically, it can be represented by a *directed line segment* five units long, as by $\overrightarrow{OP}$ in Fig. 6-5. Actually, any five-unit segment parallel (or on OP) with the same sense, or direction, as $\overrightarrow{OP}$ would do just as well. Thus, $\overrightarrow{P_1P_2}$ and $\overrightarrow{Q_1Q_2}$ also represent the vector $\overrightarrow{OP}$. The translation $\overrightarrow{OP}$ moves the point P_1 to P_2 and point Q_1 to Q_2. Therefore we have

$$\overrightarrow{OP} = \overrightarrow{P_1P_2} = \overrightarrow{Q_1Q_2}.$$

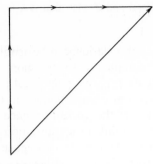

Figure 6-6

Figure 6-7

Example 2: The word *displacement* refers to the change in position of some object. For example, suppose you walk three miles north and then three miles east. The first part of your journey is a displacement of three miles in one direction, and the second leg of the journey is a displacement of three miles in another direction. Since a displacement clearly involves a magnitude and direction, it is a vector quantity, which we can once again represent graphically by a directed line segment as in Fig. 6-6. *Query:* What is the magnitude of the combined displacements? What would the final combined displacement be if you had first walked three miles east and then three miles north? Do you think that the operation of "combining" displacements is commutative?

Example 3: A satellite in space is usually under the influence of several forces: the force F_e of the earth's gravitational attraction, the force F_s of the sun's attraction, and the force F_m of the moon's attraction. Each force has a magnitude and a direction; therefore, each force is a vector quantity which you see represented by a directed line segment (Fig. 6-7). In order to determine the path of a satellite, it is necessary to study the combined effect of these force vectors on the velocity vector of the satellite.

6.1.1
EXERCISES

1. Label four points in a plane A, B, C, and A'. Construct X, Y, Z, W, and V such that: $\overrightarrow{A'X} = \overrightarrow{AB}$, $\overrightarrow{XY} = \overrightarrow{BC}$, $\overrightarrow{A'Z} = \overrightarrow{BC}$, $\overrightarrow{ZW} = \overrightarrow{AB}$, $\overrightarrow{A'V} = \overrightarrow{AC}$. Are the points X, Y, Z, W, and V distinct or do any coincide? Is this an accident resulting from your special choice of the points A, B, C, and A', or is there a general law?

2. Label five points A, B, C, D, and A'. Construct X, Y, Z, and W such that $\overrightarrow{A'X} = \overrightarrow{AB}$, $\overrightarrow{XY} = \overrightarrow{CD}$, $\overrightarrow{A'Z} = \overrightarrow{CD}$, and $\overrightarrow{ZW} = \overrightarrow{AB}$. What do you notice about the points Y and W? What is the general principle?

3. Label five points A, B, C, D, and A'. Construct X, Y, Z, U, V, W, and R such that $\overrightarrow{A'X} = \overrightarrow{AB}$, $\overrightarrow{XY} = \overrightarrow{BC}$, $\overrightarrow{YZ} = \overrightarrow{CD}$, $\overrightarrow{A'U} = \overrightarrow{AC}$, $\overrightarrow{UR} = \overrightarrow{CD}$, $\overrightarrow{A'V} = \overrightarrow{AD}$, and $\overrightarrow{XW} = \overrightarrow{BD}$. Do any of the points X, Y, Z, U, V, W, and R coincide? Is there a general principle?

4. Label four points A, B, C, and A'. Construct X, Y, and Z such that
   (a) $\overrightarrow{A'X}$ has the same direction as $\overrightarrow{AB}$ and $|\overrightarrow{A'X}| = 2|\overrightarrow{AB}|$;
   (b) $\overrightarrow{XY}$ has the same direction as $\overrightarrow{BC}$ and $|\overrightarrow{XY}| = 2|\overrightarrow{BC}|$;
   (c) $\overrightarrow{A'Z}$ has the same direction as $\overrightarrow{AC}$ and $|\overrightarrow{A'Z}| = 2|\overrightarrow{AC}|$.

5. Label four points A, B, C, and A'. Construct X, Y, and Z such that $\overrightarrow{A'X} = \overrightarrow{AB}$, $\overrightarrow{A'Y} = \overrightarrow{AC}$, and $\overrightarrow{BZ} = \overrightarrow{XY}$.

6. Label three points A, B, and A'. Construct X and Y such that $\overrightarrow{A'X} = \overrightarrow{AB}$ and $\overrightarrow{XY} = \overrightarrow{BA}$.

7. Let A, B, C be three noncollinear points (not on one line).
  (a) Find X and Y such that $\overrightarrow{CX} = \overrightarrow{AB}$ and $\overrightarrow{BY} = \overrightarrow{AC}$.
  (b) What is the relation between X and Y?
  (c) Let D be some point that is not collinear with any two of the points in your diagram. Then find Z, U, and V such that $\overrightarrow{CD} = \overrightarrow{AZ} = \overrightarrow{BU} = \overrightarrow{XV}$.
  (d) Find the unknown points. $\overrightarrow{DV} = \overrightarrow{A?}$, $\overrightarrow{UV} = \overrightarrow{Z?}$, $\overrightarrow{UD} = \overrightarrow{B?}$, and $\overrightarrow{AX} = \overrightarrow{Z?}$.
  (e) Call $\tau_1 = \overrightarrow{AB}$, $\tau_2 = \overrightarrow{AC}$, $\tau_3 = \overrightarrow{AX}$, $\tau_4 = \overrightarrow{CD}$, and find $\tau_1(\tau_1(A))$, $\tau_1(\tau_2(A))$, $\tau_1(\tau_2(Z))$, $\tau_2(\tau_1(Z))$, $\tau_1^{-1}(B)$, $\tau_1^{-1}(X)$, $\tau_1^{-1}(\tau_4(\tau_2(\tau_1(A))))$, $\tau_3^{-1}(\tau_4(X))$.

6.2

Coordinate Representation In the previous section we gave an intuitive introduction to translations and vectors. Before we proceed with coordinate representations, we want to assure you that the intuitive concepts you've used can be put on a mathematically rigorous basis. We will illustrate by defining *translation* in terms that come from our earlier development (which includes the basic ideas of euclidean geometry).

First, we give an extension of the definition of parallelism:

Definition: *Two lines l and m in a plane are called* parallel $\Leftrightarrow$ (i) $l = m \vee$ (ii) *l and m have no common point.*

(Note that this definition is tantamount to saying that l is parallel to m if and only if they have the same slope.)

Armed with this "new parallelism" we can define *translation* independent of the intuitive idea of a "shift."

Definition: *Let $\mathscr{S}$ be the set of points of a plane and τ a function on $\mathscr{S}$ to $\mathscr{S}$. Then τ is called a* translation *if and only if it is either the identity or it has the following property:*
      If P and Q are two distinct points of $\mathscr{S}$ and $P' = \tau(P)$ and $Q' = \tau(Q)$, then
(i) *PQ is parallel to $P'Q'$*, (ii) $|\overline{PP'}| = |\overline{QQ'}|$, *and* (iii) $\tau(P) \neq P$.

6.2.1
EXERCISES

1. Which of properties (i)–(iii) does the identity I have?

2. If τ is a translation and not the identity, and $\tau(Q) = Q'$, and P is on the line QQ', can $P' = \tau(P)$ be noncollinear with Q and Q'? If P is the midpoint of QQ', where is P'?

3. Suppose that τ is a translation and not the identity, $\tau(Q) = Q'$, $\tau(R) = R'$, and R is not on the line QQ'. Can R and R' be on opposite sides of the line QQ'?

If so, what does τ do to the point P where QQ' and RR' intersect? Is this consistent with property (iii)?

4. Show that the set of all translations of a given plane form an abelian group with respect to composition.

We now continue our discussion of translations (and vectors which they represent), but with points represented by their cartesian coordinates. Take a sheet of graph paper for working through the following set of exercises concerning translations and vectors relative to a coordinate system.

6.2.2
EXERCISES

1. Let $\tau : (0, 0) \rightarrow (2, 3)$. Find (x, y) such that
  (a) $\tau : (5, 7) \rightarrow (x, y)$,
  (b) $\tau : (2, -1) \rightarrow (x, y)$,
  (c) $\tau : (a, b) \rightarrow (x, y)$.

2. Let $\tau : (3, 5) \rightarrow (5, 8)$. Find (x, y) such that $\tau : (0, 0) \rightarrow (x, y)$. How does the translation of this problem compare with the translation of Exercise 1?

3. Let $\tau : (a, b) \rightarrow (c, d)$.
  (a) Find (x, y) such that $\tau : (0, 0) \rightarrow (x, y)$.
  (b) Find (r, s) such that $\tau : (m, n) \rightarrow (r, s)$.
  (c) Compute $r - m$ and $s - n$, and compare these with x and y of part (a).

4. If $\tau : (0, 0) \rightarrow (3, 4)$ and $\tau : A \rightarrow A'$, compute $|\overline{AA'}|$.

In the preceding exercises you learned the significance of the coordinates of (x, y), if $\tau : (0, 0) \rightarrow (x, y)$; and you saw that knowing the image of $(0, 0)$ enabled you to do all the computations in the questions concerning τ. Therefore, we introduce the special coordinate notation "$[x, y]$" to represent τ. That is,

$$\tau = [x, y] \Leftrightarrow \tau : (0, 0) \rightarrow (x, y).$$

Since the vector from $(0, 0)$ to (x, y) is identified with τ, we also use "$[x, y]$" as the coordinate representation of the vector. x is called the *first component* and y the *second component* of vector $[x, y]$.

5. Find x and y such that
  (a) $[2, 3]: (5, -1) \rightarrow (x, y)$,   (f) $[x, y]: (5, -1) \rightarrow (7, 2)$,
  (b) $[3, 4]: (5, -1) \rightarrow (x, y)$,   (g) $[x, y]: (a, b) \rightarrow (c, d)$,
  (c) $[-1, 2]: (5, -1) \rightarrow (x, y)$,   (h) $[x, y]: (1, 1) \rightarrow (1, 1)$,
  (d) $[0, -1]: (5, -1) \rightarrow (x, y)$,   (i) $[x, y]: (2, 3) \rightarrow (0, 0)$.
  (e) $[a, b]: (5, -1) \rightarrow (x, y)$,

6. Let $A = (1, 2)$, $B = (3, 1)$, $C = (-2, -2)$, and $A' = (2, -1)$. Find the coordinates of X, Y, Z, W, and V such that $\overrightarrow{A'X} = \overrightarrow{AB}$, $\overrightarrow{XY} = \overrightarrow{BC}$, $\overrightarrow{A'Z} = \overrightarrow{BC}$, $\overrightarrow{ZW} = \overrightarrow{AB}$, and $\overrightarrow{A'V} = \overrightarrow{AC}$.

7. Let $A = (1, 2)$, $B = (3, 1)$, $C = (-2, -2)$, $D = (-3, 4)$, and $A' = (2, -1)$. Find the coordinates of X and Y such that $\overrightarrow{A'X} = \overrightarrow{AB}$ and $\overrightarrow{XY} = \overrightarrow{CD}$.

6.3

Composition of Translations and Sums of Vectors Let τ_1 and τ_2 be two translations $\tau_1 : A \rightarrow B$ and $\tau_2 : B \rightarrow C$. As vectors we can write them $\overrightarrow{AB}$ and $\overrightarrow{BC}$, respectively. Then $\tau_2 \circ \tau_1 : A \rightarrow C$, but is $\tau_2 \circ \tau_1$ a translation? If you think of the original vectors as displacements, does the composition $\tau_2 \circ \tau_1$ represent a displacement? Justify your answer.

On a sheet of paper, label three points A, B, and C, and choose any other point A'. If $\tau_1(A) = B$ and $\tau_2(B) = C$, construct $\tau_1(A')$: then $\tau_2(\tau_1(A')) = C'$. Is $\overrightarrow{A'C'} = \overrightarrow{AC}$? If so, why? Would your conclusion hold no matter how you chose A'? If $\tau_3 = \overrightarrow{AC}$, is it true that

$$\tau_2 \circ \tau_1 = \tau_3?$$

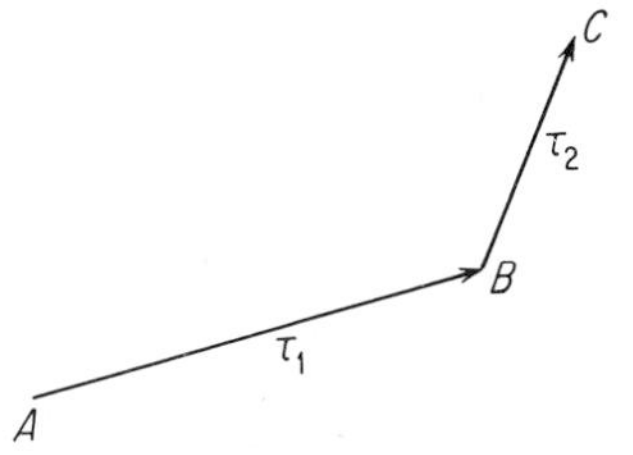

In Fig. 6-8 construct $\tau_2(A)$ and $\tau_1(\tau_2(A))$; compare with $\tau_2(\tau_1(A))$. Since you now recognize that $\tau_2 \circ \tau_1$ is a translation, you may write the composition $\tau_2 \circ \tau_1$ in vector symbolism as $\overrightarrow{AC}$.

Let's compute the composition of translations in a cartesian coordinate system. suppose the translations τ_1 and τ_2 are represented by

$$\tau_1 = [2, 3] \quad \text{and} \quad \tau_2 = [-1, 2].$$

Figure 6-8

Then

$$[0, 0] \xrightarrow{[2, 3]} [2, 3] \xrightarrow{[-1, 2]} (\underline{\quad}, \underline{\quad}). \qquad \textit{1, 5}$$

So that

$$\tau_2 \circ \tau_1 : (0, 0) \rightarrow (\underline{\quad}, \underline{\quad}). \qquad \textit{1, 5}$$

Also,

$$\tau_2 \circ \tau_1 : (-1, 5) \rightarrow (\underline{\quad}, \underline{\quad}) \qquad \textit{0, 10}$$

and

$$(a, b) \xrightarrow{[2, 3]} (\underline{\quad}, \underline{\quad}) \xrightarrow{[-1, 2]} (a + \underline{\quad}, b + \underline{\quad}). \qquad \textit{a+2, b+3, 1, 5}$$

Therefore, the translation $\tau_2 \circ \tau_1 = [x, y]$, where $x =$ _____
and $y =$ _____. If $\tau_1 = [h_1, k_1]$ and $\tau_2 = [h_2, k_2]$, then

$\qquad \tau_2 \circ \tau_1 : (0, 0) \to ($ _____, _____ $)$

and

$\qquad \tau_2 \circ \tau_1 : (0, 0) \to ($ _____, _____ $)$.

Therefore,

$\qquad \tau_2 \circ \tau_1 = \tau_1 \circ \tau_2 = [$ _____, _____ $]$.

1	
5	
	$h_1 + h_2, \; k_1 + k_2$
	$h_1 + h_2, \; k_1 + k_2$
	$h_1 + h_2, \; k_1 + k_2$

Since the composition of translations $[h_1, k_1]$ and $[h_2, k_2]$ is determined by the addition of corresponding components we adopt the notation

$$[h_1, k_1] + [h_2, k_2] = [h_1 + h_2, k_1 + k_2]$$

to represent the composition of translations $[h_1, k_1]$ and $[h_2, k_2]$. We call

$$[h_1, k_1] + [h_2, k_2]$$

the *sum of the vectors*. Addition of the vectors is defined simply as the composition of the corresponding translations. [N.B.: When we discussed functions in the previous section we defined $f + g$, the sum of f and g, by

$$(f + g)(x) = f(x) + g(x).$$

This definition was possible because $f(x)$ and $g(x)$ were numbers that could be added. If f and g are real-valued functions or complex-valued functions, then $f + g$, defined in this manner, makes sense. However, translations are point-valued functions, and we have not defined the addition of points. Therefore our definition of vector addition does not conflict with our definition of the addition of functions.]

6.3.1
EXERCISES

1. A rule for determining the geometric representation of the sum of two vectors is the following: Take geometric representations (directed line segments) of two vectors so that the origin of the second coincides with the endpoint of the first. Then the directed line segment joining the _____ of the first to the _____ of the second represents the sum of the vectors. Does this rule hold when the two vectors are parallel?

2. (a) Construct X such that $\overrightarrow{AB} + \overrightarrow{BC} = \overrightarrow{BC} + \overrightarrow{AX}$ in the case where A, B, and C are collinear as well as in the case where A, B, and C are noncollinear. This shows that addition of vectors is _____. If τ_1 and τ_2 are vectors, then $\tau_1 + \tau_2 = \tau_2 +$ _____.
  (b) Give an algebraic proof of your result in (a).

3. Let A, B, and C be noncollinear. Construct D such that $\overrightarrow{AD} + \overrightarrow{AB} = \overrightarrow{AC}$.

4. Let $ABCD$ be a parallelogram. Then

(a) $\overrightarrow{AB} = \overrightarrow{?C}$.

(b) $\overrightarrow{AD} = \overrightarrow{B?}$.

(c) The diagonal vector $\overrightarrow{AC}$ represents the sum $\overrightarrow{A?} + \overrightarrow{?C}$. (How many answers?)

(d) Give an alternate rule (to the one in Exercise 1) for constructing the sum of two nonparallel vectors.

5. Let A, B, C, and D be chosen so that no three are collinear.

(a) Construct $\overrightarrow{AB} + \overrightarrow{BC}$ and $(\overrightarrow{AB} + \overrightarrow{BC}) + \overrightarrow{CD}$.

(b) Construct $\overrightarrow{BC} + \overrightarrow{CD}$ and $\overrightarrow{AB} + (\overrightarrow{BC} + \overrightarrow{CD})$.

(c) Compare your answers to (a) and (b).

(d) Now consider whether this result would be altered by eliminating the hypothesis, "no three are collinear."

(e) What is the name of the property:

$$\forall\, a, b, c \in \mathscr{R}, \qquad a + (b + c) = (a + b) + c?$$

Can you now prove that vector addition satisfies this property? (Namely, prove

$$\overrightarrow{AB} + (\overrightarrow{CD} + \overrightarrow{EF}) = (\overrightarrow{AB} + \overrightarrow{CD}) + \overrightarrow{EF}.)$$

You have found that if A and A' are two distinct points, then there is a unique translation $\tau = \overrightarrow{AA'}$ which moves A to the position A': $\tau(A) = A'$. If $A = (a, b)$ and $A' = (a', b')$, then

$$\overrightarrow{AA'} = [a' - a, b' - b]$$

(see Exercise 3 of Sec. 6.2.2). What happens if $A' = A$? The rigorous definition of translation in Sec. 6.2 gives the answer, but for a moment let's return to our intuitive "motion" viewpoint.

The "motion" $\overrightarrow{AA}$ acts on the point A to produce the point A, i.e., this "motion" does not change A at all. Our formula yields $\overrightarrow{AA} = [0, 0]$, and if we apply this translation to any point (x, y) we obtain

$$[0, 0]: (x, y) \rightarrow (x + 0, y + 0).$$

In other words, the translation $[0, 0] = \overrightarrow{AA}$ is simply the *identity* function, which transforms each point into itself. It is more convenient to count standing still as a motion than to have exceptions to the rule that if A and B are any points, then there is a unique translation $\overrightarrow{AB}$ which moves A to the position B.

This has the further advantage that the sum of any two vectors is a vector. (In other words, the set of all vectors is closed with respect to the operation of addition.) If $\tau = \overrightarrow{AB}$, then the inverse function of τ is $\tau^{-1} = \overrightarrow{BA}$. Now even the sum of these two vectors is again a vector:

$$\tau \circ \tau^{-1} = \overrightarrow{AB} + \overrightarrow{BA} = \overrightarrow{AA}.$$

6. (a) If $\tau : A \to B$, then $\tau^{-1} \circ \tau : A \to$?.

   (b) If $A = (1, 2)$ and $B = (3, -1)$, then $\tau = \overrightarrow{AB} = [\underline{\hspace{1cm}}, \underline{\hspace{1cm}}]$ and $\tau^{-1} = \overrightarrow{BA} = [\underline{\hspace{1cm}}, \underline{\hspace{1cm}}]$.

   (c) $\tau^{-1} \circ \tau : (0, 0) \to (\underline{\hspace{1cm}}, \underline{\hspace{1cm}})$.

   (d) $\tau^{-1} \circ \tau = [\underline{\hspace{1cm}}, \underline{\hspace{1cm}}]$.

7. (a) If $\tau = [a, b]$, then $\tau^{-1} = [\underline{\hspace{1cm}}, \underline{\hspace{1cm}}]$.

   (b) $\tau^{-1} \circ \tau = [\underline{\hspace{1cm}}, \underline{\hspace{1cm}}]$ and $\tau \circ \tau^{-1} = [\underline{\hspace{1cm}}, \underline{\hspace{1cm}}]$.

The identity translation or vector $\overrightarrow{AA} = [0, 0]$, which "moves" every point into itself, is called the *zero vector*. We shall also denote it by **0**.

8. (a) $\overrightarrow{AB} + \mathbf{0} =$?,

   (b) $\mathbf{0} + \mathbf{0} =$?,

   (c) $\overrightarrow{AB} + ? = \mathbf{0}$).

9. (a) Let A, B, and C be any three points. Then $\overrightarrow{AB} + \overrightarrow{BC} + \overrightarrow{CA} =$?. (Note that we have dropped parentheses. Does it make any difference how we put them in? Why?)

   (b) Let A, B, C, and D be any four points. Then,

$$\overrightarrow{AB} + \overrightarrow{BC} + \overrightarrow{CD} + \overrightarrow{DA} = ?.$$

   (c) Generalize (a) and (b) to the case of n points $A_1, A_2, \ldots, A_n$.

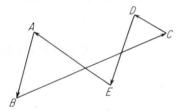

The result of Exercise 9 is sometimes stated as follows: *The sum of the vectors around any closed polygon is zero.* In Fig. 6-9 we show

$$\overrightarrow{AB} + \overrightarrow{BC} + \overrightarrow{CD} + \overrightarrow{DE} + \overrightarrow{EA} = \mathbf{0}.$$

It is interesting and useful to observe that

$$\overrightarrow{AE} = \overrightarrow{AB} + \overrightarrow{BC} + \overrightarrow{CD} + \overrightarrow{DE}.$$

Figure 6-9

A geometric picture of the zero vector is difficult, since a line segment of zero length cannot be drawn with any mark on the paper. However, as a displacement, the zero vector respresents *no motion*; as a force, the zero vector represents a force of zero magnitude (no force) operating; and as a velocity vector of a particle, the zero vector indicates that the particle is at rest. Finally, as an ordered pair, you saw above that the zero vector has the representation $[0, 0]$. We may regard the zero vector as having no direction or any direction; we shall return to this point later.

10. If several forces act on a body, the *resultant force* is the sum of the force vectors.

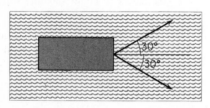

   (a) Two forces $\mathbf{F}_1$ and $\mathbf{F}_2$ act at right angles to each other. If $\mathbf{F}_1$ is 30 lb, find the magnitude of $\mathbf{F}_2$ so that the resultant force equals 50 lb.

   (b) A barge is moved at a uniform speed along a straight canal by two tugboats pulling with equal forces of 3000 lb as shown in Fig. 6-10. Find the resultant force.

Figure 6-10

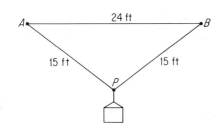

A •————— 24 ft —————• B

15 ft   15 ft

P

Figure 6-11

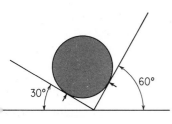

30°   60°

Figure 6-12

11. An object is said to be in static equilibrium (continues in a state of rest) if the sum of the forces acting on it is zero.

(a) A street lamp is suspended as indicated in Fig. 6-11. If the lamp weighs 16 lb, find the tension in the ropes AP and BP by considering the forces acting at P. [*Hint:* The three force vectors acting at P should form a closed triangle.]

(b) A metal sphere of 200 lb rests in a right-angled trough as shown in Fig. 6-12. Find the forces exerted on the sides of the trough at the points of contact.

12. Consider a simple dairy cooperative that deals only with butter and eggs. With each day you can associate an *inventory vector* $[x, y]$, where $x =$ pounds of butter in stock and $y =$ dozens of eggs in stock.

(a) If on successive days the inventory vectors are $[x_1, y_1]$ and $[x_2, y_2]$, then find the coordinate representation of the change vector γ, so that $[x_1, y_1] + \gamma = [x_2, y_2]$.

(b) The *change* (in inventory) *vector* is determined by the vector $[a, b]$, which represents the delivery of butter and eggs by member farmers and the vector $[r, s]$, which represents the sales of the stock. Find the change vector in terms of $[a, b]$ and $[r, s]$.

(c) A *price vector* $[p, q]$ gives the prices of the items: $p =$ price of butter per pound and $q =$ price of eggs per dozen. Determine the net change in the value of the stock if the price vector is $[p, q]$ and the change vector is $[x, y]$.

13. A company packages mixed nuts composed of almonds, cashews, and peanuts. Each mixture is described by a vector $[a, c, p]$, where $a =$ pounds of almonds, $c =$ pounds of cashews, and $p =$ pounds of peanuts.

(a) Interpret $[a_1, c_1, p_1] + [a_2, c_2, p_2]$.

(b) A *price vector* $[A, C, P]$ is defined by $A =$ price of almonds per pound, $C =$ price of cashews per pound, and $P =$ price of peanuts per pound. What is the cost of $[a, c, p]$ at price $[A, C, P]$?

Historical Note: Elaborate studies of vectors in application to geometry and physics were first carried out in the nineteenth century by Hermann G. Grassmann (1809–1877) in Germany, Josiah Willard Gibbs (1839–1903) in the United States, and Sir William Rowan Hamilton (1805–1865) in Ireland. However, the vector concept arose much earlier from attempts to mathematically characterize physical quantities such as force.

It is interesting to note that the little-known but nonetheless excellent Dutch scientist, Simon Stevin (1548–1620), experimented with two forces in an effort to determine a single force, the resultant, equivalent to the two. He discovered that the resultant was actually the force represented by the diagonal of a parallelogram of which the sides represented the two original

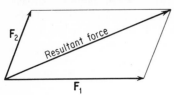

Figure 6-13

forces (see Fig. 6-13). This led to the formulation of the principle of addition of forces which he used extensively in developing a theory of equilibrium, the beginning of modern statics. (It is for this reason that the parallelogram in the figure is sometimes referred to as the *parallelogram of forces*.) Among the other accomplishments of Stevin are (1) his work on hydrostatics which laid the plans for reclaiming the below-sea-level land of Holland and (2) the development of decimal notation for numbers with the consequent methods of computation—he was the first to give a systematic treatment of decimals.†

Independently and approximately simultaneously, Galileo (1564–1642) also arrived at this law of the composition of forces.

Thus, if anyone had tried to develop a mathematical system for describing forces and their composition, the concepts of vector and vector addition could have been discovered any time after the work of these two physicists. Vector algebra could have been invented almost two centuries earlier than it actually was!

The operation of vector addition has several simple and natural physical interpretations, in terms of composition of forces, velocities, and displacements. Like all good mathematical abstractions, it yields as a bonus other valuable interpretations, including the economic interpretations given in the preceding exercises.

6.4

Other Basic Operations with Vectors   Since it becomes quite cumbersome to refer to vectors in terms of origins and endpoints, we adopt the convention that a boldface letter will also stand for a vector; and since we will have much occasion to deal with the lengths of vectors, we adopt the notation $\|\mathbf{A}\|$ to represent the lengths of the vector $\mathbf{A}$. Thus, $\|\mathbf{A}\|$ is a nonnegative real number. Adapting the notation for length of a vector to our earlier symbolism for vectors, we also have

$$\|\overrightarrow{AB}\| = \text{length of } \overrightarrow{AB},$$

$$\|[x, y]\| = \text{length of } [x, y].$$

Try your hand at a few exercises involving the new notation.

† See the chapter entitled "Stevin on Decimal Fractions" in David Eugene Smith, *A Source Book in Mathematics* (New York: Dover Publications, Inc., 1929), or J. F. Scott, *A History of Mathematics* (London: Taylor and Francis, Limited, 1958).

1. (a) $\|[1, 0]\| = $ ____,   *1*

    (b) $\|[0, 1]\| = $ ____,   *1*

    (c) $\|[0, -2]\| = $ ____,   *2*

    (d) $\|[1, 2]\| = $ ____, $\sqrt{5}$

    (e) $\|[a, b]\| = $ _____, $\sqrt{a^2 + b^2}$

    (f) $\|\mathbf{0}\| = $ ____.   *0*

2. Compare: $\|\overrightarrow{AB}\|$ ____ $\|\overrightarrow{BA}\|$. $=$

3. Compare: $\|\mathbf{A} + \mathbf{B}\|$ ____ $\|\mathbf{A}\| + \|\mathbf{B}\|$. $\leq$

4. $\|\mathbf{A} + \mathbf{B}\| = \|\mathbf{A}\| + \|\mathbf{B}\|$ if $\mathbf{A}$ and $\mathbf{B}$ are _____   *parallel*

and _____.   *have the same*   *direction*

5. $\|[2, -1] + [-1, 3]\| = $ ____. $\sqrt{5}$

6. If $O = (0, 0)$, $A = (-1, -4)$, and $B = (2, 3)$, then

$$\|\overrightarrow{AB}\| = \text{\_\_\_\_} \quad \text{and} \quad \|\overrightarrow{OA} + \overrightarrow{OB}\| = \text{\_\_\_\_},$$

                                            $\sqrt{58}, \sqrt{2}$

whereas

$$\|\overrightarrow{OA}\| + \|\overrightarrow{OB}\| = \text{_____}.$$

                                            $\sqrt{17} + \sqrt{13}$

7. (a) If $[x, y]$ has same direction as $[1, 2]$ and $\|[x, y]\| = 2\|[1, 2]\|$,
then $x = $ ____ and $y = $ ____.   *2, 4*

    (b) If $[x, y]$ has direction opposite to $[1, 2]$ and $\|[x, y]\| = 2\|[1, 2]\|$, then $x = $ ____ and $y = $ ____.   *−2, −4*

8. If $[x, y]$ has same direction as $[-2, 3]$ and $\|[x, y]\| = \frac{1}{2}\|[-2, 3]\|$,
then $x = $ ____ and $y = $ ____. $-1, \frac{3}{2}$

9. If a swimmer who can swim 800 yards per hour in still water is swimming perpendicular to a current of one mile per hour, what is his speed (magnitude of velocity)?

10. Two forces of 100 and 150 lb inclined 45° to one another combine to pull an object. What is the magnitude of the resultant force?

What vector $[x, y]$ has the same direction as $[1, 2]$ and satisfies the condition $\|[x, y]\| = 0\|[1, 2]\|$? What vector $[x, y]$ has direction opposite to $[1, 2]$ and satisfies the condition $\|[x, y]\| = 0\|[1, 2]\|$? What vector $[x, y]$ makes an angle of 30° with $[1, 2]$ and satisfies the condition $\|[x, y]\| = 0\|[1, 2]\|$?

It is easy to understand why the zero vector is thought to have no direction (if there is no motion, then there is no direction for the motion), but now your answers to the questions of the preceding paragraph show that the single vector **0** may have several directions. Imposing the condition that $\|[x, y]\| = 0$ was evidently sufficient for you to conclude that $x = y = 0$. That the condition of a direction was also imposed seemed irrelevant.

Thus, we have fulfilled our earlier promise to return to a discussion of the direction of the zero vector to explain why it is regarded as having no direction or *any direction*. The zero vector is the only vector with this property, for any nonzero vector possesses a unique direction.

We will now introduce you to another operation with vectors that you have already experienced in some earlier exercises; it is *multiplication of a vector by a scalar*.

If $\tau: (0, 0) \to (x, y)$ is a translation and **A** is the vector associated with τ, then

$$\tau \circ \tau: (0, 0) \to (\underline{\hspace{1cm}}, \underline{\hspace{1cm}}),$$ *2x, 2y*

$$\tau \circ (\tau \circ \tau): (0, 0) \to (\underline{\hspace{1cm}}, \underline{\hspace{1cm}}),$$ *3x, 3y*

and

$$\tau \circ (\tau \circ (\tau \circ \tau)): (0, 0) \to (\underline{\hspace{1cm}}, \underline{\hspace{1cm}}).$$ *4x, 4y*

But since composition of translation is the basis for vector addition, you may write $\mathbf{A} = [x, y]$,

$$\mathbf{A} + \mathbf{A} = [\underline{\hspace{1cm}}, \underline{\hspace{1cm}}],$$ *2x, 2y*

$$\mathbf{A} + \mathbf{A} + \mathbf{A} = [\underline{\hspace{1cm}}, \underline{\hspace{1cm}}],$$ *3x, 3y*

and

$$\mathbf{A} + \mathbf{A} + \mathbf{A} + \mathbf{A} = [\underline{\hspace{1cm}}, \underline{\hspace{1cm}}].$$ *4x, 4y*

Compare the direction of $\mathbf{A} + \mathbf{A}$ with that of **A**, the directions of $\mathbf{A} + \mathbf{A} + \mathbf{A}$ and $\mathbf{A} + \mathbf{A} + \mathbf{A} + \mathbf{A}$ with the direction of **A**.

Comparing lengths gives

$$\|\mathbf{A} + \mathbf{A}\| = \underline{\hspace{1cm}}\|\mathbf{A}\|, \qquad \|\mathbf{A} + \mathbf{A} + \mathbf{A}\| = \underline{\hspace{1cm}}\|\mathbf{A}\|,$$ *2, 3*

and

$$\|\mathbf{A} + \mathbf{A} + \mathbf{A} + \mathbf{A}\| = \underline{\hspace{1cm}}\|\mathbf{A} + \mathbf{A}\|.$$ *2*

Writing sums in this manner is most cumbersome and annoying, so instead we write

$$\mathbf{A} + \mathbf{A} = 2\mathbf{A}, \quad \mathbf{A} + \mathbf{A} + \mathbf{A} = 3\mathbf{A}, \quad \text{and} \quad \mathbf{A} + \mathbf{A} + \mathbf{A} + \mathbf{A} = 4\mathbf{A}.$$

A *recursive definition* of a positive integral multiple of **A** could be given by the statements

$$1\mathbf{A} = \mathbf{A}$$

and

$$n\mathbf{A} = (n - 1)\mathbf{A} + \mathbf{A} \qquad \text{for } n \in \mathcal{Z}^+ \text{ and } n \geq 2.$$

Check this definition for $n = 2$, 3, and 4. Observe that it is necessary that the definition give a "start" with $1\mathbf{A} = \mathbf{A}$, for this fact is not really known without stipulating it.

It will be interesting and worthwhile for you to prove that the direction of $n\mathbf{A}$ is the same as the direction of $\mathbf{A}$, for $n \in \mathscr{Z}^+$. (You must use the recursive definition!)

$$\|n\mathbf{A}\| = \underline{\hspace{1cm}} \|\mathbf{A}\|, \qquad n \in \mathscr{Z}^+. \qquad\qquad n$$

This statement also requires a proof (which we shall postpone) that depends on the recursive definition.

If $\mathbf{A} = [1, 2]$ and $\mathbf{B} = [-2, 3]$, then

$$2(\mathbf{A} + \mathbf{B}) = 2[\underline{\hspace{0.7cm}}, \underline{\hspace{0.7cm}}] = [\underline{\hspace{0.7cm}}, \underline{\hspace{0.7cm}}]. \qquad -1, 5, -2, 10$$

But $2\mathbf{A} = 2[1, 2] = [\underline{\hspace{0.7cm}}, \underline{\hspace{0.7cm}}]$ and $2\mathbf{B} = [\underline{\hspace{0.7cm}}, \underline{\hspace{0.7cm}}]$. $2, 4, -4, 6$

Compare $2(\mathbf{A} + \mathbf{B})$ with $2\mathbf{A} + 2\mathbf{B}$. Do they have equal lengths? $\underline{\hspace{1cm}}$ Do they have the same direction?   *Yes*

$\underline{\hspace{1cm}}$.   *Yes*

Compare $3\mathbf{A} + 4\mathbf{A}$ with $(3 + 4)\mathbf{A}$:

$$3\mathbf{A} = 3[1, 2] = [\underline{\hspace{0.7cm}}, \underline{\hspace{0.4cm}}] \quad \text{and} \quad 4\mathbf{A} = [\underline{\hspace{0.7cm}}, \underline{\hspace{0.7cm}}]. \qquad 3, 6, 4, 8$$

Also,

$$(3 + 4)\mathbf{A} = \underline{\hspace{0.7cm}}[1, 2] = [\underline{\hspace{0.7cm}}, \underline{\hspace{0.7cm}}], \qquad 7, 7, 14$$

whereas

$$3\mathbf{A} + 4\mathbf{A} = [\underline{\hspace{0.7cm}}, \underline{\hspace{0.7cm}}]. \qquad 7, 14$$

Is $(3 + 4)\mathbf{A} = 3\mathbf{A} + 4\mathbf{A}$? $\underline{\hspace{1cm}}$, (Yes/No)   *Yes*

Since $2\mathbf{A}$ is a vector, then $3(2\mathbf{A})$ is also a vector.

$$3(2\mathbf{A}) = 3(2[1, 2]) = 3[\underline{\hspace{0.7cm}}, \underline{\hspace{0.7cm}}] = [\underline{\hspace{0.7cm}}, \underline{\hspace{0.7cm}}]. \qquad 2, 4, 6, 12$$

Then

$$\|3(2\mathbf{A})\| = \underline{\hspace{0.7cm}}\|2\mathbf{A}\| = \underline{\hspace{0.7cm}}\|\mathbf{A}\|. \qquad 3, 6$$

Hence,

$$3(2\mathbf{A}) = \underline{\hspace{0.7cm}}\mathbf{A}. \qquad 6$$

Can you generalize this result so that $\mathbf{A}$ is any vector, and 3 and 2 are replaced by any positive integers? (This is another good exercise for the mathematically minded.)

Thus far you have a definition for $n\mathbf{A}$, where $n \in \mathscr{Z}^+$. We would like to extend this definition to include first $n = 0$, then $n \in \mathscr{Z}^-$, and ultimately n any real number. When a scientist attempts to extend his concepts he tries to extend in a manner that leaves his original concepts and theorems valid.

That is, the generalization should include his original work as a part. With this philosophy in mind, we extract the principal properties of $n\mathbf{A}$, $n \in \mathscr{Z}^+$, and extend the definition so that these properties still remain valid. What are these properties? And where did they arise in our development? Before proceeding with the reading you might like to try this extension on your own by giving definition(s) for $n\mathbf{A}$, where $n = 0$, $n \in \mathscr{Z}^-$, $n \in \mathscr{R}$, and pursuing the theory a bit before you see what we have to say.

We were led to a definition of $n\mathbf{A}$ from repeated compositions of τ. Now let's look at τ^{-1} and use $\mathbf{A} = [x, y]$ as the vector corresponding to the translation τ:

$$\tau^{-1} : (0, 0) \to (\underline{\qquad}, \underline{\qquad}).$$ | $-x, -y$

If $\mathbf{X} = [-x, -y]$ is the vector representing τ^{-1}, then

$$\tau^{-1} \circ \tau : (0, 0) \to [\underline{\qquad}, \underline{\qquad}].$$ | $0, 0$

In terms of addition, this is equivalent to writing

$$\mathbf{A} + \mathbf{X} = [x, y] + [\underline{\qquad}, \underline{\qquad}] = [\underline{\qquad}, \underline{\qquad}],$$ | $-x, -y, 0, 0$

or simply

$$\mathbf{A} + \mathbf{X} = \mathbf{0}.$$

If $\mathbf{A} = \overrightarrow{PQ}$, then $\mathbf{X} = \overrightarrow{Q?}$. Compare the lengths and directions of $\mathbf{A}$ and $\mathbf{X}$. | P

It seems natural at this point to call the vector $\mathbf{X}$ that represents the translation τ^{-1} by the new name $-\mathbf{A}$. Therefore the vector $-\mathbf{A}$ is merely the vector $\mathbf{A}$ with its direction reversed. In analogy with real numbers, the definition of $-\mathbf{A}$ provides the result that

$$\mathbf{A} + (-\mathbf{A}) = \mathbf{0}, \qquad \forall\, \mathbf{A}.$$

Investigating further, $\tau^{-1} \circ \tau^{-1} : (0, 0) \to (\underline{\qquad}, \underline{\qquad})$, | $-2x, -2y$
which gives $(-\mathbf{A}) + (-\mathbf{A}) = [\underline{\qquad}, \underline{\qquad}]$. Check back | $-2x, -2y$
to see how $2\mathbf{A}$ is defined and answer the following
question: Is it correct to write

$$2(-\mathbf{A}) = (-\mathbf{A}) + (-\mathbf{A})?$$ | Yes

Observe that

$$2(-\mathbf{A}) + 2\mathbf{A} = [\underline{\qquad}, \underline{\qquad}] + [\underline{\qquad}, \underline{\qquad}]$$ | $2x, 2y, -2x, -2y$

$$= [\underline{\qquad}, \underline{\qquad}].$$ | $0, 0$

Since we chose the notation $-\mathbf{V}$ to represent a vector related to $\mathbf{V}$ by the equation $\mathbf{V} + (-\mathbf{V}) = \mathbf{0}$, we infer that $-(2\mathbf{A}) = 2(-\mathbf{A})$! This suggests the definition:

$$(-2)\mathbf{A} = -(2\mathbf{A}),$$

and, in general,

$$(-n)\mathbf{A} = -(n\mathbf{A}), \qquad \text{for any } n \in \mathcal{Z}^+.$$

The one case that remains for us to consider among the integral "multiples" of a vector is 0A. How shall we define this? There are several ways you might arrive at an answer. Suppose you consider the lengths of multiples of **A**.

$$\|3\mathbf{A}\| = 3\|\mathbf{A}\|, \qquad \|5\mathbf{A}\| = 5\|\mathbf{A}\|, \qquad \|-\mathbf{A}\| = \underline{\qquad}\|\mathbf{A}\| \qquad \Big| \quad 1$$

and

$$\|-2\mathbf{A}\| = \underline{\qquad}\|\mathbf{A}\|, \qquad \text{and} \qquad \|-5\mathbf{A}\| = 5\|\mathbf{A}\|. \qquad \Big| \quad 2$$

In general,

$$\|n\mathbf{A}\| = \underline{\qquad}\|\mathbf{A}\|, \qquad n \in \mathcal{Z}^+ \text{ or } n \in \mathcal{Z}^-. \qquad \Big| \quad |n|$$

Therefore, an appropriate definition of 0A should satisfy the condition $\|0\mathbf{A}\| = \underline{\qquad}\|\mathbf{A}\|$. But the only vector of length zero is the zero vector. Hence we take $0\mathbf{A} = \mathbf{0}$.

Translation	Associated vector	Coordinate representation
τ	**A**	$[x, y]$
$\tau \circ \tau$	2**A**	$[2x, 2y]$
$\tau \circ \tau \circ \tau$	3**A**	$[3x, 3y]$
I	**0**	$[0, 0]$
τ^{-1}	$-$**A**	$[-x, -y]$
$\tau^{-1} \circ \tau^{-1}$	-2**A**	$[-2x, -2y]$
$\tau^{-1} \circ \tau^{-1} \circ \tau^{-1}$	-3**A**	$[-3x, -3y]$

Let's now extend these notions to include any real multiple of a vector.

Definition: *If r is any real number, then r**A** is a vector* (1) *whose length is given by the equation* $\|r\mathbf{A}\| = |r|\|\mathbf{A}\|$ *and* (2) *whose direction is the same as that of* **A** *if r > 0, but the opposite to that of A if r < 0. [Note that if r = 0, then* (1) *implies that r**A** = **0**.]*

Once again, taking $\mathbf{A} = [1, 2]$ and $\mathbf{B} = [-2, 3]$, then

$$\mathbf{A} + \mathbf{B} = [\underline{\qquad}, \underline{\qquad}], \qquad \Big| \quad -1, 5$$

$$\tfrac{1}{2}\mathbf{A} = [\underline{\qquad}, \underline{\qquad}], \qquad \Big| \quad \tfrac{1}{2}, 1$$

$$\tfrac{1}{2}\mathbf{B} = [\underline{\qquad}, \underline{\qquad}], \qquad \Big| \quad -1, \tfrac{3}{2}$$

$$\tfrac{1}{2}(\mathbf{A} + \mathbf{B}) = [\underline{\qquad}, \underline{\qquad}] = \underline{\qquad}\mathbf{A} + \underline{\qquad}\mathbf{B}, \qquad \Big| \quad -\tfrac{1}{2}, \tfrac{5}{2}, \tfrac{1}{2}, \tfrac{1}{2}$$

$$r\mathbf{A} = [\underline{\quad}, \underline{\quad}],$$ | $r, 2r$
$$r\mathbf{B} = [\underline{\quad}, \underline{\quad}],$$ | $-2r, 3r$
$$r(\mathbf{A} + \mathbf{B}) = [\underline{\quad}, \underline{\quad}] = \underline{\quad}\mathbf{A} + \underline{\quad}\mathbf{B},$$ | $-r, 5r, r, r$
$$\|\mathbf{A}\| = \underline{\quad},$$ | $\sqrt{5}$
$$\|\mathbf{B}\| = \underline{\quad},$$ | $\sqrt{13}$
$$\|\mathbf{A} + \mathbf{B}\| = \underline{\quad},$$ | $\sqrt{26}$
$$\|\tfrac{1}{2}\mathbf{A}\| = \underline{\quad},$$ | $\tfrac{1}{2}\sqrt{5}$
$$\|-3\mathbf{A}\| = \underline{\quad},$$ | $3\sqrt{5}$
$$\|\tfrac{2}{3}\mathbf{B}\| = \underline{\quad},$$ | $\tfrac{2}{3}\sqrt{13}$
$$2\mathbf{A} + (-3\mathbf{B}) = [\underline{\quad}, \underline{\quad}],$$ | $8, -5$
$$(-\mathbf{A}) + (-\mathbf{B}) = [\underline{\quad}, \underline{\quad}] = \underline{\quad}(\mathbf{A} + \mathbf{B}),$$ | $1, -5, -1$
$$3\mathbf{A} + (-4)\mathbf{A} = 3[1, 2] + (-4)[1, 2]$$ |
$$= [\underline{\quad}, \underline{\quad}] + [\underline{\quad}, \underline{\quad}]$$ | $3, 6, -4, -8$
$$= [\underline{\quad}, \underline{\quad}].$$ | $-1, -2$

Therefore,

$$3\mathbf{A} + (-4)\mathbf{A} = \underline{\quad}\mathbf{A},$$ | -1
$$3(-4\mathbf{A}) = 3[\underline{\quad}, \underline{\quad}] = [\underline{\quad}, \underline{\quad}]$$ | $-4, 8, -12, 24$
$$= \underline{\quad}\mathbf{A}.$$ | -12

We shall now have you apply the vector algebra you have already learned to prove a simple theorem of high school geometry: The line segment joining the midpoints of two sides of a triangle has half the length of the third side and is parallel to it.

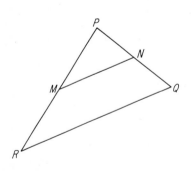

Figure 6-14

Denote the triangle by PQR, as in Fig. 6-14, with M and N the respective midpoints of sides PR and PQ. You can prove that MN is parallel to RQ if you can prove that $\overrightarrow{MN}$ and $\overrightarrow{RQ}$ satisfy the equation $\overrightarrow{MN} = r\overrightarrow{RQ}$ for some r. What must r equal if the theorem is to hold true?

As in every mathematical problem there is a hypothesis to exploit. Let's translate the hypothesis into vector language. The fact that M is the midpoint of side PR implies

(1) $$\overrightarrow{PM} = \underline{\quad} = \underline{\quad}\overrightarrow{PR}. \qquad\qquad \overrightarrow{MR}, \tfrac{1}{2}$$

That N is the midpoint of side PQ implies

(2) $$\overrightarrow{PN} = \underline{\quad} = \underline{\quad}\overrightarrow{PQ}. \qquad\qquad \overrightarrow{NQ}, \tfrac{1}{2}$$

But we are interested in the relation involving $\overrightarrow{MN}$ and $\overrightarrow{RQ}$. Summing the vectors around triangle MNP gives

(3) $$\overrightarrow{MN} = \overrightarrow{MP} + \underline{\quad}, \qquad\qquad \overrightarrow{PN}$$

and summing the vectors around triangle RQP gives

$$\overrightarrow{RQ} = \overrightarrow{RP} + \underline{\quad} \qquad\qquad \overrightarrow{PQ}$$

$$= \overrightarrow{RM} + \underline{\quad} + \overrightarrow{PN} + \underline{\quad} \qquad\qquad \overrightarrow{MP}, \overrightarrow{NQ}$$

$$= \underline{\quad}\overrightarrow{MP} + \underline{\quad}\overrightarrow{PN} \quad \text{(by (1) and (2))} \qquad\qquad 2, 2$$

$$= \underline{\quad}(\overrightarrow{MP} + \overrightarrow{PN}). \qquad\qquad 2$$

Now, using (3), you may write

$$\overrightarrow{RQ} = 2\underline{\quad}, \qquad\qquad \overrightarrow{MN}$$

which implies *two* facts:

(i) RQ is parallel to MN, and

(ii) $\|\overrightarrow{RQ}\| = 2\|\overrightarrow{MN}\|$.

Thus both parts of the theorem come out of a single vector equation!

Let's look at another approach to the same problem. Summing vectors around the closed polygon $RMNQ$, we may write

$$\overrightarrow{RQ} = \overrightarrow{RM} + \underline{\quad} + \underline{\quad}. \qquad\qquad \overrightarrow{MN}, \overrightarrow{NQ}$$

But since $\overrightarrow{RM} = \overrightarrow{MP}$ and $\overrightarrow{NQ} = \overrightarrow{PN}$,

$$\overrightarrow{RQ} = \overrightarrow{MP} + \overrightarrow{MN} + \overrightarrow{PN} = (\overrightarrow{MP} + \overrightarrow{PN}) + \overrightarrow{MN}$$

$$= \underline{\quad} + \overrightarrow{MN} = \underline{\quad}\overrightarrow{MN}. \qquad\qquad \overrightarrow{MN}, 2$$

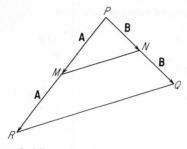

Figure 6-15

Still another streamlined version is achieved by calling

$$\mathbf{A} = \overrightarrow{PM} = \overrightarrow{MR} \text{ and } \mathbf{B} = \overrightarrow{PN} = \overrightarrow{NQ}$$

(see Fig. 6-15).

This illustration indicates the power of vectors in solving problems of geometry. You will have ample opportunity to try your hand at other problems, but first we introduce you to *vector subtraction*.

Definition *of* $\mathbf{A} - \mathbf{B}$: $\mathbf{A} - \mathbf{B} = \mathbf{A} + (-\mathbf{B})$.

Let's see what this means in geometric terms. Take directed segment representations of $\mathbf{A}$ and $\mathbf{B}$ that have the same origin. Then $-\mathbf{B}$ can be shown at various places as in Fig. 6-16(a). If we take $\mathbf{A} + (-\mathbf{B})$ in the lower half of the figure (a), then $\mathbf{A} - \mathbf{B}$ appears as drawn in Fig. 6-16(b). But $\mathbf{A} - \mathbf{B}$ is, therefore, parallel and equal in length to the line joining the endpoints of the original representations of $\mathbf{A}$ and $\mathbf{B}$ (see Fig. 6-16(c)). Observe that summing the vectors around the triangle as indicated in Fig. 6-16(c), we get $\mathbf{B} + (\mathbf{A} - \mathbf{B}) = \mathbf{A}$, which checks! For, using the definition of $\mathbf{A} - \mathbf{B}$ gives

$$\mathbf{B} + (\mathbf{A} - \mathbf{B}) = \mathbf{B} + (\mathbf{A} + (-\mathbf{B})) = \mathbf{B} + ((-\mathbf{B}) + \mathbf{A})$$

$$= (\mathbf{B} + (-\mathbf{B})) + \mathbf{A} = \mathbf{0} + \mathbf{A} = \mathbf{A}.$$

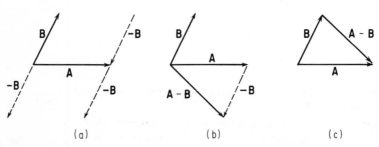

(a)   (b)   (c)

Figure 6-16

If we use subtraction in our last geometric problem we can write the proof in rather simple form:

$$\overrightarrow{RQ} = 2\mathbf{B} - 2\mathbf{A} = 2(\mathbf{B} - \mathbf{A}) = 2\overrightarrow{MN}.$$

Try your hand at the following geometric representations involving subtractions.

Written as subtractions, or differences, of two vectors (Fig. 6-17),

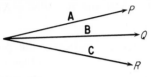

Figure 6-17

$\overrightarrow{PQ} = \underline{\quad} - \underline{\quad},$ B, A

$\overrightarrow{RQ} = \underline{\quad} - \underline{\quad},$ B, C

$\overrightarrow{PR} = \underline{\quad} - \underline{\quad}.$ C, A

In parallelogram $PQRS$ (Fig. 6-18),

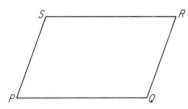

Figure 6-18

$\overrightarrow{PS} - \overrightarrow{PQ} = \overrightarrow{?},$ $\overrightarrow{QS}$

$\overrightarrow{PS} - \overrightarrow{RS} = \overrightarrow{?},$ $\overrightarrow{PR}$

$\overrightarrow{RQ} - \overrightarrow{RS} = \overrightarrow{?},$ $\overrightarrow{SQ}$

$\overrightarrow{QS} - \overrightarrow{QR} = \overrightarrow{?}.$ $\overrightarrow{RS}$

In Fig. 6-19, M is the midpoint of side PQ.

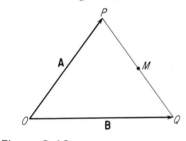

Figure 6-19

$\overrightarrow{MQ} = \underline{\quad}\overrightarrow{PQ},$ $\frac{1}{2}$

$\overrightarrow{PM} = \underline{\quad}\overrightarrow{PQ},$ $\frac{1}{2}$

$\overrightarrow{PQ} = \underline{\quad} - \underline{\quad},$ B, A

$\overrightarrow{OM} = \mathbf{A} + ?$ $\overrightarrow{PM}$

$\quad = \mathbf{A} + \underline{\quad}\overrightarrow{PQ}.$ $\frac{1}{2}$

Therefore,

$\overrightarrow{OM} = \mathbf{A} + \frac{1}{2}(\underline{\quad} - \underline{\quad}).$ B, A

Finally,

$\overrightarrow{OM} = \frac{1}{2}(\underline{\quad} + \underline{\quad}).$ A, B

The vector, with origin at O, that represents the diagonal of the parallelogram, three of whose vertices are O, P, and Q, is _____. Thus, $\|\overrightarrow{OM}\|$ is precisely equal to _____ the length of the diagonal of this parallelogram. In a rather roundabout way, we have shown that the diagonals of a parallelogram bisect each other.

$\mathbf{A} + \mathbf{B}$
one-half

Remarks: You should take note that you have proved the following:
If M is the midpoint of segment PQ, then $\overrightarrow{OM} = \frac{1}{2}(\overrightarrow{OP} + \overrightarrow{OQ})$.
It will be useful for you to remember this.

For some illustrations with coordinates, call $P = (1, 2)$, $R = (-2, 3)$, $S = (-2, -1)$, and $T = (3, -4)$. Then

$$\overrightarrow{PR} = [\underline{\quad\quad}, \underline{\quad\quad}], \quad \overrightarrow{SR} = [\underline{\quad\quad}, \underline{\quad\quad}], \qquad\qquad -3, 1, 0, 4$$

$$\overrightarrow{RT} = [\underline{\quad\quad}, \underline{\quad\quad}], \qquad\qquad 5, -7$$

$$\overrightarrow{RT} - \overrightarrow{SR} = [\underline{\quad\quad}, \underline{\quad\quad}], \qquad\qquad 5, -11$$

$$\overrightarrow{PR} - (\overrightarrow{PR} - \overrightarrow{SR}) = [\underline{\quad\quad}, \underline{\quad\quad}], \qquad\qquad 0, 4$$

$$\tfrac{1}{2}\overrightarrow{PR} + \tfrac{1}{2}\overrightarrow{RT} = [\underline{\quad\quad}, \underline{\quad\quad}], \qquad\qquad 1, -3$$

$$\tfrac{1}{2}\overrightarrow{PT} = [\underline{\quad\quad}, \underline{\quad\quad}]. \qquad\qquad 1, -3$$

In general, if $\mathbf{A}_1 = [x_1, y_1]$ and $\mathbf{A}_2 = [x_2, y_2]$, then

$$\mathbf{A}_1 - \mathbf{A}_2 = [\underline{\quad\quad}, \underline{\quad\quad}]. \qquad\qquad x_1 - x_2,$$
$$\qquad\qquad\qquad\qquad\qquad\qquad y_1 - y_2$$

If $P_1 = (x_1, y_1)$ and $P_2 = (x_2, y_2)$, then

$$\overrightarrow{P_1P_2} = [\underline{\quad\quad}, \underline{\quad\quad}]. \qquad\qquad x_2 - x_1, y_2 - y_1$$

Draw a figure labeling P_1, P_2, $\mathbf{A}_1$, $\mathbf{A}_2$ of the last two sentences and check your answers geometrically.

6.4.2
EXERCISES

1. Find $\|\mathbf{A}\|$ when
(a) $\mathbf{A} = [3, 4]$,
(b) $\mathbf{A} = [-3, 4]$,
(c) $\mathbf{A} = [-3, -4]$,
(d) $\mathbf{A} = [4, -3]$,
(e) $\mathbf{A} = [5, -7]$,
(f) $\mathbf{A} = [3, 4] - [5, -7]$,
(g) $\mathbf{A} = [5, 8]$,
(h) $\mathbf{A} = \frac{1}{5}[3, -4]$,
(i) $\mathbf{A} = \frac{1}{8}[5, -7]$,
(j) $\mathbf{A} = (1/\sqrt{89})[5, 8]$.

2. If $\mathbf{A}$ is any nonzero vector, find the length of vector $\dfrac{1}{\|\mathbf{A}\|}\mathbf{A}$.

3. A vector of length one is called a *unit vector*. Exercise 2 gives you a clue for obtaining unit vectors.
(a) If $\mathbf{A} = [3, -4]$, find a unit vector with the direction of $\mathbf{A}$.
(b) If $\mathbf{A} = [3, -4]$, find a unit vector in direction opposite to $\mathbf{A}$.
(c) If $\mathbf{A}$ and $\mathbf{B}$ are not parallel, find a unit vector in the direction of $\mathbf{A} + \mathbf{B}$. Does your answer hold if $\mathbf{A}$ and $\mathbf{B}$ are parallel?

(d) Let $O = (0, 0)$, $U_1 = (1, 0)$, and $U_2 = (0, 1)$. Find an X such that $\overrightarrow{OX}$ bisects angle U_1OU_2.

(e) If $O = (0, 0)$, $P = (1, 0)$, $Q = (-1, 5)$, find an X such that $\overrightarrow{OX}$ bisects angle POQ.

(f) Let **A** and **B** be any two vectors of equal length. If geometric representations of **A** and **B** have a common origin O, find an expression for a vector (whose origin is O) that bisects the angle formed by **A** and **B**.

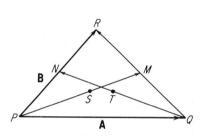

(g) If geometric representations of any two non-zero vectors **A** and **B** are taken to have a common origin O, find an expression for a vector **C** (whose origin is O) that bisects the angle formed by **A** and **B** (Fig. 6-20).

(h) If $P = (1, -2)$, $Q = (-3, 4)$, and $R = (2, 5)$, find a unit vector in the direction of $\overrightarrow{PQ}$, find $\overrightarrow{PQ} - \overrightarrow{RQ}$, and find a unit vector in the direction of $2\overrightarrow{PQ} - (4/\|\overrightarrow{PQ}\|)\overrightarrow{RQ}$.

Figure 6-20

4. Let PQR be a triangle labeled so that $\mathbf{A} = \overrightarrow{PQ}$ and $\mathbf{B} = \overrightarrow{PR}$ (Fig. 6-21).

(a) Express $\overrightarrow{QR}$ in terms of **A** and **B**.

(b) Call M the midpoint of side RQ, and find an expression for the vector $\overrightarrow{PM}$ in terms of **A** and **B**.

(c) Call N the midpoint of side PR, and find an expression for $\overrightarrow{QN}$ in terms of **A** and **B**.

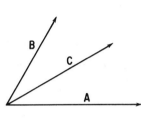

(d) If $\overrightarrow{PS} = \frac{2}{3}\overrightarrow{PM}$, find $\overrightarrow{PS}$ in terms of **A** and **B**.

Figure 6-21

(e) If $\overrightarrow{QT} = \frac{2}{3}\overrightarrow{QN}$, find $\overrightarrow{QT}$ in terms of **A** and **B**.

(f) What conclusion can you draw concerning S and T? Does this remind you of any familiar theorem? And does your work in this problem constitute a proof of the theorem?

5. Given triangle ABC with P the midpoint of side AB, Q the midpoint of side BC, and R the midpoint of side CA. Let X be any point at all, and prove that

$$\overrightarrow{XA} + \overrightarrow{XB} + \overrightarrow{XC} = \overrightarrow{XP} + \overrightarrow{XQ} + \overrightarrow{XR}.$$

6. Show by vectors that the midpoints of the sides of a quadrilateral are vertices of a parallelogram.

7. (a) If A, B, C, and D are any four points, prove that

$$\overrightarrow{AB} + \overrightarrow{AD} + \overrightarrow{CB} + \overrightarrow{CD} = 4\overrightarrow{PQ},$$

when P and Q are the midpoints of segments $\overline{AC}$ and $\overline{BD}$, respectively.

(b) Show that $\overrightarrow{PQ} + \overrightarrow{RS} = \overrightarrow{2MN}$, where P, Q, R, and S are four arbitrarily chosen points, and where M and N are the midpoints of segments $\overline{PR}$ and $\overline{QS}$, respectively. [*Hint*: Sum the vectors around the polygon $NMRS$ and $NMPQ$.] How does the problem relate to part (a)?

8. Give justifications for the following implications:
(a) $A = B \Rightarrow A + C = B + C$, for any vector C.
(b) $A = B \Rightarrow A - C = B - C$, for any vector C.
(c) $A = B$ and $C = D \Rightarrow A + C = B + D$.
(d) $A = B$ and $C = D \Rightarrow A - C = B - D$.

9. Prove that the set of vectors forms an abelian group with respect to some operation.

10. (a) Draw vectors A and B, $A + B$, mA, mB, and $m(A + B)$, and give the geometric interpretation for the statement:

$$m(A + B) = mA + mB.$$

(b) Do the same for $m(A - B) = mA - mB$.

11. Prove: If $A + B = 0$, then any two geometric representations of the nonzero vectors A and B are parallel (according to the extended definition of parallelism in Sec. 6.2).

12. (a) In Fig. 6-22(a), show how V can be represented as a sum in the form

$$V = mA + nB.$$

(b) Do the same relative to Fig. 6-22(b).
(c) Do the same relative to Fig. 6-22(c).
(d) Do the same relative to Fig. 6-22(d).
(e) For parts (a)–(d) state the cases in which m and n are positive, negative, and zero.

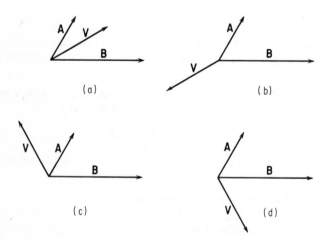

Figure 6-22

13. Let **A** and **B** be two fixed nonzero vectors in a plane such that

$$\mathbf{A} \neq m\mathbf{B} \qquad (m \in \mathscr{R}).$$

(a) Give a general geometric proof that any vector **V** in the plane of **A** and **B** can be represented as the sum

$$\mathbf{V} = h\mathbf{A} + k\mathbf{B} \qquad (h, k \in \mathscr{R}).$$

(b) Let $\mathbf{A} = [a_1, a_2]$ and $\mathbf{B} = [b_1, b_2]$; prove the same results as in part (a), but now in terms of coordinate representations.

(c) Let $\mathbf{A} = [1, 2], \mathbf{B} = [2, 1], \mathbf{V} = [-3, 4]$. Find h and k such that $\mathbf{V} = h\mathbf{A} + k\mathbf{B}$.

(d) Let $\mathbf{A} = [1, 2], \mathbf{B} = [2, 1], \mathbf{V} = [3, 4]$. Find h and k such that $\mathbf{V} = h\mathbf{A} + k\mathbf{B}$.

(e) Let $\mathbf{A} = [1, 0], \mathbf{B} = [0, 1], \mathbf{V} = [3, 4]$. Find h and k such that $\mathbf{V} = h\mathbf{A} + k\mathbf{B}$.

(f) Let $\mathbf{A} = [1, 0], \mathbf{B} = [0, 1], \mathbf{V} = [x, y]$. Find h and k such that $\mathbf{V} = h\mathbf{A} + k\mathbf{B}$.

14. Let $\mathbf{A} = [1, -2]$.

(a) $3\mathbf{A} = [\underline{\qquad}, \underline{\qquad}]$.

(b) $-2\mathbf{A} = [\underline{\qquad}, \underline{\qquad}]$.

(c) $3\mathbf{A} - 2\mathbf{A} = [\underline{\qquad}, \underline{\qquad}]$.

(d) $2(3\mathbf{A}) = 2[\underline{\qquad}, \underline{\qquad}] = [\underline{\qquad}, \underline{\qquad}] = (\underline{\qquad})\mathbf{A}$.

15. Let $\mathbf{A} = [1, -2]$.

(a) $\|\mathbf{A}\| = \underline{\qquad}$.

(b) $\|3\mathbf{A}\| = \underline{\qquad}$.

(c) $\|-2\mathbf{A}\| = \underline{\qquad}$.

(d) $\|3\mathbf{A} - 2\mathbf{A}\| = \underline{\qquad}$.

(e) If $r \in \mathscr{R}^+$, then $\|r\mathbf{A}\| = \underline{\qquad} = \underline{\qquad}\|\mathbf{A}\|$.

(f) If $r \in \mathscr{R}^-$, then $\|r\mathbf{A}\| = \underline{\qquad} = \underline{\qquad}\|\mathbf{A}\|$.

(g) In general if $r \in \mathscr{R}$, then

$$\|r\mathbf{A}\| = \underline{\qquad}\|\mathbf{A}\|.$$

6.5

Applications to Geometry of the Line Let $O = (0, 0)$. Then

$\overrightarrow{OA} = [1, -3] \Rightarrow A = (\underline{\qquad}, \underline{\qquad}),$	*1, −3*
$\overrightarrow{OB} = [4, 0] \Rightarrow B = (\underline{\qquad}, \underline{\qquad}),$	*4, 0*
$\overrightarrow{OC} = [-1, -1] \Rightarrow C = (\underline{\qquad}, \underline{\qquad}),$	*−1, −1*
$\overrightarrow{OD} = [0, 0] \Rightarrow D = (\underline{\qquad}, \underline{\qquad}).$	*0, 0*

In general, if you have the coordinate representation of a vector given as $[x, y]$, then the coordinates of its endpoint relative to the origin $(0, 0)$ are $(\underline{\qquad}, \underline{\qquad})$. *x, y*

Conversely, if $P = (x, y)$, then $\overrightarrow{OP} = [\underline{\qquad}, \underline{\qquad}]$. *x, y*

This means that we can use vectors to locate points relative to some fixed point (origin); and there should be no ambiguity, for vector $\overrightarrow{OP}$ locates the unique point P relative to the origin O.

Our first application of this principle will be to introduce some handy notation. If a vector locates point A by having its origin at O and endpoint at A, we denote the vector by $\mathbf{A}$. Simply stated,

$$\mathbf{A} = \overrightarrow{OA},$$

and when we use a vector in this manner we refer to it as a *position vector*. That is, $\mathbf{A}$ is the position vector of point A; and $[x, y]$ is the position vector of (x, y).

Let O be the origin and M the midpoint of segment $\overline{AB}$. Then $\mathbf{M} = h\mathbf{A} + k\mathbf{B}$, where $h = $ _____ and $k = $ _____. | $\frac{1}{2}, \frac{1}{2}$

The vector $\overrightarrow{AB}$ can be represented in terms of the position vectors of $\mathbf{A}$ and $\mathbf{B}$ by writing $\overrightarrow{AB} = h\mathbf{A} + k\mathbf{B}$, where $h = $ _____ and $k = $ _____. Let N be two-thirds of the way from A to B on line AB. Then the position vector $\mathbf{N}$ of point N can be written | $-1, 1$

$$\mathbf{N} = \mathbf{A} + t(\overrightarrow{AB}) = A + t(\underline{\hspace{1cm}} - \underline{\hspace{1cm}}),$$ | $\mathbf{B}, \mathbf{A}$

where $t = $ _____. Then $\mathbf{N} = h\mathbf{A} + k\mathbf{B}$, where $h = $ _____ and $k = $ _____. (Compare the representations of $\mathbf{M}$ and $\mathbf{N}$. Do you notice anything interesting about the coefficients h and k in these?) | $\frac{2}{3}, \frac{1}{3}$ $\frac{2}{3}$

Let Q be one-third of the way from A to B. Then $\mathbf{Q} = h\mathbf{A} + k\mathbf{B}$, where $h = $ _____ and $k = $ _____. Let R be four-fifths of the way from A to B. Then $\mathbf{R} = h\mathbf{A} + k\mathbf{B}$, where $h = $ _____ and $k = $ _____. Let S be on AB so that $\overrightarrow{AS} = 2\overrightarrow{AB}$. Then $\mathbf{S} = h\mathbf{A} + k\mathbf{B}$, where $h = $ _____ and $k = $ _____. Let T be on AB so that $\overrightarrow{AT} = -\overrightarrow{AB}$. Then $\mathbf{T} = h\mathbf{A} + k\mathbf{B}$, where $h = $ _____ and $k = $ _____. | $\frac{2}{3}, \frac{1}{3}$ $\frac{1}{5}, \frac{4}{5}$ -1 2 $2, -1$

Have you noticed anything special about the coefficients of $\mathbf{A}$ and $\mathbf{B}$ in all the representations of position vectors of points on AB?

Let's now try to prove a general result about the positions of points on AB. Let X be any fixed point of AB, and suppose X divides the directed segment $\overline{AB}$ in the ratio $r:s$, where $r + s = 1$. For example, if X divides $\overline{AB}$ in the ratio $2:3$, then

$$\frac{\overline{AX}}{\overline{XB}} = \frac{r}{s} = \frac{2}{3}.$$

Thus, $h = \frac{2}{5}$ and $k = \frac{3}{5}$. If X is the midpoint of $\overline{AB}$, then $r =$ _____ and $s =$ _____. If X is two-thirds of the way from A to B, then $r =$ _____ and $s =$ _____. If X is outside segment $\overline{AB}$, so that, for example, $\overrightarrow{AX} = 2\overrightarrow{AB}$, then $r =$ _____ and $s =$ _____.

$\frac{1}{2}, \frac{1}{2}$

$\frac{2}{3}, \frac{1}{3}$

$2, -1$

Returning to the general case where $\overline{AX}/\overline{XB} = r/s$ and $r + s = 1$, we can write

$$X = A + \overrightarrow{AX} = A + \underline{\quad}\overrightarrow{AB} = A + \underline{\quad}(B - A).$$

r, r

Thus, $X = sA + \underline{\quad}B$ and you have proved:

r

Theorem: *If X divides segment $\overline{AB}$ in the ratio $r:s$ where $r + s = 1$, then the position vectors of the points A, B, and X satisfy the equation*

$$X = sA + rB.$$

6.5.1
EXERCISES

1. Referring to the theorem we have just established,
(a) what happens if **A** or **B** is the zero vector?
(b) what are s and r if $X = A$?
(c) where is X if $s = \frac{3}{2}$ and $r = -\frac{1}{2}$?

2. State the converse of the theorem. Prove it true or false, as the case may be.

3. Let M be the midpoint of $\overline{AB}$, N the midpoint of $\overline{AC}$, and O be some arbitrarily chosen origin for the representation of position vectors. Then

$$N = \underline{\quad}A + \underline{\quad}C,$$

$$M = \underline{\quad}A + \underline{\quad}B,$$

$$\overrightarrow{MN} = N - M = ?.$$

What geometric result have you proved by this argument?

4. (a) Refer to Exercise 4 of Sec. 6.4.2, where you found $\overrightarrow{PS} = nA + mB$ for some n and m. Check the result of that problem to see the significance of n and m. (Be careful, for you may be caught in a booby trap!)
(b) Examine $\overrightarrow{QT}$ of that exercise in the light of the results of this section.

5. Let $P_1 = (-1, 2)$ and $P_2 = (3, 4)$.
(a) Find the midpoint $M = (m_1, m_2)$ of $\overline{P_1 P_2}$. [*Hint:* $M = \frac{1}{2}P_1 + \frac{1}{2}P_2.$]
(b) Find the coordinates of the point Q that divides $\overline{P_1 P_2}$ in the ratio $2:3$.
(c) Determine x and y so that $P = (x, y)$ divides $P_1 P_2$ in the ratio $t:(1 - t)$.

6. If $P_1 = (x_1, y_1)$ and $P_2 = (x_2, y_2)$, determine a formula for the coordinates (m_1, m_2) of the midpoint $P_1 P_2$.

7. Let $\mathbf{P}$ be the position vector of any point on line $P_1 P_2$. Then P divides segment $\overline{P_1 P_2}$ in the ratio $t : (1 - t)$, $t \in \mathscr{R}$.

(a) Find an equation for $\mathbf{P}$ in terms of $\mathbf{P}_1$ and $\mathbf{P}_2$. (This is called the *vector equation* of the line. Different values of t give rise to different points of the line.)

(b) Where is P when $0 < t < 1$?

(c) Where is P when $t < 0$?

(d) Where is P when $t > 1$?

(e) Where is P when $t = 0$, $t = 1$?

8. Continuing Exercise 7, let $P_1 = (x_1, y_1)$, $P_2 = (x_2, y_2)$ and the general point of the line be $P = (x, y)$. Then

(a) $[x, y] = (1 - t)[\underline{\hspace{1cm}}, \underline{\hspace{1cm}}] + t[\underline{\hspace{1cm}}, \underline{\hspace{1cm}}] = [\underline{\hspace{1cm}}, \underline{\hspace{1cm}}]$,

(b) $x = x_1 + \underline{\hspace{1cm}}$, $y = y_1 + \underline{\hspace{1cm}}$.

This set of equations is called the *parametric representation* of the line $P_1 P_2$; the equations are called the *parametric equations* of the line, and t is called the *parameter*.

9. Let $x = 2 + 3t$ and $y = -1 + 4t$ be the parametric representation of a line.

(a) Determine two points on the line. What values of the parameter t give rise to the two points you have found?

(b) If $t = -1$, what point of the line is given?

(c) Find the slope of the line.

10. Determine the slopes of the lines given in (a)–(e).

(a) $x = 2 + t,$
  $y = -1 + 2t.$

(b) $x = 2 + t,$
  $y = -1 + 3t.$

(c) $x = 2 + 2t,$
  $y = -1 + 6t.$

(d) $x = 2 + t,$
  $y = -1 - t.$

(e) $x = 3 + t,$
  $y = -2 - t.$

(f) Compare lines of (b) and (c) and lines of (d) and (e).

11. The parametric representation of $P_1 P_2$ can be written

$$x - x_1 = t(x_2 - x_1),$$

$$y - y_1 = t(y_2 - y_1)$$

so that the parameter t can be eliminated by dividing to get

(∗) $$\frac{y - y_1}{x - x_1} = \frac{y_2 - y_1}{x_2 - x_1}$$

(this is the *two-point form for the equation of line* $P_1 P_2$).

(a) Under what circumstances is the above division illegal?

(b) Do you recall the geometric significance of the right member of (∗)?

(c) You should now be able to determine by inspection the slope of a line from its parametric representation. Return to Exercise 10 to check your answers.

12. Let $A = (a_1, a_2)$, $B = (b_1, b_2)$, and $C = (c_1, c_2)$. Find the coordinates of the point of intersection of the medians of the triangle ABC. [*Hint:* Use the theorem on page 219.]

13. (a) Let vectors be drawn from the center of an equilateral triangle to the vertices. Prove that the sum of these *radial vectors* is the zero vector.

(b) Do the same for a square and regular pentagon.

(c) Now prove that the sum of the radial vectors of any regular polygon is the zero vector. [*Hint:* Use symmetry.]

14. Find parametric representations for the lines with the following equations:

(a) $y = 3x$, (d) $2x = 4y - 7$,

(b) $y = -2x$, (e) $2x - 5y = 3$.

(c) $3x - y + 2 = 0$,

15. Find a single equation for the lines whose parametric representations are:

(a) $x = 3 - 4t$, (d) $x = t - 4$,

$\quad y = t$ $\quad y = 3 - 3t$.

(b) $x = 1 + t$, (e) $x = 2 - 5t$,

$\quad y = 1 + t$. $\quad y = -1 - t$.

(c) $x = 2 + t$,

$\quad y = -1 + 2t$.

16. A particle moves with *uniform velocity* $\mathbf{v} = [3, 4]$ per second. That is, the particle makes equal displacements in time intervals of equal length, and its displacement each second is $\mathbf{v}$. At the time $t = 0$, the particle is at $(2, 5)$.

(a) Where is it at the time $t = 1$? It is at (x, y), where $x =$ _____ and $y =$ _____.

(b) What is the displacement during the time interval from $t = 1$ to $t = 2$? At the time $t = 2$, the particle is at (_____, _____).

(c) If $t \in \mathscr{L}^+$, then at time t the particle is at (x, y), where $x =$ _____ and $y =$ _____.

(d) What is the displacement during any time interval of $\frac{1}{2}$ second? of $\frac{1}{3}$ second? of $\frac{2}{3}$ second?

(e) What is the displacement during any time interval of length t seconds, where $t \in \mathscr{R}^+$?

(f) At the time t, $t \geq 0$, the particle is at (x, y), where

$$x = \underline{\quad\quad} + \underline{\quad\quad}, \qquad y = \underline{\quad\quad} + \underline{\quad\quad}.$$

(g) Where *was* the particle at $t = -3$, i.e., 3 seconds before we began observing it?

(h) Is the formula of part (f) valid for negative t?

(i) What kind of path does the particle traverse?

6.6

Analytic and Vector Proofs in Geometry   Geometry   is   that   branch   of mathematics that deals with, among other things, the properties of lines, curves, and surfaces. The solutions to problems in this field may be obtained by various approaches, some being more natural or stronger than others—depending on the problem at hand. The first approach you learned in high school is called the *synthetic method*, the method used by Euclid in building up geometry from *geometric* axioms (without coordinates). In Chapter 4 you learned something of the *analytic method*, which is based on coordinate systems; and now you have also learned of the *vector* approach, which can be used with or without the use of coordinates. You should be aware of the fact that coordinate systems are not intrinsic to geometry! A coordinate system should be used as a convenient instrument for attacking some problems. You, therefore, impose a coordinate system on a problem; hence, you might as well impose it so that it serves you well. You will soon have some examples that indicate how a judicious choice of the coordinate system makes things simple, while an injudicious choice renders the problem quite difficult.

Since geometric and physical facts are *independent* of coordinate systems, we keep our eyes peeled for quantities that are invariant—that do not change—when we change the coordinate system. These quantities must have intrinsic geometric meaning. For example, the angle sum of a triangle is 180° in euclidean geometry; this is a fact independent of any coordinate system.

Vectors have the property of possessing direct geometric and physical meaning. Therefore, it is advantageous to work out general problems and the general theory vectorially, whereas in practice the calculations for specific problems are done with coordinates.

In this section we will give you exercises requiring various approaches.

Let's begin with an *analytic* proof of the following theorem:

The diagonals of a parallelogram bisect each other.

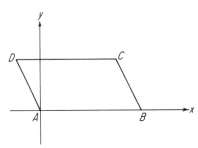

Figure 6-23

You've already proved this—synthetically in high school and vectorially on page 213. Note that this theorem has geometric significance and should therefore hold no matter where we place the coordinate axis, and no matter what coordinate system we use.

Suppose you are given parallelogram $ABCD$ (Fig. 6-23). How would you place the axes of a rectangular coordinate system? One simplification would result from placing the origin at one vertex, say A, and then placing an axis along one edge of the parallelogram.

Let the x-axis coincide with side AB. Then $A = (0, 0)$ and the y-coordinate of B equals _____. We are dealing with a general parallelogram, so we call the x-coordinate of B equal to b, an arbitrary but fixed number different from zero. Let $C = (a, c)$ and $D = (d, e)$. The slope of AB is _____. Therefore, the slope of DC is _____. But

$$\text{slope of } DC = \frac{e - ?}{? - a} = 0.$$

0
0, 0
$\dfrac{c}{d}$

Since $d \neq a$ (why?), $e - \underline{} = 0$. Therefore, $e = \underline{}$. $\quad | \quad c, c$

Thus far, you have

$$A = (0,0), \quad B = (b,0), \quad C = (a,c), \quad D = (d,c).$$

The only part of the hypothesis that has been used is the fact that DC is parallel to AB. What other hypothesis follows from the definition of the parallelogram? Let's use the fact that the other pair of opposite sides are parallel.

Slope of $AD =$ _____. $\qquad\qquad\qquad | \quad \dfrac{c}{d}$

Slope of $BC = \dfrac{c}{\underline{} - \underline{}}$. $\qquad | \quad a, b$

Since AD is parallel to BC,

$$\frac{c}{d} = \frac{c}{a-b},$$

and this implies that $d =$ _____, provided $a \neq b$. How $\quad | \quad a - b$
do you know that $a \neq b$? (Before completing the proof,
compute the lengths of the opposite sides. How does this
serve as a check?)

So far you have done nothing more than determine the coordinates of the vertices. The diagonals, and especially the midpoints of the diagonals, are the major concern. You can use the formula derived on page 219 to compute these:

Midpoint of $\overline{AC} = ($ _____, _____ $)$, $\qquad | \quad \dfrac{a}{2}, \dfrac{c}{2}$

Midpoint of $\overline{BD} = \left(\dfrac{(a-b)+b}{2}, \underline{} \right)$. $\qquad | \quad \dfrac{c}{2}$

So the midpoints of the diagonals coincide! Why does this prove the theorem?

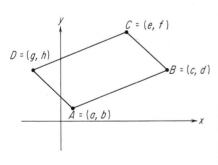

Figure 6-24

You will appreciate the simplification that resulted from our choice of co-ordinate axes if you now try to carry out the proof when the coordinate axes are taken in some general position as in Fig. 6-24.

A little more experience will enable you to see many shortcuts. You can often immediately write down the coordinates of the points involved with the hypothesis imposed so that you can get right to the heart of the problem. For example, if you were beginning on a problem involving the medians of a triangle, you could select the vertices as $A = (0,0)$, $B = (b,0)$, and $C = (c,d)$ (Fig. 6-25). Then the respective midpoints M, N, and P of sides AB, BC, and CA would be written immediately as

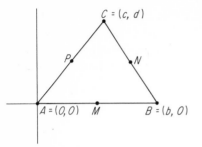

$$M = \left(\frac{b}{2},0\right), \quad N = \left(\frac{b+c}{2},\frac{d}{2}\right),$$

$$P = \left(\frac{c}{2},\frac{d}{2}\right).$$

(Incidentally, it should now be obvious that PN is parallel to AB!)

Figure 6-25

6.6.1
EXERCISES

Using analytic methods prove Statements 1–7.

1. In any triangle the sum of the squares of the lengths of the medians is equal to three-fourths the sum of the squares of the lengths of the three sides.

2. If ABC is a triangle in which M is the midpoint of side AC, then

$$|\overline{AB}|^2 + |\overline{BC}|^2 = \tfrac{1}{2}|\overline{AC}|^2 + 2|\overline{BM}|^2.$$

3. The sum of the squares of the lengths of the sides of a parallelogram is equal to the sum of the squares of the lengths of the diagonals.

4. The sum of the squares of the lengths of the four sides of any quadrilateral is equal to the sum of the squares of the lengths of the diagonals increased by four times the square of the length of the segment joining the midpoints of the diagonals.

5. The median of a trapezoid is parallel to the bases.

6. The lines joining the midpoints of the adjacent sides of a quadrilateral form a parallelogram. (Compare with the vector proof you gave in Exercise 6 of Sec. 6.4.2.)

7. In any quadrilateral the segments joining the midpoints of opposite sides intersect in a point which is the midpoint of the segment joining the midpoints of the diagonals.

8. What is the equation of the locus of points equidistant from the given points:
(a) $(-1,0)$ and $(1,0)$?
(b) $(3,0)$ and $(-1,0)$?
(c) $(3,0)$ and $(0,0)$?

9. The locus of points equidistant from two given points is always a _____. The two given points are endpoints of a segment which intersects the locus in an angle of ____°.

line
90

Let $A = (0, 0)$ and $B = (1, 2)$. The locus of points $P = (x, y)$ equidistant from A and B satisfies the equation $|\overline{PA}| = |\overline{PB}|$, which in analytic form states:

$$\sqrt{(x - \underline{\hspace{1em}})^2 + (y - \underline{\hspace{1em}})^2} = \sqrt{(\underline{\hspace{1em}} - 1)^2 + (y - \underline{\hspace{1em}})^2}.$$ | $0, 0, x, 2$

This equation implies

$$x^2 + y^2 = x^2 + y^2 + \underline{\hspace{6em}},$$ | $-2x - 4y + 5$

which reduces to $\underline{\hspace{2em}}x + \underline{\hspace{2em}}y = 5$. The slope of this line is $\underline{\hspace{2em}}$, whereas the slope of AB is $\underline{\hspace{2em}}$. | $2, 4$
 $-\frac{1}{2}, 2$

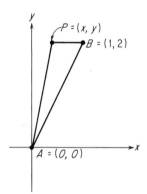

Figure 6-26

10. Let $A = (1, 0)$ and $B = (2, 3)$.

 (a) Find the equation of the perpendicular bisector of $\overline{AB}$.

 (b) What is the slope of the perpendicular bisector of $\overline{AB}$?

 (c) What is the slope of $\overline{AB}$?

11. Let $A = (1, 0)$ and $B = (-2, 4)$.

 (a) Find the equation of the perpendicular bisector of $\overline{AB}$.

 (b) What is the slope of the perpendicular bisector of $\overline{AB}$?

 (c) What is the slope of $\overline{AB}$?

Is there a simple relation between the slope of a line and the slope of the perpendicular line? If you know the relation, you can use it to check your work in Exercises 8–11, above; if not, you can use your answers to Exercises 8–11 to recall it. Although we discussed the relation between the slopes of perpendicular lines in Secs. 4.4 and 4.5 it will be instructive to do this again, perhaps a bit differently.

Suppose a line L has slope m. We might just as well take the simplest such line, the one through the origin. Its equation is $y = \underline{\hspace{2em}}x + \underline{\hspace{2em}}$. All perpendiculars | $m, 0$

to this line are parallel, so we take any two points A and B on the line L and then find the perpendicular bisector of $\overline{AB}$. Choose $A = (0, \underline{\quad})$ and $B = (1, \underline{\quad})$. Then the perpendicular bisector of $\overline{AB}$ is the locus of points $P = (x, y)$ such that

$$|\overline{AP}| = |\overline{BP}|$$

or

$$\sqrt{x^2 + \underline{\quad\quad}} = \sqrt{(x - 1)^2 + \underline{\quad\quad}}.$$

This equation implies

$$x^2 + y^2 = x^2 + y^2 + \underline{\quad\quad\quad\quad},$$

or

$$2my = \underline{\quad}x + \underline{\quad\quad}.$$

In order to determine the slope of this line we write the equation in the form

$$y = \underline{\quad}x + \underline{\quad\quad},$$

and determine that the slope is $\underline{\quad}$.

In conclusion we have proved: If a line L has slope m, then the slope of a line perpendicular to L is $\underline{\quad}$. An equivalent way of stating this is as follows:

Let L_1 and L_2 have slopes m_1 and m_2 respectively. Then $L_1 \perp L_2$ implies $m_1 m_2 = \underline{\quad}$.
But wait! This statement cannot be true! What if $m_1 = 0$? You can never multiply zero by any real number with a result of -1. Where is the trouble? Check back in the algebra to see why this case is exceptional, and discuss its geometrical significance. Also consider the converse problem: If $m_1 m_2 = -1$, can you conclude that $L_1 \perp L_2$? Explain.

Example: Suppose you wish to determine the equation of the line L' through $(1, -2)$ and perpendicular to the line L whose equation is $2x - y = 1$.

The slope of L is $\underline{\quad}$. Therefore, the slope of the perpendicular to L is $\underline{\quad}$. The desired equation can be written $y = \underline{\quad}x + b$, where b is yet to be found. We now use the fact that L' passes through $(1, -2)$ by substituting $x = \underline{\quad}$ and $y = \underline{\quad}$ in the last equation. This gives:

$$-2 = -\tfrac{1}{2}(\underline{\quad}) + b.$$

Right margin answers:

$0, m$

$y^2, (y - m)^2$

$1 + m^2 - 2x - 2my$

$-2, 1 + m^2$

$-\dfrac{1}{m}, \dfrac{1 + m^2}{2m}$

$-\dfrac{1}{m}$

$-\dfrac{1}{m}$

-1

2

$-\tfrac{1}{2}$

$-\tfrac{1}{2}$

$1, -2$

1

Therefore, $b =$ _____. The equation of L' is then

$$y = -\tfrac{1}{2}x - \tfrac{3}{2}.$$

An alternative approach, perhaps similar, is to carry out the computation in the point-slope form. Since you have determined that the slope of L' is $-\tfrac{1}{2}$, you may write the equation of L' as

$$\frac{y - \underline{\quad}}{x - \underline{\quad}} = \underline{\quad},$$

which is equivalent to the first answer you found.

$-\tfrac{3}{2}$

$-2, 1, -\dfrac{1}{2}$

6.6.2
EXERCISES

1. Find the equation of the perpendicular bisector of $\overline{AB}$ if
   (a) $A = (1, 1)$ and $B = (2, 2)$,
   (b) $A = (-1, 2)$ and $B = (3, -4)$,
   (c) $A = (1, 0)$ and $B = (-1, 0)$,
   (d) $A = (1, 0)$ and $B = (5, 0)$,
   (e) $A = (0, 5)$ and $B = (0, 1)$,
   (f) $A = (a, b)$ and $B = (c, d)$.

2. Let the equation of line L be $3x - 4y = 1$. Find the equation of the line perpendicular to L that passes through
   (a) $(0, 0)$,   (d) $(-3, 4)$,
   (b) $(1, 1)$,   (e) $(5, 0)$,
   (c) $(1, -2)$,   (f) (a, b).

3. Find the equation of the line L' through $(-1, 2)$ that is perpendicular to L, if the slope of L is
   (a) 0,   (f) 16,
   (b) 1,   (g) undefined,
   (c) -1,   (h) $1 - a \ (a \neq 1)$,
   (d) 2,   (i) $\pi/2$.
   (e) $-\tfrac{1}{2}$,

4. Let $A = (1, 1)$, $B = (3, 1)$, and $C = (4, 3)$. Find the equations of the altitudes of triangle ABC. Find the intersection of each pair of altitudes. Did you discover anything?

5. Geometric symmetry, when it exists, may be a powerful hypothesis. (See Ex. 13 of Sec. 6.57.) Now that you are doing geometry with the aid of algebra, we suggest that you be on the lookout for algebraic symmetry as well. For example, suppose you are faced with the problem of finding the equations of the medians of triangle ABC, where

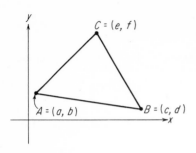

Figure 6-27

$A = (a, b)$, $B = (c, d)$, and $C = (e, f)$ (Fig. 6-27). Call M the midpoint of $\overline{AB}$. Then

$$M = \left(\frac{a + c}{2}, \frac{b + d}{2}\right).$$

We seek the equation of line CM:

$$\frac{y - f}{x - e} = \frac{f - \frac{b + d}{2}}{e - \frac{a + c}{2}},$$

provided $e \neq$ _____. If $e \neq$ _____, the equation of one median is

$$y - f = \frac{2f - b - d}{2e - a - c}(x - e).$$

The equations for the other medians can now be written down directly because, algebraically, the process of determining the equation of one median is the same for all. That is, we have algebraic symmetry! Some people prefer to say, "Just interchange the names of the vertices." At any rate, the equation for the median through B is:

$$y - d = \frac{2d - f - b}{2c - e - a}(x - c), \qquad \text{provided} \underline{\hspace{3cm}}.$$

Now write the equation for the remaining median by the principle of symmetry, and then check by deriving it from first principles. (Sometimes a choice of notation helps to display the symmetry. Try, for example, $A = (a_1, a_2)$, $B = (b_1, b_2)$, and $C = (c_1, c_2)$.)

6. Let $A = (a, b)$, $B = (c, d)$, and $C = (e, f)$.
(a) Find the equation of the altitude on side AB.
(b) Use the symmetry principle to determine the altitudes on the other sides.
(c) Check your answers against those of Exercise 4.

7. Find an equation for the line passing through the origin and perpendicular to vector $\mathbf{A}$, if
(a) $\mathbf{A} = [0, 1]$,
(b) $\mathbf{A} = [1, 0]$,
(c) $\mathbf{A} = [2, 1]$,
(d) $\mathbf{A} = [1, 2]$,
(e) $\mathbf{A} = [-3, 4]$,
(f) $\mathbf{A} = [a, b]$.

8. (a) If $\mathbf{A} = [a, b]$, then the equation of the line perpendicular to $\mathbf{A}$ and passing through the origin is _____$x +$ _____$y =$ _____.
(b) If $\mathbf{A} = [a, b]$, then the equation of the line perpendicular to $\mathbf{A}$ and passing through (x_1, y_1) is $ax +$ _____$y =$ _____. Is your answer correct if $b = 0$?
(c) Therefore, you can immediately write the coefficients of x and y of an equation perpendicular to a given vector. Is the converse true? Are there any exceptional cases?

9. (a) Write a vector [_____, _____] perpendicular to the line L whose equation is $3x + 4y = 1$.

(b) Write a unit vector [_____, _____] perpendicular to L.

(c) Write still another unit vector perpendicular to L.

10. (a) Write a vector [_____, _____] perpendicular to the line L whose equation is $ax + by + c = 0$.

(b) Write a unit vector perpendicular to the line L of part (a).

11. A vector is determined by its magnitude and direction. How can you describe the magnitude and direction of a vector if you are given the components? That is, suppose $\mathbf{V} = [a, b]$.

(a) Find a formula $\|\mathbf{V}\|$ in terms of a and b.

(b) Describe the slope of $\mathbf{V}$ in terms of a and b.

12. (a) Using the result of Exercise 11(a), the *vector equation* of a circle of radius r centered at the origin is $\|\mathbf{P}\| = r$. If $\mathbf{P}$ is the position vector of $P = (x, y)$, i.e., if $\mathbf{P} = [x, y]$, then the equation of the locus is $\|[x, y]\| = r$. Use Exercise 11(a) to rewrite this in nonvector form.

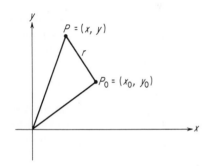

(b) Let $P_0 = (x_0, y_0)$. Then the vector equation of the circle of radius r centered at P_0 is

$$\|\mathbf{P} - \mathbf{P}_0\| = r.$$

Let $\mathbf{P} = [x, y]$, and use Exercise 11(a) to rewrite this vector equation of the circle in analytic form.

(c) Determine the vector form and the nonvector form for the equation of a sphere of radius r, centered at $P_0 = (x_0, y_0, z_0)$.

Figure 6-28

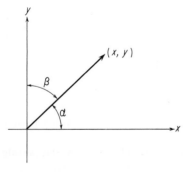

13. Every vector is parallel to some unit vector, so let's consider the unit vectors in the plane.

(a) If $[x, y]$ is a unit vector with inclination α, then

$$x = \underline{\quad\quad} \qquad (\sin \alpha/\cos \alpha/\tan \alpha)$$

and

$$y = \underline{\quad\quad}.$$

(Incidentally, when you have completed this part you will have determined a parametric representation of the unit circle centered at $(0, 0)$!)

(b) Find a parametric representation of a circle of radius r centered at $(0, 0)$.

(c) If β is the angle that $[x, y]$ makes with

Figure 6-29

the y-axis, then

$$y = \underline{\quad\quad} \qquad (\sin \beta/\cos \beta/\tan \beta).$$

(d) α and β are called the *direction angles* of the vector; and $\cos \alpha$, $\cos \beta$ are called the *direction cosines* of the vector. Since $\alpha = \pi/2 - \beta$, the direction cosines satisfy the relation

$$\cos^2 \alpha + \cos^2 \beta = \underline{\hspace{1cm}}.$$

(e) (Optional) Let α, β, and γ be the angles that a vector makes with the x, y, and z axes, respectively; i.e., let α, β, γ be the direction angles of a vector $\mathbf{V}$. Find the unit vector $(1/\|\mathbf{V}\|)\mathbf{V}$ in the form $[x, y, z]$, and prove that the direction cosines satisfy a relation analogous to the one in part (d).

14. (a) Find an equation of the line tangent to the circle $x^2 + y^2 = 4$ at $(1, \sqrt{3})$. [*Hint:* Use perpendicularity.]
(b) Find the equation of the line tangent to the circle

$$(x - 1)^2 + (y + 2)^2 = 10$$

at $(2, 1)$.
(c) Find the equation of the line tangent to the circle of part (b) at $(2, -5)$.

15. The translation $\tau: (0, 0) \rightarrow (r, \theta)$, where (r, θ) is the polar representation of a point in the plane, can be written in component form $[r, \theta]$. On a piece of polar graph paper draw
    (a) $[2, \pi/6]$,   (d) $[1, \pi/2] - [3, \pi]$,
    (b) $[2, 4\pi/3]$,   (e) $[0, 30°] + [\pi/2, 60°]$.
    (c) $[2, \pi/6] + [1, 2\pi/3]$,

16. Continuing with the use of polar component representation for vectors, find a unit vector perpendicular to
    (a) $[2, \pi/6]$,   (d) $[1, 0]$,
    (b) $[2, 4\pi/3]$,   (e) $[0, 1]$.
    (c) $[1, 60°]$,

17. (a) If $[x, y]$ is the rectangular component representation of a vector $\mathbf{A}$, find a polar component representation of $\mathbf{A}$.
(b) If $[r, \theta]$ is a polar component representation of a vector $\mathbf{B}$, find the rectangular component representation of $\mathbf{B}$.

18. (Optional) Let $[x, y, z]$ be a vector in rectangular component form.
(a) Find its length.
(b) Invent a three-dimensional coordinate system analogous to polar coordinates. Take a hint from the geography of the earth.

6.7

Abstract Vector Spaces   In Sec. 6.2, when we showed how *translation* could be defined carefully within our logical framework, we refrained from giving a definition of "vector," Our point of view was that you could continue to work quite adequately with the physicists' notion that *a vector is a quantity possessing magnitude and direction* or the geometers' notion that *a vector is a directed line segment*. We were waiting for you to gain some more experience with concrete applications of vectors before introducing the abstraction that mathematicians have developed so richly in the past century. Now that you have this experience, we are ready to proceed.

Our aim is to develop the vector concept *abstractly*, so that it can be applied to physics, geometry, economics, and—if we are lucky—to other areas as well. In order to do this we take the term *vector* as undefined, and construct several postulates that "we want" vectors to obey. That is, we broaden the range of possible applications of the vector concept by concentrating on properties and mathematical behavior rather than restricting ourselves by saying what a vector *is* in some very specific way. Thus, we shall define an *abstract vector space*.

Let $\mathscr{F}$ be a field whose elements we call *scalars*. As usual, 0 and 1 will be the additive and multiplicative identities, respectively. A *vector space* $\mathscr{V}$ over $\mathscr{F}$ is a set of elements called *vectors* satisfying the following properties:

(i) There is an operation called *vector addition*, denoted by "+," under which $\mathscr{V}$ is an abelian group; the identity of the group is denoted by "**0**."

(ii) There is an operation, called *multiplication by scalars*, which associates with each $a \in \mathscr{F}$ and $\alpha \in \mathscr{V}$ a *product* $a\alpha \in \mathscr{V}$; that is, $\mathscr{V}$ is *closed with respect to multiplication by scalars*.

(iii) $1\alpha = \alpha, \forall \alpha \in \mathscr{V}$;

(iv) $(a + b)\alpha = a\alpha + b\alpha, \forall a, b \in \mathscr{F}, \forall \alpha \in \mathscr{V}$;

(v) $a(\alpha + \beta) = a\alpha + a\beta, \forall a \in \mathscr{F}, \forall \alpha, \beta \in \mathscr{V}$;

(vi) $a(b\alpha) = (ab)\alpha, \forall a, b \in \mathscr{F}, \forall \alpha \in \mathscr{V}$.

Note that an adequate description of a vector space requires you to identify the field $\mathscr{F}$ as well as the vectors; you must also specify the operations; and in some cases it may be necessary to give an elucidation of the meaning of equality for vectors. The exercises below are designed to give you some practice.

6.7.1
EXERCISES

1. Explain why no logical ambiguity results from using "+" to denote both (vector) addition in $\mathscr{V}$ and addition in $\mathscr{F}$.

2. (a) Let $\mathscr{R}_2 = \{[x, y] \mid x, y \in \mathscr{R}\}$. Define vector addition and multiplication by scalars, so that $\mathscr{R}_2$ is a vector space. (Be sure to prove that $\mathscr{R}_2$ satisfies all the properties (i)–(vi).)

(b) Let $\mathscr{R}a_3 = \{[x, y, z] \mid x, y, z \in \mathscr{R}a\}$. Define vector addition and multiplication by scalars so that $\mathscr{R}a_3$ is a vector space.

(c) Let $\mathscr{F}$ be any field and $\mathscr{F}_n$ the set of all ordered n-tuples $\alpha = [x_1, x_2, \ldots, x_n]$ of scalars $x_i \in \mathscr{F}$. Can addition and multiplication by scalars be defined so that $\mathscr{F}_n$ is a vector space?

(d) Verify that the set of all translations of a plane form a vector space.

3. Let $\mathscr{P}_2$ be the set of all polynomial functions of the form

$$P: x \to a_0 + a_1 x, \qquad a_i \in \mathscr{R}.$$

(a) If $Q: x \to b_0 + b_1 x$, then

$$P + Q: x \to ?.$$

(b) Show that $\mathscr{P}_2$ is an abelian group with respect to function addition.
(c) What else is necessary in order to establish that $\mathscr{P}_2$ is a vector space?

4. (a) What are the zero vectors in the particular vector spaces $\mathscr{F}_n$ and $\mathscr{P}_2$?
(b) $\forall\, P \in \mathscr{P}_2,\ 0P = \underline{\hspace{1cm}}\,;\forall\, \alpha \in \mathscr{F}_n,\ 0\alpha = \underline{\hspace{1cm}}$.
(c) If your answers in (b) are particular instances of a general theorem for abstract vector spaces, then you should be able to prove that

$$\alpha + 0\alpha = \underline{\hspace{1cm}}, \qquad \forall \alpha \in \mathscr{V}.$$

(d) Using property (iii) to begin, you may write

$$\alpha + 0\alpha = (\underline{\hspace{0.8cm}})\alpha + 0\alpha = (\underline{\hspace{0.8cm}} + \underline{\hspace{0.8cm}})\alpha = (\underline{\hspace{0.8cm}})\alpha = \underline{\hspace{0.8cm}}.$$

Is this true for every $\alpha \in \mathscr{V}$?
Hence, $\forall \alpha \in \mathscr{V}$,

$$0\alpha = \underline{\hspace{1cm}}.$$

5. (a) If $-\alpha$ denotes the additive inverse of vector α,

$$\alpha + (-\alpha) = (-\alpha) + \underline{\hspace{0.8cm}} = \underline{\hspace{0.8cm}}, \qquad \forall \alpha \in \mathscr{V}.$$

(b) Taking a hint from Exercise 4, show that

$$(-1)\alpha = -\alpha.$$

6. In Exercise 4 you showed that multiplying the zero scalar with any vector yields the zero vector. Now we ask you to investigate the product of any scalar with the zero vector.
(a) Examine some particular vector spaces you know and formulate a conjecture:

$$a0 = \underline{\hspace{1cm}}, \qquad \forall\, a \in \mathscr{F},$$

(b) Try to prove your conjecture in (a) before looking at the hints in (c) and (d).
(c) $\forall\, a \in \mathscr{F},\ \forall \alpha \in \mathscr{V}$,

$$a\alpha + a0 = \underline{\hspace{0.8cm}}(\alpha + \underline{\hspace{0.8cm}}) = \underline{\hspace{0.8cm}}\alpha = \underline{\hspace{0.8cm}} + 0.$$

Now, using the group properties of $\mathscr{V}$, solve for $a0$.
(d) Another approach is to let b be any nonzero element in $\mathscr{F}$ and $\alpha \in \mathscr{V}$. Then

$$\alpha + b0 = \underline{\hspace{0.8cm}}\alpha + b0$$
$$= \underline{\hspace{0.8cm}}b^{-1}\alpha + b0$$
$$= \underline{\hspace{0.8cm}}(\underline{\hspace{0.8cm}} + 0).$$

Finish the proof of the fact that $b0 = 0$. (Note that by Exercise 4 you already have $00 = 0$. Thus $a0 = 0$, $\forall\, a \in \mathscr{F}$.)

7. (a) Prove the converse of your result in Exercise 6, namely

$$a\alpha = \mathbf{0} \Rightarrow (a = 0 \lor \alpha = \mathbf{0}).$$

[*Hint:* What is the consequence of $(a\alpha = \mathbf{0} \land a \neq 0)$?]

(b) Let $a \in \mathscr{F}, \alpha \in \mathscr{V}, \beta \in \mathscr{V}$. Investigate the consequence of

$$a\alpha = a\beta \land a \neq 0.$$

(c) Let $a, b \in \mathscr{F}$ and $\alpha \in \mathscr{V}$. Investigate the consequence of

$$a\alpha = b\alpha \land \alpha \neq \mathbf{0}.$$

8. Geometric Vectors. In order to build the set of directed segments into a group, we must first state the definition of equality for directed segments.

(a) Discuss the relationship between the definition of equality of directed segments and the definition of vector addition.

(b) Verify that the set of directed segments in a plane, relative to the usual definitions of equality, addition, and multiplication by scalars, forms a vector space over $\mathscr{R}$.

(c) What is the geometric significance of the commutative property

$$\alpha + \beta = \beta + \alpha$$

if α, β are directed segments?

9. Fields as Vector Spaces

(a) Consider the set $\mathscr{C}$ of complex numbers. Verify that $\mathscr{C}$ is a vector space over $\mathscr{R}$.

(b) Consider the set $\{a + b\sqrt{2} \,|\, a, b \in \mathscr{R}a\}$. Test to see whether this field is a vector space.

(c) Consider the set $\{a + \sqrt{2} \,|\, a \in \mathscr{R}\}$. What property or properties of a vector space are not satisfied? Is this set a field? (Booby.)

(d) Is the set $\{a + b\sqrt{2} + c\sqrt[3]{2} \,|\, a, b, c \in \mathscr{R}a\}$ a vector space? Is it a field?

10. Verify that the *inventory vectors* (Exercise 12 of Sec. 6.3.1) are "really" vectors. What is the meaning of the zero vector as an inventory vector? What does the inventory vector $[-3, 2]$ mean?

11. (a) Consider the set of all $[x, y]$ such that

$$x + y = 0,$$
$$x + 2y = 0.$$

Test to see whether this set is a vector space.

(b) Consider the set of all $[x, y]$ such that

$$x + y = 0,$$
$$x + 2y = 1.$$

Test to see whether this set is a vector space.

(c) Consider the set of all $[x, y, z]$ such that

$$x - y + 2z = 0,$$
$$-x + y + z = 0,$$
$$x - y + 5z = 0.$$

Does this set form a vector space? How many elements does the set have?

12. (a) Let $\mathscr{S}$ be any set and $\mathscr{V}$ the set of all functions on $\mathscr{S}$ to $\mathscr{R}$. Show that $\mathscr{V}$ is a vector space over $\mathscr{R}$, in which addition and multiplication by scalars have the usual meanings for functions.

(b) Let $\mathscr{W}$ be the set of all functions on $\mathscr{S}$ to $\mathscr{R}a$. Is $\mathscr{W}$ also a vector space?

(c) Generalize (a) and (b).

6.8

Work. The Dot Product In physics the word *work* is given precise mathematical meaning in contrast to its everyday usage. The layman says "I work" or "work is done." The word "work" is generally used to denote activity that requires muscular or mental effort; but sometimes even great muscular effort, such as playing a game of tennis, is said to be "play, not work." The scientist, however, says that physical work is done only if:

(i) a force acts on a body, and

(ii) the body experiences a displacement.

Note that the two requirements—force and displacement—are vector quantities.

In the precise words of physicists:

> The *work* done by a constant force acting on a body while the body is displaced along a straight line is a scalar quantity defined as the product of the magnitude of the displacement by the component of the force in the direction of the displacement.†

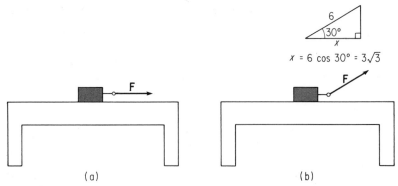

Figure 6-30

† George Shortley and Dudley Williams, *Elements of Physics* (4th ed.; Englewood Cliffs, N.J.: Prentice-Hall, Inc., 1965), p. 104.

Therefore, if a horizontal force **F** of magnitude 6 lb displaces a block 5 ft along a tabletop [see Fig. 6-30(a)], the work done is 30 ft-lb. However, if **F** acts at an inclination of 30° to the horizontal, as in Fig. 6-30(b), then the work done is $3\sqrt{3} \cdot 5 = 15\sqrt{3}$ ft-lb.

Although the notion of component may be intuitively clear, the general concept has not been introduced; let us do so now for completeness. Let the (geometric) vector **V** and the nonzero (geometric) vector **U** have a common origin O. The *component of* **V** *in the direction of* **U** *is defined as*

$$\text{comp}_U V = \|V\| \cos \theta,$$

where θ is the angle made by **V** and **U** at O. Therefore, if $\|V\| \neq 0$, the component of **V** in the direction of **U** is

   (i) positive if θ is acute;
   (ii) negative if θ is obtuse;
   (iii) zero if $\theta = 90°$;
   (iv) $\|V\|$ if $V \parallel U$.

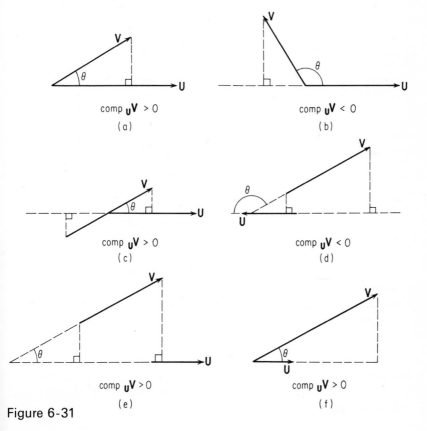

Figure 6-31

Note that the requirement that the two vectors have a common origin is superfluous. You need only drop perpendiculars from the origin and endpoint of **V** to the "line of action" of **U**; the distance between the feet of the perpendiculars is the magnitude of comp$_U$**V** (see Fig. 6-31). What tells you whether the component is positive or negative?

Exercise: Check the definition of component given in Sec. 6.2, and show that it is a special case of the definition given in the preceding paragraph.

With the new definition of component, we can give a formula for the work W done by force vector **F** effecting the displacement **S**:

$$W = \|\mathbf{F}\| \, \|\mathbf{S}\| \cos \theta,$$

where θ is the angle formed by **F** and **S**.

The definition of work involves the "multiplication" of two vectors (**F** and **S**) to yield a scalar W. This type of product is therefore called a *scalar product*. We give a formal definition:

The scalar product *of* **A** *and* **B** *is denoted by* **A** · **B**, *and is defined by*

(1) $$\mathbf{A} \cdot \mathbf{B} = \|\mathbf{A}\| \, \|\mathbf{B}\| \cos \theta,$$

where θ is the angle formed by **A** *and* **B** *when the two vectors are considered to emanate from the same point.*

The *scalar product* is also called the *dot product*, as a consequence of the standard notation (dot) in (1).

6.8.1
EXERCISES

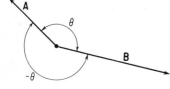

Figure 6-32

1. (a) Show that **A** · **B** is independent of "which way the angle is measured." That is, the dot product is the same whether you take θ or $-\theta$ as the angle between **A** and **B**.
   (b) If **A** = **0**, then **A** · **B** = _____, ∀**B**.
   (c) What conclusion would you draw from the fact that **A** · **B** = 0? (Be careful!)

2. By exerting a force of 12 lb on a rope attached to a sled, a man pulls the sled across the ice on the surface of a pond. If the rope makes an angle of 45° with the direction of motion, how much work does the man do in moving the sled a distance of 90 ft?†

3. (a) Explain why work can be negative. Give two examples.
   (b) Suppose you are pushing a lawn mower and the force **F** you exert is along the handle (see Fig. 6-33). Construct a diagram showing the geometric representation

† From Shortley and Williams, *Elements of Physics.*

of the horizontal component F_h and the vertical component F_v. How would you push the mower to minimize the "wasted" component F_v and maximize the "useful" component F_h?

(c) Continuing part (b), use the dot product to show that no work is done if **F** is vertical, even if you work all afternoon.

Figure 6-33

4. Prove that the dot product, defined by (1), obeys the commutative law.

5. (a) Express the length of **A** in terms of the dot product **A · A**.

(b) Use part (a) to express comp_B **A** completely in terms of dot products (assuming **B** ≠ **0**).

(c) Express comp_A **B** completely in terms of dot products.

(d) If neither **A** nor **B** is the zero vector, find the condition(s) under which

$$\text{comp}_B \mathbf{A} = \text{comp}_A \mathbf{B}.$$

6. Prove

(2) $$\mathbf{A} \cdot \mathbf{B} = (\text{comp}_B \mathbf{A})\|\mathbf{B}\| = (\text{comp}_A \mathbf{B})\|\mathbf{A}\|.$$

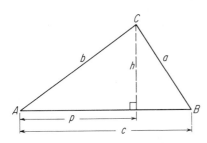

7. Refer to Fig. 6-34. The length p is usually referred to as the perpendicular projection (or the orthogonal projection) of side AC on side AB.

(a) If h is the length of the altitude on AB, then

$$h^2 = b^2 - \underline{\quad} = a^2 - (\underline{\quad} - \underline{\quad})^2.$$

(b) Solve for a^2 in terms of b, c, and p.

(c) Notice that p depends only on b and the angle A. In fact, $p = bF(A)$, where F is some function. Do you know what $F(A)$ is equal to?

Figure 6-34

(d) Express p completely in terms of dot products, using only the vectors $\overrightarrow{AB}$ and $\overrightarrow{AC}$.

8. Area. If K represents the area of the triangle in Fig. 6-34, then $K^2 = \frac{1}{4}h^2c^2$.

(a) Find K^2 in terms of the lengths of the sides.

(b) Establish Heron's formula:

$$K = \sqrt{s(s - a)(s - b)(s - c)},$$

where $s = \frac{1}{2}(a + b + c)$. (If you look up Heron, sometimes called *Hero*, you will probably be amazed at the date of discovery of this elegant formula. Incidentally, some historians credit Archimedes with the first discovery of Heron's formula.)†

---

† See B. L. Van der Waerden, *Science Awakening* (Fair Lawn, N.J.: Oxford University Press, Inc., 1961), p. 228.

(c) Explain why the existence of a formula for the area, in terms of the sides alone, could have been predicted from high school geometry.

The geometric idea behind the notion of component is that of a projection—more accurately, a perpendicular projection—of one vector onto another to obtain a scalar. Therefore, we can—if we wish—turn the picture around and use facts from geometry to explore the algebraic properties of components and dot products. For example, a simple but very useful result that is immediate from geometry is

(3) $\text{comp}_C (A + B) = \text{comp}_C A + \text{comp}_C B.$

Exercise: Refer to Fig. 6-35 and give a complete argument for (3).

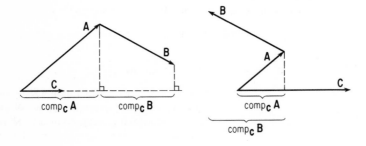

Figure 6-35

Using (2) and (3) we can investigate to see whether the dot product is distributive:

$(A + B) \cdot C = \text{comp}_C (\underline{\hspace{2cm}}) \|C\|$ (why?) $A + B$

$= (\text{comp}_C A + \underline{\hspace{1.5cm}}) \|C\|$ (why?) $\text{comp}_C B$

$= \text{comp}_C A \|C\| + \underline{\hspace{1.5cm}} \|C\|$ $\text{comp}_C B$

$= A \cdot C + \underline{\hspace{1cm}} \cdot C.$ B

Therefore, we have the following:

Theorem: $(A + B) \cdot C = A \cdot C + B \cdot C.$

Other properties and further applications of dot products appear in the following set of exercises.

6.8.2
EXERCISES

1. (a) Prove the left-distributive law:

$$\mathbf{A} \cdot (\mathbf{B} + \mathbf{C}) = \mathbf{A} \cdot \mathbf{B} + \mathbf{A} \cdot \mathbf{C}.$$

(b) Prove the corollary:

$$(\mathbf{A} + \mathbf{B}) \cdot (\mathbf{C} + \mathbf{D}) = \mathbf{A} \cdot \mathbf{C} + \mathbf{A} \cdot \mathbf{D} + \mathbf{B} \cdot \mathbf{C} + \mathbf{B} \cdot \mathbf{D}.$$

(c) Prove that if n is any scalar,

$$(n\mathbf{A}) \cdot \mathbf{B} = \mathbf{A} \cdot (n\mathbf{B}) = n(\mathbf{A} \cdot \mathbf{B}),$$

for every pair of vectors $\mathbf{A}$, $\mathbf{B}$.

2. Recall that the zero vector may be assigned any direction at all. With this understanding, you should be able to prove the following easily remembered theorem.

$$\mathbf{A} \cdot \mathbf{B} = 0 \Leftrightarrow \mathbf{A} \perp \mathbf{B}.$$

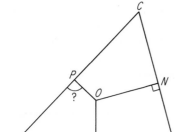

Figure 6-36

3. We will assist you in obtaining a vector proof that the perpendicular bisectors of the sides of a triangle meet in a point.

Let ABC be the given triangle, and suppose the perpendicular bisectors of AB and BC meet at O. Let M, N, and P be the midpoints of the sides, as shown in Fig. 6-36. If we can show that $OP \perp AC$, we will have proved what is desired. Explain why!

There will be less to write if we take advantage of the notation introduced in Sec. 6.5 for dealing with position vectors. This means, for example, that

$$\overrightarrow{OM} = \mathbf{M}, \quad \overrightarrow{ON} = \underline{\quad} \quad \text{and} \quad \overrightarrow{AB} = \underline{\quad} - \underline{\quad}. \qquad \text{N, B, A}$$

What we hope to show is that

$$(*) \qquad \mathbf{P} \cdot (\underline{\quad} - \mathbf{A}) = \underline{\quad}. \qquad \text{C, 0}$$

According to the hypothesis,

$$\mathbf{M} \cdot (\mathbf{B} - \mathbf{A}) = \underline{\quad}. \qquad 0$$

But since $\mathbf{M}$ is the midpoint of side AB,

$$\mathbf{M} = \underline{\quad}\mathbf{A} + \underline{\quad}\mathbf{B}. \qquad \tfrac{1}{2}, \tfrac{1}{2}$$

Therefore,

$$(\underline{\quad}\mathbf{A} + \underline{\quad}\mathbf{B}) \cdot (\mathbf{B} - \mathbf{A}) = 0. \qquad \tfrac{1}{2}, \tfrac{1}{2},$$

Expanding, in accordance with your result in Exercise 1(b),

$$\underline{\quad}\mathbf{B} \cdot \mathbf{B} - \underline{\quad}\mathbf{A} \cdot \mathbf{A} = 0. \qquad \tfrac{1}{2}, \tfrac{1}{2}$$

Hence, $\mathbf{A} \cdot \mathbf{A} = \mathbf{B} \cdot \mathbf{B}$, which implies $\|\mathbf{A}\| = \|\mathbf{B}\|$. Similarly, you can show that $\mathbf{C} \cdot \mathbf{C} = \mathbf{B} \cdot \mathbf{B}$.

This is all very nice, but what are we after? Looking at (∗) tells us that we need to compute the dot product $\mathbf{P} \cdot (\mathbf{C} - \mathbf{A})$:

$$\mathbf{P} \cdot (\mathbf{C} - \mathbf{A}) = (\tfrac{1}{2}\underline{\quad} + \tfrac{1}{2}\underline{\quad}) \cdot (\mathbf{C} - \mathbf{A}) \qquad\qquad \mathbf{A, C}$$

$$= \tfrac{1}{2}\mathbf{C} \cdot \underline{\quad} - \tfrac{1}{2}\mathbf{A} \cdot \underline{\quad}. \qquad\qquad \mathbf{C, A}$$

One more step and we will have established (∗).

4. Use dot products to give a vector proof that an angle inscribed in a semicircle is a right angle. [*Hint:* Let segment AB be a diameter, O the center, and P any point on the circle. What is the relationship between $\overrightarrow{OA}$ and $\overrightarrow{OB}$? Evaluate $\overrightarrow{AP} \cdot \overrightarrow{BP}$.]

5. Prove by vector methods:

(a) The sum of the squares of the lengths of the diagonals of a parallelogram is equal to the sum of the squares of the lengths of the sides.

(b) The sum of the squares of the lengths of the sides of any quadrilateral exceeds the sum of the squares of the lengths of the diagonals by four times the square of the length of the segment joining the midpoints of the diagonals.

(c) If two circles intersect, the line joining their centers is perpendicular to the line joining their points of intersection.

6. Taking a hint from Exercise 3 of this set, prove that the altitudes of a triangle meet in a point.

7. (a) Let $\mathbf{F}$ be the sum of n forces $\mathbf{F}_1, \mathbf{F}_2, \ldots, \mathbf{F}_n$, all acting at point O. Then the work W done by $\mathbf{F}$ producing a displacement $\mathbf{S}$ is

$$W = \mathbf{F}_1 \cdot \mathbf{S} + \mathbf{F}_2 \cdot \mathbf{S} + \cdots + \mathbf{F}_n \cdot \mathbf{S}.$$

Justify this statement.

(b) Also, if $\mathbf{F}$ results in n consecutive displacements $\mathbf{S}_1, \mathbf{S}_2, \ldots, \mathbf{S}_n$, then the work done is

$$W = \mathbf{F} \cdot \mathbf{S}_1 + \mathbf{F} \cdot \mathbf{S}_2 + \cdots + \mathbf{F} \cdot \mathbf{S}_n.$$

Why?

The coordinate representations in Exercises 8–10 are assumed to be relative to a rectangular coordinate system.

8. (a) $[1, 0] \cdot [0, 1] = ?, [2, 0] \cdot [0, -3] = ?$.

(b) $[1, 0] \cdot [1, 0] = ?, [1, 1] \cdot [1, 1] = ?, [3, -4] \cdot [3, -4] = ?$.

(c) $[3, -4] \cdot [1, 0] = (\underline{\quad}[1, 0] + \underline{\quad}[0, 1]) \cdot [1, 0] = ?$.

(d) $[3, -4] \cdot [2, 0] = \underline{\quad}([3, -4] \cdot [1, 0]) = ?$.

(e) $[a, b] \cdot [1, 0] = (\underline{\quad}[1, 0] + \underline{\quad}[0, 1]) \cdot [1, 0] = ?$.

9. In order to simplify the computation we shall write the basic vectors $\mathbf{i} = [1, 0]$ and $\mathbf{j} = [0, 1]$.

(a) $[3, -4] = \underline{\quad}\mathbf{i} + \underline{\quad}\mathbf{j}, [a_1, a_2] = \underline{\quad}\mathbf{i} + \underline{\quad}\mathbf{j}$.

(b) $\mathbf{i} \cdot \mathbf{i} = ?, \mathbf{j} \cdot \mathbf{j} = ?, \mathbf{i} \cdot \mathbf{j} = ?, \mathbf{j} \cdot \mathbf{i} = ?$.

(c) $[a_1, a_2] \cdot [b_1, b_2] = (\underline{\hspace{1cm}} \mathbf{i} + \underline{\hspace{1cm}} \mathbf{j}) \cdot (\underline{\hspace{1cm}} \mathbf{i} + \underline{\hspace{1cm}} \mathbf{j})$

$= \underline{\hspace{1cm}} \mathbf{i} \cdot \mathbf{i} + \underline{\hspace{1cm}} \mathbf{i} \cdot \mathbf{j} + \underline{\hspace{1cm}} \mathbf{j} \cdot \mathbf{i} + \underline{\hspace{1cm}} \mathbf{j} \cdot \mathbf{j} = \underline{\hspace{1cm}} + \underline{\hspace{1cm}}.$

(d) If $\mathbf{F} = 3\mathbf{i} + 4\mathbf{j}$ represents a force, find the magnitude of the force, the component of $\mathbf{F}$ in the direction of the x-axis, and the component of $\mathbf{F}$ in the direction of the y-axis.

(e) Show that the component of $\mathbf{F}$ in the direction of $\mathbf{A} = -\mathbf{i} + 5\mathbf{j}$ is $17/\sqrt{26}$.

10. (a) If $\mathbf{U}$ is a unit vector, then $\text{comp}_{\mathbf{U}} \, \mathbf{F} = \mathbf{F} \cdot (\underline{\hspace{1cm}}).$

(b) If $\mathbf{A}$ is any nonzero vector,

$$\left\| \frac{\mathbf{A}}{\mathbf{A} \cdot \mathbf{A}} \right\| = \,?.$$

(c) If $\mathbf{A}$ is any nonzero vector

$$\text{comp}_{\mathbf{A}} \, \mathbf{F} = \mathbf{F} \cdot (\underline{\hspace{1cm}}).$$

6.9

Further Applications of the Dot Product Since the definition of the dot product was geometric, we found that we could make use of it to prove geometric results. In fact, length and angle can be expressed in terms of dot products:

(1) $$\|\mathbf{A}\| = \sqrt{\mathbf{A} \cdot \mathbf{A}},$$

(2) $$\cos \theta = \frac{\mathbf{A} \cdot \mathbf{B}}{\sqrt{\mathbf{A} \cdot \mathbf{A}} \sqrt{\mathbf{B} \cdot \mathbf{B}}},$$

where θ is the angle formed by the two nonzero vectors $\mathbf{A}$ and $\mathbf{B}$.

In Sec. 6.8.2 we found that if the vectors are expressed as ordered pairs relative to a rectangular coordinate system, so that

$$\mathbf{A} = a_1 \mathbf{i} + a_2 \mathbf{j}, \qquad \text{i.e., } \mathbf{A} = [a_1, a_2],$$
$$\mathbf{B} = b_1 \mathbf{i} + b_2 \mathbf{j}, \qquad \text{i.e., } \mathbf{B} = [b_1, b_2],$$

then

(3) $$\mathbf{A} \cdot \mathbf{B} = a_1 b_1 + a_2 b_2.$$

This formula, in particular, puts us in a good position to exploit the dot product in applications to analytic geometry.

6.9.1
EXERCISES

1. Let $\mathbf{A} = 2\mathbf{i} - 3\mathbf{j}$ and $\mathbf{B} = -2\mathbf{i} + \mathbf{j}$.
(a) Find $\mathbf{A} \cdot \mathbf{B}$.
(b) Find $\text{comp } \mathbf{A}_{\mathbf{B}}$ and $\text{comp } \mathbf{B}_{\mathbf{A}}$.

(c) Find a unit vector parallel to **A** and with the same orientation as **A**.

(d) Find the work done by force vector **A** in moving a particle from the origin to $(1, 2)$.

2. Find a vector **Z** perpendicular to $\mathbf{V} = 2\mathbf{i} - 3\mathbf{j}$, such that $\|\mathbf{Z}\| = 4\|\mathbf{V}\|$. How many such vectors are there?

3. (a) If $\mathbf{A} = [a_1, a_2]$ and $\mathbf{B} = [b_1, b_2]$ are nonzero vectors, find a formula for the cosine of the angle made by **A** and **B** in terms of their coordinates.

(b) If θ is the angle made by **A** and **B** in Exercise 1, find $\cos\theta$. Is θ acute?

4. (a) Let $\mathbf{A} = \mathbf{i} + \mathbf{j}$. Find an equation for the line through the origin and perpendicular to **A**. Write it in the form $ax + by = c$, and compute b/a.

(b) Let $\mathbf{B} = \mathbf{i} + 2\mathbf{j}$. Find an equation for the line through the origin perpendicular to **B**. Write it in the form $ax + by = c$, and compute b/a.

(c) Let $\mathbf{C} = x_1\mathbf{i} + y_1\mathbf{j} \neq \mathbf{0}$. Find an equation for the line through the origin and perpendicular to **C**. Write it in the form $ax + by = c$ and compute b/a.

(d) Let $\mathbf{D} = 3\mathbf{i} - 4\mathbf{j}$. Find an equation of the line perpendicular to **D** and through $(1, -1)$.

5. Let L be a line whose equation is $ax + by = 0$, with $b \neq 0$.

(a) Find the coordinates of the y-intercept of L.

(b) Find y_1 so that $(1, y_1)$ is on L.

(c) The vector joining the points found in (a) and (b) is

$$\mathbf{V} = \underline{\qquad}\mathbf{i} + \underline{\qquad}\mathbf{j}.$$

(d) Compute $\mathbf{A} \cdot \mathbf{V}$, where $\mathbf{A} = a\mathbf{i} + b\mathbf{j}$.

6. (a) Find a vector $\mathbf{N}_1$ perpendicular to the line L_1 whose equation is $2x - 3y = 12$.

(b) Find a vector $\mathbf{N}_2$ perpendicular to the line L_2 whose equation is $2x - 5y = 12$.

(c) If α is the acute angle formed by L_1 and L_2 and β is the angle formed by $\mathbf{N}_1$ and $\mathbf{N}_2$, what is the relation between α and β. (Careful, there may be a booby trap.)

(d) Find $\cos\alpha$.

7. If $P = (x, y)$ is the general point of line L which is perpendicular to $\mathbf{N} = a\mathbf{i} + b\mathbf{j} \neq \mathbf{0}$, and if $P_0 = (x_0, y_0)$ is a given point of L, we know that

$$\overrightarrow{P_0P} \cdot \mathbf{N} = \underline{\qquad}.$$

Therefore, rewriting this in coordinate form,

$$[(x - \underline{\qquad})\mathbf{i} + (y - \underline{\qquad})\mathbf{j}] \cdot (a\mathbf{i} + b\mathbf{j}) = \underline{\qquad}.$$

Hence

$$a(x - \underline{\qquad}) + b(y - \underline{\qquad}) = \underline{\qquad}$$

is the equation of line L.

8. Let $\mathbf{U} = (\cos\alpha)\mathbf{i} + (\cos\beta)\mathbf{j}$.

(a) Give geometric interpretations for α and β. [*Hint*: Use components.]

(b) Find $\|\mathbf{U}\|$.

(c) Find the equation of the line tangent to the unit circle at $(\frac{1}{2}, \sqrt{3}/2)$.

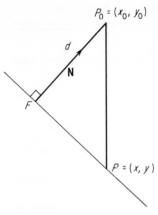

$P_0 = (x_0, y_0)$

d

N

F

$P = (x, y)$

Figure 6-37

9. Distance From a Point to a Line. Let the equation of a line be given by

$$ax + by + c = 0.$$

(a) Find a nonzero vector **N** perpendicular to L.

(b) Let P_0 be any given point and P some given point on L. Then, referring to Fig. 6-37, the distance d from P_0 to L is given by

$$d = |\text{comp}\underline{}|.$$

(c) $\overrightarrow{PP_0} = (\underline{})\mathbf{i} + (\underline{})\mathbf{j}$ and

$$\text{comp}_{\mathbf{N}}\overrightarrow{PP_0} = [(\underline{}\mathbf{i} + \underline{}\mathbf{j}) \cdot (a\mathbf{i} + b\mathbf{j})]\frac{1}{\sqrt{a^2 + b^2}}$$

$$= \frac{\underline{}x_0 + \underline{}y_0 - ax - by}{\sqrt{a^2 + b^2}}.$$

Since (x, y) is on L, we know that $-ax - by = \underline{}$. Hence,

$$\text{comp } PP_0{}_{\mathbf{N}} = \frac{\underline{}x_0 + \underline{}y_0 + \underline{}}{\sqrt{a^2 + b^2}}$$

and

$$d = \frac{|\underline{}x_0 + \underline{}y_0 + \underline{}|}{\sqrt{a^2 + b^2}}.$$

(d) It is a dangerous and wasteful policy to memorize formulas that can easily be derived. The formula obtained in (c) is one such example. You would do well to think through afresh each problem that requires finding the distance from a given point to a given line. We might suggest one simplification which is shown in the following computation.

Problem: To find the distance from $P_0 = (1, 3)$ to the line $L: y = \frac{1}{2}x - 1$. The equation for L should be written

$$\underline{}x + \underline{}y + \underline{} = 0.$$

Then a vector perpendicular to L is

$$\mathbf{N} = \underline{}\mathbf{i} + \underline{}\mathbf{j}.$$

A unit vector perpendicular to L is

$$\mathbf{U} = \frac{1}{\sqrt{5}}\mathbf{i} + \underline{}\mathbf{j}.$$

Then

$$d = |\text{comp}_{\mathbf{U}} \overrightarrow{P_0P_1}|,$$

where P_1 is any point of L.

A simple choice for P_1 is $(0, \underline{\hspace{1cm}})$. Hence

$$d = |\overrightarrow{P_0 P_1} \cdot \mathbf{U}|.$$

Justify this statement and complete the computation for d.

(e) Solve the problem of part (d) using $P_1 = (2, 0)$.

(f) Show that you can solve the problem of (d) using $P_1 = (x_1, y_1)$. [*Hint:* $x_1 - 2y_1 = 2$.]

10. Find the distance from $(1, 2)$ to $x - 2y = 5$.

(b) Find the distance from $(1, -2)$ to $x - 2y = 5$.

(c) Find the distance from $(1, -2)$ to $-x + 2y + 5 = 0$.

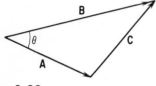

11. (a) Let ABC be an isosceles triangle with $\overline{AB} = \overline{AC}$. Prove by vectors that the median from A is perpendicular to BC.

(b) Referring to Fig. 6-38, write $\mathbf{C}$ in terms of $\mathbf{A}$ and $\mathbf{B}$. Call $\|\mathbf{A}\| = a$, $\|\mathbf{B}\| = b$, and $\|\mathbf{C}\| = c$. Express c^2 in terms of a, b, and θ. Do you recognize your result?

Figure 6-38

12. The definition of dot product given in Sec. 6.8 was *independent of the coordinate system*. Thus, it has intrinsic geometric significance. In fact, if we know the values of the dot product of all vectors, we could use the dot product to *define* length and angle; for

$$\|\mathbf{A}\| = \sqrt{\mathbf{A} \cdot \mathbf{A}}$$

and $\cos \theta = ?$ (in terms of dot product), where θ is the angle.

Taking a hint from this discussion, we see that we can introduce geometric concepts into an abstract vector space if we can only find a function that behaves like the dot product. We shall pursue this further.

(a) The dot product is a function whose domain is ordered pairs of vectors. Its range is \underline{\hspace{1cm}}. Among its fundamental properties are:

$$\mathbf{A} \cdot \mathbf{B} = \mathbf{B} \cdot \underline{\hspace{1cm}},$$

$$\mathbf{A} \cdot (\mathbf{B} + \mathbf{C}) = \underline{\hspace{1cm}} + \underline{\hspace{1cm}},$$

$$\mathbf{A} \cdot \mathbf{A} \geq 0,$$

$$\mathbf{A} \cdot \mathbf{A} = 0 \Leftrightarrow \mathbf{A} = \underline{\hspace{1cm}},$$

$$(c\mathbf{A} \cdot \mathbf{B}) = c(\underline{\hspace{1cm}} \cdot \underline{\hspace{1cm}}).$$

(b) Any function on ordered pairs of vectors that satisfies the conditions of part (a) is called a *real inner product*. By means of a real inner product we can define length and angle. Give the suitable definitions.

(c) Define a real inner product for the vector space $\mathscr{P}_3$ of polynomial functions

$$a_0 + a_1 I + a_2 I^2, \qquad a_i \in \mathscr{R}.$$

(d) Show that if distance (length) is defined by the inner product, then it satisfies the two properties ascribed to distance in Exercise 1 of Sec. 2.5.1. [Note that you may use only the properties of inner product given in (a).]

(e) Referring to part (c), find a polynomial perpendicular to $3 - 2I + I^2$.

13. (a) Using the fact that $|\cos \theta| \leq 1$, prove the Cauchy inequality

$$(x_1 y_1 + x_2 y_2)^2 \leq (x_1^2 + x_2^2)(y_1^2 + y_2^2)$$

for any real numbers x_1, x_2, y_1, and y_2.

(b) Under what conditions does equality hold in the Cauchy inequality?

14. Prove that $\forall\, a, b, x \in \mathscr{R}$.

$$|a \sin x + b \cos x| \leq \sqrt{a^2 + b^2}.$$

15. According to Exercise 13, the Cauchy inequality may be expressed in terms of dot products:

$$(\mathbf{X} \cdot \mathbf{Y})^2 \leq (\mathbf{X} \cdot \mathbf{X})(\mathbf{Y} \cdot \mathbf{Y}).$$

Moreover, if the real inner product $(\mathbf{A}, \mathbf{B})$, is defined for every pair of vectors $\mathbf{A}$, $\mathbf{B}$ of an abstract vector space, then one possible generalization of the Cauchy inequality is

(4) $$(\mathbf{A}, \mathbf{B})^2 \leq (\mathbf{A}, \mathbf{A})(\mathbf{B}, \mathbf{B}).$$

This inequality, *which is expressed entirely in terms of inner products*, can indeed be proven by using only the properties of inner products. We shall assist you in constructing such a proof in Sec. 7.10.

Meanwhile, assuming (4), prove that if distance (length) is defined in an abstract vector space, as done in Exercise 12(b), then distance satisfies the triangle inequality.

Chapter Seven Numerical Solution of Equations

Section 7.1 discusses the importance of systems of linear equations in many scientific problems and reviews the methods of solution familiar to the reader from earlier courses. In Sec. 7.2, the elements of logic learned in Chapter 3 are used to analyze linear systems and their solutions. Extensions to systems of more than two equations are treated in Sec. 7.3. Section 7.4 discusses methods of finding approximate solutions when the initial data (the coefficients) are given as approximations. Linear systems are interpreted geometrically, as transformations, in Sec. 7.5, and Sec. 7.6 reviews the transformation viewpoint in terms of vectors. The work in Secs. 7.5 and 7.6 leads to the use of matrices as interpretations of linear transformations and as a shorthand to express the algebra of linear equations. Section 7.8 gives several iteration methods for finding solutions of equations. Methods of iteration (and error estimates) are applied to quadratic and other equations in Secs. 7.9 through 7.11.

7.1

Exact Solution of Two-by-Two Equations   We begin with the problem of calculating the currents in an electrical circuit. Let us summarize briefly some of the concepts and terms that arise in the study of electrical circuits:

Current: The flow of electrons which, for example, has the effect of heating a wire, lighting a bulb, or running a fan. Current is measured in *amperes* (abbreviated *amp*) after the French scientist, André M. Ampère (1775–1836).

Voltage source: A source of energy such as a battery or generator which has the effect of producing a flow of current. Voltage is measured in *volts*, after the pioneering Italian scientist, Count Alessandro Volta (1745–1827).

Resistance: A part in an electric circuit that resists the flow of current, thereby using energy. An obvious example is an electric light bulb. Resistance is measured in *ohms*, after the German physicist Georg S. Ohm (1787–1854).

Quantity	Mathematical symbol	Unit
Current	I	ampere
Voltage	E or V	volt
Resistance	R	ohm

Voltage, in a sense, is the "driving pressure" of current and is sometimes referred to as *electromotive force* or *emf*. (The name "electromotive force" is a poor one, since it suggests an erroneous mechanical description of voltage.) As energy is used by a resistance, there is a decrease in the electromotive force. This decrease is called the *voltage drop* across the resistance. If E is the voltage drop across a resistance of R ohms and a current of I amperes passes through the resistance, then

$$E = RI$$

by Ohm's law.

Another fundamental law we will need is *Kirchoff's law: The algebraic sum of all the voltage drops around any loop (or mesh) is zero*. Stated in another way, the voltage supplied by the voltage source (e.g., battery) is equal to the sum of the voltage drops in the loop. [Gustav Kirchoff (1824–1887) formulated two fundamental laws for electrical networks. The above is one—you should look up the other in an elementary physics book.]

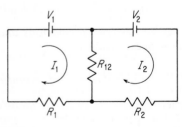

Suppose we are faced with the problem of calculating currents in a circuit, given the voltages and resistances. In Fig. 7-1 we have indicated voltage sources by the symbol ‖, resistances by ⋀⋀⋀⋀⋀, with straight line segments indicating wire conductors of current that have negligible resistance. The magnitudes of voltages, currents, and resistances are denoted by

Figure 7-1

the usual letters. We can refer to the left loop as mesh 1 and the right loop as mesh 2. Note that R_{12} is the resistance common to meshes 1 and 2. The arrow indicates the direction of flow of the current. If either I_1 or I_2 turns out to be negative, then the current in that mesh goes in the direction opposite to the one indicated in the diagram.

The voltage drop across resistance R_1 is, by Ohm's law, equal to $R_1 I_1$. If we consider mesh 1 according to the directions specified, the current through R_{12} is $I_1 - I_2$. (Note that the total current through R_{12} is $I_1 - I_2$, or $I_2 - I_1$, according to which direction we are considering.) Therefore, the voltage drop across resistance R_{12} is _____. Applying Kirchoff's law to mesh 1, we have

$$R_{12}(I_1 - I_2) + R_1 I_1 = V_1.$$

Kirchoff's law applied to mesh 2 yields

$$\underline{\hspace{4cm}} = V_2.$$

(Note that the current through R_{12} in this mesh is $I_2 - I_1$.) We have two equations with two unknowns I_1 and I_2. We can put these into a standard form

$$(R_1 + R_{12})I_1 - R_{12}I_2 = V_1,$$

$$\underline{\hspace{1.5cm}}I_1 + (\underline{\hspace{1.5cm}})I_2 = V_2.$$

These equations are *linear*. That is, the equations involve only first powers of the unknowns I_1 and I_2. If you were to sketch a graph of the equation

$$(R_1 + R_{12})I_1 - R_{12}I_2 = V_1$$

on a rectangular coordinate system $[(I_1, I_2)\text{-axes}]$, the locus would be a _____.

Try your hand at a few examples.

(right margin answers)

$R_{12}(I_1 - I_2)$

$R_{12}(I_2 - I_1)$
$+ I_2 R_2$

$-R_{12}, R_2 + R_{12}$

line

7.1.1
EXERCISES

1. Given the circuit in Fig. 7-1 with $R_1 = R_2 = R_{12} = 1$ ohm and $V_1 = V_2 = 6$ volts.
(a) Use Ohm's and Kirchoff's laws to set up the equations for finding I_1 and I_2.
(b) Determine I_1 and I_2 by solving the pair of linear equations you found in part (a).
(c) Sketch the graphs of these linear equations in the (I_1, I_2)-plane. What point represents the graphic solution to the equations? How does your graphic solution compare with your algebraic solution in accuracy?
2. Given a circuit as described in Fig. 7-1 but with $V_1 = 3$ volts, $V_2 = 6$ volts, $R_1 = 1$ ohm, $R_2 = 2$ ohms, and $R_{12} = 1$ ohm. Find I_1 and I_2.

3. The set of linear equations that you have solved in Exercises 1 and 2 can be written

$$ax - by = d,$$
$$-bx + cy = f.$$

Solve this system of equations for x and y.

In practice, physicists can measure the current in any part of a circuit by means of an instrument called an *ammeter*. Since a physical determination of currents is possible, we can turn the problem around and use electrical circuits to solve certain algebraic problems. For example, if we had the simple system

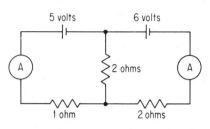

Figure 7-2

$$3x - 2y = 5,$$
$$-2x + 4y = 6,$$

we could solve for x and y by inserting ammeters, symbolized by Ⓐ, as shown in the circuit diagram of Fig. 7-2. The reading on the ammeter on the left would give the value of x, and the reading on the ammeter on the right would give the value of y. Of course, these would be only approximations to the exact solution to the given algebraic equation, with the accuracy depending upon the precision of measurement of the resistances and voltages as well as the precision of the ammeters that yield the solution. Similarly, our equations give only an approximate mathematical model of the physical problem since, for example, we have neglected the resistances of the wires. We shall speak more of approximations later.

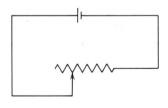

Figure 7-3

The method of solving a set of linear equations by electrical methods, as described above, is quite inefficient. However, physicists and electrical engineers have instruments to facilitate such mathematical analyses. For example, the *rheostat* is a device for varying the resistance in a circuit with a voltage source. The diagram (Fig. 7-3) attempts to suggest that the arrow may be moved to any part of the resistance. A large resistance is introduced when the wire (↑) touches the open end of the symbol ⋀⋀⋀⋀⋀⋀ , and if the wire (↑) is moved to the right the resistance may be reduced to zero.

Therefore, by introducing rheostats (Fig. 7-4) to achieve resistances R_1, R_2, and R_{12}, we have an electric circuit that would yield the solution

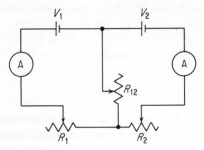

Figure 7-4

for x and y in any system of equations of the form

$$ax - by = V_1,$$
$$-bx + cy = V_2,$$

where $b \geq 0$, $a \geq b$ and $c \geq b$. Quick turns of three dials set the three rheostats to desired positions for a given system, and the answer can be immediately read off from the ammeters. Such an electric circuit is, in fact, a computer. We set up a physical situation which is governed by the equations we wish to solve, and we solve our mathematical problem by *measuring* the physical quantities. This type of computer is called an *analog computer*. Its accuracy depends on that of our measuring instruments. The computer we have described in the figure is of the most rudimentary type, solving only one type of mathematical problem. Needless to say, a greater facility with electrical circuits would enable you to build increasingly complex computers that would solve more complex problems as well as a great variety of problems.

Let's now move to another example from elementary physics. Consider a thin rectangular metal plate $ABCD$, as shown in Fig. 7-5. The top and

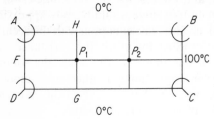

Figure 7-5

bottom are kept at 0°C by melting ice packed against them. The sides are kept at 100°C by boiling water. (These temperatures cannot be maintained at the corners, but this is irrelevant in our problem.) The problem is to determine the equilibrium temperatures t_1 and t_2 at the interior points P_1 and P_2. We shall assume a property of heat conduction: the temperature at any interior point is the average of the temperatures at the "neighboring" points. For example, the points neighboring P_1 are F, G, H, and P_2. Therefore,

$$t_1 = \frac{100 + 0 + 0 + t_2}{4}$$

and

$$t_2 = \frac{t_1 + 0 + 0 + 100}{4}$$

This pair of equations can be rewritten

$$4t_1 - t_2 = 100.$$
$$-t_1 + 4t_2 = 100.$$

Again, we have a linear system. Moreover, this system of equations can be solved by the electrical circuit that we analyzed in the first illustration! Therefore, solving a problem in electrical circuits solves a related problem in heat conduction. Or, in still other words, solving one mathematical problem gives a solution to a problem in electric circuits and a solution to a problem in heat conduction. Once again we have an illustration of the power of the abstraction in mathematics. By analyzing not the specific problem in physics but the general abstract mathematical problem that arises from the given physical problem, we obtain a mathematical theory which has many concrete interpretations. The theory of linear equations is an excellent example of a theory with a wide range of applications in social sciences such as psychology and economics as well as in all of the physical sciences.

Since an abstract mathematical problem may have many concrete interpretations, we can solve the abstract problem and apply the result in any of the concrete situations. Or, we can set up an experiment corresponding to one of the interpretations, measure the unknown quantities, and we will have the solution of the abstract problem; an analog computer performs this function.

In many branches of science—in meteorology and economics, for example —it is important to be able to solve, at least approximately, simultaneous linear equations with as many as a thousand unknowns. Such problems have stimulated the research of some outstanding mathematicians. Recent developments have been reported in several symposia conducted by the National Bureau of Standards and in other publications.†

7.1.2
EXERCISES

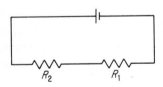

Figure 7-6

1. Given the circuit in Fig. 7-6 $R_1 = 2$ ohms, $R_2 = 3$ ohms, and the voltage drop across R_1 is 6 volts. Find the current through R_2 and the voltage drop across R_2.

2. (a) Solve the system of linear equations

$$3x = 4,$$
$$4y = -7.$$

† F. L. Alt, ed., *Advances in Computers*, Vols. 1 and 2 (New York: Academic Press, Inc., 1960, 1961); L. J. Paige and O. Taussky, eds., *Simultaneous Linear Equations and the Determination of Eigenvalues*, National Bureau of Standards Applied Mathematics Series, Vol. 29 (Washington, D.C., 1953); O. Taussky, ed., *Contributions to the Solution of Linear Equations and the Determination of Eigenvalues*, National Bureau of Standards Applied Mathematics Series, Vol. 39 (Washington, D.C., 1954); John Todd, ed., *A Survey of Numerical Analysis* (New York: McGraw-Hill Book Company, 1962).

(b) Sketch the graphs of these equations and label the point which represents the solution of the system.

(c) Solve the system for x and y:

$$ax = b,$$
$$cy = d.$$

3. Solve for x and y:

(a) $3x - 4y = 12,$
$\quad 4y = 3.$

(b) $4x + 3y = 12,$
$\quad 4x = -3.$

(c) $ax + by = u, a \neq 0,$
$\quad\quad\quad\quad y = v.$

(d) $ax + by = u,$
$\quad\quad cy = v.$

Was the method you used to answer (d) valid for all values of a, b, and c? If not, what assumptions must you make about these numbers?

4. From Exercise 3 you see that it is rather simple to solve a pair of simultaneous linear equations if one unknown is absent from one of the equations. Let's review the solution to Exercise 3(d). Examining the second equation, we have

$$cy = v \Rightarrow y = \underline{\quad\quad}, \quad\quad \text{provided} \underline{\quad\quad} \neq 0. \quad\quad \left| \quad \frac{v}{c}, c \right.$$

We then substitute this value of y into the first equation and obtain

$$ax + b\left(\frac{v}{c}\right) = u.$$

Therefore,

$$ax = u + \underline{\quad\quad} = \frac{?}{c} \quad\quad \left| \quad \frac{-bv}{c}, cu - bv \right.$$

and

$$x = \frac{?}{ac}, \quad\quad \left| \quad cu - bv \right.$$

provided also that $\underline{\quad\quad} \neq 0.$ $\quad\quad \left| \quad a \right.$
The provision that

$$a \neq 0 \quad \wedge \quad c \neq 0$$

may be united in the statement that $ac \neq 0$. (Why?)

(a) Now suppose you are given the system

$$x - y = 2$$
$$x + y = 1.$$

If a given x and y satisfy these equations, then they also satisfy the equation

$$(x - y) - (x + y) = \underline{\quad\quad} - \underline{\quad\quad}.$$

Simplify this equation and solve it. Then complete the solution of the given system.

(b) We solved the system in part (a) by *eliminating* x from the given pair of equations. The equation we obtained, together with either of the given equations, forms a system of the type discussed in Exercise 3. Solve the system in part (a) by eliminating y from the given pair of equations.

(c) The process of ridding an equation of an unknown as you did in part (a) is called *elimination*. By "adding the equations" in (a) you eliminated y, and by "subtracting one equation from the other" you eliminated x. Now how would you eliminate x in the system

$$2x - 3y = 1,$$

$$x + y = 3?$$

Do it, and solve for x and y.

(d) Solve the system of part (b) by first eliminating y.

(e) What is the algebraic (logical) justification for the steps you took in solving by elimination?

(f) Solve for x and y:

$$3x - y = 6,$$

$$2y - 6x = 18.$$

(g) Solve for x and y:

$$4x + 8y + 7 = 0,$$

$$3x + 4y + 3 = 0.$$

(h) Solve for x and y:

$$(2x - 3y) = \tfrac{5}{2}(2x - 3),$$

$$\tfrac{1}{2}(8x + 5y) = 6 + \tfrac{1}{7}(10x - 2y).$$

5. A rectangle whose length is 10 ft greater than its width has a perimeter of 40 ft. Find the length and width.

6. Suppose you have two solutions of nitric acid in the laboratory, one 10 per cent strength and the other 3 per cent strength. If you desire 100 cc of a 6 per cent solution, what quantities of each would you use?

We'll assist you in this "mixture problem." Then we'll give you several problems to try without any help. If you let $A = $ cc of 10 per cent solution and $B = $ cc of 3 per cent solution that will be used in the mixture, you get the relation

(1) $\qquad\qquad A + B = $ _____. | *100*

Another relation (linear, we hope) can be found by considering the amount of nitric acid in the mixture. Ten per cent of A is nitric acid and 3 per cent of B is nitric acid. Therefore,

(2) $\qquad 0.10A + $ _____$B = ($_____$)100.$ | *0.03, 0.06*

Equations (1) and (2) constitute a pair of linear equations which, from the conditions of the problem, must both be true simultaneously. These are equivalent to

(1′) $$A + B = 100,$$

(2′) $$10A + \underline{\hspace{1cm}}B = \underline{\hspace{1cm}}.$$

3, 600

Suppose we wish to eliminate A. Solving for A in the first equation gives

$$A = \underline{\hspace{2cm}}.$$

100 − B

and substituting this value for A into equation (2′) yields

(3) $$10(100 - B) + 3B = 600.$$

Thus we have eliminated A and can readily solve for B. This method of elimination is sometimes referred to as *elimination by substitution*. Solving for B in equation (3) gives

$$B = \underline{\hspace{1cm}} \text{ cc.}$$

$\frac{400}{7}$

Now substituting this value for B in (a), we can solve for A, getting $A = \underline{\hspace{1cm}}$ cc.

$\frac{300}{7}$

An alternative method for eliminating A would be as follows. We multiply both members of equation (1) by 10 to obtain the equations

(1″) $$10A + 10B = 1000,$$

(2′) $$10A + 3B = 600.$$

Then we subtract (2′) from (1″), getting

$$\underline{\hspace{1cm}}B = \underline{\hspace{1cm}}.$$

7, 400

This method of elimination is sometimes called *elimination by addition or subtraction*.

7. One ton of copper alloy that is 70 per cent copper is to be made by fusing a 65 per cent alloy with an 85 per cent alloy. How many pounds of each alloy must be used? (One ton = 2000 lb.)

8. One solution of HCl was made with 14 liters of water and 4 liters of pure HCl. A second was made with 6 liters of water and 3 liters of pure HCl.

(a) If the two solutions are now mixed, what percentage of the mixture is pure HCl?

(b) How many liters of pure HCl should be added to the second solution in order to obtain a 25 per cent solution?

9. Determine the linear polynomial $L(x) = ax + b$, finding the values of a and b if

(a) $L(0) = 0$ and $L(1) = 1$,

(b) $L(0) = 0$ and $L(1) = 3$,

(c) $L(0) = 1$ and $L(1) = \dfrac{1 + \sqrt{2}}{-3}$,

(d) $L(0) = \dfrac{1 + \sqrt{2}}{-3}$ and $L(2) = 1$,

(e) $L(1) = 1$ and $L(-3) = 1$,

(f) $L(1) = 1$ and $L(352) = 1$.

10. If you are given the system of linear equations

$$3x + 4y = 1,$$

$$x - 2y = 2,$$

the solution can be expressed in set-builder notation as

$$\mathscr{S} = \{(x, y)|3x + 4y = 1 \land x - 2y = 2\}.$$

For this reason the set $\mathscr{S}$ is called the *solution set* to the given system. How large is the solution set for the above system?

Suppose you multiply both members of the first equation by 5 and both members of the second by 2. How does the solution set

$$\{(x, y)\,|\,15x + 20y = 5 \land 2x - 4y = 4\}$$

compare with $\mathscr{S}$?

11. (a) Find the solution set of the system

$$x + y = 0,$$

$$x - y = 0.$$

(b) Let $L_1 = x + y$ and $L_2 = x - y$. Find the solution set:

$$\{(x, y)\,|\,L_1 = 0 \land 2L_2 = 0\}.$$

(c) Find the solution set: $\{(x, y)\,|\,L_1 = 0 \land -3L_2 = 0\}$.

(d) Find the solution set: $\{(x, y)\,|\,L_1 = 0 \land aL_2 = 0\}$, where a is any real number other than zero.

(e) Find the solution set: $\{(x, y)\,|\,L_1 = 0 \land 0 \cdot L_2 = 0\}$.

(f) Find the solution set: $\{(x, y)\,|\,2L_2 = 0 \land -5L_2 = 0\}$.

(g) If two systems of equations have the same solution set, they are called *equivalent*. Which of the systems of equations in (b)–(f) are equivalent to the one given in part (a)?

12. Given:

$$L_1 = x + y,$$

$$L_2 = x - y.$$

Graph the equations (a)–(d) on one set of axes.

(a) $L_1 + L_2 = 0$,

(b) $L_1 - L_2 = 0$.

(c) $L_1 + 2L_2 = 0$.

(d) $3L_1 - 2L_2 = 0$.

(e) Find the solution set:

$$\mathscr{S}_1 = \{(x, y)\,|\,L_1 = 0 \land L_2 = 0\}.$$

(f) Find the solution set:

$$\mathscr{S}_2 = \{(x, y) \mid L_1 = 0 \wedge L_1 + L_2 = 0\}.$$

(g) Find the solution set:

$$\mathscr{S}_3 = \{(x, y) \mid L_1 = 0 \wedge L_1 + \mu L_2 = 0, \mu \in \mathscr{R}\}.$$

(h) Under what condition will $\mathscr{S}_3$ consist of more than one ordered pair?

(i) If

$$\mathscr{S} = \{(x, y) \mid L_1 = 0 \wedge \lambda L_1 + \mu L_2 = 0; \lambda, \mu \in \mathscr{R} \wedge \mu \neq 0\},$$

compare $\mathscr{S}$ with $\mathscr{S}_1, \mathscr{S}_2$, and $\mathscr{S}_3$.

(j) Which of these systems are equivalent?

$$L_1 = 0 \wedge L_2 = 0,$$

$$L_1 = 0 \wedge L_1 + 2L_2 = 0,$$

$$L_1 = 0 \wedge L_1 + \mu L_2 = 0 \quad (\mu \neq 0),$$

$$L_1 = 0 \wedge \lambda L_1 + \mu L_2 = 0 \quad (\mu \neq 0),$$

$$\lambda L_1 = 0 \wedge 0 \cdot L_1 + \mu L_2 = 0,$$

$$L_1 = 0 \wedge \lambda L_1 + 0 \cdot L_2 = 0.$$

13. Given:

$$L_1 = x - y + 1,$$

$$L_2 = 2x + 3y - 3.$$

(a) Find the solution set: $\{(x, y) \mid L_1 = 0 \wedge L_2 = 0\}$.

(b) Find the solution set: $\{(x, y) \mid L_2 = 0 \wedge 2L_1 - L_2 = 0\}$.

(c) On one set of axes draw graphs of $L_1 = 0, L_2 = 0$, and $L_1 - L_2 = 0$.

14. Let's think of L_1 and L_2 as functions whose domains are sets of points (ordered pairs) and whose function values are given as follows:

$$L_1(x, y) = x - y + 1 \quad \text{and} \quad L_2(x, y) = 2x + 3y - 3.$$

Then, since $(1, 2)$ is on the graph of $L_1 = 0$, we have $L_1(1, 2) =$ _____. In general, if (x_0, y_0) is on the graph $L_1 = 0$, we have $L_1(x_0, y_0) =$ _____. And if (x_0, y_0) is on the graph of $L_2 = 0$, then $L_2(x_0, y_0) = 0$. Thus,

$$L_1(x_0, y_0) + L_2(x_0, y_0) = \underline{\qquad}.$$

For any real numbers λ, μ, we also have

$$\lambda L_1(x_0, y_0) + \mu L_2(x_0, y_0) = \underline{\qquad}.$$

0

0

0

0

Hence, if λ and μ are not both zero, the line representing $\lambda L_1(x, y) + \mu L_2(x, y) = 0$ is a line passing through the point of intersection of original pair: $L_1 = 0$ and $L_2 = 0$. In fact, *any line* through the point of intersection (x_0, y_0) of $L_1 = 0$ and $L_2 = 0$ has an equation of the form

$$\lambda L_1 + \mu L_2 = 0.$$

The set of all lines through a single point is called a *pencil of lines*.

(a) Find a value of μ so that the line represented by $L_1 + \mu L_2 = 0$ passes through the origin.

(b) Find the value of λ that forces the line whose equation is $\lambda L_1 + L_2 = 0$ to have a slope of zero.

(c) Find the member of the pencil of lines $\lambda L_1 + \mu L_2 = 0$ that is vertical.

(d) Find the member of the pencil $\lambda L_1 + \mu L_2 = 0$ that passes through $(1, 2)$.

(e) Find the member of the pencil $\lambda L_1 + \mu L_2 = 0$ that is perpendicular to $L_2 = 0$.

15. Given the system

$$2x + y = 4,$$

$$x - y = 1.$$

(a) Solve for x and y.

(b) Find the vertical member of the pencil of lines determined by the two equations.

(c) Find the member of the pencil that is horizontal.

(d) What is the relation of the lines found in (b) and (c) to the solution you found in (a)?

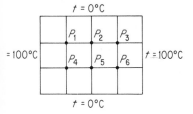

Figure 7-7

16. The equations we set up for our heat-conduction problem give us only a very crude approximation to the solution. We can obtain a better approximation if we use a finer grid such as the one shown in Fig. 7-7. Let $t_1, t_2, \ldots, t_6$ be the equilibrium temperatures at points $P_1, \ldots, P_6$. We set up the equation which states that the temperature t, P_1 is the average of the temperatures at its neighboring points:

$$t_1 = \frac{0 + 100 + t_2 + t_4}{4}.$$

The equation corresponding to the temperature at point P_2 is

$$t_2 = \frac{\underline{} + \underline{} + \underline{} + \underline{}}{4}. \qquad t_1, 0, t_3, t_5$$

(What are the neighbors of P_2?) Set up the equations corresponding to the other interior points in the grid. How many equations do you have? How many unknowns?

7.2

Logical Analysis of Linear Systems   We shall begin with a discussion of the logic employed in solving systems of linear equations. The work you did in Exercises 10–12 of Sec. 7.1.2 may be summarized as follows: If we are given linear equations $L_1(x, y) = 0$ and $L_2(x, y) = 0$, the problem of finding the solution boils down to finding an equivalent system of the form $x = x_0$ and $y = y_0$. The logical equivalence

$$[L_1(x, y) = 0 \land L_2(x, y = 0] \Leftrightarrow [x = x_0 \land y = y_0]$$

represents the procedure. In this event, the set $\{(x_0, y_0)\}$, consisting of one ordered pair, is the solution set.

The first task is to examine the logic of the algebra involved in the step-by-step procedure of obtaining a system of the form

$$x = x_0,$$

$$y = y_0.$$

Exercises 7.2.1 are designed to start you on this examination. In these exercises, the symbols L, L_1, etc. stand for expressions of the form $ax + by + c$, where a, b, and c are real constants.

7.2.1
EXERCISES

1. (a) If $L_1 = 0$, then $3L_1 = $ _____.
(b) If $3L_1 = 0$, then $L_1 = $ _____.
(c) Can one of the equations $L_1 = 0$ and $3L_1 = 0$ be true without the other being true?
(d) What about the equations $L_1 = 0$ and $\lambda L_1 = 0$, where λ is any real number different from 0?

2. (a) Let $L_1 = 3x + 4y - 5$. Find λ such that

$$\lambda L_1 = x + by + c, \qquad \forall\, x, y \in \mathcal{R}$$

for some real constants b and c.
(b) If $L_1 = Ax + By + C$, where A, B, and C are given constants, find a number $\lambda \in \mathcal{R}$ such that the coefficient of x in λL_1 is equal to 1. For which value of A is this impossible?

3. (a) If $L_1 = x + By + C$ and $L_2 = ax + by + c$, find a number $\lambda \in \mathcal{R}$ such that the coefficient of x in $\lambda L_1 + L_2$ is 0. Does such a number λ always exist?
(b) If $L_2 = by + c$, find numbers μ and y_0 such that $\mu L_2 = y - y_0$ for all y.
(c) If $L_2 = by + c$, find a number y_0 such that

$$L_2 = 0 \Leftrightarrow y = y_0.$$

For which values of b does such a number y_0 exist?
(d) If $L_1 = x + By + C$ and $L_2 = by + c$ and $b \neq 0$, find numbers x_0 and y_0 such that

$$L_1 = 0 \land L_2 = 0 \Leftrightarrow x = x_0 \text{ and } y = y_0.$$

For which values of b do such numbers x_0 and y_0 exist?

(e) Apply the method of Exercise 3(a) to the case

$$L_1 = x + y - 1 \quad \text{and} \quad L_2 = x + y - 2.$$

Find all points (x, y) such that $L_1 = 0 \wedge L_2 = 0$.
  (f) Apply the method of Exercise 3(a) to the case

$$L_1 = x - 2y - 1 \quad \text{and} \quad L_2 = -3x + 6y + 3.$$

Find all points (x, y) such that $L_1 = 0 \wedge L_2 = 0$.

By the above results,

$$L_1 = 0 \Leftrightarrow \lambda L_1 = 0$$

for any number $\lambda \neq 0$. If the coefficient of x in $L_1 = ax + by + c$ is different from 0, then there is an equation (of the form $\lambda L_1 = 0$) equivalent to the equation $L_1 = 0$, in which the coefficient of x is 1.
  If, in the system of linear equations $L_1 = 0 \wedge L_2 = 0$, the coefficient of x in L_1 is different from 0, then there is an equation

$$\mu L_1 + L_2 = 0$$

in which the coefficient of x is 0. The system $L_1 = 0 \wedge L_2 = 0$ is equivalent to the system

$$L_1 = 0 \quad \wedge \quad \mu L_1 + L_2 = 0.$$

In general, the latter equation is equivalent to an equation of the form $y = y_0$. Then the given system is equivalent to one of the desired form

$$x = x_0 \quad \wedge \quad y = y_0.$$

It may happen, as in Exercises 3(e) and 3(f) above, that, for some numbers λ and μ not both equal to 0, the coefficients of both x and y in $\lambda L_1 + \mu L_2$ are equal to 0.
  In Exercise 3(e), we have $L_1 - L_2 = 1$, so that

$$L_1 = 0 \wedge L_2 = 0 \Rightarrow L_1 - L_2 = 1 = 0.$$

Therefore, there is no point (x, y) such that $L_1 = 0 \wedge L_2 = 0$. The equations $L_1 = 0$ and $L_2 = 0$ are *inconsistent*. In this case the system of equations $L_1 = 0 \wedge L_2 = 0$ has no solution.
  In Exercise 3(f), we have $3L_1 + L_2 = 0$, or $L_2 = -3L_1$. Therefore, any solution of the equation $L_1 = 0$ is also a solution of the system $L_1 = 0 \wedge L_2 = 0$. The system is *redundant*, since the equation $L_2 = 0$ gives us no additional information about the point (x, y). All points (x, y) on the line $L_1 = 0$ satisfy the system $L_1 = 0 \wedge L_2 = 0$. The system has, then, infinitely many solutions which form the line $L_1 = 0$.

1. Fill the blanks. The equation $2x - y = 1$ is inconsistent with

(a) _____ $- 2y = 4,$ $4x$

(b) $x -$ _____ $= 4,$ $\frac{1}{2}y$

(c) _____ $+ y = 1.$ $-2x$

The system

$$3x - 4y = 1$$

$$3x - 4y = k$$

is inconsistent if $k \neq$ _____. If $k = 1$, the system is _____   *1, consistent*
(consistent/inconsistent).

If you write

$$L_1 = 3x - 4y - 1$$

and

$$L_2 = 3x - 4y - 2,$$

then the graph of $L_1 + L_2 = 0$ is a line of slope _____, and the $\frac{3}{4}$
graph of $2L_1 - 3L_2 = 0$ is a line of slope _____. The line whose $\frac{3}{4}$
equation is $L_1 + \mu L_2 = 0$, with $\mu \neq -1$, has slope equal to _____. $\frac{3}{4}$
(Examine the case $\mu = -1$.) We can extend the notion of a pencil $\frac{3}{4}$
of lines to include this case by calling the set of lines

$$\{L_1 + \mu L_2 = 0 \mid \mu \in \mathcal{R} \wedge \mu \neq -1\}$$

a *pencil of parallel lines.* Of course, this pencil may be written

$$\{\lambda L_1 + \mu L_2 = 0 \mid \lambda, \mu \in \mathcal{R} \wedge \lambda \neq -\mu\},$$

which conforms to the original definition of pencil. The member
of the pencil determined by $\lambda = 1$ and $\mu = -2$ has an x-intercept
of _____ and a y-intercept of _____. The member of the pencil $1, -\frac{3}{4}$
which passes through $(-3, 0)$ may be written with $\lambda = 1$ and
$\mu =$ _____. The member of the pencil that passes through the $-\frac{10}{11}$
midpoint of the segment joining $(1, -3)$ to $(-5, 1)$ is $3x - 4y =$
_____. (Can you think of a method of answering the last question -2
without first finding values for λ and μ?) Finally, the equation of
the line that passes through the origin and is perpendicular to
each member of the given pencil is _____ $= 0.$ $4x + 3y$

2. Let $L_1 = x - 2y + 1$ and $L_2 = 3 - 3x + 6y.$
(a) Graph the equations $L_1 = 0$ and $L_2 = 0.$
(b) Graph the equation $\lambda L_1 + L_2 = 0$ for any real number $\lambda \neq 3.$

3. What is the geometric interpretation of a redundant system, and how would you
give a geometric description of its solution?

4. Thus far you have examples of systems of two linear equations that have one
solution, no solution, and infinitely many solutions. Can you find an example of a
system of two linear equations with exactly two solutions? Explain your answer
geometrically.

5. Determine whether the following systems are consistent, inconsistent, or redundant, and find the solution sets:

(a) $2x - y = 2,$
$3x + 2y = 3.$

(b) $x + 2y = 3,$
$2x - y + \frac{1}{2} = 0.$

(c) $2x - y = 2,$
$y - 2x = 2.$

(d) $x = 4y + 3,$
$x = 4y + 1.$

(e) $x = 4y + 3, \quad x = -4y + 3.$

(f) $3x - y + 1 = 0,$
$y - 3x = 1.$

(g) $2x - y = 3,$
$10x - 5y = 15.$

(h) $2x - 3y = 8,$
$3x = \frac{1}{2}(24 + 9y).$

(i) $2x - 3y = \frac{5}{2}(2x - 3),$
$\frac{1}{2}(8x - 5y) = 6 + \frac{1}{7}(10x - 2y).$

6. You have now solved several systems of linear equations. Suppose you consider the possibility of finding a formula for the solution to a pair of equations, much the same as you discovered a formula for the solution to the general quadratic equation

$$ax^2 + bx + c = 0, \qquad a \neq 0.$$

A formula for the solution to a system of linear equations might be useful in several capacities: (a) it would provide an automatic method of solution without requiring particular algebraic devices for each new system; (b) if we had a machine to assist in computing the solution, we would be able to give the machine one set of instructions that would suffice for all—or at least a large class of systems; and (c) a formula might even help us gain insight into the mathematical theory, as an analysis of the quadratic formula enabled us to derive criteria for the nature of the roots of a quadratic equation.

Therefore, we begin with the general linear system consisting of the two equations

$$a_1 x + b_1 y = c_1,$$
$$a_2 x + b_2 y = c_2.$$

If you choose to eliminate x by multiplying the first equation by a_2 ($\neq 0$), you would multiply the second by _____ (_____ $\neq 0$). The resulting system, equivalent to the original, is

$$a_1 a_2 x + a_2 b_1 y = a_2 c_1,$$
$$\underline{\quad} a_2 x + \underline{\quad} b_2 y = \underline{\quad} c_2.$$

Subtracting the first equation from the second yields

$$(\underline{\quad} - a_2 b_1)y = (\underline{\quad} - a_2 c_1).$$

Therefore,

$$y = \frac{a_1 c_2 - a_2 c_1}{a_1 b_2 - a_2 b_1}, \qquad \text{provided} \underline{\hspace{3cm}} \neq 0.$$

You could now solve for x by either eliminating y as you did x or substituting the value of y that was found in the equation above. In either case the result would be

$$x = \frac{b_2 c_1 - b_1 c_2}{\Delta}, \qquad \text{where } \Delta = \underline{\hspace{3cm}} \neq 0.$$

a_1, a_1

a_1, a_1, a_1

$a_1 b_2, a_1 c_2$

$a_1 b_2 - a_2 b_1$

$a_1 b_2 - a_2 b_1$

Notice that the provision $\Delta \neq 0$ in the formula for x is precisely the same as that found for the formula for y. Let's examine this restriction on our new-found formula. What sort of a system is it that has

$$\Delta = a_1 b_2 - a_2 b_1 = 0?$$

Let's see. $\Delta = 0 \Rightarrow a_1 b_2 = $ _____, which states that

$$\frac{a_1}{b_1} = \frac{a_2}{b_2} \quad \text{(provided _____)}.$$

The ratios of the coefficients are the same! The geometric concept related to the ratio of the coefficients in a linear equation is the _____ of the _____ which is the graph of the equation. If the graph of the first equation is not a vertical line, then its slope is ____; and similarly, the slope of the second line is ____. Therefore, if $a_1/b_1 = a_2/b_2$, the graphs of the equations in the given system are _____, unless the lines coincide. If the two equations are independent (i.e., not redundant), then the system is (consistent/inconsistent).

Now you should examine on your own the results of the equations having graphs with no slope (vertical lines).

[margin notes] $a_2 b_1$

$b_1 \neq 0 \wedge b_2 \neq 0$

slope, line

$-a_1/b_1, -a_2/b_2$

parallel

inconsistent

7. Find solutions to the following systems, applying the formula derived in Exercise 6. (Note that Exercises (d)–(f) can be transformed into linear systems.)

(a) $4x - 8y = 17$,
$12x + 16y = -9$.

(d) $\dfrac{1}{1 + y} = \dfrac{1}{1 - x}$,

$\dfrac{2}{1 - x} - \dfrac{1}{2 - y} = 0$.

(b) $5x - 2y - 7 = 0$,
$2x + y - 1 = 0$.

(e) $\dfrac{a}{a + y} = \dfrac{b}{b - x}$,

$\dfrac{c}{d - x} - \dfrac{d}{c - y} = 0$.

(c) $2x + 3y + 6 = 0$,
$4x + 3y = 4$.

(f) $\dfrac{6}{x + y} - \dfrac{3x + y}{y + x} = -1$,

$\dfrac{x + 1}{y} + \dfrac{12 - x}{y - 5} = 0$.

8. Suppose a computing machine takes s seconds to perform a single addition or subtraction and m seconds for a multiplication or division. How long would the computer take to solve a system of two linear equations (a) by elimination and (b) by formula?

9. Often given equations are not linear, but they can be converted to linear equations. Each of the systems below can be reduced to a linear system by judicious substitutions. Solve each system by this technique.

(a) $\dfrac{1}{x} + \dfrac{2}{y} = 9,$

$\dfrac{3}{x} - \dfrac{5}{y} - 5 = 0.$ *Hint:* Let $u = \dfrac{1}{x}$ and $v = \dfrac{1}{y}.$

(b) $\dfrac{5}{x} + \dfrac{6}{y} = \dfrac{5}{2},$

$\dfrac{4}{x} - \dfrac{5}{y} + \dfrac{19}{15} = 0.$

(c) $\dfrac{2}{x-1} - \dfrac{3}{y+2} = -4,$

$\dfrac{1}{x-1} + \dfrac{2}{y+2} = 5.$

(d) $3x - \dfrac{2}{2y-7} - 14 = 0,$

$5x - \dfrac{3}{7-2y} + 2 = 0.$

10. The economic concept *demand* is defined as a relation between price p and quantity q. If consumers are willing to purchase $q = d(p)$ units of a product when the price is p dollars per unit, then we speak of d as the *demand function*. The *supply function* s is defined by the equation $q = s(p)$, where q represents the quantity that the seller will offer for sale at the price p dollars per unit. When the quantity and price "demanded" by a buyer coincide with the quantity and price offered by the sellers, the so-called *equilibrium point* is reached. That is, equilibrium is obtained when

$$q = d(p) \quad \wedge \quad q = s(p).$$

(a) If the demand for a good is given by $q = 100 - p$ and the supply is given by $q = p - 50$, determine the equilibrium price and quantity of the good exchange.

(b) A real estate speculator has exactly five lots for sale. What is the supply function? Find the equilibrium price and quantity if the demand function is

$$d(p) = 10 - \tfrac{1}{10}p.$$

Exhibit a graphical solution.

(c) If $d(p) = \dfrac{600}{p + 10} - 10$ and $s(p) = \dfrac{1}{5}p - 10$ are the demand and supply functions for a good, find the equilibrium price and quantity.

(d) Assuming that the demand and supply functions are both linear, state a condition that would assure the existence of an equilibrium point (p_0, q_0).

(e) If the demand function d and supply function s are given by

$$d = \{(p, q) \mid 2q + p = 100 \wedge p > 0 \wedge q > 0\}$$

and

$$s = \{(p, q) \mid q - p = -50 \wedge p > 0 \wedge q > 0\},$$

find the equilibrium price.

11. Let $C(x)$ denote the cost of producing x units of a good and $G(x)$ denote the gross income from selling x units of the good.

(a) If the selling price is p dollars per unit, write an expression for $G(x)$.
If $G(x) - C(x) > 0$, then the firm is making a profit equal to _____ per

unit; if $G(x) - C(x) < 0$, the firm is losing _____ per unit; and if $G(x) - C(x) = 0$, the firm is breaking even.

(b) If the selling price of a good is $2 per unit and $C(x) = x + 20$, find the point at which the company breaks even. (This is called the *break-even point*.)

(c) Graph $y = G(x)$ and $y = C(x)$ for the data given in part (b). If (x_0, y_0) is the break-even point, is the firm profiting or losing when $x > x_0$? when $x < x_0$? (A chart with graphs of the gross income function and the cost function, which so conveniently shows when a business will show a loss, make a profit, or break even, is called a *break-even chart*.)

12. Suppose that the selling price of a good is p dollars per unit and the cost function C of the good is a first-degree polynomial function. That is, $C(x) = ax + b$.

(a) Find the coordinates of the break-even point in terms of the data a, b, and p.

(b) It would seem that the break-even point would occur when the cost of producing a unit (cost per unit) was exactly equal to the price. Verify this. Does your result depend on the nature of the cost function?

13. If the gross income function G and the cost function C are defined as

$$G = \{(x, y) \mid y = \tfrac{3}{2}x, x \geq 0\},$$

$$C = \{(x, y) \mid y = x^{1/3} + 10, x \geq 0\},$$

(a) make a break-even chart and find the break-even point;

(b) what will the profit be if 27 units are manufactured and sold?

14. If $L_1 = 2x - y$ and $L_2 = 2x + y$, graph the following relations:

(a) $L_1 = 0$,

(b) $L_2 = 0$,

(c) $L_1 + L_2 = 0$,

(d) $L_1 = 0 \wedge L_2 = 0$,

(e) $L_1 = 0 \vee L_2 = 0$,

(f) $L_1^2 = 0$,

(g) $L_1^2 + L_2^2 = 0$,

(h) $L_1 \cdot L_2 = 0$.

15. If $L_1 = 3x + 4y - 5$ and $L_2 = 6x - 7y + 8$, graph the following relations:

(a) $L_1 \cdot L_2 = 0$,

(b) $L_1^2 + L_2^2 = 0$,

(c) $L_1 = 1$,

(d) $L_1 = 2$,

(e) $L_1 = 5$.

7.3

Systems of More Than Two Linear Equations Suppose you are faced with the problem of determining the equation of a circle through three given points of the plane. (Could you solve this problem by means of a straight-edge and compass construction?) For example, let's assume that the points given, relative to a cartesian coordinate system, are $(0, 0)$, $(0, 1)$, and $(1, -1)$.

You already know (from Sec. 5.6) that the equation of a circle can always be written in the form

(1) $$x^2 + y^2 + Ax + By + C = 0.$$

(See Exercise 3 of Sec. 5.6.1.) The problem, therefore, is to determine the specific values of A, B, and C so that (1) becomes the equation of the circle that passes through the given points.

If the circle passes through $(0, 0)$, then equation (1) must be a true statement when $x = 0 \wedge y = 0$. Therefore,

$$0^2 + 0^2 + A \cdot 0 + B \cdot 0 + C = 0,$$

which tells you that

(2) $\qquad\qquad C = \underline{}.$ | 0

Imposing the condition that $(0, 1)$ is on the circle, whose equation is (1), gives

$\qquad 0^2 + (\underline{})^2 + A(\underline{}) + B(\underline{}) + C = 0.$ | $1, 0, 1$

Simplifying gives

(3) $\qquad (\underline{})A + (\underline{})B + C = \underline{}.$ | $0, 1, -1$

Finally, imposing the condition that $(1, -1)$ is on the circles gives

(4) $\qquad (\underline{})A + (\underline{})B + C = \underline{}.$ | $1, -1, -2$

Equations (2), (3), and (4) constitute a system of three linear equations in three unknowns. The elimination method can easily be applied by substituting the value of C, given by equation (2), into equations (3) and (4). This substitution yields

(3′) $\qquad\qquad\qquad B = -1,$

(4′) $\qquad\qquad\qquad A - B = -2.$

Solving this system is now a trivial matter. Returning to the original problem, the equation of the circle through the given points is

$\qquad x^2 + y^2 + (\underline{})x + (\underline{})y = 0.$ | $-3, -1$

Let's try a more difficult problem. Suppose the given points $(1, 1)$, $(2, -1)$, and $(3, 2)$. That $(1, 1)$ is on the circle gives the equation

(5) $\qquad\qquad A + B + C = \underline{}.$ | -2

That $(2, -1)$ is on the circle gives the equation

(6) $\qquad\qquad (\underline{})A - B + C = \underline{}.$ | $2, -5$

And, $(3, 2)$ on the circle implies the equation

(7) $\qquad\qquad (\underline{})A + (\underline{})B + C = \underline{}.$ | $3, 2, -13$

If this system of three equations in three unknowns can be reduced to two equations in two unknowns, we can then rely on the methods discussed in this chapter. Therefore we proceed by *eliminating* one unknown, say C.

Elimination of C from equations (5) and (6) yields

(8) $(\underline{\quad})A + (\underline{\quad})B = 3.$ $-1, 2$

Elimination of C from (5) and (7) yields

(9) $(\underline{\quad})A + (\underline{\quad})B = 11.$ $-2, -1$

Now equations (8) and (9) constitute a system you can
solve for A and B. When you do, you get $A = \underline{\quad}$ and -5
$B = \underline{\quad}$. Substituting these values for A and B into (5), -1
(6), or (7) of the original system, you get $C = \underline{\quad}$. 4

This process of elimination can be applied to linear systems of any
number of equations to reduce the problem to that of solving systems
consisting of fewer equations. Reducing a new problem to one that we
already know how to solve is an approach that permeates all of mathematics. It would be valuable to establish it in your repertoire of problem
solving techniques.

7.3.1
EXERCISES

1. (a) Solve the system of equations (5), (6), and (7) by eliminating C from (5) and (6),
and from (6) and (7).

(b) Solve the same system by eliminating B first, reducing the problem to two
equations involving unknowns A and C.

(c) Find the centers and radii of the circles found in the illustrative problems just
solved.

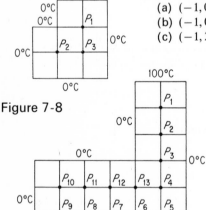

Figure 7-8

Figure 7-9

2. Find the equation of the circle through the points
  (a) $(-1, 0), (3, 0), (2, 1)$;
  (b) $(-1, 0), (3, 0), (4, 1)$;
  (c) $(-1, 2), (-2, 1), (2, -2)$.

3. Given the thin plate with temperatures indicated at the boundaries shown in Fig. 7-8.
Find the temperatures at P_1, P_2, and P_3. (If
necessary, refer to the related example in Sec.
7.1.)

4. Given the thin plate in Fig. 7-9, find the
temperatures at the thirteen points $P_1, P_2, \ldots, P_{13}$.
(This problem leads to a system of thirteen equations in thirteen unknowns!)

5. Solve the following systems and check your
results:

  (a) $x + 2y - 3z = -5,$
    $2x - 3y + z = 11,$
    $3x + 5y + 4z = 0.$

(b) $3r - 2s - t = -\frac{1}{2}$,
   $2r + 3s - 4t = 27$,
   $4r - s + t = -1$.

(c) $\dfrac{2}{x} - \dfrac{3}{y} + \dfrac{5}{z} = 7$,

   $\dfrac{1}{x} + \dfrac{3}{y} - \dfrac{2}{z} = -1$,

   $\dfrac{3}{x} + \dfrac{5}{y} - \dfrac{4}{z} = 3$.

(d) $-2A + B + D = -4$,
   $-B + C + 2D = -3$,
   $A + 2B - 3C = -14$,
   $-3A + 2B + 3D = -13$.

6. (a) If the time that a computer requires for an addition or subtraction is s seconds and the time for a multiplication or division is m seconds, how long will it take the computer to solve a linear system of three equations in three unknowns by elimination?

(b) Derive a formula for the solution of such a system and find the time required for the computer to solve the system by means of your formula.

7. Let $\mathscr{L} = \{ax + by + c \mid a, b, c \in \mathscr{R}\}$. We shall define a relation $\approx$ among the elements of $\mathscr{L}$. If

$$L_1 = a_1x + b_1y + c_1 \quad \text{and} \quad L_2 = a_2x + b_2y + c_2,$$

then

$$L_1 \approx L_2 \Leftrightarrow a_1 = a_2 \wedge b_1 = b_2 \wedge c_1 = c_2.$$

(a) A relation that is *reflexive, symmetric*, and *transitive* is called an *equivalence relation*, since these three properties are the essential properties of equality (see Exercise 2 of Sec. 3.2.1). Is $\approx$ an equivalence relation?

(b) Relative to the operation $+$ and the relation $\approx$ (which we shall now call "equals"), is $\mathscr{L}$ an abelian group? Prove your answer.

(c) Let $L_1 \sim L_2 \Leftrightarrow L_1 = mL_2$, where m may be any nonzero real number. Is $\sim$ an equivalence relation? And, is $\mathscr{L}$ an abelian group relative to the operation $+$ and the relation $\sim$?

8. (a) Let $a_0 = 1_1, a_1 = 1$, and $a_{n+2} = a_{n+1} + a_n$ for $n \geq 0$. Compute a_n for $n \leq 16$.

(b) Solve the system

$$a_nx - a_{n+1}y = 0,$$

$$a_{n-1}x - a_ny = 1,$$

for $n = 13, 14, 15$.

(c) Solve the systems

$$(a_n + \varepsilon)x - a_{n+1}y = 0,$$

$$a_{n-1}x - a_ny = 1,$$

for $n = 13, 14, 15$, and $\varepsilon = \pm 0.1$.

(d) If the coefficient A in the system

$$Ax - a_{n+1}y = 0,$$

$$a_{n-1}x - a_ny = 1,$$

is known to differ from a_n by at most 0.1, to what approximation are x and y determined? Can you tell whether x is positive or negative?

7.4

Approximate Solutions   In problems that involve measurement we frequently do not have exact values for the quantities measured. For example, if you were measuring voltages you would be able to determine the voltages only approximately, within some margin of error that would depend on the precision of the voltmeter. Then, if these voltage readings, along with measurements of resistances, were used for determining the currents in a two-mesh network, you would be faced with the question of how accurate an answer can be obtained in this manner. In other words, if the coefficients of a two-by-two system are given only within some margin, what is the margin of error in the answer you determine by formula or elimination?

If we were to use a digital rather than an analog computer, then the numbers would be represented by their digits, not as physical quantities. Such a computer may work with numbers represented by ten digits in decimal notation, or it may use 35-digit numbers in binary notation. As long as the numbers are not beyond the capacity of the computer, the computations can be handled exactly. Therefore, it may appear that work with a digital computer does not involve approximation. However, a second glance tells us otherwise; problems of approximation will arise even with the simple operation of multiplication, since the product of two ten-digit numbers is a 20-digit number that will usually be *rounded off*. Thus, with digital computers, too, we must analyze errors in connection with round-off.

Let's begin with a simple example. Suppose a is measured to equal 3, and we know the measurement is off by at most 0.1. It is most convenient to express this by saying that $|a - 3| < 0.1$. Suppose also that $|b - 2| < 0.03$. Now suppose we are asked to solve for x in the equation

$$ax = b.$$

If the measurements were exact with $a = 3$ and $b = 2$, then $x = \frac{2}{3}$. Thus, we are faced with the problem of determining the maximum error in the statement $x = \frac{2}{3}$. If we can arrive at a value for E in the inequality $|x - \frac{2}{3}| < E$, then we have *an* answer. Of course, we would have a *best answer* if we were sure that we had the smallest value for E for which the inequality is true.

Now $|a - 3| < 0.1 \Rightarrow a = 3 + \alpha$, where $|\alpha| < 0.1$, and $|b - 2| < 0.03$ $\Rightarrow b = 2 + \beta$, where $|\beta| < 0.03$.

Therefore,

$$\left| x - \frac{2}{3} \right| = \left| \frac{b}{a} - \frac{2}{3} \right| = \left| \frac{2 + \beta}{3 + \alpha} - \frac{2}{3} \right| = \left| \frac{3\beta - 2\alpha}{3(3 + \alpha)} \right|.$$

Hence,

$$\left| x - \frac{2}{3} \right| = \left| \frac{3\beta - 2\alpha}{3(3 + \alpha)} \right|.$$

We will examine the right member of this result, utilizing the properties of absolute values.

$$|3\beta - 2\alpha| \le |3\beta| + |2\alpha| = 3|\beta| + 2|\alpha| < 3(0.03) + 2(0.1) = 0.29$$

and $|3 + \alpha| \ge |3| - |\alpha|$. (Can you justify this step? Would it be valid if $\alpha = 4$? if $\alpha = -4$?)

$$|3 + \alpha| > 3 - 0.1 = 2.9.$$

Therefore,

$$\left| x - \frac{2}{3} \right| < \frac{0.29}{3(2.9)} = 0.0333\ldots.$$

Notice that in attempting to get $\left| x - \frac{2}{3} \right|$ less than some quantity, we attempted to find the largest possible value for $\left| \dfrac{3\beta - 2\alpha}{3(3 + \alpha)} \right|$; and this was accomplished by finding the largest possible value of the numerator and the *smallest* possible value of the denominator.

Let's do this same problem with a different strategy, but now we will call on you for assistance. Given $|a - 3| < 0.1$, $|b - 2| < 0.03$, and $ax = b$. We know that $x = \frac{2}{3} + \xi$; and we ask, how large might ξ be? We begin, as above, by letting $a = 3 + \alpha$ and $b = 2 + \beta$. Then $ax = b$ becomes

$$(3 + \underline{\quad})(\tfrac{2}{3} + \underline{\quad}) = 2 + \beta.$$	α, ξ

Then

$$2 + 3\underline{\quad} + \tfrac{2}{3}\alpha + \underline{\quad} = 2 + \beta.$$	$\xi, \alpha\xi$

Simplifying, we obtain

$$3\xi = \underline{\quad} - \underline{\quad} - \alpha\xi.$$	$\beta, \tfrac{2}{3}\alpha$

We now estimate the right-hand side,

$$3|\xi| = |3\xi| = |\underline{\quad} - \underline{\quad} - \alpha\xi|,$$	$\beta, \tfrac{2}{3}\alpha$

making use of the principle that $|A + B| \le |A| + |B|$. We obtain

$$3|\xi| < |\underline{\qquad}| + |\underline{\qquad}| + |\alpha\xi| \qquad\qquad \beta, \tfrac{2}{3}\alpha$$

$$< 0.03 + \underline{\qquad} + 0.1|\xi|. \qquad\qquad 0.0667$$

Now we can solve for $|\xi|$:

$$(3 - 0.1)|\xi| \le \underline{\qquad}, \qquad\qquad 0.0967$$

or

$$|\xi| \le \frac{\quad}{2.9} < 0.034. \qquad\qquad 0.0967$$

7.4.1
EXERCISES

1. (a) If $|a - 3| < \varepsilon$, $|b - 2| < \delta$, and $ax = b$, estimate $\xi = x - \tfrac{2}{3}$ in terms of ε and δ.

(b) If $\varepsilon \le 1$, prove that $|x - \tfrac{2}{3}| < (3\delta + 2\varepsilon)/6$.

(c) If $\varepsilon < 3$, prove that $|\xi| < (\delta + \tfrac{2}{3}\varepsilon)/(3 - \varepsilon)$.

2. Suppose you wish to find the solution to the general problem: If $ax = b$ and you are given the approximations a_1 and b_1 for a and b, respectively, find the maximum error in $x_1 = b_1/a_1$ as an approximation to x.

Of course, this problem cannot be solved unless you are also given the margin of error in the given values for a and b, so suppose you know that $|a - a_1| < \varepsilon$ and $|b - b_1| < \delta$. We may write

$$a_1 = a + \alpha \quad \text{and} \quad b_1 = b + \beta,$$

with $|\underline{\quad}| < \varepsilon$ and $|\beta| < \underline{\quad}$. We shall assume that $a > 0$. $\qquad \alpha, \delta$
x_1 can be expressed as

$$x_1 = \frac{b + \underline{\quad}}{a + \alpha}. \qquad\qquad \beta$$

The maximum error is then

$$\left| x_1 - \frac{b}{a} \right| = \left| \frac{b + \underline{\quad}}{a + \alpha} - \frac{b}{a} \right| \qquad\qquad \beta$$

$$= \left| \frac{a\beta - \underline{\quad}}{a(a + \alpha)} \right| \qquad\qquad b\alpha$$

$$\le \frac{|a\beta| \; ? \; |\underline{\quad}|}{|a(a + \alpha)|} \qquad\qquad +, \, b\alpha$$

$$\le \frac{|a||\beta| + |b||\alpha|}{|a||a + \alpha|} < \frac{|a|\delta + |b|\underline{\quad}}{|a||a + \alpha|}. \qquad\qquad \varepsilon$$

To estimate the last fraction, we apply the principle that if we divide by less we obtain a ———— (larger/smaller) number. Therefore, if we decrease the denominator, replacing it by a smaller positive number, we obtain a ———— (larger/smaller) result. So we try to estimate $|a + \alpha|$ from below. We have

larger

larger

$$|a + \alpha| \geq |a| - \underline{\quad} \qquad \text{(Why? Explain.)}$$

$|\alpha|$

$$\geq a - \underline{\quad},$$

ε

which will be positive provided that $a > \underline{\quad}$. Then we can complete our estimate:

ε

$$\left| x_1 - \frac{b}{a} \right| \leq \frac{a\delta + |b|\varepsilon}{a(\underline{\quad})}$$

$a - \varepsilon$

if $\varepsilon < a$.

What would you do if $a < 0$?

3. The demand function relating the price p of a hundredweight of pork with the quantity q of hundredweights demanded is given by the relation

$$q = \frac{p - a}{b}.$$

If $a = 100 + \alpha$, with $|\alpha| < 2$, $b = 5 + \beta$, with $|\beta| < 0.02$, and $q = 16 + \gamma$, with $|\gamma| < 0.01$, find the maximum fluctuation in price p.

4. In $x + ay = b$, $cy = 1$, with $|a - 1| < \frac{1}{10}$, $|b + 1| < \frac{1}{10}$, and $|c - 1| < \frac{1}{10}$, find the maximum error in computing x and y from the given equations.

If $a = 1$, $b = -1$, and $c = 1$, then $x = \underline{\quad}$ and $y = \underline{\quad}$. If you think of $x = -2 + \xi$ and $y = 1 + \eta$, then finding the maximum error in x and y requires finding ———— and ————. Let $a = 1 + \alpha$, $b = -1 + \beta$, and $c = 1 + \gamma$. Then you know that $|\alpha| < \underline{\quad}$, $|\beta| < \underline{\quad}$, and $|\gamma| < \underline{\quad}$. The second equation of this given system can be written

$-2, 1$

$|\xi|, |\eta|$

$\frac{1}{10}, \frac{1}{10}, \frac{1}{10}$

$$(1 + \gamma)y = 1 \quad \text{or} \quad y = 1 + \underline{\quad}.$$

$\dfrac{-\gamma}{1 + \gamma}$

Therefore, $\eta = \underline{\quad}$ and

$\dfrac{-\gamma}{1 + \gamma}$

$$|\eta| = \left| \frac{-\gamma}{1 + \gamma} \right| = \frac{|\gamma|}{|1 + \gamma|} \leq \frac{|\gamma|}{1 - \underline{\quad}}.$$

$|\gamma|$

Therefore,

$$|\eta| < \frac{\frac{1}{10}}{1 - \frac{1}{10}} = \underline{\quad}.$$

$\frac{1}{9}$

Returning to the first equation, you may write

$$x = b - ay = (-1 + \underline{\quad}) - (1 + \underline{\quad})(1 + \eta),$$

β, α

or $-2 + \xi = -2 + \beta - \alpha - \eta - \underline{\quad}$.

$\alpha\eta$

Simplifying and taking absolute values of both members gives

$$|\xi| = |\beta - \alpha - \alpha\eta| \le |\beta| + |\alpha| + |\alpha||\eta|,$$

so the numerical bound for $|\xi|$ is given by the inequality

$$|\xi| < \underline{\qquad}.$$

$\frac{29}{90}$

5. In the system $x + ay = b$, $cy = d$, find the maximum error in x and y, if
   (a) $|a - 1| < 0.1$, $|b + 1| < 0.1$, $|c - 1| < 0.1$, and $|d - 1| < 0.1$.
   (b) $|a - 2| < 0.01$, $|b + 2| < 0.1$, $|c - 1| < 0.1$, and $|d - 1| < 0.1$.

6. In the system $ax + by = u$, $cx + dy = v$, if $|a - 13| < 0.0001$, $|b - 17| < 0.0001$, $|c - 16| < 0.0001$, $|d - 21| < 0.0001$, $u = 1$, and $v = 0$, what is the maximum error in x and y?

If the exact values of the coefficients were $a = 13$, $b = 17$, $c = 16$, and $d = 21$, then we would have $x = \underline{\qquad}$ and $y = \underline{\qquad}$.
We can, therefore, write $x = 21 + \xi$ and $y = -16 + \eta$, so the maximum errors in x and y are given by $|\underline{\qquad}|$ and $|\underline{\qquad}|$, respectively. Let's write

21, −16
ξ, η

$$a = 13 + \alpha, \quad b = 17 + \beta, \quad c = 16 + \gamma, \quad d = 21 + \delta.$$

Then $|\alpha| < \underline{\qquad}$, $|\beta| < \underline{\qquad}$, $|\gamma| < 0.0001$, and $|\delta| < 0.0001$. Multiplying out and rearranging terms, we obtain

0.0001, 0.0001

$$13\xi + 17\eta = -21\alpha + 16\beta - \alpha\xi - \beta\eta = r,$$

$$16\xi + 21\eta = \underline{\qquad}\gamma + \underline{\qquad}\delta - \underline{\qquad}\xi - \underline{\qquad}\eta = s.$$

−21, 16, γ, δ

We can solve for ξ and η in terms of r and s:

$$\xi = \underline{\qquad}r + \underline{\qquad}s, \qquad \eta = \underline{\qquad}r + \underline{\qquad}s.$$

21, −17, −16, 13

Let $\varepsilon = \max \{|\xi|, |\eta|\}$ be the larger of $|\xi|$ and $|\eta|$. Then we can estimate $|r|$ and $|s|$:

$$|r| \le 21|\alpha| + 16|\beta| + |\alpha||\xi| + |\beta||\eta|$$

$$\le 0.0021 + \underline{\qquad} + 0.0001\varepsilon + \underline{\qquad}\varepsilon$$

$$\le \underline{\qquad} + \underline{\qquad}\varepsilon.$$

0.0016, 0.0001
0.0037, 0.0002

Therefore, we can also estimate $|\xi|$ and $|\eta|$

$$|\xi| \le 21|r| + 17|s|$$

$$\le 21(0.0037 + 0.0002\varepsilon) + 17(\underline{\qquad} + \underline{\qquad}\varepsilon)$$

$$\le \underline{\qquad} + \underline{\qquad}\varepsilon;$$

0.0037, 0.0002
0.1406, 0.0076

and

$$|\eta| \le \underline{\qquad} + \underline{\qquad}\varepsilon.$$

0.1073, 0.0058

But ε is the larger of $|\xi|$ and $|\eta|$, so that we obtain

$$\varepsilon \leq \underline{\hphantom{0.1406}} + 0.0076\varepsilon. \qquad\qquad 0.1406$$

Solving this inequality, we obtain

$$\varepsilon \leq \frac{0.1406}{\underline{\hphantom{0.9924}}} = \underline{\hphantom{0.142}} < 0.15. \qquad\qquad 0.9924, 0.142$$

Carry out a similar estimation for $|s|$.

7. (a) Work Exercise 6 with the assumptions $|a - 13| < 0.01$, $|b - 17| < 0.01$, $|c - 16| < 0.01$, and $|d - 21| < 0.01$.

(b) Solve the system of equations with $\alpha = -0.0001 = \delta$, $\beta = \gamma = -\alpha$. How does the above estimate for ε compare with the actual value?

(c) Solve the equations with $\alpha = \delta = -0.01$, $\beta = \gamma = -\alpha$. How does your estimate for ε in part (a) compare with the actual value?

8. Suppose that $x_1 = x + \xi$, $y_1 = y + \eta$, and $|\xi| \leq \varepsilon$, $|\eta| \leq \varepsilon$.

(a) What is the greatest possible value of $|(x_1 + y_1) - (x + y)|$?

(b) What is the greatest possible value of $|3x_1 - 3x|$?

(c) If a is a given constant, what is the greatest possible value of $|ax_1 - ax|$?

(d) If $|x| \leq A$, $|y| \leq A$, what is the greatest possible value of $|x_1 y_1 - xy|$?

(e) If $|x| \leq A$, what is the greatest possible value of $|x_1^2 - x^2|$?

(f) If $|x| \leq A$, $\varepsilon \leq 1$, find a constant C such that $|x_1^2 - x^2| \leq C\varepsilon$.

(g) If $n \in \mathscr{Z}^+$, $|x| \leq A$, and $\varepsilon \leq 1$, find a constant C_n such that $|x_1^n - x^n| \leq C_n \varepsilon$.

(h) If $0 \leq x \leq A$ and $0 \leq x_1 \leq A$, what is the greatest possible value of

$$\left| \sqrt{x_1} - \sqrt{x} \right|?$$

(i) If $0 \leq x \leq A$, $0 \leq x_1 \leq A$, and $n \in \mathscr{Z}^+$, what is the greatest possible value of $\left| \sqrt[n]{x_1} - \sqrt[n]{x} \right|$?

(j) If $0 < h \leq |x| \leq A$, what is the greatest possible value of $|x_1^{-1} - x^{-1}|$? For which values of ε is this maximum finite?

(k) If the function $P = 3 + 4I - 8I^2$ and $|x| \leq A$, $\varepsilon \leq 1$, find a constant C such that $|P(x_1) - P(x)| \leq C\varepsilon$.

(l) If $|a_0| \leq 8$, $|a_1| \leq 8$, $|a_2| \leq 8$, $P = a_0 + a_1 I + a_2 I^2$, and $|x| \leq A$, $\varepsilon \leq 1$, find a constant C such that $|P(x_1) - P(x)| \leq C\varepsilon$.

7.5

Interpretation by Transformation   In many applications of mathematics, we meet the problem of solving a large number of systems of equations of the form

(1)
$$5x - 2y = u,$$
$$-2x + 3y = v.$$

The system (1) is typical of those encountered in the study of two-mesh electrical networks with given resistances but *arbitrary voltages u and v*. Electrical engineers and physicists who study such networks have devices called *potentiometers* by means of which they can vary the voltages in a network. (The volume control of a radio or television set is a simple example a potentiometer.) Just a single two-mesh network with a pair of potentiometers is sufficient to provide a physical model for a infinite number of systems given by (1).

In geometric terms, the given equations can be considered to define a transformation of an (x, y)-plane onto a (u, v)-plane (Fig. 7-10). Since our experience has shown that geometry can serve to assist in understanding algebra, we will devote this section to the study of linear equations as geometric transformations. Later, we shall turn the picture around and use the algebra of linear equations to assist in the study of geometry.

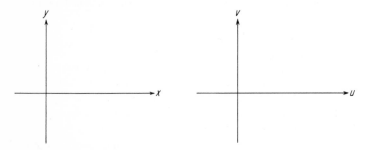

Figure 7-10

We begin with a pair of equations

$$3x + 4y = u,$$

$$2x + 3y = v.$$

As remarked above, these equations can be considered, geometrically, to define a transformation

$$T : (x, y) \rightarrow (u, v)$$

from an (x, y)-plane to a (u, v)-plane. We can represent T explicitly by writing

(2) $$T : (x, y) \rightarrow (u, v) = (3x + 4y, 2x + 3y)$$

or merely

$$T : (x, y) \rightarrow (3x + 4y, 2x + 3y).$$

If you wish to see how T transforms the point whose coordinates are $(3, 5)$ (Fig. 7-11), you write

$$T : (3, 5) \rightarrow (3(3) + 4(5), 2(3) + 3(5)) = (29, 21).$$

Thus,

$$T: (3, 5) \rightarrow (29, 21).$$

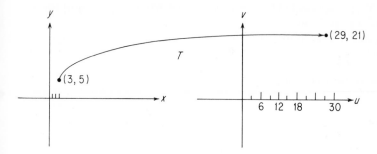

Figure 7-11

In these new terms the old problem of solving for the unknowns in a system of linear equations is equivalent to finding the point (x, y) such that $T: (x, y) \rightarrow$ a given point (u, v).

The transformation T may be regarded as a function (see Exercise 3 below) which operates on points in the (x, y)-plane to produce points in the (u, v)-plane. Thus, we shall also exploit the functional notation and write $T(x, y) = (u, v)$.

7.5.1
EXERCISES

In this entire set of exercises, T refers to the transformation defined by (2), namely, $T: (x, y) \rightarrow (3x + 4y, 2x + 3y)$.

1. $T(0, 0) = ?$, $T(1, 1) = ?$, $T(-1, -1) = ?$, $T(2, 2) = ?$ In each case compute v/u.

2. $T(1, 2) = ?$, $T(2, 4) = ?$, $T(-1, -2) = ?$, $T(a, 2a) = ?$ In each case, compute v/u.

3. Does T make each point (x, y) correspond to a unique point (u, v)? Is T really a function?

4. (a) Find (A, B) such that $T(A, B) = (1, 0)$.
  (b) Find (C, D) such that $T(C, D) = (0, 1)$.
  (c) Compute $T(A + C, B + D)$.
  (d) Compute $T(2A + C, 2B + D)$.
  (e) Compute $T(2A - 3C, 2B - 3D)$.
  (f) Compute $T(5A + 3C, 5B + 3D)$.
  (g) Find (x, y) such that $T(x, y) = (7, 2)$.
  (h) Find (x, y) such that $T(x, y) = (u, v)$. How is this solution related to the solutions of parts (a) and (b)? Can this principle be generalized?
  (i) If h and k are fixed real numbers, compute $T(hA + kC, hB + kD)$.

275

(j) If $T(x, y) = (u, v)$, compute $Au + Cv$ and $Bu + Dv$.

(k) How many points (x, y) are transformed by T into a given point (u, v)?

5. (a) The locus in the (x, y)-plane defined by the equation $y = x$ is transformed by T into a locus in the (u, v)-plane. Find the new locus and describe it by an equation.

(b) Do similarly for the locus defined by $y = 3x$.

(c) Do similarly for the locus defined by $y = mx$.

(d) Complete the conjecture: The transformation T transforms lines through the origin of the (x, y)-plane into _____.

(e) Prove your contention in part (d).

6. (a) $T(1, 6) = ?$.

(b) $T(3, 8) = ?$.

(c) $T(1 + 3, 6 + 8) = ?$.

(d) $T(7 \cdot 1, 7 \cdot 6) = ?$.

(e) $T(-5 \cdot 1, -5 \cdot 6) = ?$.

(f) If k and m are fixed real numbers, compute $T(k, 6k), T(3m, 8m)$, and $T(k + 3m, 6k + 8m)$.

7. (a) Is there an ordered pair (a, b) that transforms into itself; that is, $T(a, b) = (a, b)$?

(b) How many ordered pairs (a, b) satisfy $T(a, b) = (a, b)$?

(c) Find a point $(x, 1)$ such that $T(x, 1) = (kx, k)$. For how many values of k is there such a point?

(d) What does T do to the line joining the origin to one of the points $(x, 1)$ which you found in part (c)?

8. Let the transformation U be defined by

$$U(x, y) = (Ax + Cy, Bx + Dy),$$

where A, B, C, and D are as in Exercise 4.

(a) Compute $U(T(2, 1))$.

(b) Compute $T(U(7, 2))$.

(c) What is $T \circ U$?

(d) What is $U \circ T$?

9. Let $T(x, y) = (u, v) = (3x + 4y, 2x + 3y)$.

(a) What is the set of (x, y) such that $v = 0$?

(b) What is the set of (x, y) such that $v = 2$?

(c) What is the set of (x, y) such that $v = 2u$?

(d) What is the set of (u, v) such that $x = 1$? If the position of a point at time t is given by $x = 1$ and $y = t$, what is the path of the point? What is the path of the corresponding point (u, v)?

(e) Describe the locus defined by the set

$$\{(u, v) \mid x = 1 - t \wedge y = t\}.$$

(f) In the (u, v)-plane, graph the set

$$\{(u, v) \mid x = 1 + t \wedge y = 6 + 7t\}.$$

(g) Find m such that $\{(x, y) \mid v = mu\}$ is a line parallel to the y-axis.

The problem of finding the solution to the system of equations

$$3x + 4y = 7,$$

$$2x + 3y = 2,$$

is the problem of finding (x, y) such that $T(x, y) = (7, 2)$. In the light of the discussion above, we can put this problem in the context of trans-formations as follows: We have $T: (x, y) \rightarrow (7, 2)$. If we knew the *inverse of T*, assuming its existence and calling it V for the moment, we could apply V to the ordered pair $(7, 2)$ to obtain $V(7, 2) = (x, y)$. This reasoning is indicated pictorially in Fig. 7-12. Thus, the problem of finding (x, y) such that $T(x, y) = (u, v)$ reduces to that of finding the inverse V, of T, so that

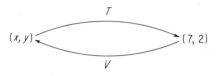

Figure 7-12

$$V(u, v) = (x, y).$$

In Exercises 7.5.1, where

$$T: (x, y) \rightarrow (u, v) = (3x + 4y, 2x + 3y),$$

you found, by solving for (u, v), that

$$V: (x, y) = (3u - 4v, -2u + 3v).$$

Therefore, $V(7, 2) = (\underline{\quad}, \underline{\quad})$, which should check with your answer to Exercise 4(g). In general, if you are given any point (u_0, v_0) in the (u, v)-plane, it is a simple matter to determine the (x_0, y_0) such that $T(x_0, y_0) = (u_0, v_0)$. You merely compute (x_0, y_0) by operating with V:

$$V(u_0, v_0) = (x_0, y_0).$$

Knowing V enables you to solve an infinity of systems of equations, namely all those of the form

$$3x + 4y = \underline{\quad\quad},$$

$$2x + 3y = \underline{\quad\quad},$$

no matter what numbers appear in the blanks. You can now begin to appreciate the economy of the "transformation point of view." Furthermore, you observe that the key to solving systems of equations lies mainly in the coefficients of the unknowns, for these are the numbers that define the given transformation whose inverse we seek.

If you had many systems of the form

$$T(x, y) = (u, v)$$

to solve, and you had an assistant who knew only arithmetic, you could instruct him to calculate x like this:

(1) Write u.
(2) Write v.
(3) Multiply the number in (1) by 3.
(4) Multiply the number in (2) by 4.
(5) Subtract the number in (4) from the number in (3).

You could also program these instructions for computer use. How would you write out such instructions for computing y?

If T and V are given as above, you get $V(T(1, 2)) = (\underline{\hspace{1cm}}, \underline{\hspace{1cm}})$ and $T(V(7, 2)) = (\underline{\hspace{1cm}}, \underline{\hspace{1cm}})$. Was very much computing required to fill these blanks? You shouldn't have done any! Since $V(T(x, y)) = (\underline{\hspace{1cm}}, \underline{\hspace{1cm}})$ and $T(V(u, v)) = (\underline{\hspace{1cm}}, \underline{\hspace{1cm}})$, V does, in fact, satisfy the conditions which define *the inverse function* of T; for

$$V \circ T = T \circ V = I,$$

where I denotes the identity function or transformation. We therefore say that

$$V = T^{-1}, \qquad \cdot$$

which explicitly denotes the relationship between V and T.

7.5.2
EXERCISES

1. Find the inverses of the following transformations:
 (a) $A(x, y) = (x + 5y, y)$,
 (b) $B(x, y) = (-y, x)$,
 (c) $C(x, y) = (5x + 8y, 8x + 13y)$,
 (d) $D(x, y) = (4x + 9y, 9x + 12y)$,
 (e) $E(x, y) = (13x - 8y, -8x + 5y)$.

2. (a) Let $(u, v) = A(x, y)$ and $(r, s) = A(u, v)$, where A is defined in Exercise 1. Then $(r, s) = (A \circ A)(x, y) = (ax + by, cx + dy)$, for some numbers a, b, c, d. Compute these numbers.

(b) Compute the transformations $B \circ B$, $A \circ B$, $B \circ A$, $A \circ C$, $C \circ A$, $C \circ E$, $E \circ C$, as suggested in part (a) of this problem.

Since the transformation T is completely determined by the coefficients of x and y in its defining equations, it is convenient to use the symbol

$$\begin{pmatrix} 3 & 4 \\ 2 & 3 \end{pmatrix}$$

as a name for T. Such a symbol is called a *matrix*. The transformation T is represented by a 2×2 matrix (two rows, two columns). In the same way we can represent the transformations A, B, and C in Exercise 1 of Sec. 7.5.2 by the matrices

$$\begin{pmatrix} 1 & 5 \\ 0 & 1 \end{pmatrix}, \quad \begin{pmatrix} 0 & -1 \\ 1 & 0 \end{pmatrix}, \quad \text{and} \quad \begin{pmatrix} 5 & 8 \\ 8 & 13 \end{pmatrix},$$

respectively.

Write the matrices representing D, E, V, and the identity transformation I.

Let us compute the matrix of the transformation $C \circ T$. If $(r, s) = C(u, v)$ and $(u, v) = T(x, y)$, then

$$r = 5u + 8v = 5(3x + 4y) + 8(2x + 3y)$$

$$= \underline{\quad\quad} x + \underline{\quad\quad} y \qquad\qquad \textit{31, 44}$$

and

$$s = 8u + 13v = 8(\underline{\quad} x + \underline{\quad} y) + 13(\underline{\quad} x + \underline{\quad} y) \qquad \textit{3, 4, 2, 3}$$

$$= \underline{\quad\quad} x + \underline{\quad\quad} y. \qquad\qquad\qquad \textit{50, 71}$$

Therefore, the transformation $C \circ T$ is represented by the matrix

$$\begin{pmatrix} \underline{\quad\quad} & \underline{\quad\quad} \\ \underline{\quad\quad} & \underline{\quad\quad} \end{pmatrix}. \qquad\qquad \textit{31, 44}$$
$$\textit{50, 71}$$

In general, if the transformations G and Γ have the matrices

$$G : \begin{pmatrix} a & b \\ c & d \end{pmatrix} \quad \text{and} \quad \Gamma : \begin{pmatrix} \alpha & \beta \\ \gamma & \delta \end{pmatrix},$$

then the matrix of $G \circ \Gamma$ is

$$\begin{pmatrix} \underline{\quad} + \underline{\quad} & \underline{\quad} + \underline{\quad} \\ \underline{\quad} + \underline{\quad} & \underline{\quad} + \underline{\quad} \end{pmatrix}. \qquad \begin{matrix} a\alpha,\ b\gamma,\ a\beta,\ b\delta \\ \\ c\alpha,\ d\gamma,\ c\beta,\ d\delta \end{matrix}$$

We call this the *product* of the matrices for G and Γ, and write

$$\begin{pmatrix} a & b \\ c & d \end{pmatrix} \begin{pmatrix} \alpha & \beta \\ \gamma & \delta \end{pmatrix} = \begin{pmatrix} a\alpha + b\gamma & a\beta + b\delta \\ c\alpha + d\gamma & c\beta + d\delta \end{pmatrix}.$$

The number in the first row and second column of the product is obtained by multiplying the numbers in the _____ row of the first factor by the corresponding numbers in the _____ column of the second factor, and adding the results.

first
second

In the same way, the number in the second row and first column of the product is obtained by multiplying the numbers in the _____ row of the first factor by the corresponding numbers in the _____ column of the second factor, and adding.

second
first

This is the beginning of an algebra of matrices. The formulas for the elements in the product of two matrices suggest that we can consider our transformations as examples of matrix multiplication. Look at the product

$$\begin{pmatrix} 3 & 4 \\ 2 & 3 \end{pmatrix}\begin{pmatrix} x \\ y \end{pmatrix}.$$

Note that we have represented the point (x, y) by a 2×1 matrix (two rows, one column). If we apply the above rule (since the second factor has only one column, the product will also be a _____ × _____ matrix), we obtain the number in the first row and first (and only) column of the product by multiplying the numbers in the _____ row of the first factor by the numbers in the _____ column of the second factor, and adding. This gives $3x + 4y$. Lo and behold, this is the formula for _____! In the same way, the number in the second row and first column of the product is obtained by multiplying the numbers in the _____ row of the first factor by the numbers in the _____ column of the second factor, and adding. This gives

2, 1

first
first

u

second
first

$$\text{_____}x + \text{_____}y.$$

2, 3

We see that

$$\begin{pmatrix} 3 & 4 \\ 2 & 3 \end{pmatrix}\begin{pmatrix} x \\ y \end{pmatrix} = \begin{pmatrix} \text{_____} + \text{_____} \\ \text{_____} + \text{_____} \end{pmatrix},$$

3x, 4y

2x, 3y

so that T can be represented by

$$T : \begin{pmatrix} x \\ y \end{pmatrix} \rightarrow \begin{pmatrix} 3 & 4 \\ 2 & 3 \end{pmatrix}\begin{pmatrix} x \\ y \end{pmatrix} = \begin{pmatrix} u \\ v \end{pmatrix}.$$

The composition of transformations corresponds to the multiplication of matrices.

1. Compute the following products:

(a) $\begin{pmatrix} 1 & 0 \\ 0 & 1 \end{pmatrix}\begin{pmatrix} \alpha & \beta \\ \gamma & \delta \end{pmatrix}$,

(b) $\begin{pmatrix} a & b \\ c & d \end{pmatrix}\begin{pmatrix} 1 & 0 \\ 0 & 1 \end{pmatrix}$,

(c) $\begin{pmatrix} 5 & 6 \\ 2 & 3 \end{pmatrix}\begin{pmatrix} 3 & -2 \\ -6 & 5 \end{pmatrix}$,

(d) $\begin{pmatrix} 3 & -2 \\ -6 & 5 \end{pmatrix}\begin{pmatrix} 5 & 6 \\ 2 & 3 \end{pmatrix}$,

(e) $\begin{pmatrix} 2 & 0 \\ 0 & 2 \end{pmatrix}\begin{pmatrix} \alpha & \beta \\ \gamma & \delta \end{pmatrix}$,

(f) $\begin{pmatrix} a & b \\ c & d \end{pmatrix}\begin{pmatrix} 2 & 0 \\ 0 & 2 \end{pmatrix}$,

(g) $\begin{pmatrix} 0 & 1 \\ 1 & 0 \end{pmatrix}\begin{pmatrix} \alpha & \beta \\ \gamma & \delta \end{pmatrix}$,

(h) $\begin{pmatrix} a & b \\ c & d \end{pmatrix}\begin{pmatrix} 0 & 1 \\ 1 & 0 \end{pmatrix}$,

(i) $\begin{pmatrix} 0 & 1 \\ 0 & 0 \end{pmatrix}\begin{pmatrix} 0 & 0 \\ 0 & 1 \end{pmatrix}$,

(j) $\begin{pmatrix} 0 & 0 \\ 0 & 1 \end{pmatrix}\begin{pmatrix} 0 & 1 \\ 0 & 0 \end{pmatrix}$,

(k) $\begin{pmatrix} 1 & 2 \\ 3 & 4 \end{pmatrix}\begin{pmatrix} 5 & 6 \\ 7 & 8 \end{pmatrix}$,

(l) $\begin{pmatrix} 5 & 6 \\ 7 & 8 \end{pmatrix}\begin{pmatrix} 9 & 10 \\ 11 & 12 \end{pmatrix}$,

(m) $(12 \quad 34)\begin{pmatrix} 111 & 122 \\ 151 & 166 \end{pmatrix}$.

2. Let

$$\begin{pmatrix} a & b \\ c & d \end{pmatrix}\begin{pmatrix} \alpha & \beta \\ \gamma & \delta \end{pmatrix} = \begin{pmatrix} t & u \\ v & w \end{pmatrix}.$$

Compute $(tw - uv) - (ad - bc)(\alpha\delta - \beta\gamma)$.

3. Let the transformation H have the matrix

$$\begin{pmatrix} 1 & 1 \\ 0 & 1 \end{pmatrix}.$$

Compute the matrix of H^n for $n = \pm 1, \pm 2, \pm 3, \dots, \pm 10$.

4. How would you define the product of a 1×2 matrix with a 2×1 matrix:

$$(a \quad b)\begin{pmatrix} x \\ y \end{pmatrix}?$$

5. How would you define the product of a 2×1 matrix with a 1×2 matrix:

$$\begin{pmatrix} x \\ y \end{pmatrix}(a \quad b)?$$

6. How would you define the product of a 1×1 matrix with a 1×1 matrix: $(a)(x)$?

7. How would you define the product of a 1×1 matrix with a 2×2 matrix:

$$(x)\begin{pmatrix} a & b \\ c & d \end{pmatrix}?$$

8. If T is the transformation considered above, i.e., defined by (2), compute
   (a) $T(5, -6)$,
   (b) $T(10, -12)$,
   (c) $T(-8, 7)$,
   (d) $T(5 + (-8), (-6) + 7)$,
   (e) $T(x_1 + x_2, y_1 + y_2)$.

9. (a) How does

$$\begin{pmatrix} 3 & 4 \\ 2 & 3 \end{pmatrix} \begin{pmatrix} 7x \\ 7y \end{pmatrix}$$

compare with

$$\begin{pmatrix} 3 & 4 \\ 2 & 3 \end{pmatrix} \begin{pmatrix} x \\ y \end{pmatrix} ?$$

   (b) How does

$$\begin{pmatrix} 3 & 4 \\ 2 & 3 \end{pmatrix} \begin{pmatrix} x_1 + x_2 \\ y_1 + y_2 \end{pmatrix}$$

compare with

$$\begin{pmatrix} 3 & 4 \\ 2 & 3 \end{pmatrix} \begin{pmatrix} x_1 \\ y_1 \end{pmatrix} \quad \text{and} \quad \begin{pmatrix} 3 & 4 \\ 2 & 3 \end{pmatrix} \begin{pmatrix} x_2 \\ y_2 \end{pmatrix} ?$$

10. What is the effect of T operating on a line in the (x, y)-plane?
   (a) Let $x = x_0 + at$, $y = y_0 + bt$, $t \in \mathcal{R}$ be a parametric representation of the given line. Compute

$$\begin{pmatrix} 3 & 4 \\ 2 & 3 \end{pmatrix} \begin{pmatrix} x_0 + at \\ y_0 + bt \end{pmatrix}.$$

   (b) If $u = u_0 + a't$, $v = v_0 + b't$, find u_0, v_0, a', and b'.
   (c) What is the image in the (u, v)-plane of the given line in the (x, y)-plane?
   (d) If a line L is given by $y = 2x - 1$, find the image of L under T. What is the slope of the image of L?
   (e) If line M is given by $y = 2x$, find $T(M)$ by the matrix method and determine its slope.
   (f) If line N is given by $y = 2x + 1$, find $T(N)$ and determine its slope.
   (g) An alternative method for finding the images under T is the following. Consider the problem of finding $T(L)$, where L is given by $y = 2x - 1$. From

$$3x + 4y = u$$

$$2x + 3y = v,$$

find u and v in terms of x alone. Then eliminate x from the resulting equations to obtain an equation in u and v. Use this method to find the images of M and N, checking the results you obtained by the matrix method in (e) and (f).

7.6

Transformations of Vectors. Linearity In order to achieve a geometric view of a system of linear equations, we considered the ordered pairs (x, y) as points transformed into points designated by ordered pairs (u, v). From this point of view, we observed that the equations define a function whose domain is the set of ordered pairs:

$$\{(x, y)|x, y \in \mathcal{R}\}.$$

However, we recall that ordered pairs were encountered as vectors as well as points. Hence, a transformation T, defined by a pair of linear equations, also has an interpretation as a transformation of vectors into vectors. That is,

$$T: [x, y] \to [u, v].$$

Let's examine the effect of T on vectors, first considering this effect on the sum of two vectors. Let

$$\mathbf{X}_1 = [x_1, y_1],$$
$$\mathbf{X}_2 = [x_2, y_2].$$

We ask: How is $T(\mathbf{X}_1 + \mathbf{X}_2)$ related to $T(\mathbf{X}_1)$ and $T(\mathbf{X}_2)$?
Suppose we call $T(\mathbf{X}_1) = [u_1, v_1]$ and $T(\mathbf{X}_2) = [u_2, v_2]$.
In coordinate form $\mathbf{X}_1 + \mathbf{X}_2 = [\underline{\hspace{1cm}}, \underline{\hspace{1cm}}]$. Thus, applying the defining equations for T [see (2) on p. 274] to determine $T(\mathbf{X}_1 + \mathbf{X}_2)$, we have

$x_1 + x_2,$
$y_1 + y_2$

$$3(x_1 + x_2) + 4(\underline{\hspace{1cm}}) = (3x_1 + 4y_1) + (3x_2 + 4y_2),$$

$y_1 + y_2$

$$2(x_1 + x_2) + 3(y_1 + y_2) = (2x_1 + 3y_1) + \underline{\hspace{1cm}}.$$

$2x_2 + 3y_2$

But

$$\underline{\hspace{0.5cm}}x_1 + \underline{\hspace{0.5cm}}y_1 = u_1 \quad \text{and} \quad \underline{\hspace{0.5cm}}x_2 + \underline{\hspace{0.5cm}}y_2 = u_2,$$

3, 4, 3, 4

and

$$\underline{\hspace{0.5cm}}x_1 + \underline{\hspace{0.5cm}}y_1 = v_1 \quad \text{and} \quad \underline{\hspace{0.5cm}}x_2 + \underline{\hspace{0.5cm}}y_2 = v_2.$$

2, 3, 2, 3

You have, therefore, shown that

$$T(\mathbf{X}_1 + \mathbf{X}_2) = [\underline{\hspace{1cm}} + u_2, \underline{\hspace{1cm}}],$$

$u_1, v_1 + v_2$

and the vector

$$T(\mathbf{X}_1) + T(\mathbf{X}_2) = [\underline{\hspace{1cm}}, \underline{\hspace{1cm}}].$$

$u_1 + u_2,$
$v_1 + v_2$

The answer to our first question is then

(1) $$T(\mathbf{X}_1 + \mathbf{X}_2) = T(\mathbf{X}_1) + T(\mathbf{X}_2).$$

The next question we pose is: If **X** is a vector and c a real number, how is the vector $T(c\mathbf{X})$ related to the vector $T(\mathbf{X})$?

Let $\mathbf{X} = [x_0, y_0]$ and

$$T(\mathbf{X}) = [u_0, v_0] = [3x_0 + 4y_0, 2x_0 + 3y_0].$$

Then $c\mathbf{X} = [\underline{\quad}, \underline{\quad}]$. $T(c\mathbf{X})$ can be computed by utilizing the defining equations for T. Thus,

$$T(c\mathbf{X}) = [3\underline{\quad} + 4\underline{\quad}, 2(cx_0) + 3(cy_0)]$$

$$= [\underline{\quad}(3x_0 + 4y_0), c(2x_0 + 3y_0)]$$

$$= \underline{\quad}[3x_0 + 4y_0, 2x_0 + 3y_0] = \underline{\quad}T(\mathbf{X}).$$

(right margin) cx_0, cy_0

$(cx_0), (cy_0)$

c

c, c

Therefore, you have the answer to our second question:

(2) $\qquad\qquad T(c\mathbf{X}) = cT(\mathbf{X}).$

A transformation which satisfies the properties (1) and (2) is called a *linear transformation*. Since a transformation T performs an *operation* on vectors, it is sometimes called an *operator*. Thus an operator L is called a *linear operator* if it satisfies the two conditions:

$$L(\mathbf{X}_1 + \mathbf{X}_2) = L(\mathbf{X}_1) + L(\mathbf{X}_2),$$

for any vectors $\mathbf{X}_1$ and $\mathbf{X}_2$; and

$$L(c\mathbf{X}) = cL(\mathbf{X}),$$

where c is any scalar and **X** is any vector.

7.6.1
EXERCISES

1. Let T be represented by the matrix

$$\begin{pmatrix} 3 & 4 \\ 2 & 3 \end{pmatrix}$$

(a) Find $T(1, 0)$ by computing

$$\begin{pmatrix} 3 & 4 \\ 2 & 3 \end{pmatrix}\begin{pmatrix} 1 \\ 0 \end{pmatrix}.$$

(b) $\qquad\qquad \begin{pmatrix} 3 & 4 \\ 2 & 3 \end{pmatrix}\begin{pmatrix} 0 \\ 1 \end{pmatrix} = ?.$

(c) Call $\varepsilon_1 = [1, 0]$ and $\varepsilon_2 = [0, 1]$, and find $T(\varepsilon_1 + \varepsilon_2)$ in two different ways.

(d) $[3, -2] = \underline{\quad}\varepsilon_1 + \underline{\quad}\varepsilon_2$. Thus, to compute $T(3, 2)$, you need only compute $\underline{\quad}T(\varepsilon_1) + \underline{\quad}T(\varepsilon_2)$.

(e) Using the linearity properties of T, compute $T(-1, -1)$, $T(2, 2)$, $T(1, 2)$, and $T(2, 4)$ and check your answers with Exercises 1 and 2 of Sec. 7.5.1.

(f) Using the linearity properties of T, compute $T(1, 6)$, $T(3, 8)$, $T(4, 14)$, $T(7, 42)$, and $T(-5, -30)$ and compare answers with those obtained in Exercise 5 of Sec. 7.5.1.

2. (a) Let $O = (0, 0)$, $A = (1, 0)$, $B = (1, 1)$, and $C = (0, 1)$ denote points in the (x, y)-plane. What shape figure is the square $OABC$ transformed into by the transformation T?

(b) Answer the same question with regard to the square $PQRS$ in the (x, y)-plane, where $P = (0, 1)$, $Q = (1, 1)$, $R = (1, 2)$, and $S = (0, 2)$. Draw the figures in the (x, y)-plane and the (u, v)-plane.

3. Let L_1 and L_2 be two parallel lines in the (x, y)-plane. Suppose

$$T: L_1 \to L_1' \quad \text{and} \quad T: L_2 \to L_2'.$$

Do L_1' and L_2' intersect always? sometimes? never? Prove your answer.

4. Let OAB be a triangle in the (x, y)-plane, where $O = (0, 0)$, $A = (1, 0)$, and $B = (1, 1)$. Let

$$T: O \to O', \qquad T: A \to A', \qquad T: B \to B'.$$

(a) What is the area of triangle OAB?

(b) What is the area of triangle $O'A'B'$?

(c) Triangle OAB has a "counterclockwise orientation" in the (x, y)-plane. What is the orientation of triangle $O'B'C'$?

5. Let $O = (0, 0)$, $B = (1, 1)$, and $C = (-1, 1)$, and

$$T: O \to O', \qquad T: B \to B', \qquad T: C \to C'.$$

(a) Compare the areas of triangle OBC and triangle $O'B'C'$.

(b) Compare the orientations.

6. Let $O = (0, 0)$, $E = (x_1, y_1)$, and $F = (x_2, y_2)$ and let

$$T: O \to O', \qquad T: E \to E', \qquad T: F \to F'.$$

(a) What is the area of triangle OEF?

(b) What is the area of triangle $O'E'F'$?

(c) Do you think the orientations of triangles OEF and $O'E'F'$ are the same or do you think they are opposite?

Virtually all the work of this section and the preceding section has been concerned with the transformation T represented by the matrix

$$\begin{pmatrix} 3 & 4 \\ 2 & 3 \end{pmatrix}.$$

When we are working with a fixed coordinate system, we shall often identify a linear transformation with its matrix and use the same letter as a name for both:

$$T = \begin{pmatrix} 3 & 4 \\ 2 & 3 \end{pmatrix}.$$

We may then speak of "the linear transformation

$$\begin{pmatrix} 3 & -2 \\ -4 & 3 \end{pmatrix}."$$

Since composition of linear transformations corresponds to multiplication of their matrices, we shall often use the notations $A \circ B$ and AB interchangeably.

To compute $T(2, 1)$, which may also be written $T\binom{2}{1}$ or $T[2, 1]$, we write

$$\begin{pmatrix} 3 & 4 \\ 2 & 3 \end{pmatrix}\begin{pmatrix} 2 \\ 1 \end{pmatrix} = \begin{pmatrix} 3 \cdot 2 + 4 \cdot 1 \\ 2 \cdot 2 + 3 \cdot 1 \end{pmatrix} = \begin{pmatrix} 10 \\ 7 \end{pmatrix}.$$

Thus, $T: [2, 1] \to [10, 7]$.

7. (a) If

$$U = \begin{pmatrix} 1 & 0 \\ 0 & 1 \end{pmatrix},$$

find

$$U\begin{pmatrix} 1 \\ 1 \end{pmatrix}, \quad U\begin{pmatrix} 2 \\ 1 \end{pmatrix}, \quad U\begin{pmatrix} -2 \\ 1 \end{pmatrix}, \quad \text{and} \quad U\begin{pmatrix} a \\ b \end{pmatrix}.$$

(b) Let

$$V = \begin{pmatrix} a & b \\ c & d \end{pmatrix},$$

and suppose

$$V\begin{pmatrix} 1 \\ 0 \end{pmatrix} = \begin{pmatrix} 1 \\ 0 \end{pmatrix} \quad \text{and} \quad V\begin{pmatrix} 0 \\ 1 \end{pmatrix} = \begin{pmatrix} 0 \\ 1 \end{pmatrix}.$$

Find a, b, c, and d.

8. Let

$$S = \begin{pmatrix} 2 & 0 \\ 0 & 2 \end{pmatrix}.$$

(a) Find

$$S\begin{pmatrix} 1 \\ 0 \end{pmatrix}, S\begin{pmatrix} 0 \\ 1 \end{pmatrix}, \quad \text{and} \quad S\begin{pmatrix} r \\ s \end{pmatrix}.$$

(b) If $k \in \mathcal{R}$, define the transformation

$$K: [x, y] \to k[x, y].$$

Is K a linear transformation? What is the matrix representation of K?

(c) If the 2×1 matrix $\begin{pmatrix} x \\ y \end{pmatrix}$ is used to represent the vector $[x, y]$, define $k\begin{pmatrix} x \\ y \end{pmatrix}$ so that it represents the vector $k[x, y]$.

(d) Define

$$k\begin{pmatrix} a & b \\ c & d \end{pmatrix}$$

so that the "associative law"

$$\left(k\begin{pmatrix}a & b \\ c & d\end{pmatrix}\right)\begin{pmatrix}x \\ y\end{pmatrix} = k\left(\begin{pmatrix}a & b \\ c & d\end{pmatrix}\begin{pmatrix}x \\ y\end{pmatrix}\right)$$

holds.

9. Let

$$V = \begin{pmatrix}-1 & 1 \\ 1 & 0\end{pmatrix} \quad \text{and} \quad W = \begin{pmatrix}1 & -1 \\ 1 & 0\end{pmatrix}.$$

(a) Find

$$W\left(V\begin{pmatrix}1 \\ 0\end{pmatrix}\right) \quad \text{and} \quad V\left(W\begin{pmatrix}1 \\ 0\end{pmatrix}\right).$$

(b) Find

$$W\left(V\begin{pmatrix}x \\ y\end{pmatrix}\right) \quad \text{and} \quad V\left(W\begin{pmatrix}x \\ y\end{pmatrix}\right).$$

(c) Write the system of linear equations which represents the transformation

$$W\left(V\begin{pmatrix}x \\ y\end{pmatrix}\right) = \begin{pmatrix}u \\ v\end{pmatrix},$$

and exhibit the matrix representation of $V \circ W$.

(d) $W \circ V = \begin{pmatrix}? \end{pmatrix}$.

10. Let $O = (0, 0)$, $A = (1, 2)$, and $B = (-1. 1)$.

(a) Find the area of triangle OAB.

(b) Let V be the same as in Exercise 9, and find the area of the triangle $V(O)V(A)V(B)$.

(c) Is the orientation of the transformed triangle the same or the opposite of the original?

11. Let

$$Z = \begin{pmatrix}-1 & 1 \\ 2 & 0\end{pmatrix} \quad \text{and} \quad W = \begin{pmatrix}1 & -1 \\ 1 & 0\end{pmatrix},$$

and call $O = (0, 0)$, $A = (1, 2)$, and $B = (-1, 1)$.

(a) Compare the areas of triangle OAB and triangle $Z(O)Z(A)Z(B)$.

(b) Find $Z \circ W$ and $W \circ Z$.

(c) Does W^{-1} exist? If so, find it.

12. (a) Let

$$T = \begin{pmatrix}3 & 4 \\ 2 & 3\end{pmatrix} \quad \text{and} \quad Z = \begin{pmatrix}-1 & 1 \\ 2 & 0\end{pmatrix}$$

be linear transformations. Let the transformation S be defined by

$$S: [x, y] \to T[x, y] + Z[x, y].$$

Compute

$$S[kx, ky] - kS[x, y]$$

and

$$S([x_1, y_1] + [x_2, y_2]) - (S[x_1, y_1] + S[x_2, y_2]).$$

Is S a linear transformation? If so, what is its matrix?

(b) Repeat part (a) with

$$T = \begin{pmatrix} a & b \\ c & d \end{pmatrix} \quad \text{and} \quad Z = \begin{pmatrix} \alpha & \beta \\ \gamma & \delta \end{pmatrix}.$$

(c) Let

$$J = \begin{pmatrix} t & u \\ v & w \end{pmatrix},$$

and let V and W be the transformations defined by

$$W: [x, y] \to (JT)[x, y] + (JZ)[x, y],$$

and

$$V: [x, y] \to J(S[x, y]).$$

Are V and W linear? If so, what are their matrices? What about the transformation $S \circ J$?

13. Let $O = (0, 0)$, $A = (1, 2)$, $B = (-2, 7)$, and

$$Z = \begin{pmatrix} -1 & 1 \\ 2 & 0 \end{pmatrix}.$$

Denote $Z(O)$ by O', $Z(A)$ by A', etc.

(a) Find the midpoint of AB and call it M.
(b) Find the midpoint of $A'B'$ and compare with $Z(M)$.
(c) How is the vector $\frac{1}{2}[1, 2] + \frac{1}{2}[-2, 7]$ related to the point M?
(d) Use linearity properties to simplify

$$Z(\tfrac{1}{2}[1, 2] + \tfrac{1}{2}[-2, 7]).$$

14. Let's investigate the general question of whether "midpoints transform into midpoints." If we wish to phrase the question precisely, we state: Let L be a linear transformation and P, Q a pair of distinct points in the domain of L. Let M be the midpoint of PQ. Is $L(M)$ the midpoint of the segment whose endpoints are $L(P)$ and $L(Q)$?

This question can certainly be answered by a coordinate approach, assigning general coordinates to P and Q and computing. We would like to assist you in carrying through an investigation using the properties of vectors and the linearity of transformation L. First, we designate the position vectors of P, Q, and M by **P**, **Q**, and **M**, respectively. Since M is the midpoint of PQ, you may write

$$\mathbf{M} = \underline{\hspace{1cm}}\mathbf{P} + \underline{\hspace{1cm}}\mathbf{Q}.$$

Then $L(\mathbf{M}) = L(\underline{\hspace{1cm}}\mathbf{P} + \underline{\hspace{1cm}}\mathbf{Q})$. Since L is linear, this last equation may be written

$$L(\mathbf{M}) = \tfrac{1}{2}L(\mathbf{P}) + \underline{\hspace{1cm}}L(\underline{\hspace{1cm}}),$$

which shows that $L(\mathbf{M})$ is the position vector of the _____ of the segment joining $L(\mathbf{P})$ to _____. What is the answer to the question we posed? Can you state a generalization that you can prove in a similar manner?

$\tfrac{1}{2}, \tfrac{1}{2}$
$\tfrac{1}{2}, \tfrac{1}{2}$
$\tfrac{1}{2}, \mathbf{Q}$
midpoint
$L(\mathbf{Q})$

15. We define a function η whose domain is $\{(x, y) \mid x, y \in \mathscr{R}\}$ as follows:

$$\eta(x, y) = y.$$

This function is sometimes called a *selector function* for it merely selects the second member of the ordered pair as its value. Then

$$\eta(3, 4) = 4, \qquad \eta(3, -4) = \underline{\hspace{1cm}}, \qquad \text{and} \quad \eta(5, \underline{\hspace{1cm}}) = 2.$$

(a) Compute $\dfrac{\eta(3, 4) - \eta(3, -4)}{\eta(3, 2) - \eta(3, 0)}$.

(b) If

$$Z = \begin{pmatrix} -1 & 1 \\ 2 & 1 \end{pmatrix},$$

compute $\dfrac{\eta(Z(3, 4)) - \eta(Z(3, -4))}{\eta(Z(3, 2)) - \eta(Z(3, 0))}$.

(c) Compute $\dfrac{\eta(Z(3, a)) - \eta(Z(3, b))}{\eta(Z(3, c)) - \eta(Z(3, d))}$.

Let's continue analyzing linear transformations with the aid of geometry. But now let us think of a transformation as a mapping of the (x, y)-plane into *itself*. Suppose we examine the linear transformation

$$T = \begin{pmatrix} 2 & 1 \\ 0 & 1 \end{pmatrix}$$

to see its geometric effect on a plane. Consider the effect of T on the unit square $OABC$ (see Fig. 7-13). We see that T maps the square into a parallelogram. It appears that the line T maps into itself has the equation _____. Does each point of this line map into itself? _____ (Yes/no.) Let's ask the more general

$y = 0$
no

question: What vectors map into themselves under the transformation T? If $[a, b]$ maps into itself, then

$$T\begin{pmatrix} a \\ b \end{pmatrix} = \ ? \ .$$

$\begin{pmatrix} a \\ b \end{pmatrix}$

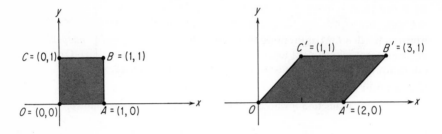

Figure 7-13

If you equate corresponding elements on both sides,

$$2a + \underline{\hspace{1cm}} b = a,$$ *1*

$$\underline{\hspace{1cm}} a + \underline{\hspace{1cm}} b = b.$$ *0, 1*

This system simplifies to read

$$\underline{\hspace{1cm}} a + \underline{\hspace{1cm}} b = 0,$$ *1, 1*

$$\underline{\hspace{1cm}} a + \underline{\hspace{1cm}} b = 0,$$ *0, 0*

which has the solution $b = \underline{\hspace{1cm}}$. Thus all vectors of the $-a$
form $[a, \underline{\hspace{1cm}}]$ map into themselves. Such vectors are $-a$
said to be *fixed* or *invariant* under the transformation T.
  The result of the last paragraph proves that every
point of the line $y = \underline{\hspace{1cm}}$ maps into itself. If $D = (1, -1)$, $-x$
the triangle OBD maps into the triangle $OB'D$, since O
and D are fixed points.

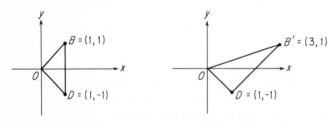

Figure 7-14

Compare the areas of $OABC$ and $OA'B'C'$, and compare the areas of triangles OBD and $OB'D$ (Fig. 7-14).

You already know that a linear transformation maps every line through the origin into a line which passes through (_____, _____). Suppose we ask: Which of these lines map into themselves? You can probably answer this by more than one method that you have learned in this section, but now we wish to acquaint you with an approach to this problem that takes advantage of the vector concept and the linearity of T.

0, 0

Suppose T maps the line OP into itself (Fig. 7-15). Then $T(P) = Q$ is also a point on the line OP. Thus, if $P = (a, b)$, we know that

$$Q = \lambda P = [\lambda a, \lambda b]$$

for some number λ. Conversely, suppose $T(P) = \lambda P$ for some number λ. Then, if R is any point on line OP, we have

$$R = \mu P$$

and

$$T(R) = T(\mu P) = \mu T(P)$$

$$= \mu(\lambda P) = \lambda \mu P$$

$$= \lambda R,$$

which shows that $T(R)$ is also on OP. So our problem reduces to that of answering the question: Which vectors $[x, y]$ other than the zero vector map into scalar multiples of themselves?

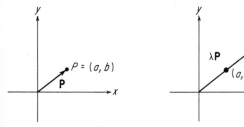

Figure 7-15

We now apply this approach to the given transformation T:

$$\begin{pmatrix} 2 & 1 \\ 0 & 1 \end{pmatrix}\begin{pmatrix} x \\ y \end{pmatrix} = \begin{pmatrix} \lambda x \\ \lambda y \end{pmatrix}.$$

This matrix equation is equivalent to the system

$$2x + y = \lambda x$$

$$y = \lambda y,$$

or

$$(2 - \lambda)x + y = 0$$

$$(1 - \lambda)y = 0.$$

The second equation of the system is the simpler, having the solution

$$1 - \lambda = 0 \quad \vee \quad y = 0;$$

that is,

$$\lambda = 1 \quad \vee \quad y = 0.$$

If $\lambda \neq 1$, then $y = 0$, and the first equation yields $(2 - \lambda)x = 0$, which has the solution

$$x = 0 \quad \vee \quad 2 - \lambda = 0.$$

Therefore, the zero vector $\begin{pmatrix} 0 \\ 0 \end{pmatrix}$ maps into a scalar multiple of itself. Is this news?

Our result is that $\lambda = 1$ or $\lambda = 2$ or $x = y = 0$, and we discard the last solution, which is trivial. Let's find x and y when $\lambda = 2$:

$$2x + y = 2x,$$

$$y = 2y.$$

We find that $y = 0$ and x may be any number! Therefore, all vectors of

the form $\begin{pmatrix} x \\ 0 \end{pmatrix}$ map into $\begin{pmatrix} 2x \\ 0 \end{pmatrix}$. Check this result.

Thus the line $y =$ _____ maps into itself. However, the only *point* of this line that maps into itself is (_____, 0).

Now, let's return to the postponed case of $\lambda = 1$. Putting this value for λ in the original system gives

$$2x + y = x,$$

$$y = y.$$

or _____ $+ y = 0$, whose solution can be represented parametrically by $x = t \wedge y =$ _____. Therefore, the line $y =$ _____ maps into itself. In this case, every point of the line maps into itself.

0

0

x

−t

−x

Review the problem and answer the following questions: Is there a vector $\mathbf{V}$ such that $T(\mathbf{V}) = -\mathbf{V}$? Is there a vector $\mathbf{V}$ such that $T(\mathbf{V}) = 3\mathbf{V}$? How many values of λ are there for which there are vectors $\mathbf{V}$ satisfying $T(\mathbf{V}) = \lambda\mathbf{V}$? How many values of λ are there for which this equation has a solution $\mathbf{V} \neq \mathbf{0}$?

From the preceding discussion, we see that the key to finding the fixed lines under a linear transformation T is finding the values of λ for which

(1) $$T(\mathbf{V}) = \lambda\mathbf{V},$$

for some nonzero vector $\mathbf{V}$. These values of λ are most frequently called the *eigenvalues* of T. (The word "eigenvalue" is the illegitimate offspring of the pure German name "eigenwert" and the pure English name "characteristic value." Eigenvalues are also called "latent values," "proper values," and "spectral values.") A vector $\mathbf{V}$ satisfying (1) is called an *eigenvector* corresponding to the eigenvalue λ. The following exercises are designed to give you some geometric insights into the significance of eigenvalues. You will find other important and diverse applications of these notions throughout all of mathematics. And if you go on to study the physics of quantum theory, you may anticipate a most startling appearance of eigenvalues as numbers which correspond to the energy levels of an atom.

7.6.2
EXERCISES

1. Let

$$U = \begin{pmatrix} 2 & 5 \\ 0 & 3 \end{pmatrix}$$

represent a linear transformation.

(a) Find the eigenvalues and associated eigenvectors of U.

(b) Are there any fixed vectors? That is, are there any vectors $\mathbf{V}$ such that $U(\mathbf{V}) = \mathbf{V}$?

(c) Find all the fixed points.

(d) Find the lines through the origin that map into themselves.

(e) Let $O = (0,0)$, $A = (a_1, a_2)$, and $B = (b_1, b_2)$, and call $U(A) = A'$ and $U(B) = B'$. Find the ratio

$$\frac{\text{area of } \triangle OAB}{\text{area of } \triangle OA'B'}.$$

2. Let

$$I = \begin{pmatrix} 1 & 0 \\ 0 & 1 \end{pmatrix}.$$

(a) What is the *transform* (i.e., image) of a square under the linear transformation I?

(b) What is the transform of a circle under I?

(c) How many eigenvalues satisfy the equation $I(\mathbf{V}) = \lambda\mathbf{V}$, for some nonzero vector $\mathbf{V}$?

(d) What are the fixed points of the transformation?

(e) What are the fixed lines?

3. Let T be any linear transformation. In order for T to have any fixed points other than the origin, one eigenvalue λ must be _____.

(b) Is I the only linear transformation of the plane that fixes every line? (This is a booby trap. Think before you answer!)

4. (a) Study the transformation

$$\begin{pmatrix} 3 & 0 \\ 0 & 3 \end{pmatrix}$$

and describe its geometric effect on regions. How does the transformation affect areas?

(b) Do the same with the transformation

$$\begin{pmatrix} -3 & 0 \\ 0 & -3 \end{pmatrix}.$$

(c) Find the fixed lines through $(0, 0)$ of the transformations in (a) and (b).

5. (a) Study the transformation

$$\begin{pmatrix} 1 & 0 \\ 0 & -1 \end{pmatrix}.$$

Describe its geometric effect on points and find its inverse.

(b) Find all the fixed points and all fixed lines through the origin.

6. (a) Study the transformation

$$\begin{pmatrix} -1 & 0 \\ 0 & 1 \end{pmatrix},$$

describing its geometric effect on regions.

(b) What does the transformation do to areas?

(c) Is orientation preserved or changed by the transformation?

7. (a) Study the transformation

$$\begin{pmatrix} -1 & 0 \\ 0 & -1 \end{pmatrix}$$

in a manner similar to the one you followed in Exercises 4, 5, and 6.

(b) Do the same for $\begin{pmatrix} 0 & 1 \\ 1 & 0 \end{pmatrix}.$

(c) Do the same for $\begin{pmatrix} 0 & -1 \\ -1 & 0 \end{pmatrix}$.

(d) Find the inverses of the transformation in parts (a), (b), and (c).

8. Let

$$S = \begin{pmatrix} 3 & 1 \\ -4 & -2 \end{pmatrix}.$$

(a) Find the nonzero values of λ for which there are solutions to the equation $S(V) = \lambda V$.

(b) Find the lines through the origin that are fixed under the transformation S.

(c) If

$$L = \begin{pmatrix} a & b \\ c & d \end{pmatrix}$$

represents any linear transformation, what is the maximum number of eigenvalues of L?

9. Let the transformation

$$P = \begin{pmatrix} 1 & 0 \\ 0 & 0 \end{pmatrix}.$$

(a) Find $P[1, 2]$, $P[2, 2]$, $P[-\sqrt{2}, 2]$, and $P[P[-3, 2]]$.

(b) Find the matrix representation for the transformation $P \circ P$.

(c) Describe the geometric effect of P. What happens to areas?

(d) Find P^{-1} if it exists.

10. Discuss the transformation

$$O = \begin{pmatrix} 0 & 0 \\ 0 & 0 \end{pmatrix}.$$

11. What happens to circles under linear transformations? Let

$$T = \begin{pmatrix} 1 & -1 \\ -1 & -1 \end{pmatrix}.$$

The system of equations related to T is

$$x - y = u$$
$$-x - y = v.$$

First, we ask: What happens to the unit circle centered at the origin?

If you solve for x and y in terms of u and v, you should be able to eliminate x and y from the equation of the unit circle, which is $x^2 + y^2 = $ _____.

(a) Fill in the blanks:

$$\text{\_\_\_\_}u + \text{\_\_\_\_}v = x,$$
$$\text{\_\_\_\_}u + \text{\_\_\_\_}v = y.$$

(b) $x^2 + y^2 = ($_____$u + $_____$v)^2 + ($_____$u + $_____$v)^2 = 1$. This implies

_____$u^2 + $_____$v^2 + $_____$uv = 1$.

(c) Graph the equation determined in (b) in the (u, v)-plane.

(d) Compare the area of the unit circle in the (x, y)-plane with the area enclosed by its transform.

(e) The set of all circles centered at the origin is sometimes referred to as a *family* of circles. You have so far considered one member of this family—namely, the circle of radius 1. The member of this family that has a radius equal to r has equation: $x^2 + y^2 = $ _____.

(f) Find the equation of the transform of the circle of part (e), under the given transformation T.

(g) What is the value of the ratio $(u^2 + v^2)/(x^2 + y^2)$? Does this ratio have geometric significance? Does it depend on the magnitude of the vector $[x, y]$? Does it depend on the direction of the vector $[x, y]$?

Optional Problems for Geometric Investigation

12. Give an example of a linear transformation that shrinks areas by a factor of one-half. How is the area shrinking related to the elements of the matrix?

13. What happens to the family of circles with center as the origin under the transformation

$$\begin{pmatrix} a & b \\ b & -a \end{pmatrix}?$$

If there is an area change, how is it related to the matrix?

14. Answer Exercise 13 for the linear transformation

$$\begin{pmatrix} a & b \\ a & -b \end{pmatrix}.$$

15. **(a)** Find the curves which map into circles with center at origin, under the general linear transformation

$$\begin{pmatrix} a & b \\ c & d \end{pmatrix}.$$

(b) Investigate the transforms of the circles with center at the origin under the general linear transformation

$$\begin{pmatrix} a & b \\ c & d \end{pmatrix}.$$

So far we have studied the linear transformations

$$T : x \rightarrow ax$$

which map a line, a one-dimensional space, into a one-dimensional space and the transformation

$$T : (x, y) \to (ax + by, cx + dy)$$

which transforms a plane, a two-dimensional space, into a two-dimensional space. Let us now look at linear transformations which transform a plane, a two-dimensional space, into a line, a one-dimensional space.

We consider then a linear transformation T:

$$T : (x, y) \to u$$

which transforms points (x, y) (or vectors $[x, y]$) into numbers u. The conditions that T be linear are

$$T(c\mathbf{X}) = cT(\mathbf{X})$$

and

$$T(\mathbf{X}_1 + \mathbf{X}_2) = T(\mathbf{X}_1) + T(\mathbf{X}_2)$$

for any vectors $\mathbf{X}, \mathbf{X}_1, \mathbf{X}_2$, and any number c.

Suppose that $T(1, 0) = 3$ and $T(0, 1) = -5$. Then we can compute $T(2, 4)$ easily since $[2, 4] = 2[1, 0] + 4[0, 1]$. In fact, we have

$$T([2, 4]) = T(2[1, 0] + 4[0, 1])$$

$$= T(2[1, 0] + T(\underline{\quad}[0, 1])$$ *4*

$$= \underline{\quad}T([1, 0]) + \underline{\quad}T([0, 1])$$ *2, 4*

$$= (2 \cdot \underline{\quad}) + (4 \cdot \underline{\quad}).$$ *3, −5*

More generally, since

$$[x, y] = \underline{\quad}[1, 0] + \underline{\quad}[0, 1],$$ *x, y*

we obtain by the same method

$$T([x, y]) = \underline{\quad}x + \underline{\quad}y$$ *3, −5*

Thus the linear transformation is uniquely determined by the numbers $T(1, 0)$ and $T(0, 1)$. More generally, if T is a linear transformation of the plane into the line, and $T(1, 0) = a$ and $T(0, 1) = b$, then

$$T(x, y) = \underline{\quad}x + \underline{\quad}y, \quad \forall\, x, y \in \mathscr{R},$$ *a, b*

which is, then, the general form of a linear transformation of a plane into a line. We can also express it in terms of the product of a 1×2 matrix with a 2×1 matrix:

$$(\underline{\quad} \quad \underline{\quad}) \begin{pmatrix} x \\ y \end{pmatrix} = ax + by.$$ *a, b*

Recalling the work of Secs. 6.8 and 6.9, we note that this expression can be considered as the dot product of two vectors:

$$[a, b] \cdot [x, y] = ax + by.$$

7.6.3
EXERCISES

1. Show that the dot product is linear. [If $F_A(X)$ represents the dot product of **A** with **X**, you must show that

$$F_A(X_1 + X_2) = ? \quad \text{and} \quad F_A(cX) = ?,$$

where c is any scalar.]

2. (a) Show that

$$(x \quad y)\begin{pmatrix} a & b \\ c & d \end{pmatrix}\begin{pmatrix} x \\ y \end{pmatrix}$$

is a scalar (i.e., a 1×1 matrix).
(b) What is the condition on a, b, c, and d that makes

$$[x, y] \cdot \left(\begin{pmatrix} a & b \\ c & d \end{pmatrix}[x, y] \right) = 0, \quad \forall\, x, y \in \mathcal{R}?$$

3. If a linear transformation T maps the (x, y)-plane into a line of the plane, the line always passes through _____.

4. Compute
(a) $[1, 0] \cdot [0, 1]$,
(b) $[x, y] \cdot [-y, x]$,
(c) $([a, b] \cdot [x, y]) - ([x, y] \cdot [a, b])$.

5. If you recalled the properties of dot product, the result in Exercise 4(c) could have been obtained without computation. Take this hint and find:
(a) $(c[a, b]) \cdot [x, y] - c([a, b] \cdot [x, y])$,
(b) $\{[a, b] \cdot ([x, y] + [z, w])\} - ([a, b] \cdot [x, y])$.

Research Problem

6. Let

$$T = \begin{pmatrix} a & b \\ c & d \end{pmatrix}.$$

(a) What condition on a, b, c, and d guarantees that T is length-preserving?
(b) What condition on a, b, c, and d guarantees that T is angle-preserving?
(c) What condition on a, b, c, and d guarantees that T is length-preserving and orientation-preserving?
(d) What condition on a, b, c, and d guarantees that T is length-preserving and orientation-reversing?

7.7

Algebra of Matrices   In the last two sections you learned to represent a linear transformation

$$T : (x, y) \rightarrow (u, v)$$

where $u = ax + by$, $v = cx + dy$, by a matrix

$$T = \begin{pmatrix} a & b \\ c & d \end{pmatrix}.$$

In this notation the transformation can be expressed in terms of matrix multiplication:

$$T\begin{pmatrix} x \\ y \end{pmatrix} = \begin{pmatrix} u \\ v \end{pmatrix}.$$

You learned an operation of *multiplying* matrices: If

$$A = \begin{pmatrix} \alpha & \beta \\ \gamma & \delta \end{pmatrix},$$

then

$$TA = \begin{pmatrix} a & b \\ c & d \end{pmatrix}\begin{pmatrix} \alpha & \beta \\ \gamma & \delta \end{pmatrix} = \begin{pmatrix} a\alpha + b\gamma & a\beta + b\delta \\ c\alpha + d\gamma & c\beta + d\delta \end{pmatrix}.$$

This definition agrees with the equation

$$(TA)\begin{pmatrix} x \\ y \end{pmatrix} = T\left(A\begin{pmatrix} x \\ y \end{pmatrix}\right).$$

In Exercise 12 of Sec. 7.6.1 you discovered that if T and A are linear transformations, then the transformation S defined by

$$S : (x, y) \rightarrow (T(x, y) + A(x, y))$$

is also a linear transformation. We call S the *sum* of T and A, and write

$$S = T + A.$$

The matrix of S is

$$S = \begin{pmatrix} a & b \\ c & d \end{pmatrix} + \begin{pmatrix} \alpha & \beta \\ \gamma & \delta \end{pmatrix} = \begin{pmatrix} a + \alpha & b + \beta \\ c + \gamma & d + \delta \end{pmatrix}.$$

The identity I is a special linear transformation with the matrix

$$I = \begin{pmatrix} 1 & 0 \\ 0 & 1 \end{pmatrix}$$

In many ways it is analogous to the number 1. More generally, the matrices

$$kI = \begin{pmatrix} k & 0 \\ 0 & k \end{pmatrix}$$

resemble the corresponding numbers k.

For example, we have

$$aI + bI = (a + b)I, \qquad (aI)(bI) = (ab)I.$$

The *inverse* of the matrix T is the matrix T^{-1} such that

$$TT^{-1} = T^{-1}T = I.$$

The matrix T^{-1} exists if and only if $\Delta = ad - bc \neq 0$, and then we have the formula

$$T^{-1} = \begin{pmatrix} d/\Delta & -b/\Delta \\ -c/\Delta & a/\Delta \end{pmatrix}.$$

We identify multiplication of a matrix T by a number k with the multiplication of T by kI:

$$kT = (kI)T = \begin{pmatrix} ka & kb \\ kc & kd \end{pmatrix}.$$

In the exercises of Secs. 7.5 and 7.6 you also discovered that the algebra of matrices obeys the following laws analogous to those for numbers:

M1. If A and B are matrices, then $A + B$, $A - B$, and AB are uniquely determined matrices.

M2. If A and B are matrices, then $A + B = B + A$.

M3. If A, B, and C are matrices, then

$$(A + B) + C = A + (B + C)$$

and

$$(AB)C = A(BC).$$

M4. If A, B, and C are matrices, then

$$A(B + C) = (AB) + (AC)$$

and

$$(B + C)A = (BA) + (CA).$$

M5. If A and B are matrices, then $B - A = X$ is the unique solution of the equation

$$A + X = B.$$

M6. If A is a matrix, then $IA = AI = A$.

The *zero* matrix is $A - A$, and is independent of A:

$$A - A = \begin{pmatrix} 0 & 0 \\ 0 & 0 \end{pmatrix}.$$

There is no danger of ambiguity if we denote the zero matrix simply by "0".

M7. If A is a matrix, then

$$A + 0 = 0 + A = A$$

and

$$A0 = 0A = 0.$$

Of course, all of this discussion has been confined to 2×2 matrices. Properties M1–M7 tell us that the 2×2 matrices form an algebraic structure called a *ring*, and that 0 is the identity with respect to addition and I is the identity with respect to multiplication. Multiplication in this ring is not commutative, in general, so we need to use both distributive laws. This ring has *divisors of 0*, i.e., matrices A and B such that

$$A \neq 0, \qquad B \neq 0, \quad \text{and} \quad AB = 0.$$

In general, division is impossible. Can you see why?

When division is possible, we must be careful about the order. If

$$A = \begin{pmatrix} a & b \\ c & d \end{pmatrix} \quad \text{and} \quad \Delta = ad - bc \neq 0,$$

then the solution X of the equation $AX = B$ is $X = A^{-1}B$, whereas the solution Y of the equation $YA = B$ is $Y = BA^{-1}$.

If we consider 2×2 matrices with *real* numbers as elements, then they form also an example of a *linear algebra* over the field of real numbers. There is an operation of multiplication of a matrix by a number which obeys the laws:

If a and b are numbers and A, B, and C are matrices, then

$$a(AB) = (aA)B, \quad a(bC) = (ab)C,$$

$$a(A + B) = (aA) + (aB), \quad (a + b)A = (aA) + (bA),$$

$$0A = 0_2, \quad 1A = A, \quad a0_2 = 0_2.$$

Here we have used 0_2 to denote the 2×2 zero matrix.

The linear algebra of 2×2 matrices of real numbers is *four-dimensional*. We can express every such matrix in the form

$$A = ae_{11} + be_{12} + ce_{21} + de_{22},$$

where a, b, c, and d are real numbers, and the matrices e_{11}, e_{12}, e_{21}, and e_{22} are the following "units":

$$e_{11} = \begin{pmatrix} 1 & 0 \\ 0 & 0 \end{pmatrix}, \qquad e_{12} = \begin{pmatrix} 0 & 1 \\ 0 & 0 \end{pmatrix}$$

$$e_{21} = \begin{pmatrix} 0 & 0 \\ 1 & 0 \end{pmatrix}, \qquad e_{22} = \begin{pmatrix} 0 & 0 \\ 0 & 1 \end{pmatrix}.$$

The matrices $e_{11}, e_{12}, e_{21}, e_{22}$ form a *basis* for the algebra of 2×2 matrices. There are many other ways to choose a basis consisting of four matrices.

The 2×2 matrices of complex numbers also form a four-dimensional linear algebra over the field of complex numbers. We can also choose the matrices $e_{11}, \ldots, e_{22}$ as a basis for this algebra. We may also regard this algebra as a linear algebra over the field of real numbers with the basis $e_{11}, ie_{11}, e_{12}, ie_{12}, e_{21}, ie_{21}, \ldots$. How many dimensions does this linear algebra have?

These algebras have many interesting *subalgebras*.

If $P = a_0 + a_1 I + \cdots + a_n I^n$ is a polynomial, and A is a matrix, we define $P(A)$ as the matrix

$$P(A) = a_0 I + a_1 A + a_2 A^2 + \cdots + a_n A^n.$$

[Note that in the definition of P, "I" denotes the identity function, whereas in the definition of $P(A)$, "I" denotes the identity matrix. This should not cause any confusion.]

7.7.1
EXERCISES

1. (a) Let

$$A = \begin{pmatrix} x & 1 \\ 0 & x \end{pmatrix}.$$

Compute $A^2 = AA$, $A^3 = A^2A$, $A^4 = A^3A$, ... up to A^{20}.

(b) If P is the polynomial defined by

$$P(x) = 17 + x + x^2 + x^3 + x^4 + x^5 - 3x^{10} \qquad \text{for all } x,$$

find polynomials Q and R such that

$$P(A) = \begin{pmatrix} Q(x) & R(x) \\ 0 & Q(x) \end{pmatrix}.$$

2. Let

$$B = \begin{pmatrix} 0 & 1 \\ 1 & 1 \end{pmatrix}.$$

(a) Compute B^n for $1 \le n \le 10$.

(b) Compute B^{-1} and then $B^{-n} = (B^{-1})^n$ for $1 \le n \le 10$.

(c) Let

$$B^n = \begin{pmatrix} a_n & b_n \\ c_n & d_n \end{pmatrix}.$$

Compute $c_n - b_n$, $a_{n+1} - b_n$, $d_n - b_n$, and $a_n d_n - b_n c_n$.

(d) Compute $B^2 - B$.

(e) What are the eigenvalues of B? For each eigenvalue, find a corresponding eigenvector.

(f) Let $\mathbf{X}_1 = [x_1, y_1]$ and $\mathbf{X}_2 = [x_2, y_2]$ be eigenvectors of B corresponding to two different eigenvalues. Find formulas for u and v in the expression

$$[x, y] = u\mathbf{X}_1 + v\mathbf{X}_2$$

of an arbitrary vector $[x, y]$ in terms of $\mathbf{X}_1$ and $\mathbf{X}_2$.

(g) Let $B[x, y] = U\mathbf{X}_1 + V\mathbf{X}_2$, where $\mathbf{X}_1$ and $\mathbf{X}_2$ are as in part (f), and $U, V \in \mathcal{R}$. Find formulas for U and V in terms of u and v. Find formulas for U_n and V_n in the equation

$$B^n[x, y] = U_n\mathbf{X}_1 + V_n\mathbf{X}_2.$$

Find u, v, U_n, and V_n when $x = 1$, $y = 0$. Give a formula for b_n [in part (c)] in terms of U_n and V_n.

3. Let

$$A = \begin{pmatrix} a & b \\ c & d \end{pmatrix} = xI - B, \qquad B = \begin{pmatrix} \alpha & \beta \\ \gamma & \delta \end{pmatrix},$$

where B is a given matrix. Let P be the polynomial defined by

$$P(x) = \Delta = ad - bc, \qquad \forall x \in \mathcal{R}.$$

(a) Solve the equation $P(x) = 0$. Work out the special cases $\alpha = 0$, $\beta = \gamma = \delta = 0$.

(b) Compute $P(B)$.

4. If A, B, and C are given matrices and A^{-1} and B^{-1} exist, solve the equation $AXB = C$ for the unknown matrix X.

5. Consider the set $\mathcal{C}$ of matrices of the form $A = aI + bJ$, where $a, b \in \mathcal{R}$ and

$$J = \begin{pmatrix} 0 & 1 \\ -1 & 0 \end{pmatrix}.$$

(a) Compute J^2. Compute

$$(aI + bJ)(cI + dJ), \qquad (cI + dJ)(aI + bJ).$$

(b) Find real numbers x and y such that

$$(aI + bJ)(xI + yJ) = I = 1I + 0J.$$

What is the inverse of $aI + bJ$? For which values of a and b does $(aI + bJ)^{-1}$ fail to exist?

(c) Is the set $\mathscr{C}$ closed with respect to addition? With respect to multiplication?

(d) Find the solutions Z in $\mathscr{C}$ of the equation

$$Z^2 = -I = (-1)I.$$

(e) Compute $(aI + bJ)(aI - bJ)$.

6. Consider the set $\mathscr{D}$ of matrices of the form $A = aI + be_{12}$, where a and b are real numbers.

(a) Compute $(aI + be_{12})(cI + de_{12})$.

(b) Find real numbers x and y such that

$$(aI + be_{12})(xI + ye_{12}) = I.$$

For which values of a and b does $(aI + be_{12})^{-1}$ fail to exist?

(c) Compute $(xI + ye_{12})^n$ for $n = 2, 3, 4$. What is the formula for general n? If P is the polynomial defined by

$$P(x) = 1 + \frac{x}{1!} + \frac{x^2}{1!} + \cdots + \frac{x^{10}}{10!} \qquad \text{for all } x,$$

compute $P(xI + ye_{12})$.

(d) Is $\mathscr{D}$ closed with respect to addition? With respect to multiplication? What are the divisors of zero, if any, in $\mathscr{D}$?

7. Let $\mathscr{H}$ be the set of matrices of the form

$$tI + x\varepsilon_1 + y\varepsilon_2 + z\varepsilon_3,$$

where $t, x, y, z \in \mathscr{R}$ and

$$\varepsilon_1 = \begin{pmatrix} i & 0 \\ 0 & -i \end{pmatrix}, \qquad \varepsilon_2 = \begin{pmatrix} 0 & 1 \\ -1 & 0 \end{pmatrix}, \qquad \varepsilon_3 = \begin{pmatrix} 0 & i \\ i & 0 \end{pmatrix},$$

and $i^2 = -1$.

(a) Compute $\varepsilon_1^2, \varepsilon_2^2, \varepsilon_3^2, \varepsilon_1\varepsilon_2, \varepsilon_2\varepsilon_3, \varepsilon_3\varepsilon_1, \varepsilon_2\varepsilon_1, \varepsilon_3\varepsilon_2, \varepsilon_1\varepsilon_3$.

(b) Compute $(a\varepsilon_1 + b\varepsilon_2 + c\varepsilon_3)(x\varepsilon_1 + y\varepsilon_2 + z\varepsilon_3)$.

(c) Compute $(dI - a\varepsilon_1 - b\varepsilon_2 - c\varepsilon_3)(dI + a\varepsilon_1 + b\varepsilon_2 + c\varepsilon_3)$.

(d) Solve for t, x, y, z:

$$(dI + a\varepsilon_1 + b\varepsilon_2 + c\varepsilon_3)(tI + x\varepsilon_1 + y\varepsilon_2 + z\varepsilon_3) = I.$$

For which values of d, a, b, and c does

$$(dI + a\varepsilon_1 + b\varepsilon_2 + c\varepsilon_3)^{-1}$$

fail to exist?

(e) Is $\mathscr{H}$ closed with respect to addition? With respect to multiplication?

8. Find all matrices of real numbers

$$X = \begin{pmatrix} a & b \\ c & d \end{pmatrix}$$

such that $X^2 = I$. How many solutions does this equation have?

9. Let α and β be given numbers, $\beta \neq \alpha$. Find all matrices of real numbers

$$X = \begin{pmatrix} a & b \\ c & d \end{pmatrix}$$

which satisfy the "quadratic" equation

$$X \begin{pmatrix} \alpha & 0 \\ 0 & \beta \end{pmatrix} X = I.$$

(a) If $\beta \neq 0$ and $\alpha \neq 0$, how many solutions are there? Do the signs of α and β matter?

(b) If $\beta = 0$ and $\alpha \neq 0$, how many solutions are there?

10. Let

$$A = \begin{pmatrix} 1 & k \\ 0 & 1 \end{pmatrix},$$

where k is real. Find all solutions X of the "linear" equation

$$AX - XA = 0, \qquad X = \begin{pmatrix} a & b \\ c & d \end{pmatrix},$$

(b) Find all solutions of the equation $AX - XA = I$. How many solutions are there?

11. If A and B are matrices, define $[A, B] = AB - BA$. This matrix is a measure of the extent to which A and B commute.

(a) Compute $[A, P(A)]$, where P is any polynomial.
(b) Compute

$$[A, B + C] - ([A, C] + [B, C]),$$
$$[A, BC] - ([A, B]C + B[A, C]),$$

and

$$[A, B] + [B, A].$$

(c) Suppose that $[A, B] = I$. Compute $[A, B^n]$ for $n = 2, 3, 4$. What is the general formula?

(d) Let $f_3(A, B, C) = A[B, C] - B[A, C] + C[A, B]$ and

$$f_4(A, B, C, D) = A f_3(B, C, D) - B f_3(A, C, D) + C f_3(A, B, D) - D f_3(A, B, C).$$

Compute $f_4(A, B, C, D)$ for any particular matrices A, B, C, D.

12. A *rotation* about the origin is a transformation T which leaves unchanged, or invariant, the distance from a point to the origin. Let

$$T = \begin{pmatrix} a & b \\ c & d \end{pmatrix}$$

be the matrix of a rotation about the origin, so that if

$$T\begin{pmatrix} x \\ y \end{pmatrix} = \begin{pmatrix} u \\ v \end{pmatrix},$$

then $u^2 + v^2 = x^2 + y^2$ for all points (x, y).
   (a) Let $a = \frac{3}{5}$. Find all possible values for b, c and d.
   (b) Compute $a^2 + c^2$, $b^2 + d^2$, $ab + cd$, if T is a rotation.
   (c) If T and

$$U = \begin{pmatrix} \alpha & \beta \\ \gamma & \delta \end{pmatrix}$$

are rotations about the origin, is TU a rotation? (Compare with the research problems in Exercise 6 of Sec. 7.6.3.)

13. In the theory of relativity, events on a line are described by coordinates t and x, t measuring time from a fixed moment, and x the distance from a given point. If units are chosen so that c, the velocity of light, is 1, then the *interval* between an event at $(0, 0)$ and an event at (t, x) is

$$\sqrt{t^2 - x^2}.$$

A *Lorentz transformation* is one which leaves the intervals between events invariant— these are the allowed transformations of coordinates in passing from one observer to another in the special theory of relativity.
   Let $\tau = at + bx$, $\xi = ct + dx$ be a Lorentz transformation, so that

$$\tau^2 - \xi^2 = t^2 - x^2 \qquad \text{for all } (t, x).$$

   (a) What are the conditions on a, b, c, and d?
   (b) If $c = 2\lambda/(1 - \lambda^2)$, where λ is a given number, find all possible values for a, b, and d.

14. Let J be defined as in Exercise 5.
   (a) Compute J^3, J^4, J^{21}, J^{54}.
   (b) Let $\mathscr{S} = \{J, J^2, J^3, J^4\}$. Is $\mathscr{S}$ closed with respect to matrix multiplication?
   (c) Is $\mathscr{S}$ an abelian group with respect to matrix multiplication?

15. Prove that the set $\mathscr{C}$, defined in Exercise 5, is a field with respect to matrix addition and multiplication.

7.8

Approximating Solutions by Iteration   In very many mathematical problems it is difficult and sometimes even impossible to get an *exact* numerical solution. Yet the engineer, the economist—the applied scientist in general— requires a numerical answer to work with even though it be only an approximation to the exact solution. Consequently, many methods have been developed for getting approximate numerical solutions to mathematical problems. In this section we introduce several such methods for solving systems of linear equations. Of course, simple two-by-two systems can readily be solved for exact solutions, so you may think that our methods are most impractical. However, keep in mind that this is an *introduction to new methods*, which can also be applied to systems of 1000 equations in 1000 unknowns.

Consider the system

$$5x - 2y = -1,$$

$$-2x + 3y = 2.$$

If you solve the first equation for x and the second for y, you get

$$x = \underline{\hspace{1cm}},$$

$$y = \underline{\hspace{1cm}}.$$

$$\frac{2y - 1}{5}$$

$$\frac{2x + 2}{3}$$

Suppose you guess at a solution for x. Let's say your guess is $x = 1$. On the basis of this guess you can determine a corresponding value for y. Substituting $x = 1$ in the second equation, which is already solved for y, you get $y = \underline{\hspace{1cm}}$. Now on the basis of this value of y you can return to the first equation to get a new value for x, namely $x = \underline{\hspace{1cm}}$. This process can now be repeated again and again. Let's carry out some further computations and analyze the procedure to determine whether or not we are getting closer to the solution in the successive steps of the computation. However, before we go on we had better organize the computations into a systematic procedure so that we can keep track of the succession of values of x and y.

$$\frac{4}{3}$$

$$\frac{1}{3}$$

Call the initial guess $x = x_1$. From this you compute $y = y_1$ using the second equation. (Above you had $x_1 = 1$ and found $y_1 = \frac{4}{3}$.) From $y = y_1$ you compute $x = x_2$ by substituting back into the first equation. Fill in the blanks:

n	x_n	y_n
1	1	$\frac{4}{3}$
2	___	$\frac{8}{9}$
3	___	___
4	___	$\frac{1496}{2025}$

$$\frac{1}{3}$$

$$\frac{7}{45}, \frac{104}{135}$$

$$\frac{73}{675}$$

The equations used to determine x_n and y_n can be written in the form

$$x_{n+1} = \frac{2(\underline{\hspace{1cm}}) - 1}{5},$$

$$y_n = \frac{2x_n + 2}{3}.$$

$$y_n$$

This pair of equations actually describes the entire process, which is called an *iterative* procedure since the successive computations are repetitions of earlier steps with different numbers. In general, an *iterative method* for solving an equation or set of equations consists of repeating certain operations over and over again.

Are the values of x bunching up? Are the values of y bunching up? Calculate $x_{n+1} - x_n$ and $y_{n+1} - y_n$ to answer these questions.

$x_2 - x_1 =$ _____,	$y_2 - y_1 =$ _____,		$-\frac{2}{2}, -\frac{4}{9}$
$x_3 - x_2 =$ _____,	$y_3 - y_2 =$ _____,		$-\frac{8}{45}, -\frac{16}{135}$
$x_4 - x_3 =$ _____,	$y_4 - y_3 =$ _____.		$-\frac{32}{675}, -\frac{64}{2025}$

Are the values of x_n, y_n that you have computed getting closer to each other?

Are the values of x_n and y_n getting closer to the exact solution of the system? Suppose (x, y) is the exact solution and $\xi_n = x_n - x$ and $\eta_n = y_n - y$ are the errors. Then

$$x_n = x + \xi_n, \qquad y_n = \underline{\quad} + \underline{\quad}. \qquad\qquad y, \eta_n$$

Substitute into the above equations:

$$x_{n+1} = x + \xi_{n+1} = \frac{2(y + \underline{\quad}) - 1}{5} \qquad\qquad \eta_n$$

$$= \frac{2y - 1}{5} + \underline{\quad}\eta_n \qquad\qquad \frac{2}{5}$$

and

$$y_n = y + \underline{\quad} = \frac{2(\underline{\quad} + \underline{\quad}) + 2}{3} \qquad\qquad \eta_n, x, \xi$$

$$= \frac{2x + 2}{3} + \underline{\quad}\xi_n. \qquad\qquad \frac{2}{3}$$

Since (x, y) is the exact solution of the system, we know that

$$\frac{2y - 1}{5} = \underline{\quad} \quad\text{and}\quad \frac{2x + 2}{3} = \underline{\quad}. \qquad x, y$$

Therefore we find that

$$\xi_{n+1} = \underline{\quad}\eta_n \qquad\qquad \frac{2}{5}$$

and

$$\eta_n = \underline{\quad}\xi_n. \qquad\qquad \frac{2}{3}$$

It follows that

$$\xi_{n+1} = \underline{\quad}\xi_n. \qquad\qquad \frac{4}{15}$$

Is $|\xi_{n+1}|$ greater or less than $|\xi_n|$? _____ (greater/less).
    Also

$$\eta_{n+1} = \text{_____} \xi_{n+1}$$

$$= \text{_____} \eta_n.$$

Therefore, as n increases, $|\eta_n|$ _____ (increases/decreases). Are x_n and y_n getting closer to x and y? _____ (yes/no).

    Let's now look at our iterative process geometrically. Sketch, on one graph, the loci described by the two equations

$$5x - 2y = -1,$$

$$-2x + 3y = 2.$$

Since y_1 was computed by substituting x_1 for x in the _____ (first/second) equation, the point (x_1, y_1) lies on the locus of the _____ (first/second) equation. Now draw a line from (x_1, y_1) to (x_2, y_1). This line is _____ (horizontal/vertical). The point (x_2, y_1) is on the locus of the _____ (first/second) equation. You have begun a drawing that geometrically describes the iteration above. Suppose we say that the iteration gives the points (x_1, y_1), $(x_2, y_1), (x_2, y_2), \ldots, (x_{n+1}, y_n), (x_{n+1}, y_{n+1}), \ldots.$
Carry out the iteration geometrically by joining these points in the given order. What do you learn from the drawing?

    Let's now take the same system,

$$5x - 2y = -1$$

$$-2x + 3y = 2,$$

but this time substitute the approximation x_1 into the first equation (rather than the second). We will follow the same iteration process but this time the first equation plays the role of the second in the earlier example; and the second now plays the role of the first. Therefore, we solve the first equation for y and the second for x, getting

$$y = \text{_____},$$

$$x = \text{_____}.$$

If $x_1 = 1$, then $y_1 = $ _____. Substituting y_1 for y in the second equation, you find that $x_2 = $ _____. The iterative procedure can be described by the equations

$$y_n = \frac{5(\text{_____}) + 1}{2},$$

Answers column:

less

$\frac{2}{3}$

$\frac{4}{15}$

decreases

yes

second
second
horizontal

first

$\dfrac{5x + 1}{2}$

$\dfrac{3y - 2}{2}$

3

$\dfrac{7}{2}$

x_n

$$x_{n+1} = \frac{3(\underline{\hspace{1cm}}) - 2}{2},$$

y_n

for $n = 1, 2, 3, \ldots$. Now carry out the computations for the first three approximations, filling in the table below:

n	x_n	y_n	$x_{n+1} - x_n$	$y_{n+1} - y_n$
1				
2				
3				

Sketch a graph of the system and show the process just completed by joining (x_1, y_1) to (x_2, y_1), (x_2, y_1) to (x_2, y_2), and (x_2, y_2) to (x_3, y_2). Do you find this iteration more or less effective than the first in obtaining an approximate solution to the system?

7.8.1
EXERCISES

1. Use the method of iteration described above to compute approximate solutions to the following systems of linear equations. Carry out the first four steps until you obtain (x_5, y_5), and draw a graph exhibiting the iteration geometrically in each case. Compute $x_{n+1} - x_n$ and $y_{n+1} - y_n$ for $n = 1, 2, 3, 4$ to see whether your approximations are "bunching up" and "converging" upon the solution.

(a) $2x + y = 1$,
$\quad 2x + 2y = 1$.
$\quad 2x - y = 1$,
$\quad 2x - 2y = 1$.

(c) $x - y = -1$,
$\quad 2x + y = -1$.
(d) $3x - y = 1$,
$\quad 3x + y = 3$.

2. Consider the system

$$3x - 2y = -1,$$

$$x - y = 1,$$

calling L_1 the line represented by the first equation and L_2 the line represented by the second equation.

(a) What are the slopes of L_1 and L_2?
(b) Graph L_1 and L_2 on one set of axes.
(c) Draw in a geometric iteration which "converges" upon the solution. If the first step, from (x_1, y_1) to (x_2, y_1), is horizontal, on which line would you pick (x_1, y_1)? This line has _____ (smaller/greater) slope than the other.
(d) The formula for iteration is then (which one?)

$$\begin{cases} 3x_{n+1} - 2y_n = -1, \\ x_n - y_n = 1, \end{cases} \quad \text{or} \quad \begin{cases} x_{n+1} - y_n = 1, \\ 3x_n - 2y_n = -1. \end{cases}$$

3. In Exercise 2 the slopes of both lines were positive. Consider a system that defines two lines L_1 and L_2, both of negative slope:

$$L_1: 3x + 2y = -1,$$

$$L_2: x + y = 1.$$

Carry out the same type of analysis that you did in Exercise 2, and give the iteration formula in the form

$$\underline{\hspace{1cm}} x_{n+1} + \underline{\hspace{1cm}} y_n = \underline{\hspace{1cm}},$$

$$\underline{\hspace{1cm}} x_n + \underline{\hspace{1cm}} y_n = \underline{\hspace{1cm}}.$$

4. Suppose you are given the system

$$ax + by = u,$$

$$cx + dy = v,$$

the graphs of the respective lines being called L_1 and L_2. Suppose you are given that the slopes of L_1 and L_2 are of the same sign and that $|ad| > |bc|$.
   (a) Must L_1 and L_2 intersect?
   (b) If both slopes are positive, would the iteration procedure

$$ax_{n+1} + by_n = u,$$

$$cx_n + dy_n = v,$$

"converge" upon the solution, or would it lead away from the solution?
   (c) What is the answer to the question in part (b) if both slopes are negative?

5. Now examine a system which represents two lines whose slopes differ in sign:

$$L_1: 5x + 2y = -1,$$

$$L_2: -2x + 3y = 2.$$

Carry out an analysis as you did in the last three exercises and give the iteration formula you would use to approximate the solution in the form

$$\underline{\hspace{1cm}} x_{n+1} + \underline{\hspace{1cm}} y_n = \underline{\hspace{1cm}},$$

$$\underline{\hspace{1cm}} x_n + \underline{\hspace{1cm}} y_n = \underline{\hspace{1cm}}.$$

6. Consider the system

$$L_1: ax + by = u,$$

$$L_2: cx + dy = v,$$

where (i) the slopes of L_1 and L_2 differ in sign and (ii) $|ad| > |bc|$.
   (a) The iteration procedure that "converges" upon the solution is

$$\underline{\hspace{1cm}} x_{n+1} + \underline{\hspace{1cm}} y_n = \underline{\hspace{1cm}},$$

$$\underline{\hspace{1cm}} x_n + \underline{\hspace{1cm}} y_n = \underline{\hspace{1cm}}.$$

Where did you use the hypothesis (i)?

(b) Compare with your results of Exercise 3 and try to formulate a general policy you would follow in selecting an iterative procedure of the form

$$\underline{\quad} x_{n+1} + \underline{\quad} y_n = \underline{\quad},$$

$$\underline{\quad} x_n + \underline{\quad} y_n = \underline{\quad}.$$

7. The results of your observations in these exercises can be summarized by the following theorem: Given the system

$$ax + by = u,$$

$$cx + dy = v,$$

the iteration procedure

$$ax_{n+1} + by_n = u,$$

$$cx_n + dy_n = v,$$

"converges" upon the solution provided $|?| > 1$.

8. Consider the iteration

$$x_{n+1} = \frac{2y_n - 1}{5}, \qquad y_n = \frac{2x_n + 2}{5}$$

for approximating the solution of the system

$$x = \frac{2y - 1}{5}, \qquad y = \frac{2x + 2}{5}.$$

(a) Express x_{n+1} in terms of x_n:

$$x_{n+1} = \underline{\quad} x_n + \underline{\quad}.$$

(b) Let $\xi_n = x_n - x$ be the error in approximating the true value of x (incidentally, what is it?). Substitute

$$x_n = x + \xi_n, \qquad x_{n+1} = x + \xi_{n+1},$$

into the equation in part (a), and find a constant C such that $\xi_{n+1} = C\xi_n$. Is $|C|$ greater or less than 1?

(c) Find a formula for ξ_n/ξ_0. For which values of n is

$$\left| \frac{\xi_n}{\xi_0} \right| \geq 0.001?$$

(d) Do the analogues of parts (a)–(c) for the other process

$$x_{n+1} = \frac{3y_n - 2}{2}, \qquad y_n = \frac{5x_n + 1}{2}$$

discussed in the text.

9. Consider the transformation $T: x \rightarrow ax + b$.

(a) What is the fixed point of the transformation T, i.e., the solution of the equation $x = T(x) = ax + b$? Does T have a fixed point for all values of a and b?

(b) Form a sequence by iteration:

$$x_{n+1} = T(x_n) = ax_n + b, \qquad x_0 \text{ arbitrary.}$$

Let $\xi_n = x_n - x$, where x is the fixed point of T. For which values of a and b is $|\xi_{n+1}|/|\xi_n|$ less than 1?

(c) Show how the result of part (b) yields the solution of Exercise 7.

The geometric pictures of the iteration procedure you have been working on have led to some very suggestive names: the *staircase solution* in the event that the slopes of the two lines have the same sign, and the *spiral* or *cobweb solution* in the case where the slopes have opposite signs.

Let's now try to apply the staircase-spiral iteration method to find the solution to a system, one equation of which is quadratic:

$$y = x^2 - 1,$$
$$y = 4x - 2.$$

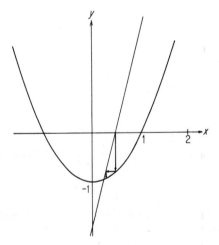

Figure 7-16

We begin by sketching a graph, since graphs usually assist us in making an analysis. An iterative procedure that "converges" upon the "lower" inter-section point is shown on the graph in Fig. 7-16. It begins at the x-intercept of the line, where $y =$ _____. If this starting point is called (x_1, y_1), then $y_1 =$ _____ and $x_1 =$ _____. Now the path of the iteration is vertically down from the line to the graph of the quadratic function, so in order to compute y_2 you write

$$y_2 = (\text{\_\_\_\_\_})^2 - 1.$$

| 0 |
| $0, \frac{1}{2}$ |
| $\frac{1}{2}$ |

Then, since $y_2 = 4x_2 - 2$, you solve for the numerical value of x_2, getting $x_2 = $ _____. You should now be able to write the general formula for this iteration. It is

0.312

$$y_{n+1} = (\underline{\quad})^2 - 1,$$

x_n

$$x_n = \frac{(\underline{\quad}) + 2}{4}.$$

y_n

Finish this example by carrying out the iteration until it coincides with the exact solution (which you can find algebraically) in the first two decimal places for the x- and y-values. Carry the calculation out to three decimal places; then round off to two.

If you were interested only in the x-value of the solution above you could have dispensed with the y's entirely by eliminating them. Rewriting the second equation with a subscript of $n + 1$ you get

$$x_{n+1} = \frac{(\underline{\quad}) + 2}{4}.$$

y_{n+1}

Now you can eliminate the y's by substituting from the first equation into the second, getting

$$x_{n+1} = \frac{[(\underline{\quad})^2 - 1] + 2}{4}$$

x_n

or simply

$$x_{n+1} = \frac{(\underline{\quad})^2 + (\underline{\quad})}{4}.$$

x_n, *1*

This, you will recall, is a *recursive* definition of the x_i. It completely determines x_i for every nonnegative integer i, provided you are told how to begin. Since we had $x_1 = \frac{1}{2}$, a complete recursive formula for the x_i is given by

$$x_1 = \tfrac{1}{2},$$

$$x_{n+1} = \frac{x_n^2 + 1}{4}.$$

From each approximate solution x_n, the recursion formula shows how to proceed to another approximate solution x_{n+1}.

We return now to the start of the last problem to see what happens in eliminating the y_n as we did in the last paragraph. If we eliminate y from the system

$$y = x^2 - 1,$$

$$y = 4x - 2,$$

we get $4x - 2 = x^2 - 1$. The numbers in the sequence $\{x_n\}$ in the iteration above are then approximations to a root of this polynomial equation, which can be written in the standard form

$$x^2 - 4x + \underline{\hspace{1cm}} = 0.$$

1

If we isolate x on one side of the equals sign, we get

$$x = \underline{\hspace{1cm}}.$$

$$\frac{x^2 + 1}{4}$$

Compare this with the recursion formula for iteration. What do you now think about the possibility of using our method of iteration for finding the real roots of quadratics? Do you think this idea can be extended to find roots of cubics and other polynomial equations?

Let's return to the problem of finding the second solution to the system

$$y = x^2 - 1,$$

$$y = 4x - 2,$$

which can be reduced to the problem of finding the second root of the quadratic equation $x^2 - 4x + 1 = 0$. You recall that we chose the initial point (x_1, y_1) on the line and moved vertically down to the graph of the quadratic function. This gave a staircase approach to the solution. Examine the figure and experiment to see whether starting elsewhere on the line would lead you to the second intersection point. Don't read further until you've done this experimentation.

In order to achieve an approach to the second point of intersection by starting with (x_1, y_1) on the line, you must move \underline{\hspace{2cm}} (horizontally/vertically) to the graph of the quadratic. Therefore, x_2 is determined by substituting y_1 for y in the equation

horizontally

$$y = \underline{\hspace{1cm}}$$

$x^2 - 1$

and solving for x.

$$x_2 = \underline{\hspace{1cm}}.$$

$\pm\sqrt{y_1 + 1}$

(How do you know what sign to choose?)

Then

$$y_2 = \underline{\hspace{1cm}}.$$

$4x_2 - 2$

The general formula for this iteration is then

$$y_n = 4\underline{\hspace{1cm}} - 2,$$

x_n

$$x_{n+1} = \sqrt{\underline{\hspace{1cm}} + 1}.$$

y_n

1. (a) Carry out three steps of the iteration to determine the second solution to the system

$$y = x^2 - 1,$$

$$y = 4x - 2.$$

(b) Eliminate the y's so that your formula is a straightforward iterative method for finding the larger root of the quadratic equation $x^2 - 4x + 1 = 0$.

(c) How many steps of the iteration of part (b) are necessary for the answer to coincide with the exact answer in the first two decimal places?

2. The solutions of the general quadratic equation $ax^2 + bx + c = 0$ can be expressed by a relatively simple formula, which you know as the *quadratic formula*, involving the four rational operations and the extraction of roots. This formula was known to the Greeks, probably as early as 500 B.C. A similar although more complicated formula for the solutions to the cubic equation $ax^3 + bx^2 + cx + d = 0$ was discovered by Tartaglia (1500–1557); and a formula for the quartic equation was found shortly thereafter. However, *no such formula exists* for the solution of the general quintic equation

$$ax^5 + bx^4 + cx^3 + dx^2 + ex + f = 0.$$

In 1824, at the age of 22, the highly gifted Norwegian mathematician Niels Henrik Abel† (1802–1829) proved the remarkable result that it is *impossible* to solve the general quintic by means of a formula that involves only the rational operations of arithmetic together with root extractions.‡ Thus, approximate methods and, in particular, iterative techniques become essential to the solution of polynomial equations of degree five or higher.

Suppose you are given the quintic equation

$$5x^5 - 5x - 1 = 0,$$

with the problem of finding the real solutions.

† Although Abel died at the early age of 26, he left significant contributions in many branches of mathematics, and for these he is generally regarded as among the greatest mathematicians of history. Abel learned and created mathematics under the most oppressive conditions of poverty and poor health; and most of his learning was done virtually "on his own" as many of you are now learning mathematics. You can read about this fascinating genius in an interesting biography written by Professor Oystein Ore of Yale, *Niels Henrik Abel, Mathematician Extraordinary* (Minneapolis: University of Minnesota Press, 1957).

‡ This result is usually known as *Abel's theorem*, and Abel certainly deserves this honor. However, Evariste Galois (1811–1832), working in France, and Paolo Ruffini (1765–1822), in Italy, also obtained the theorem independently, and therefore they also deserve to be honored. In 1799 Ruffini presented his proof, which was considered too vague for acceptance by the leading mathematicians of that day. The work of Galois was perhaps the most general, establishing criteria for solvability of nth-degree polynomial equations. Thus, Galois obtained Abel's theorem as a special case of his general theory. Although Galois died at 20, he left a mark that places him among the greatest mathematicians of all time. The story of his tumultuous and frustrated life is told most interestingly by Professor Leopold Infeld in the historical novel, *Whom the Gods Love* (New York: Whittlesey House, 1948).

(a) Solve for x^4, writing $x^4 = $ _____ + _____.

(b) Draw the graphs of $y = x^4$ and $y = 1 + 1/5x$.

(c) Examine iterative methods suggested by (b) to approximate one of the three real roots to the original quintic equation. Does this iterative method work to obtain all three of the real roots?

[*Ans.* The roots correct to five decimal places are: -0.20032, -0.94209, and 1.04476.]

(d) Solving for x to get $x = x^5 - \frac{1}{5}$ suggests an iterative process using the equations $y = x$ and $y = x^5 - \frac{1}{5}$. Draw the graphs to see whether any iteration based on these equations leads to a solution.

3. (a) Sketch on one set of axes graphs of the equations

$$y = 2x$$

$$y = x + \frac{3}{x}.$$

(b) How many points of intersection are there? Does this agree with your algebraic solution to the system?

(c) Analyze your graph and derive an iteration formula for the first-quadrant solution in the form

$$y_{n+1} = 2\text{\underline{\ \ \ \ }},$$

$$y_{n+1} = \text{\underline{\ \ \ \ }} + \frac{3}{\text{\underline{\ \ \ \ }}}.$$

(d) Eliminate the y's in your answer to part (c) and get an iteration formula in the form

$$x_{n+1} = f(x_n).$$

This iteration formula provides a solution to a polynomial equation. What is the equation?

(e) If $\alpha = \sqrt{3}$, then the equation of part (d) takes the form

$$x_{n+1} = \frac{1}{2}\left(x_n + \frac{\alpha^2}{x_n}\right).$$

Let $z_n = (x_n - \alpha)/(x_n + \alpha)$ and find a formula for z_{n+1} in terms of z_n. Find the exponent k_n such that

$$z_n = z_0^{k_n}.$$

For which values of x_0 is $|z_0| < 1$?

Find a formula for $x_n - \alpha$ in terms of z_n. For which values of z_n is $|x_n - \alpha| < 0.001$?

(f) Can you use what you have learned to discover an iterative procedure for approximating $\sqrt{2}$? $\sqrt{5}$? $\sqrt{a}$ if $a > 0$?

The iteration for $\sqrt{a}$, $a > 0$, that you discovered in this problem, namely,

$$x_{n+1} = \frac{1}{2}\left(x_n + \frac{a}{x_n}\right),$$

is usually associated with the name of Isaac Newton (1642–1727), the codiscoverer of calculus. However, it was used more than 1800 years earlier by Heron of Alexandria (about 100 B.C.) for computing square roots. This is very likely the first appearance of an iteration method in the history of mathematics.

4. Using the iteration formula derived in Exercise 3, find $\sqrt{2}$ and $\sqrt{3}$, accurate to three decimal places, taking $x_1 = 1$. Would you say that this method is efficient?

5. Possible iteration formulas for solving the equation $x^2 - 2x - 1 = 0$ are:

(i) $x_1 = 3$,
$x_{n+1} = x_n^2 - x_n - 1$.

(ii) $x_1 = 2$,
$x_{n+1} = x_n^2 - x_n - 1$.

(iii) $x_1 = 2$,
$x_{n+1} = \frac{1}{2}(x_n^2 - 1)$.

(iv) $x_1 = 3$,
$x_{n+1} = \frac{1}{2}(x_n^2 - 1)$.

(v) $x_1 = -1$,
$x_{n+1} = \frac{2x_n + 1}{x_n}$.

Which of these recursion formulas are satisfactory for approximating the roots of the equation? Which root do you get in each case?

Research Problem

6. For the solution to the linear system

$$ax + by = u,$$
$$cx + dy = v,$$

a possible iterative method is

$$ax_{n+1} + by_n = u,$$
$$cx_n + dy_{n+1} = v.$$

Investigate the conditions under which this iteration converges to a solution. Can you prove a theorem analogous to the one stated in Exercise 7 of Sec. 7.8.1 for staircase-spiral iteration?

We will now investigate another iteration method for solving a linear system of two equations in two unknowns. We shall first look at the method graphically, so we let L_1 and L_2 be the graphs of the two equations, and let P_0 be the intersection point of the lines L_1 and L_2 (Fig. 7-17). (We assume L_1 and L_2 are distinct nonparallel lines.) Point P_0 represents the solution, so we desire an iteration scheme which will get us closer and closer to P_0.

We pick any point P_1 on line L_1 as a first approximation to the solution. Then from P_1 we drop a perpendicular to L_2, and we call the foot of the perpendicular P_2. From P_2 we drop a perpendicular to L_1 and call the foot of this second

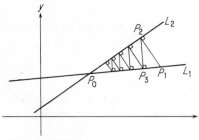

Figure 7-17

perpendicular P_3. We continue this process which clearly defines a sequence of points $\{P_n\}$. How do you know that the points P_n are getting closer to P_0 as you go further out in the sequence? What geometric argument can you give to prove that the distance $\overline{|P_0P_1|}$ is greater than $\overline{|P_0P_2|}$? Can you give a vector proof? Under what circumstances, if any, does $\overline{|P_0P_1|} = \overline{|P_0P_2|}$?

This iteration procedure might be called the *method of projection*, for the orthogonal projection of segment P_0P_1 on L_2 is segment P_0P_2 and the orthogonal projection of segment P_0P_2 on L_1 is segment P_0P_3. In general, each segment P_0P_{i+1} is an orthogonal projection of the preceding segment P_0P_i. How would you describe this in terms of components?

Let's see if you can derive a formula for the projection method of iteration. We will help, but we ask you to do most of the work. Call the system

$$L_1: ax + by = u,$$

$$L_2: cx + dy = v.$$

Let the coordinates of P_n be (x_n, y_n), $n = 0, 1, 2, 3, \ldots,$ where $P_0 = (x_0, y_0)$ represents the solution. If $P_1 = (x_1, y_1)$ is on L_1, then the line joining P_1 to P_2 is perpendicular to line _____. Therefore, the slope of line P_1P_2 equals _____, provided _____ $\neq 0$. (We shall assume that none of the coefficients $a, b, c,$ or d is zero.) The plan is to find formulas for x_2 and y_2 in terms of the coordinates x_1 and y_1 of the starting point. You have the slope of line P_1P_2 and you know that this line passes through (x_1, y_1), so it should be an easy job to determine the equation of line P_1P_2. Check back, if necessary, to write this line in the parametric form	L_2 $d/c, c$

(1)
$$x = x_1 + \underline{\qquad}t,$$ c

$$y = y_1 + \underline{\qquad}t$$ d

where t, the parameter, takes on all the real values. We seek (x_2, y_2), the intersection of P_1P_2 and line _____. Therefore, you must solve the system of equations of these two lines. This can be done by substituting equations (1) into the equation for line _____, namely	L_2 L_2

(2)
$$\underline{\qquad}x + \underline{\qquad}y = \underline{\qquad}.$$ c, d, v

Substituting equation (1) into (2) gives

$$c(x_1 + \underline{\qquad}t) + d(y_1 + \underline{\qquad}t) = v.$$ c, d

The value of t which makes (3) a true sentence is the value of t that defines the point _____. Solving for t gives

$$t = \dfrac{v - \underline{\qquad}x_1 - \underline{\qquad}y_1}{\underline{\qquad}}.$$

(margin answers: P_2; c, d; $c^2 + d^2$)

You can determine x_2 and y_2 by substituting this value of t into (1). Therefore,

$$x_2 = x_1 + c\left(\frac{v - cx_1 - dy_1}{c^2 + d^2}\right),$$

$$y_2 = y_1 + d\left(\frac{v - cx_1 - dy_1}{c^2 + d^2}\right).$$

Solving for x_3, y_3 in terms of x_2, y_2 follows the same algebraic procedure as solving for x_2, y_2 in terms of x_1, y_1, except that the roles of c, d, and v are taken over by _____, _____, and _____, respectively. Therefore, you can immediately write the solution for x_3, y_3 as

(margin answer: a, b, u)

$$x_3 = x_2 + \underline{\qquad\qquad},$$

$$y_3 = y_2 + \underline{\qquad\qquad}.$$

(margin answers: $\dfrac{a(u - ax_2 - by_2)}{a^2 + b^2}$; $\dfrac{b(u - ax_2 - by_2)}{a^2 + b^2}$)

If k is an integer, then $2k$ is always _____ (odd/even) and $2k + 1$ is always _____. The general iteration formula for all integers is given by the following four equations (fill the blanks!):

(margin answers: even; odd)

$$x_{2k} = \underline{\qquad\qquad}, \qquad x_{2k+1} = \underline{\qquad\qquad},$$

$$y_{2k} = \underline{\qquad\qquad}, \qquad y_{2k+1} = \underline{\qquad\qquad}.$$

7.8.3
EXERCISES

1. Carry out four steps of the iteration by projection for the solutions to the systems below. These are systems that you solved in Exercise 1 of Sec. 7.8.1, so you can compare the efficiency of the two methods.

(a) $2x + y = 1,$
 $2x + 2y = 1.$

(b) $2x - y = 1,$
 $2x - 2y = 1.$

(c) $x - y = -1,$
 $2x + y = -1.$

(d) $3x - y = 1,$
 $3x + y = 3.$

2. At one time the demand function d and the supply function s for meat were given as

$$d = \{(p, y) \,|\, y = 83 - 2p \wedge p > 0\},$$

$$s = \{(p, y) \,|\, y = 2p - 11\},$$

where p represents price. What was the equilibrium price? Calculate by carrying out four steps of the iteration. Is the staircase-spiral method suitable for this problem?

3. A manufacturing firm finds that its cost function c and its revenue function r are given by

$$c = \{(x, y) \mid y = 1.7x + 12\},$$
$$r = \{(x, y) \mid y = 0.3x\},$$

where x is the number of units sold. Find, by an iterative process, the "break-even point."

If the staircase-spiral method is used for approximating the "break-even point," you can make a safe prediction on the geometric nature of the approach. What is this prediction and why are you sure of its validity?

7.9

Falling Body. Iteration and Error Estimates for Square Roots
In Chapter 1 we discussed the motion of a falling body and some of the mathematical equations related to this motion. Let's now turn to the task of solving some equations that arise from problems of motion. We begin with one of the simplest (Fig. 7-18):

(1) $$s = 16t^2.$$

Equation (1) tells us the distance s (in feet) that a body falls in t seconds, if it is under the influence of gravity alone. (Do you recall where the "16" came from?)

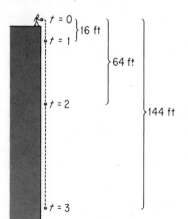

Figure 7-18

One type of question that the physicist would ask concerning the motion is : How long does it take for the body to fall 10 feet? 100 feet? In general, how long does it take for the body to fall b feet? If the body falls b feet, we can substitute in (1) and get

(2) $$b = 16t^2.$$

The solution to the problem can be found by taking square roots. In fact, the solution to (2) is

$$t = \sqrt{?}.$$

(Why does only the positive square root appear as an answer to this problem?)

This simple expression for the solution is satisfactory for the algebraist but not for the physicist. The physicist requires a numerical answer that he can measure on a rule or feed into a computer. In short, the applied scientist is interested in a rational approximation to the answer, so we return to equation (2) with this idea in mind.

Equation (2) is equivalent to an equation of the form

(3) $$x^2 - c = 0.$$

For example, if we ask how long it takes for the body to fall 48 feet, then the equation to be solved is

$$t^2 - \underline{\hspace{1cm}} = 0.$$

| *3*

The algebraic solution to this equation is $t = \sqrt{\underline{\hspace{1cm}}}$.

| *3*

Refer to the previous section for a simple iteration process for determining square roots. The recursion formula that you discovered for computing $\sqrt{3}$ is

$$x_{n+1} = \frac{1}{2}\left(\underline{\hspace{1cm}} + \frac{\underline{\hspace{1cm}}}{x_n}\right).$$

| x_n, *3*

Pick $x_1 = 1$. Then $x_2 = \underline{\hspace{1cm}}$ $x_3 = \underline{\hspace{1cm}}$,

| *2, 1.75*

and $x_4 = \underline{\hspace{1cm}}$.

| *1.732*

From these results the sequence of terms appears to "converge." But do the terms really "converge"? Do they get closer and closer to $\sqrt{3}$? The geometric analysis that you made in the last section might have been convincing, but that was *not* a satisfactory mathematical proof. The question of whether x_n is getting closer and closer to the $\sqrt{3}$ as n gets larger is really an arithmetic question, and we must be able to prove an arithmetic statement in order to answer this question. For example, if we could prove that

$$|x_{n+1} - \sqrt{3}| < |x_n - \sqrt{3}|, \qquad \text{for all } n > 1,$$

then we would know that the x_n are getting closer to $\sqrt{3}$ as n gets larger and larger. And, if, in addition, we could perhaps prove that

$$|x_n - \sqrt{3}| < \frac{1}{10^n},$$

then we would know that x_k is surely within one-thousandth of $\sqrt{3}$ if $k \geq \underline{\hspace{1cm}}$; in fact we would now know that the numbers x_n found by the iteration give approximations to $\sqrt{3}$ to any desired accuracy!

| *3*

Before we try to give a complete answer to the question of convergence to $\sqrt{3}$, we shall help you to examine the procedure to determine some of its essential characteristics.

Check your recent computations and the results of the previous section to see whether the sequence elements that you found increase toward, decrease toward, or oscillate about the number you know to be the square root. Note that the first step x_1 should not be considered as part of the pattern since the first guess is arbitrary. What have you found? Suppose you wish to *prove* that this is so for all $n > 1$, namely that

$$x_{n+1} ? x_n. \qquad (\leq \text{ or } \geq ?)$$

$\leq$

You could prove this inequality if you could prove

$$\frac{1}{2}\left(x_n + \frac{3}{x_n}\right) ? x_n$$

$\leq$

(using the iteration for $\sqrt{3}$). And, if $x_n > 0$, this would follow from

$$x_n^2 + 3 ? \underline{\qquad}.$$

$\leq 2x_n^2$

Subtracting x_n^2 from both members, we have the equivalent inequality $x_n^2 ? 3$, which follows from $x_n \geq \sqrt{3}$.

$\geq$

Summarizing the reasoning so far, we have

$$x_n \geq \sqrt{3} \Rightarrow x_{n+1} \leq x_n \qquad \text{for } n > 1.$$

Now if we could prove $x_n - \sqrt{3} \geq 0$, the result $x_{n+1} \leq x_n$ would be proved.

Rewrite $x_n - \sqrt{3}$ using the recursion relation:

$$x_n - \sqrt{3} = \frac{1}{2}\left(\underline{\qquad} + \frac{3}{\underline{\qquad}}\right) - \sqrt{3}.$$

x_{n-1}, x_{n-1}

Putting the right member over a common denominator,

$$x_n - \sqrt{3} = \frac{(\underline{\qquad})^2 + 3 - (\underline{\qquad})\sqrt{3}}{2x_{n-1}}.$$

$x_{n-1}, 2x_{n-1}$

Do you see how the numerator of the right member might be written in a simpler form?

(4) $\qquad x_n - \sqrt{3} = \frac{(\underline{\qquad})^2}{2x_{n-1}} \qquad (n \geq 2).$

$x_{n-1} - \sqrt{3}$

If $x_{n-1} > 0$, what deduction can you make about the right member? It is _____ (positive/negative/ nonpositive/nonnegative).

nonnegative

Finally, you have that $x_n - \sqrt{3} \geq 0$, which is just what is needed to clinch the argument. Reviewing the reasoning, we established

(a) $n \geq 2 \Rightarrow x_n \geq \sqrt{3}$, and

(b) $x_n \geq \sqrt{3} \Rightarrow x_{n+1} \leq x_n$.

Part (b) can be written more deftly once we see how to handle the inequalities. For example,

$$x_n \geq \sqrt{3} \Rightarrow x_n^2 \geq 3$$

$$\Rightarrow 2x_n^2 \geq 3 + x_n^2$$

$$\Rightarrow x_n \geq \frac{1}{2}\left(\frac{3}{x_n} + x_n\right) = x_{n+1}.$$

The last inequality can be deduced only if $x_n > 0$. How can you be sure that $x_n > 0$?

If we start the iteration with $x_1 > \sqrt{3}$, then each term of the sequence is less than or equal to its predecessor. However, this alone is not sufficient to conclude that the terms of the sequence $\{x_n\}$ converge upon $\sqrt{3}$, where

$$x_{n+1} = \frac{1}{2}\left(x_n + \frac{3}{x_n}\right).$$

For example, the terms might be decreasing and getting closer to $\sqrt{3}$, but they might be always larger than $\sqrt{3} + \frac{1}{4}$. That is, even though the x_n would be decreasing, it is conceivable that

$$x_n - \sqrt{3} > \tfrac{1}{4}.$$

In this case one would hardly say that the x_n are converging upon $\sqrt{3}$. (The x_n might possibly be converging upon $\sqrt{3} + \frac{1}{4}$.) So let us examine the quantity $x_n - \sqrt{3}$ to see what we can prove about its magnitude.

From (4) you know that

(5) $\qquad 0 \leq x_{n+1} - \sqrt{3} = \dfrac{(\underline{\qquad})^2}{2x_n}.$ $\qquad\qquad\Big|\; x_n - \sqrt{3}$

The quantity in parentheses is precisely the one we are focusing on, for it is the difference between a sequence element and $\sqrt{3}$. We can, therefore, get each difference, $x_{n+1} - \sqrt{3}$, in terms of the preceding difference $x_n - \sqrt{3}$. Perhaps we can show that

(6) $\qquad x_{n+1} - \sqrt{3} = a(x_n - \sqrt{3}),$ $\qquad$ where $0 \leq a < 1.$

This would tell us that the difference $x_{n+1} - \sqrt{3}$ is a fraction $(a/1)$ of the previous difference $x_n - \sqrt{3}$. And if we had some precise information about a, we would know how close the sequence terms get to $\sqrt{3}$.

Proceeding in the direction of obtaining something like (6), let's start the sequence with $x_1 > 1$, so if we replace x_n in the denominator of (5) by 1 we make the fraction _____ (larger/smaller). Therefore, | *larger*

(7) $\qquad x_{n+1} - \sqrt{3} ? \dfrac{(x_n - \sqrt{3})^2}{2}.$ $\qquad (\leq \text{ or } \geq ?)$ | $\leq$

Can you strengthen the inequality by replacing $x_n - \sqrt{3}$ by a larger number? Above, as noted in (a), you learned that $x_n - \sqrt{3} \geq 0$ (for which n?), so if you choose $x_1 > \sqrt{3}$, the inequality $x_n - \sqrt{3} \geq 0$ will hold for all n. Also from above, as noted in (b), you learned that

$$x_{n+1} \leq x_n \leq x_{n-1} \leq \cdots \leq x_2,$$

so if you select $x_1 \leq 2$, then it is certain that

$$x_n - \sqrt{3} ? 1. \qquad (\leq \text{ or } \geq ?)$$ | $\leq$

With this information, (5) can be modified to read

$$x_{n+1} - \sqrt{3} = \frac{(x_n - \sqrt{3})}{2x_n} \cdot (x_n - \sqrt{3})$$

$$? \frac{1}{2 \cdot 1}(x_n - \sqrt{3}). \qquad (\leq \text{ or } \geq ?)$$ | $\leq$

Applying (7) to this inequality enables you to write

$$x_{n+1} - \sqrt{3} \leq \tfrac{1}{2}(x_n - \sqrt{3}) \leq \underline{\qquad}(x_{n-1} - \sqrt{3}).$$ | $(\tfrac{1}{2})^2$

[Now you see the strategy behind getting an inequality of the form of (6).] You can carry out this procedure until you get the right member of the inequality in terms of the initial member of the sequence. The result is

$$x_{n+1} - \sqrt{3} \leq (\tfrac{1}{2})^n (x_1 - \sqrt{3}).$$ | n

And if you choose $x_1 - \sqrt{3} \leq 1$, you have

(8) $\qquad\qquad x_{n+1} - \sqrt{3} \leq (\tfrac{1}{2})^n.$ | n

The right member of (8) gets smaller and smaller, less than any prescribed positive number, as n increases. Therefore, by taking n large enough, x_n can be brought as close to $\sqrt{3}$ as you would like. If someone asked you for a term of the sequence that differs from $\sqrt{3}$ by less than $\frac{1}{100}$, how large would you take n? The smallest exponent k for which $(\frac{1}{2})^k < \frac{1}{100}$ is _____. Taking $n = 7$, | 7

$n + 1 =$ _____. Therefore, $x_? - \sqrt{3} < \frac{1}{100}$. And | 8

$x_i - \sqrt{3} < \frac{1}{100}$ whenever $i \geq$ _____. We can now assert | 8

that the terms x_n do really converge upon $\sqrt{3}$. Inequality (8) establishes the convergence, and it also gives us an estimate of the error if we choose to use any particular member of the sequence as an approximation. An approximation method is actually of little value unless we know how good the approximation is. Therefore, we will continue to get estimates of the error whenever we discuss approximations; and soon we will ask you to find error estimates for some of the methods developed in the last section.

7.9.1
EXERCISES

1. (a) Let

$$x_{n+1} = \frac{1}{2}\left(x_n + \frac{2}{x_n}\right), \qquad n = 1, 2, 3, \ldots.$$

Let x_1 be chosen positive. Prove $x_2 \geq \sqrt{2}$, and prove the more general result that $x_n \geq \sqrt{2}$ for $n > 1$.
 (b) Let

$$x_{n+1} = \frac{1}{2}\left(x_n + \frac{a}{x_n}\right),$$

where $a > 0$ and $n = 1, 2, 3, \ldots$. Prove $x_n \geq \sqrt{a}$, for $n > 1$, if $x_1 > 0$.
 (c) Can the inequalities in parts (a) and (b) be strengthened to read $x_n > \sqrt{2}$ and $x_n > \sqrt{a}$ ($n > 1$) if it is specified that $x_1 > 0$ and x_1 is rational? Justify your answer.

2. At first glance it is not always easy to tell the best way to establish convergence. Even the experienced mathematician must play with the inequalities to construct an argument and get an estimate. Of course, the more experience you get, the better you learn to play. Suppose you were playing with the iteration

$$x_{n+1} = \frac{1}{2}\left(x_n + \frac{3}{x_n}\right)$$

in a way different from the one we showed you, and you began your argument by saying that the x_n converge to $\sqrt{3}$ if the x_n are positive and $x_n^2 - 3$ gets closer and closer to zero. Then the way to proceed would be to examine the quantity $x_n^2 - 3$. This can most easily be done by using the recursion formula to write

$$x_{n+1}^2 - 3 = \frac{1}{4}\left(\underline{} + \underline{} + \frac{9}{x_n^2}\right) - 3$$

$$= \frac{(\underline{})^2}{4x_n^2}.$$

(What deduction can you make about this quantity?) Therefore, $x_{n+1}^2 - 3 \geq \underline{}$, which implies $x_k^2 \geq \underline{}$ for $k > 1$. The question of convergence must be pursued by finding a bound on $x_n^2 - 3$, so we assist you by writing

$$0 \leq x_{n+1}^2 - 3 \leq \frac{x_n^2 - 3}{4x_n^2}(\underline{}).$$

Continue this argument to show that the x_n converge to $\sqrt{3}$. Assume $x_1 > 0$ and $x_1^2 - 3 > 0$, and prove

$$x_n^2 - 3 \leq (\tfrac{1}{4})^{n-1}(x_1^2 - 3) \qquad \text{for } n > 1.$$

Can you reduce the right-hand member of this inequality to show that the approximation is better than it appears in this statement?

3. If $x_1 \geq 1$ and

$$x_{n+1} = \frac{1}{2}\left(x_n + \frac{a}{x_n}\right), \qquad a > 0,$$

prove that the terms of the sequence $\{x_n\}$ converge to $\sqrt{a}$.

4. Using the recursion formula of Exercise 3, determine a value N so that $x_n - \sqrt{a} < \frac{1}{1000}$ for all $n \geq N$. Take
   (a) $a = 2$,
   (b) $a = 5$,
   (c) $a = 10$.
Check your answers in a table of square roots.

The first four exercises were concerned with the convergence and the estimate of error for the iteration leading to the square root. In the succeeding exercises we shall take you back to the iterations for the solution to

$$ax + by = u,$$

$$cx + dy = v,$$

to see if you can prove convergence and estimate the error. Perhaps you will be able to deduce conditions that will guarantee the convergence.

5. Let the iteration be defined by

$$ax_{n+1} + by_{n+1} = u,$$

$$cx_n + dy_{n+1} = v.$$

Marginal answers:

$x_n^2, 6$

$x_n^2 - 3$

$0, 3$

$x_n^2 - 3$

Call (x_0, y_0) the exact solution and (x_n, y_n) the approximate solution at the nth step of the iteration. The error at the nth step can be given in terms of the numbers ξ_n, η_n, where

$$\xi_n = x_n - x_0 \quad \text{and} \quad \eta_n = y_n - y_0.$$

The strategy will be to show that ξ_n and η_n decrease to zero as you go further in the iteration, i.e., as n gets larger.

$$\xi_{n+1} = \underline{\qquad} - x_0 \quad \text{and} \quad \eta_{n+1} = \underline{\qquad} - y_0. \qquad\qquad x_{n+1}, y_{n+1}$$

Substituting for x_n, x_{n+1}, y_{n+1} in the recursion formula gives

$$a(\underline{\qquad} + x_0) + b(\underline{\qquad} + y_0) = u, \qquad\qquad \xi_{n+1}, \eta_{n+1}$$

$$c(\underline{\qquad} + x_0) + d(\underline{\qquad} + y_0) = v. \qquad\qquad \xi_n, \eta_{n+1}$$

Expanding and regrouping, you get

$$a\underline{\qquad} + b\underline{\qquad} + (ax_0 + by_0) = u, \qquad\qquad \xi_{n+1}, \eta_{n+1}$$

$$c\underline{\qquad} + d\underline{\qquad} + (cx_0 + dy_0) = v. \qquad\qquad \xi_n, \eta_{n+1}$$

But look at the quantities in parentheses! What is $ax_0 + by_0$ equal to? [*Hint:* What is the definition of (x_0, y_0)?] Using this fact reduces the system to

$$a\xi_{n+1} + b\eta_{n+1} = \underline{\qquad}, \qquad\qquad 0$$

$$c\xi_n + d\eta_{n+1} = \underline{\qquad}. \qquad\qquad 0$$

Since ξ_n comes from an earlier stage of the iteration than ξ_{n+1} and η_{n+1}, solve for ξ_{n+1} and η_{n+1} in terms of ξ_n.

$$\eta_{n+1} = \underline{\qquad}\xi_n \quad (\underline{\qquad} \neq 0), \qquad\qquad -\dfrac{c}{d}, \ d$$

$$\xi_{n+1} = \underline{\qquad}\eta_{n+1} = \underline{\qquad}\xi_n \quad (\underline{\qquad} \neq 0). \qquad\qquad -\dfrac{b}{a}, \dfrac{bc}{ad}, \ ad$$

In order to compare the magnitude of the errors at the $(n + 1)$st step with the magnitude of the error at the nth step, you should find the absolute value of these errors.

$$|\xi_{n+1}| = \left|\underline{\qquad}\xi_n\right| = \left|\underline{\qquad}\right|\,|\xi_n|. \qquad\qquad \dfrac{bc}{ad}, \dfrac{bc}{ad}$$

This is a recursion formula for the error at each stage of the iteration. If you apply it again, you get

$$|\xi_{n+1}| = \left|\underline{\qquad}\right|\,|\xi_n| = \left|\underline{\qquad}\right|^2|\xi_{n-1}|, \qquad\qquad \dfrac{bc}{ad}, \dfrac{bc}{ad}$$

and if you continue you can get $|\xi_{n+1}|$ in terms of the initial error ξ_1. Thus,

$$|\xi_{n+1}| = \left|\dfrac{bc}{ad}\right|^{?}|\xi_1|. \qquad\qquad n$$

Now you have a formula for the error in x_{n+1} in terms of the initial error ξ_1. What is the corresponding error in y_{n+1} in terms of ξ_1?

The errors decrease as n gets larger provided _____ < 1. In fact if _____ < 1, then you know that the errors $|\xi_n|$ decrease to zero as n gets larger. Thus, you finally have conditions under which the given iteration converges to the solution. This condition is _____. Is this condition a necessary and sufficient condition? Check this result with the theorem you proved about this iteration in the previous chapter.

$$\left|\frac{bc}{ad}\right|$$
$$\left|\frac{bc}{ad}\right|$$
$$\left|\frac{bc}{ad}\right| < 1$$

6. Another recursion formula that you used for the two-by-two linear system was

$$ax_{n+1} + by_n = u,$$

$$cx_n + dy_{n+1} = v.$$

(a) Define the errors ξ_i, η_i as in the last exercise and prove that

$$a\xi_{n+1} + b\eta_n = 0,$$

$$c\xi_n + d\eta_{n+1} = 0.$$

(b) Let $\delta_n = \max\{|\xi_n|, |\eta_n|\}$, and prove inequalities of the form

$$|\xi_{n+1}| \le (\underline{\hspace{1cm}})\delta_n, \qquad |\xi_{n+2}| \le (\underline{\hspace{1cm}})\delta_n.$$

(c) From part (b) deduce an inequality of the form

$$|\xi_{n+1}| \le (\underline{\hspace{1cm}})\delta_0.$$

(d) Under what condition does $|\xi_i|$ approach zero as i increases? Does the same hold true for $|\eta_i|$?

(e) What are the conditions necessary for convergence of this iteration method? Compare this with the solution (if you obtained one) to the research problem in Exercise 6 of Sec. 7.8.2. Did you find this approach—the analytic approach—easier or harder than the geometric approach suggested earlier?

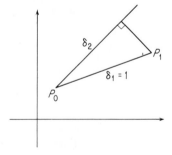

7. Analyze the projection method of iteration. Let P_0 represent the exact solution and let P_1 represent the initial guess at the solution (Fig. 7-19). Call $\delta_n = |P_0P_n|$. This represents the error at the nth step of the iteration. Call $\delta_2/\delta_1 = k$.

(a) No matter how large δ_1 is, k is less than _____.

(b) Derive a recursion formula of the form $\delta_{n+1} = $ _____ δ_n.

(c) Derive a result of the form $\delta_{n+1} = $ _____ δ_0.

(d) Why does this prove convergence upon the exact solution? How does this proof compare with the proof based on vectors?

Figure 7-19

8. We will now show you an iteration method very much like others you saw in the previous section. Suppose you are given the system

$$-0.9x - 0.3y + 5 = 0,$$

$$0.2x - 0.6y + 7 = 0.$$

If you add x to both members of the first equation and y to both members of the second equation, you get a system of the form

$$x = \underline{}x + \underline{}y + 5, \qquad\qquad\qquad 0.1, -0.3$$

$$y = \underline{}x + \underline{}y + 7. \qquad\qquad\qquad 0.2, 0.4$$

Then a reasonable approach to iteration would be to guess at a solution and substitute it into the right-hand members, getting another approximation. Then repeat the process. This can be described by the equations

$$x_{n+1} = 0.1x_n - 0.3y_n + 5,$$

$$y_{n+1} = 0.2x_n + 0.4y_n + 7.$$

But does this iteration really converge upon the exact solution (x_0, y_0)?

(a) Call the errors $\xi_i = x_i - x_0, \eta_i = y_i - y_0$ and substitute in the iteration formula. Using the fact that (x_0, y_0) is the exact solution, you should get a system of the form

$$\xi_{n+1} = \underline{}\xi_n + \underline{}\eta_n,$$

$$\eta_{n+1} = \underline{}\xi_n + \underline{}\eta_n.$$

(b) Call $\delta_n = \max\{|\xi_n|, |\eta_n|\}$, and derive results of the form

$$|\xi_{n+1}| \le (\underline{})\delta_n,$$

$$|\eta_{n+1}| \le (\underline{})\delta_n.$$

(c) Using the results of (b), derive a bound on the errors by proving inequalities of the form

$$|\xi_{n+1}| \le \underline{}\delta_0,$$

$$|\eta_{n+1}| \le \underline{}\delta_0.$$

9. The system

$$ax + by = u,$$

$$cx + dy = v,$$

can be rewritten

$$x = Ax + By + u,$$

$$y = Cx + Dy + v.$$

Using the method illustrated in Exercise 8, prove that the iteration

$$x_{n+1} = Ax_n + By_n + u,$$

$$y_{n+1} = Cx_n + Dy_n + v$$

converges if $(|A| + |B| < 1) \wedge (|C| + |D| < 1)$. Would you say that the coefficients in Exercise 8 were judiciously chosen?

10. Given the system

$$4.4x + 3.2y + 21 = 0,$$

$$2x - 3y + 6 = 0.$$

Exhibit an iteration formula for solving the system by the method of the last two exercises. Does your formula really converge to the solution? How do you know?

7.10

General Quadratic Equations   The height h of a projectile at time t (Fig. 7-20) is given by the equation

$$h = h_0 + v_0 t - 16t^2.$$

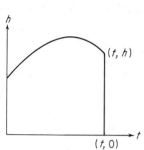

Figure 7-20

What is the height of the body at $t = 0$? Do you recall the significance of the number v_0?

How would you go about answering the question: When does the body hit the ground? When the body hits the ground, its height is _____. Therefore, you set $h =$ _____, which gives

$$0 = h_0 + v_0 t - 16t^2.$$

0, 0

Now you are left with the problem of solving for t. The equation to be solved is a more general quadratic equation than those you were working with in Sec. 7.9; it is of the form

$$at^2 + bt + c = 0, \qquad a \neq 0.$$

In this section we shall discuss this general quadratic and a number of mathematical problems relating to it.

Let's begin with a specific case

(1) $-16t^2 + 64t + 20 = 0$

and ask: Can we reduce this quadratic equation to the type that we treated in the last section? That is, can we reduce the quadratic under discussion to the form

$$x^2 - A = 0?$$

The leading coefficient can be changed to 1 by dividing, but then we are left with the problem of eliminating the linear (first-power) term.

We begin with the easy step. Equation (1) is

$$t^2 + (\underline{\quad})t + (\underline{\quad}) = 0.$$

$-4, -\frac{5}{4}$

In order to eliminate the t-term we try a substitution of the form $t = x + k$, where x will be the new unknown. Why have we chosen this kind of substitution (sometimes called a change of variable)? The reason is simple: We want to change a given quadratic equation into another quadratic equation. That is, the degree of the given equation and the degree of the new equation are to be equal. Therefore, the simplest degree-preserving substitutions available are

$$t = ax \quad \text{and} \quad t = nx + k.$$

[Can you think of still another type of substitution that would preserve the degree of (1)?] The first will not eliminate the t-term (why not?), so we try the second type with $n = 1$. This gives

$$(x + k)^2 - 4(x + k) - \tfrac{5}{4} = 0,$$

which can be simplified to read

$$x^2 + (\underline{\qquad})x + k^2 - 4k - \tfrac{5}{4} = 0.$$

$2k - 4$

The linear term will be eliminated if its coefficient is zero. Algebraically, this condition can be written

$$\underline{\quad}k - 4 = 0,$$

2

or

$$k = \underline{\quad}.$$

2

Therefore, if we select $k = \underline{\quad}$, the substitution $t = x + k$ will reduce the given quadratic to a quadratic without a linear term. Carrying out the algebra in this case gives

2

(2) $$x^2 - \underline{\quad} = 0.$$

$\frac{21}{4}$

Now, if you were after a numerical answer to the question of when the body hit the ground, you could begin by using one of the iteration methods of Sec. 7.9 to solve (2). Suppose you got $x = x_0$ as your solution. How would you find the time t when the body hit the ground? Your answer would be

$$t = x_0 + \underline{\quad}.$$

2

Let's see what this algebraic transformation means in geometric terms. The graphs of the equations

$$y = t^2 - 4t - \tfrac{5}{4} \quad \text{and} \quad y = x^2 - \tfrac{21}{4}$$

are shown in Fig. 7-21. How are the graphs related? If you wished to change the position of the y-axis in the first figure so that it would be in the same relation to the graph as in the second, how far would you shift it? What is the relation of this shift to the change in variable $t = x + k$? An equivalent way of looking at this shift is to hold the axes in the first figure and shift the graph of $y = t^2 - 4t - \tfrac{5}{4}$ to the (left/right) so that the first figure would then look the same as the second. Have you ever seen shifts of this type before? What was the name of this type of transformation? Check back, if necessary, to see how the substitution $t = x + k$ fits the algebraic description of the "shift" transformation.

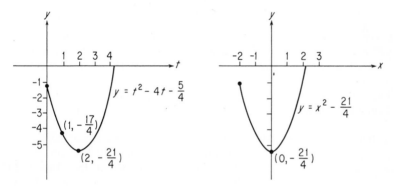

Figure 7-21

7.10.1
EXERCISES

1. (a) Carry out the reduction of the general quadratic equation

$$at^2 + bt + c = 0$$

to the form $x^2 - A = 0$.

(b) If $t = x + k$, what value of k did you use in part (a)?

(c) Using the fact that $x = \pm\sqrt{A}$, find t in terms of the original coefficients a, b, and c. Do you recognize this formula for t?

(d) How was this formula for t derived the first time you saw it in this book (or in your high school textbook)? Is the new derivation simpler than the old?

2. In the illustration, $h = -16t^2 + 64t + 20$, the body appears to reach its maximum height when $t =$ _____. How can we prove this?

(a) Write $h = -16(t^2 - $ _____ $t) + 20$.

(b) Complete the square of the term in parentheses so that

$$h = -16(\underline{\hspace{1cm}})^2 + \underline{\hspace{1cm}}.$$

(c) h attains its maximum value when the squared term is zero. This occurs when $t = \underline{\hspace{1cm}}$.

3. (a) If $y = t^2 - 4t - \frac{5}{4}$, does y attain a maximum value? a minimum value? Find the maximum and/or minimum value of y, whichever exists. For what value of t does this extreme value of y occur?

(b) If $y = x^2 - \frac{21}{4}$, clearly y does not reach a maximum value. Does y have a minimum value? If so, for what value of t does it occur?

(c) Compare your answers to Exercises 2(c), 3(a), and 3(b) and explain the phenomenon.

4. Consider the general case

$$y = ax^2 + bx + c, \qquad a \neq 0.$$

If $a > 0$, then y will have a _____ (minimum/maximum) value. If $a < 0$, then y will have a _____ value. If y attains a minimum or maximum value y_m at x_m, then we have referred to y_m as an *extreme value*. The point (x_m, y_m) is also called an *extreme* point.

(a) Find a formula for x_m that holds for the general quadratic.
(b) Find a formula for y_m.

5. The graph of $y = f(x)$ is called *symmetric about the y-axis* if and only if the following condition holds: If (x_0, y_0) is on the graph, then so is $(-x_0, y_0)$. (See Fig. 7-22.) In functional notation the condition is expressed

$$y_0 = f(x_0) \Rightarrow y_0 = f(-x_0).$$

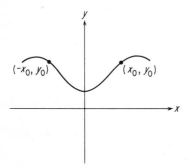

Figure 7-22

Similarly, we can define *symmetric* with respect to the *x*-axis. Which of the following have graphs that exhibit symmetry with respect to one of the axes?

(i) $y = x^2$,
(ii) $2y = x^2$,
(iii) $2y = -x^2$,
(iv) $y = 2x^2 + 3$,
(v) $y = |x|$,
(vi) $y = -16x^2 + 64x + 20$,
(vii) $y = x^2 - \frac{21}{4}$,
(viii) $y^2 = (3 - x)$,
(ix) $(y - 1)^2 = (x + 2)^2$,
(x) $|y| + |x| = 1$.

6. The notion of symmetry with respect to an axis is a special case of *symmetry about a line*. Imagine a figure drawn on a sheet of paper, and suppose the paper can be folded along line l so that when the paper is folded all the points of the figure on one side of l fall on points of the figure on the other side of l. In this case, we would say that the figure is symmetric about l. The line l is called the *axis of symmetry*. (See Fig. 7-23.)

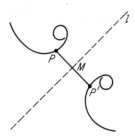

Figure 7-23

A more precise definition begins as follows: The plane figure $\mathscr{F}$ is said to be symmetric about line l if and only if the following condition holds: If point P is on $\mathscr{F}$, then there is also a point P' on $\mathscr{F}$ so that l is the perpendicular bisector of PP' (Fig. 7-23). What remains to be said if P is on l?

(a) Is the graph of $y = t^2 - 4t - \frac{5}{4}$ symmetric with respect to any line? If your answer is yes, give the equation of the axis of symmetry.

(b) What is the equation of the axis of symmetry of the graph of

$$y = x^2 - c?$$

(c) What is the equation of the axis of symmetry of the graph of

$$y = ax^2 + bx + c \qquad (a \neq 0)?$$

(d) Prove that the extreme point of the graph of

$$y = ax^2 + bx + c \qquad (a \neq 0)$$

occurs on the axis of symmetry.

7. Suppose that the graph of $y = f(x)$ is symmetric with respect to the line whose equation is $y = x$. Let $P_0 = (x_0, y_0)$ be on the graph. Then the point $P'_0 = (\underline{\hspace{1cm}}, \underline{\hspace{1cm}})$ must also be on the graph. In mathematical language this says:

$$y_0 = f(x_0) \Rightarrow \underline{\hspace{1cm}} = f(\underline{\hspace{1cm}}).$$

8. Recall that a figure $\mathscr{F}$ is said to be invariant under a transformation T if T maps the figure $\mathscr{F}$ onto $\mathscr{F}$.

(a) Prove that the graph of $y = -x^2$ is invariant under the linear transformation

$$R = \begin{pmatrix} -1 & 0 \\ 0 & 1 \end{pmatrix}.$$

(b) Prove that the graph of $y^2 = -x + 3$ is invariant under the linear transformation

$$S = \begin{pmatrix} 1 & 0 \\ 0 & -1 \end{pmatrix}.$$

(c) Prove that any figure $\mathscr{F}_y$ that is symmetric with respect to the y-axis remains invariant under R, and any figure $\mathscr{F}_x$ that is symmetric with respect to the x-axis is invariant under S.

(d) Prove that the axes of symmetry of $\mathscr{F}_y$ and $\mathscr{F}_x$ are pointwise invariant under R and S, respectively.

(e) Suppose a locus $\mathscr{L}$ is invariant under the transformation

$$T = \begin{pmatrix} 0 & 1 \\ 1 & 0 \end{pmatrix}.$$

What kind of symmetry does $\mathscr{L}$ have?

(f) Suppose a locus $\mathscr{L}$ is invariant under the linear transformation

$$U = \begin{pmatrix} 0 & -1 \\ -1 & 0 \end{pmatrix}.$$

What is the axis of symmetry of $\mathscr{L}$?

Since extracting square roots appears to be so essential in solving quadratics and other problems, we shall use the remaining exercises to introduce a rather different method for the approximation of square roots. Perhaps this method is not as practical as the iteration of Sec. 7.9; you be the judge. We will illustrate by calculating $\sqrt{3}$.

It is clear that $2 < 3 < 4$. This implies that $1 < \sqrt{3} < 2$ (why?). Then

$$(\underline{}) - \sqrt{3} < 1. \qquad \text{(Fill in with an integer.)}$$

Calling the left member θ, we have

$$\theta = \underline{} - \sqrt{3} \wedge 0 < \theta < 1,$$

$$\theta^2 = (\underline{}) - (\underline{})\sqrt{3} \wedge 0 < \theta^2 < 1,$$

$$\theta^3 = (\underline{}) - (\underline{})\sqrt{3} \wedge 0 < \theta^3 < 1.$$

For every integer n, θ^n is of the form

$$\theta^n = a_n - b_n\sqrt{3}. \qquad \text{(Prove this!)}$$

Is a_n always an integer? Is b_n always an integer? Can a_n equal zero? Can b_n equal zero? The a_n are _____ (always/sometimes/never) positive. The b_n are _____ (always/sometimes/never) positive. Settle all questions in this paragraph before reading on.

Let's try to get formulas for the a_n and b_n. A recursion formula can be obtained easily by noting that

$$a_{n+1} - b_{n+1}\sqrt{3} = (a_n - b_n\sqrt{3})(\underline{})$$

$$= (2a_n + 3b_n) - (\underline{})\sqrt{3}.$$

Therefore,

$$a_{n+1} = 2a_n + \underline{},$$

and
$$b_{n+1} = a_n + \underline{\qquad}.$$

Check these formulas against the computations you made for $n = 1, 2, 3$.

By dividing both members of the equation $a_n - b_n\sqrt{3} = \theta^n$ by b_n, we get

$$0 < \frac{a_n}{b_n} - \sqrt{3} = \frac{\theta^n}{b_n}$$

and

$$\frac{a_n}{b_n} - \sqrt{3} \le \theta^n. \qquad \text{(Why?)}$$

This inequality shows that a_n/b_n is an approximation to $\sqrt{3}$ and the error is at most θ^n. But as n gets larger, θ^n decreases to zero! Therefore the a_n/b_n converge to $\sqrt{3}$. The computation of the a_n/b_n is done readily by means of the recursion formulas, which are very simple. If you had begun with $a_1 = 2$ and $b_1 = 1$, what θ would you use to estimate the maximum error? Which of the following would be satisfactory choices for θ: 0.2, 0.3, 0.4, 0.5?

10. Modify the reasoning of Exercise 9 to determine a sequence $\{a_n/b_n\}$ converging upon $\sqrt{3}$ based on the fact that

$$0 < \theta = |1 - \sqrt{3}| < 1.$$

11. (a) Find the integer k such that $k < \sqrt{5} < k + 1$.

(b) Letting $\theta = (k + 1) - \sqrt{5}$, use the method of Exercise 9 to determine a sequence $\{a_n/b_n\}$ that converges to $\sqrt{5}$.

(c) Use the sequence of part (b) to compute $\sqrt{5}$ accurate to two decimal places.

(d) Determine a sequence $\{a_n/b_n\}$, converging to $\sqrt{5}$, based on the fact that

$$0 < |k - \sqrt{5}| = \theta < 1.$$

(e) Observing that $8^2 - 7 \cdot 3^2 = 1$, apply the methods of this problem to compute $\sqrt{7}$ to the nearest one-thousandth.

(f) Can the method of this problem be applied to compute $\sqrt{a}$ for any integer $a > 0$?

Returning to the study of the projectile whose motion is described by the equation

$$h = -16t^2 + 64t + 20, \qquad t \ge 0$$

we ask: At what time will the projectile be 80 ft high? In order to answer this question you substitute _____ for | *80*

h in the equation of motion and solve the resulting quadratic equation

$$-16t^2 + 64t + \underline{\hspace{1cm}} = 0.$$

−60

This equation simplifies to become

$$4t^2 + (\underline{\hspace{1cm}})t + \underline{\hspace{1cm}} = 0,$$

− 16, 15

which can be factored into two linear factors with integer coefficients:

$$(\underline{\hspace{0.6cm}}t - \underline{\hspace{0.6cm}})(\underline{\hspace{0.6cm}}t - \underline{\hspace{0.6cm}}) = 0.$$

2, 3, 2, 5

This statement is true when $t = \underline{\hspace{1cm}}$ or $t = \underline{\hspace{1cm}}$. Thus, the answer to the original question is that the projectile is at a height of 80 ft at two different times: at $t = \underline{\hspace{1cm}}$ sec and at $t = \underline{\hspace{1cm}}$ sec after it has begun its flight. Graphically, these solutions are given by the points of intersection of the graphs of

$\frac{3}{2}, \frac{5}{2}$

$\frac{3}{2}, \frac{5}{2}$

$$h = -16t^2 + 64t + 20,$$

$$h = \underline{\hspace{1cm}}.$$

80

At what time will the projectile be 100 ft high? Following the same reasoning, you write

$$-16t^2 + 64t + 20 = \underline{\hspace{1cm}}.$$

100

Simplifying leads to the equation

$$t^2 + (\underline{\hspace{1cm}})t + \underline{\hspace{1cm}} = 0.$$

−4, 5

This equation does not seem to factor readily. You should be able to prove that it cannot be factored into linear factors with integer coefficients. (Can you prove this?) So we use the quadratic formula to get

$$t = \frac{4 \pm \sqrt{\underline{\hspace{1cm}}}}{2},$$

−4

which simplifies to give

$$t = 2 \pm \sqrt{\underline{\hspace{1cm}}}.$$

−1

But the square root of a negative number is not a real number. Using the familiar notation $i = \sqrt{-1}$, our answer can be expressed

$$t = 2 \pm i.$$

338
NUMERICAL SOLUTION OF EQUATIONS
SECTION 7.10

What do these answers mean in our problem? The scale we use for time is the *real number scale*, or part of the real number scale. Therefore, there is no time at which the projectile reaches a height of 100 ft. What does this mean graphically? Draw the figure and see. To check this answer you might also determine the maximum height attained by the projectile. If you haven't worked Exercise 2 of Sec. 7.10.1, then you should do it now.

Let's take another simple problem: A rectangle has an area of four square units, and its length is three units longer than its width. Find the dimensions.

If you let x = width, then the length = _____. Since the area of a rectangle is the product of its length and width you have

$$x(\underline{\hspace{2cm}}) = 4.$$

This quadratic can be put in simple standard form.

$$x^2 + (\underline{\hspace{1cm}})x + (\underline{\hspace{1cm}}) = 0.$$

Factoring gives

$$(x + (\underline{\hspace{1cm}}))(x + (\underline{\hspace{1cm}})) = 0,$$

which implies that $x = 1$ or $x = $ _____.

$x + 3$
$x + 3$
$3, -4$
$-1, 4$
-4

Check the first answer to see if it fulfills the conditions of the problem. What about the second answer?

From the two illustrations given you find that the mathematical solution of a problem does not always have physical meaning or meaning in the applied problem from which the mathematics arose. A field -50 ft long may be meaningless to a surveyor, but \$-50 may mean that you have overdrawn your checking account. A projectile attaining a height of 100 ft at time $t = 2 + i$ may be nonsense, but an answer of $2 + i$ can be very meaningful in an electric circuit problem. Negative numbers and imaginary numbers are not simply creations of the mathematician to develop elegant solutions to his problems. These concepts are extremely useful in applied science, although they were not always so regarded. The Italian mathematician Cardan (1501–1576) referred to the nonreal roots of polynomials as "ingenious though useless." This is another one of the many instances in history when a development in pure science was judged prematurely. Not only is it difficult—it is *impossible* to always predict applicability and usefulness. This is precisely why you should master as much mathematical knowledge as you possibly can early in your training. You may even discover a new application for it.

Let's return to study the general quadratic to see if we can predict the nature of the roots without actually determining them. We confine

PROGRAMMED TEXT
FOLLOWS

attention to quadratics with real coefficients, that is,

$$ax^2 + bx + c = 0, \qquad a \neq 0, \quad a, b, c \in \mathscr{R}.$$

The quadratic formula gives the roots:

$$x = \frac{-b \pm \sqrt{b^2 - 4ac}}{2a}.$$

Is it possible for the two roots to coincide? The condition
on the coefficients that implies the equality of two roots
is _____ = 0. $b^2 - 4ac$

The roots are imaginary if the quantity under the
square root sign is _____. Otherwise, the roots   *negative*
are real. Algebraically, this is stated:

_____ $\geq 0 \Rightarrow$ roots are _____; $b^2 - 4ac$, *real*

_____ $< 0 \Rightarrow$ roots are _____. $b^2 - 4ac$,
                                                                  imaginary

In answering each of the questions we posed about the nature of the
roots, you used the quantity $b^2 - 4ac$. Because it gives us so much information we shall give it a name: *discriminant*. It is actually the discriminant
of the quadratic equation, for there are discriminants of cubics, quartics,
and so on. Let's write

$$\text{disc} = \text{discriminant} = b^2 - 4ac,$$

$$\text{disc} = 0 \Rightarrow \text{equal roots},$$

$$\text{disc} > 0 \Rightarrow \text{real unequal roots},$$

$$\text{disc} < 0 \Rightarrow \text{imaginary roots}.$$

(Can these implications be reversed?)

7.10.2
EXERCISES

1. Determine a formula for the height h (in feet) of a projectile under the force of
gravity if
  (a) it begins its motion at a height of 30 ft and it is again 30 ft high after 1 sec.
  (b) it begins its flight 10 ft below the ground level and it attains a height of 80 ft
above ground level after 2 sec.
  (c) it attains its maximum height of 55 ft after 2 sec of flight. Where was this
projectile at $t = 0$, and when does it hit the ground?

2. On one set of axes sketch graphs of the functions
  (i) $f(x) = x^2 - 4x - 1$,
  (ii) $g(x) = x^2 - 4x + 4$,
  (iii) $h(x) = x^2 - 4x + 8$.

(a) From the graph and the computations you have made, deduce whether the discriminant is less than, equal to, or greater than zero in each case. Check by computing the discriminants.

(b) If the discriminant is negative, then the graph of the quadratic function will _____ (always/sometimes/never) cross the x-axis. If the discriminant is negative, then the graph will _____ (always/sometimes/never) cross the y-axis.

(c) If the discriminant equals zero, the graph of the quadratic function will intercept the x-axis _____ (once/twice/not at all).

3. (a) If the discriminant of the quadratic function defined by

$$f(x) = ax^2 + bx + c, \qquad a < 0$$

is negative, then the graph of $y = f(x)$
 (i) lies entirely above the x-axis,
 (ii) lies entirely below the x-axis,
 (iii) crosses the x-axis.
Which of (i), (ii), (iii) is correct? Give a proof that your choice is correct by proving one of

$$f(x) > 0, \ \forall \, x \in \mathscr{R}, \qquad f(x) < 0, \ \forall \, x \in \mathscr{R}, \qquad f(x) = 0 \text{ for some } x \in \mathscr{R}.$$

(b) Let $f(x) = 2.4x^2 - 8.35x - 15.62$. Without plotting and without solving a quadratic equation, answer the following: Does the graph of $y = f(x)$ lie entirely above the x-axis? lie entirely below the x-axis? cross the x-axis?

4. Application to Cauchy Inequality. In Exercise 13 of Sec. 6.9.1 we promised to return to a proof of the Cauchy inequality for abstract vector spaces (over $\mathscr{R}$) for which a real inner product has been defined. We are now in a position to make good our promise.

Let the real inner product of $\mathbf{A}$ and $\mathbf{B}$ be denoted by $(\mathbf{A}, \mathbf{B})$. If the Cauchy inequality is to be generalized, we must be able to prove

(∗) $(\mathbf{A}, \mathbf{B})^2 \leq (\mathbf{A}, \mathbf{A})(\mathbf{B}, \mathbf{B})$

using only the properties of inner product.

(a) Review the properties of inner product (see Sec. 6.9).

(b) Consider the vector $\mathbf{A} + \lambda\mathbf{B}$, where $\mathbf{A}$ and $\mathbf{B}$ are any vectors of the abstract vector space and $\lambda \in \mathscr{R}$.

$$(\mathbf{A} + \lambda\mathbf{B}, \mathbf{A} + \lambda\mathbf{B}) \geq 0 \qquad \text{(why?)}$$

$$\Rightarrow (\mathbf{A}, \mathbf{A}) + \lambda(\underline{\quad\quad}) + \lambda^2(\underline{\quad\quad}) \geq 0.$$

If we write the left member as $Q(\lambda)$, then Q is a quadratic function. What is its discriminant?

Since $Q(\lambda) \geq 0$, its discriminant satisfies the inequality

$$\text{disc } Q \underline{\quad} 0 \qquad (\leq / \geq).$$

Thus,

$$[2(A, B)]^2 - 4(\underline{\quad})(\underline{\quad}) \leq 0.$$

Complete the proof of (∗).

5. Determine the values of k for which the roots of the following equations are *real* and *equal*.
   (a) $x^2 - 5x + k = 0$,
   (b) $x^2 + 4x + 9k = -2kx$.

6. Without finding the roots, determine whether any real values of x can satisfy the equations:
   (a) $2x^2 - 6x + 7 = 0$,
   (b) $0.24x + 0.0025 - x^2 = 0$.

7. If $ax^2 + bx + c = 0$ $(a \neq 0)$ the roots r_1 and r_2 are:

$$r_1 = \underline{\hspace{1.5cm}} \quad \text{and} \quad r_2 = \underline{\hspace{1.5cm}}.$$

   (a) Find $r_1 + r_2$.
   (b) Find $r_1 \cdot r_2$.
   (c) The given quadratic can be reduced to the form

$$(x - r_1)(x - r_2) = 0.$$

Expand this factorization to check your answers to (a) and (b).

8. Construct a quadratic so that:
   (a) one root is 6 and the other root is $-\frac{7}{2}$,
   (b) the sum of the roots is 4 and the product of the roots is 1,
   (c) the sum of the roots is zero and the product of the roots is -1,
   (d) the roots are r/s and s/r, where r and s are the roots of

$$ax^2 + bx + c = 0,$$

   (e) the roots are $-7 \pm 2\sqrt{5}$.

9. (a) Are the roots of $2x^2 + x - 0 = 0$ rational?
   (b) Are the roots of $2x^2 + x - 3 = 0$ rational?
   (c) Is the discriminant any help in determining whether the roots are rational or irrational? Prove: If a, b, and c are rational numbers, then the roots of

$$ax^2 + bx + c = 0 \quad (a \neq 0)$$

are also rational if the discriminant is \underline{\hspace{3cm}}. Is the converse true?

10. If a polynomial of degree n is given by

$$a_n x^n + a_{n-1} x^{n-1} + \cdots + a_1 x + a_0, \qquad a_n \neq 0,$$

find a formula for (a) the sum of its roots and (b) the product of its roots. [*Hint:* Refer to Exercise 7.]

11. Have you ever proved the fact that a quadratic equation cannot have more than two roots? Try it before accepting our assistance below.

Suppose the quadratic equation $ax^2 + bx + c = 0$ has three *distinct* roots r_1, r_2, and r_3. (The roots' being distinct implies that $r_1 \neq r_2$, $r_1 \neq r_3$, and $r_2 \neq r_3$.) Then it is true that

(A) $a(\underline{\hspace{1.5cm}})^2 + b(\underline{\hspace{1.5cm}}) + c = 0,$

(B) $a(\underline{\hspace{1.5cm}})^2 + b(\underline{\hspace{1.5cm}}) + c = 0,$

(C) $a(\underline{\hspace{1.5cm}})^2 + b(\underline{\hspace{1.5cm}}) + c = 0.$

Eliminate c from (A) and (B). Simplify further, using the fact that *the roots are distinct*. Call the result (D).

Eliminate c from (B) and (C), simplify, and call the result (E). From (D) and (E) you should be able to force a contradiction.

12. Find the coefficients of the quadratic equation whose roots are:
   (a) $1 + 2i$ and $1 - 2i$,
   (b) $-2 + i$ and $-2 - i$,
   (c) $-3 + \sqrt{2}$ and $-3 - \sqrt{2}$,
   (d) $2 + i\sqrt{3}$ and $2 - i\sqrt{3}$,
   (e) $2 - i\sqrt{3}$ and -5.

13. If a, b, and c are real and if the quadratic equation

$$ax^2 + bx + c = 0 \qquad (a \neq 0)$$

has

   (a) one root equal to $1 - i\sqrt{2}$, then the other root equals \underline{\hspace{1cm}};
   (b) one root equal to $-5i$, then the other root equals \underline{\hspace{1cm}};
   (c) one root equal to $-5 - \sqrt{3}i$, then the other root equals \underline{\hspace{1cm}};
   (d) one root equal to $a + bi$, then the other root equals \underline{\hspace{1cm}}.

14. At sea level sound travels 1088 ft/sec. How deep is a well if a stone dropped from the surface is heard to hit bottom after 5 sec? [*Hint:* Use formula for distance traveled by a freely falling body.]

15. (a) If $x^2 + bx + c = 0$ has roots r_1 and r_2, find the quadratic equation whose roots are r_1^2 and r_2^2.
   (b) Find the polynomial whose roots are r_1^4 and r_2^4.

7.11

The Bernoulli Iteration In this section we shall continue our study of the general quadratic equation, using it mainly as a vehicle for the introduction of still another important iteration procedure.

First, we take a short detour to solve a related problem: Are there functions f that satisfy the *functional equation*

(1) $$f(n + 2) - 3f(n + 1) + f(n) = 0$$

for every nonnegative integer n?

We begin the investigation by letting $n = 0$, in which case

(2) $$f(2) - 3f(1) + f(0) = 0.$$

A solution satisfying (2) can easily be found by noting the relationship between (2) and a quadratic equation:

$$f(2) - 3f(1) + f(0) = 0, \qquad \begin{pmatrix} f(n) \\ \downarrow \\ x^n \end{pmatrix}$$
$$\downarrow \qquad \downarrow \qquad \downarrow$$
$$x^2 - 3x + 1 = 0$$

Thus, if r is a root of this quadratic, then

(3) $$f(2) = r^2, \qquad f(1) = r, \qquad f(0) = 1 = r^0$$

provides a solution to (2)—in fact, two solutions—since the related quadratic equation has two roots.

Can you extend the solutions given by (3)? For $n = 1$, the diagram

(4) $$f(3) - 3f(2) + f(1) = 0,$$
$$\downarrow \qquad \downarrow \qquad \downarrow$$
$$? - 3r^2 + r = 0,$$

gives a hint. Then condition (4) is also satisfied if $f(3) = $ _____ . If $n = 2$,
$$f(4) - 3f(3) + f(2) = 0,$$
$$\downarrow \qquad \downarrow \qquad \downarrow$$
$$? - 3r^3 + r^2 = 0,$$

you see that the solution we have can be extended by taking $f(4) = $ _____ . Continuing the process to determine a solution to the original functional equation (1), you get $f(n) = $ _____ . More precisely, if r_1 and r_2 are the roots of

$$x^2 - 3x + 1 = 0,$$

then two solutions to (1) are

$$f(n) = r_1^- \quad \text{and} \quad f(n) = r_2^-.$$

Is there any way to obtain new solutions from a known solution? Suppose f_1 is a solution, i.e.,

$$f_1(n + 2) - 3f_1(n + 1) + f_1(n) = 0$$

for $n \geq 0$. Let $f(n) = Af_1(n)$ for $n \geq 0$, where A is any constant. Then

$$f(n + 2) - 3f(n + 1) + f(n)$$
$$= Af_1(n + 2) - 3A\text{_____} + A\text{_____}$$
$$= A(\text{_____} - 3\text{_____} + \text{\_\_\_\_\_}) $$
$$= A \cdot \text{\_\_\_\_\_} = \text{\_\_\_\_\_} \quad \text{for} \quad n \geq 0.$$

(margin notes:)

r^3

r^4

r^n

n, n

$f_1(n + 1), f_1(n)$

$f_1(n + 2),$
$f_1(n + 1), f_1(n)$
$0, 0$

Therefore f is also a solution. This yields these two families of solutions:

$$f(n) = Ar_1^n \quad \text{and} \quad f(n) = Br_2^n$$

where A and B are any fixed numbers. Now we shall show you how to combine two solutions to obtain a third.

Let f_1 and f_2 be two solutions. Substituting $f_1 + f_2$ for f in the left member of (1), you get

$$[f_1(n+2) + f_2(n+2)] - 3[f_1(n+1) + f_2(n+1)] + [f_1(n) + f_2(n)]$$

$$= [f_1(n+2) - 3f_1(n+1) + f_1(n)] + [\underline{\hspace{3cm}}]$$

$$= 0 + \underline{\hspace{1cm}}$$

$$= \underline{\hspace{1cm}}.$$

$f_2(n+2) -$
$3f_2(n+1) +$
$f_2(n)$
0
0

What does this computation show? It proves that the sum of any two solutions is also a solution! Therefore, if A and B are any fixed numbers, and r_1, r_2 are the two roots of $x^2 - 3x + 1 = 0$, then

(5) $f(n) = A\underline{\hspace{1cm}} + B\underline{\hspace{1cm}}$ r_1^n, r_2^n

is a solution to (1). This solution is called the *general solution*, because it includes every solution as a special case. This fact is established by the following argument.

If $f(0)$ and $f(1)$ are known, then $f(2)$ is uniquely determined by the equation

$$f(2) - 3f(1) + f(0) = 0,$$

$f(3)$ is uniquely determined by

$$f(3) - 3f(2) + f(1) = 0,$$

and, in general, $f(n)$ is uniquely determined for every integer $n \geq 2$ by

$$f(n) - 3f(n-1) + f(n-2) = 0, \qquad n \geq 2.$$

Thus, there is a unique solution to the functional equation if the two values $f(0)$ and $f(1)$ are specified. We shall now find it. For any given pair of values $f(0)$ and $f(1)$, we can determine A and B such that

$$f(0) = A + B,$$

$$f(1) = Ar_1 + Br_2.$$

Since $f(0)$ and $f(1)$ are supposed to be given, this gives us _____ equations for the _____ unknowns A and B. Solve them. | *two, two*

$$A = \frac{\underline{\hspace{1cm}} - \underline{\hspace{1cm}}}{r_1 - r_2},$$ | $r_2 f(0), f(1)$

$$B = \frac{\underline{\hspace{1cm}} - \underline{\hspace{1cm}}}{r_1 - r_2}.$$ | $f(1), r_1 f(0)$

Then

$$f(2) = 3f(1) - f(0)$$

$$= A(3\underline{\hspace{1cm}} - r_1) + B(3\underline{\hspace{1cm}} - r_2)$$ | r_1, r_2

$$= A r_1^- + B r_2^-.$$ | $2, 2$

Similarly,

$$f(3) = 3f(2) - f(1)$$

$$= A(3\underline{\hspace{1cm}} - 1) + B(3\underline{\hspace{1cm}} - 1),$$ | r_1^2, r_2^2

and, in general,

$$f(n) = A\underline{\hspace{1cm}} + B\underline{\hspace{1cm}}.$$ | r_1^n, r_2^n

Therefore, we see that every solution can be expressed in the form (5).

The particular functional equation we have been discussing is an example of a *difference equation*. It is sometimes written in a form

$$y_{n+1} - 3y_n + y_{n-1} = 0, \qquad n = \mathscr{Z}^+,$$

where y_n is an abbreviation for $f(n)$. Difference equations have a variety of applications. In recent years social scientists, especially economists, have found them to be of great value.† Our aim in introducing difference equations is to show how they can be used to find approximate solutions to polynomial equations. This technique was first discovered by Daniel Bernoulli (1700–1784), one of the famous family of Swiss scientists.

For the given equation

$$y_{n+1} - 3y_n + y_{n-1} = 0, \qquad n \in \mathscr{Z}^+,$$

† See P. A. Samuelson, *Foundations of Economic Analysis* (Cambridge, Mass.: Harvard University Press, 1948) and W. J. Baumol, *Economic Dynamics* (New York: Macmillan, 1951).

pick y_0, y_1 arbitrarily, say $y_0 = 1$ and $y_1 = 2$. (You now know that this choice completely determines the solution.) Make a table for computing y_n and their successive ratios:

n	y_n	
0	1	
1	2	
2	_____	*5*
3	_____	*13*
4	_____	*34*
5	_____	*89*

$$\frac{y_3}{y_2} = \text{\_\_\_\_\_},$$ *2.60*

$$\frac{y_4}{y_3} = \text{\_\_\_\_\_},$$ *2.62*

$$\frac{y_5}{y_4} = \text{\_\_\_\_\_}.$$ *2.62*

The roots of the given quadratic equation

$$x^2 - 3x + 1 = 0,$$

accurate to two decimal places, are

$$r_1 = \text{\_\_\_\_\_} \quad \text{and} \quad r_2 = \text{\_\_\_\_\_}.$$ *2.62, 0.38*

Do you observe anything interesting?
   Fill in the table:

$$\frac{y_2}{y_3} = \text{\_\_\_\_\_},$$ *0.38*

$$\frac{y_3}{y_4} = \text{\_\_\_\_\_},$$ *0.38*

$$\frac{y_4}{y_5} = \text{\_\_\_\_\_}.$$ *0.38*

Do you find this a surprise?
   Let's analyze the foregoing procedure to see if we can explain the coincidences. We know that the solution for y_n is given by

$$y_n = Ar_1^n + Br_2^n.$$

Therefore,

$$\frac{y_{n+1}}{y_n} = \frac{A\rule{1.5cm}{0.4pt} + B\rule{1.5cm}{0.4pt}}{Ar_1^n + Br_2^n}.$$

The right member can be written in the form

$$r_1 + \text{remainder},$$

so

$$\frac{y_{n+1}}{y_n} = r_1 + \frac{\rule{2cm}{0.4pt}}{Ar_1^n + Br_2^n}.$$

What happens to the remainder R as n gets large? Dividing the numerator and denominator of the remainder by r_1^n, it becomes

$$R = \frac{B(\rule{1cm}{0.4pt})^n(r_2 - r_1)}{A + B(r_2/r_1)^n}.$$

Suppose $|(r_2/r_1)| < 1$. Then as n gets larger $|(r_2/r_1)^n|$ gets $\rule{1.5cm}{0.4pt}$ (larger/smaller). In fact, $|(r_2/r_1)^n|$ approaches closer and closer to the value $\rule{1cm}{0.4pt}$. Thus, the absolute value of the numerator of R approaches $\rule{1cm}{0.4pt}$, and the absolute value of the denominator approaches $|\rule{1cm}{0.4pt}|$. This means that, as n gets larger, $|R|$ approaches the value $\rule{1cm}{0.4pt}$.

The reasoning in the preceding paragraph can be made more explicit as follows:

Let $\delta = |(r_2/r_1)|$. We are assuming $0 < |\delta| < 1$. Then

$$|R| = \frac{|B(r_2/r_1)^n(r_2 - r_1)|}{|A + B(r_2/r_1)^n|} = \frac{|B(r_2 - r_1)| \, |(r_2/r_1)^n|}{|A + B(r_2/r_1)^n|}$$

$$\leq \frac{|B(r_2 - r_1)| \, |(r_2/r_1)^n|}{||A| - |B(r_2/r_1)^n||} \quad \text{(why?)}$$

$$\leq \frac{|B(r_2 - r_1)|\delta^n}{||A| - |B|\delta^n|}.$$

As n increases, the right member of this inequality approaches zero. Therefore, R also approaches zero as n gets larger.

Finally, this means: If $|r_1| > |r_2|$, then the sequence of ratios y_{n+1}/y_n converges to r_1, *the root that is larger in absolute value*. This is the reason why your calculations of y_{n+1}/y_n in the example brought you close to $(3 + \sqrt{5})/2$.

The method of determining r_1 approximately by computing the sequence of ratios y_{n+1}/y_n is the promised *Bernoulli iteration method*. We will ask you to explore it further in the exercises.

7.11.1
EXERCISES

1. Carry out the justification for obtaining r_2, the root that is smaller in absolute value, by means of the Bernoulli iteration.

2. Use the Bernoulli iteration to find the roots of

$$3x^2 - 5x - 1 = 0.$$

3. Use the Bernoulli iteration method to find both roots of

$$x^2 + 0.12x - 1.3 = 0.$$

4. (a) Replace x by $1/z$ in the equation $x^2 - 3x + 1 = 0$. This replacement gives a new polynomial

$$(\underline{\hspace{1cm}})z^2 + (\underline{\hspace{1cm}})z + (\underline{\hspace{1cm}}) = 0.$$

How are the roots s_i of this equation related to the roots r_i of the original? (Assume $|s_1| > |s_2|$.)

(b) Use the Bernoulli iteration method, carrying it to y_5/y_4 to determine s_1. From s_1 obtain an approximation to r_2.

5. Let $f(x)$ be a polynomial function. Form a new polynomial $f(x) \cdot f(-x)$.

(a) The graph of $y = f(x) \cdot f(-x)$ is symmetric with respect to one of the axes. Which one?

(b) This implies that only _____ (even/odd) powers of x appear in the product $f(x) \cdot f(-x)$.

(c) Let $z = x^2$. Then the degree of the resulting polynomial $g(z)$ is the same as the degree of $f(x)$. How are the roots of $g(z) = 0$ related to the roots of $f(x) = 0$?

6. (a) Find a quadratic equation $z^2 + b_1 z + c_1 = 0$, whose roots are r_1^2 and r_2^2. Find a quadratic equation $w^2 + b_2 w + c_2 = 0$, whose roots are r_1^4 and r_2^4.

(b) If you carry this procedure through n times, you get a polynomial of the form $y^2 + b_n y + c_n = 0$. Give recursive formulas for b_n and c_n.

(c) The roots of $y^2 + b_n y + c_n = 0$ are r_1^2 and r_2^2.

(d) Express b_n and c_n in terms of the roots in part (c).

(e) Write $b_n = -r_1^{2^n}[1 + (\underline{\hspace{1cm}})]$.

(f) Assuming $|r_1| > |r_2|$, then the sequence $\{b_{n+1}/b_n\}$ converges to _____, and the sequence $\{c_{n+1}/c_n\}$ converges to _____.

(g) Utilizing your result of part (f), get approximations for r_1 and r_2, carrying the process through for $n = 3$.

7. The method of approximating roots given in Exercise 6 is called the *Graeffe root-squaring method*. It has the advantage of producing both roots simultaneously, but programming the computation on an electronic computer is not as simple as programming the Bernoulli method. As a research problem investigate the validity of the Graeffe method in the cases where (a) $r_1 = r_2$ and (b) r_1, r_2 complex.

Research Problem

8. (a) Investigate the outcome of the Bernoulli iteration for a quadratic whose roots are real and equal.

(b) Investigate the procedure when the roots are complex.

Chapter Eight **Estimation of Errors** *The previous chapter discussed, to some extent, the errors in using approximation methods in solving equations. The current chapter extends this discussion, completing the analysis of errors for the various methods used in Chapter 8. In Sec. 8.2, matrices and vectors are used to obtain a better understanding of iterative methods applied to linear systems. Section 8.4 gives a (noncalculus) treatment of Newton's method for computation of roots and a discussion of the error. The study of the sequences obtained from iterations and the training the reader obtains in utilizing inequalities in this chapter will be of great assistance in grasping the important ideas of* limits *in the next chapter.*

8.1

Linear Equations   You have been introduced to a variety of methods for finding approximate solutions to equations. In some cases you have studied the behavior of the errors. Now we begin a somewhat systematic discussion of the estimation of errors.

We start with linear equations. The simplest type is

(1)
$$ax = b,$$

where a and b are given numbers. If $a \neq 0$, there is a unique solution

$$x = \frac{b}{a}.$$

In Exercise 2 of Sec. 7.4.1, you proved that if

$$|a_1 - a| < \varepsilon, \qquad |b_1 - b| < \delta, \quad \text{and} \quad 0 < \varepsilon < a,$$

then the solution x_1 of the equation $a_1 x_1 = b_1$ is an approximate solution of (1), with the error estimate

$$|x_1 - x| < \frac{a\delta + |b|\varepsilon}{a(a - \varepsilon)}$$

Thus if the data, the numbers a and b, are known to within small errors, the solution x is determined to within a small error.

The exact solution of (1) is so simple that we need no fancy method for computing the solution approximately. Nevertheless, it is useful to examine a simple iterative process for solving such an equation. The reasoning will serve as a model for the treatment of more complicated problems.

In Sec. 7.8, we were led to study sequences of the form

$$x_{n+1} = ax_n + b \qquad (n \geq 0),$$

where x_0 is given. We may regard such a sequence as an iterative method for solving the equation

(2)
$$x = ax + b = f(x).$$

In other words, we look for the *fixed points* of the transformation f, and try to approximate a fixed point by iterating the operation f:

$$x_{n+1} = f(x_n),$$

starting with the guess x_0.

In Exercises 8 and 9 of Sec. 7.8.1, you found that if $\xi_n = x_n - x$ is the error in approximating the exact solution x of (2) by x_n, then

$$|\xi_{n+1}| < |\xi_n|$$

if $|a| < 1$. Under this condition, then, the error decreases as more and more iterations are performed.

How small does the error become? If we perform enough iterations, can we make the error less than 0.000001, or less than any other assigned positive number?

You found that

$$\xi_{n+1} = x_{n+1} - x = f(x_n) - f(x)$$
$$= a(x_n - x) = a\xi_n,$$

so

$$\xi_1 = a\xi_0, \qquad \xi_2 = a\xi_1 = a^2\xi_0;$$

and, in general,

$$\xi_n = a^n\xi_0,$$

$$|\xi_n| = |a|^n|\xi_0|.$$

The problem is reduced to that of studying the behavior of the powers of a fixed number.

8.1.1
EXERCISES

1. Find the value of x, the fixed point of f. Is it unique? For which values of a and b is there a fixed point?

2. If $|a| \geq 1$, does $|\xi_n|$ decrease as n increases? Is there an n such that $|\xi_n| < |\xi_0|$?

3. Let

$$a_{n+1} = (1 + h)a_n \qquad \text{for } n \geq 0, \qquad a_0 = 1, \qquad h \in \mathcal{R},$$

so that $a_n = (1 + h)^n$, and let $b_n = a_n - (1 + nh)$.

(a) Compute $b_{n+1} - (1 + h)b_n$ in terms of n and h. For which values of n and h is this difference negative?

(b) If $h > -1$, find the first value of n for which b_n is negative. Can b_0 be negative? If $n > 0$ and n is the *first* integer for which b_n is negative, then b_{n-1} ____ $0 \,(\leq/\geq)$ but b_n ____ $0 \,(</=/>)$. Is this possible?

(c) If $h > -1$, which is larger: a_n or $1 + nh$? In consequence of your answer, write an inequality:

$$(1 + h)^n \text{ ____ } 1 + nh, \qquad h > -1, \qquad n \in \mathcal{Z}^+.$$

[NOTE: The inequality you proved in (c) is a most important result. We shall use it a great deal in subsequent chapters, so it would be very wise to keep it in mind.]

(d) If $h > 0$, find a $N_1 \in \mathcal{Z}^+$ such that

$$a_n > 2, \qquad \forall n \geq N_1.$$

If A is any given positive number, find a number $N_2 \in \mathscr{Z}^+$ such that

$$a_n > A, \qquad \forall\, n \geq N_2.$$

4. Suppose that $|a| < 1$. Find a number h such that

$$\frac{1}{|a|} = 1 + h.$$

(a) Is h positive or negative?

(b) Apply Exercise 3(c) to obtain the following result: If $|a| < 1$ and $n \in \mathscr{Z}^+$, then

$$|a|^n \leq \frac{1}{(1 + h)^n} \leq \frac{|a|}{\underline{\qquad}}.$$

(c) Find a number $N_1 \in \mathscr{Z}^+$ such that $|a|^n < \frac{1}{2}$, $\forall\, n \geq N_1$. Find a number $N_2 \in \mathscr{Z}^+$ such that $|a|^n < \varepsilon$, $\forall\, n \geq N_2$, where ε is any given positive number.

[NOTE: While you can obtain an estimate of N_2 by using the result of Exercise 3(c) directly, you can obtain a much better estimate in terms of the value of N_1 and the value of the first integer k such that $1 \leq 2^k \varepsilon$.]

5. By using the relations

$$x_n = x + \xi_n,$$

$$\xi_n = a^n \xi_0,$$

and the solution of Exercise 1 of this section, you can obtain a formula for x_n in terms of a, b, x_0, and n. You can obtain an alternative formula as follows:

(a) Let $y_n = x_n/a^n$. Compute $y_{n+1} - y_n$ from the recursion formula for x_{n+1} on page 352.

(b) Compute y_n from this formula and

$$y_n = y_0 + (y_1 - y_0) + (y_2 - y_1) + \cdots + (y_n - y_{n-1}).$$

(c) Now use the relation $x_n = a^n y_n$.

(d) By comparing your two formulas for x_n, compute the sum

$$1 + 0.05 + (0.05)^2 + \cdots + (0.05)^9.$$

This is x_n, according to the result of part (c), for $x_0 = 0$, $b = 1$, $n = 10$, and $a = \underline{\qquad}$.

6. Suppose you have a computer which can add, subtract, and multiply. You could compute reciprocals by means of the sequence

$$x_{n+1} = x_n(2 - yx_n) \qquad \text{for } n \geq 0,$$

where x_0 is given.

(a) Let $z_n = 1 - x_n y$. Find a number k such that $z_{n+1} = z_n^k$ for $n \geq 0$.

(b) Give a formula for z_n in terms of z_0. For which values of z_0 is $|z_n| < 1$?

(c) If x_0 is chosen so that $|z_n| < 1$ for all n, what happens to z_n as n increases? Does x_n approach some number x? Is x a fixed point of f, where

$$f(x) = x(2 - yx) \qquad \text{for } x \text{ real?}$$

(d) What is a good choice of x_0 if $y = 3.4$? if $y = 0.34$? In each case find an n such that $|x_n - x| < 0.0001$.

8.2

Matrix Methods Let us now look at a 2×2 system of equations

(1)
$$ax + by = u,$$
$$cx + dy = v.$$

In Sec. 7.2, you found the solution to be

$$x = \frac{du - bv}{\Delta},$$

$$y = \frac{av - cu}{\Delta},$$

where $\Delta = ad - bc$, providing that $\Delta \neq 0$.

The result can be put in a more suggestive form. (If we choose a suitable notation, it sometimes seems that the symbols are brighter than we are!) We introduce the matrix

$$A = \begin{pmatrix} a & b \\ c & d \end{pmatrix}$$

and the vectors

$$\mathbf{X} = \begin{pmatrix} x \\ y \end{pmatrix} \quad \text{and} \quad \mathbf{B} = \begin{pmatrix} u \\ v \end{pmatrix}$$

and write (1) in the form $A\mathbf{X} = \mathbf{B}$. The solution is

$$\mathbf{X} = A^{-1}\mathbf{B}, \quad \text{if } \Delta \neq 0,$$

where A^{-1} is the inverse matrix of A:

$$A^{-1} = \begin{pmatrix} \dfrac{d}{\Delta} & \dfrac{-b}{\Delta} \\ \dfrac{-c}{\Delta} & \dfrac{a}{\Delta} \end{pmatrix}.$$

This result is just like the formula for the solution of the single linear equation $ax = b$.

We can summarize the results of Chapter 7 on systems of linear equations in the following way:

(a) If $\Delta \neq 0$, then A^{-1} exists, and system (1) has a unique solution for an arbitrary vector $\mathbf{B}$. The linear transformation A maps the (x, y)-plane one-to-one onto the (u, v)-plane.

(b) If $\Delta = 0$ but $A \neq 0$ (i.e., if a, b, c, and d are not all 0), then A maps the (x, y)-plane onto a line in the (u, v)-plane. If **B** is not on this line, the system (1) has no solution, i.e., the equations are inconsistent. If **B** is on this line, then the set of solutions **X** of (1) forms a line in the (x, y)-plane. The general solution of (1) can be expressed in the form

$$\mathbf{X} = \mathbf{X}_0 + \mathbf{Y},$$

where $\mathbf{X}_0$ is any particular solution and **Y** is a solution of the equation

(2) $$AY = 0.$$

The set of all **Y**'s can be expressed in the form

$$\mathbf{Y} = t\mathbf{Y}_0, \qquad t \in \mathcal{R},$$

where $\mathbf{Y}_0$ is any solution of (2) other than the zero vector.

(c) If $A = 0$ (i.e., $a = b = c = d = 0$), then A maps the whole (x, y)-plane onto a single point, the origin of the (u, v)-plane.

In Exercises 6 and 7 of Sec. 7.4.1, you estimated the error in the solution when the coefficients of a specific equation are known to within certain errors. We can apply the same method to the general problem (1). (See Exercise 2 below.)

Most of the approximate methods for solving systems like (1) have the form

$$\mathbf{X}_{n+1} = A\mathbf{X}_n + \mathbf{B} = T(\mathbf{X}_n), \qquad n \geq 0,$$

where A is a given matrix, **B** is a given vector, and $\mathbf{X}_0$ is an initial guess at a solution. We would expect, if the process works, to obtain approximations to the solution of the system

$$\mathbf{X} = A\mathbf{X} + \mathbf{B} = T(\mathbf{X}),$$

or

(3) $$(I - A)\mathbf{X} = \mathbf{B}.$$

Our study of the one-dimensional problem, $x = ax + b$ in Sec. 8.1, suggests that such a procedure will work if A is, in some sense, a sufficiently "small" matrix. If

$$A = \begin{pmatrix} a & b \\ c & d \end{pmatrix},$$

then the system (3) has the form:

$$(1 - a)x - by = u,$$
$$-cx + (1 - d)y = v.$$

If A is "small," i.e., a, b, c, and d are small, then the coefficients, $1 - a$ and $1 - d$, down the main diagonal are approximately 1, while the other coefficients are small. The system (3) is then said to have a *dominating main diagonal.*

If the system (1) has a dominating main diagonal, i.e., if $|a|$ is much larger than $|b|$, and $|d|$ is much larger than $|c|$, then (1) can be put in the form (3). Simply divide each equation in the system by the coefficient on the main diagonal; that is, divide the first equation by a and the second by d.

These procedures also work for systems with many equations and unknowns, and are well adapted to modern high-speed computers.

The procedure which we used in Exercise 6 of Sec. 7.4.1 can be used to transform quite general linear systems into systems with dominating main diagonals. (See Exercises 4–6 below.)

8.2.1
EXERCISES

1. In many problems of the type (1) it is important to estimate $\mathbf{B}$ for given A and $\mathbf{X}$ or to estimate $\mathbf{X}$ with given A and $\mathbf{B}$.

(a) In (1) let $a = 3$ and $b = 4$. If $|x| \leq 1$ and $|y| \leq 1$, what is the greatest possible value for $|u|$? For which values of x and y is the maximum of $|u|$ attained?

(b) Assume that $|x| \leq 1$ and $|y| \leq 1$. Find the greatest possible value of $|u|$ in each of the following cases:

a	b	max $|u|$	maximum attained for $[x, y] =$
3	-4		
-3	4		
-3	-4		

(c) The general result is: If a and b are given, then for $|x| \leq 1$ and $|y| \leq 1$ the greatest possible value of $|ax + by|$ is _____. This maximum is attained for

$$[x, y] = \pm[\text{\_\_\_\_}, \text{\_\_\_\_}].$$

[*Hint:* The function sgn, defined as follows,

$$\text{sgn } t = \begin{cases} +1 & \text{for } t > 0, \\ -1 & \text{for } t < 0, \\ 0 & \text{for } t = 0, \end{cases}$$

may be useful in expressing your answer.]

(d) More generally, if a, b, and ξ are given, then the greatest possible value for $|ax + by|$, for $|x| \leq \xi$ and $|y| \leq \xi$, is ($\text{\_\_\_\_} + \text{\_\_\_\_}$)$\xi$. The maximum is attained for $[x, y] = \pm[\text{\_\_\_\_}, \text{\_\_\_\_}]$.

(e) You can apply the result of part (d) to estimate $|v|$: If c, d, and ξ are given and $\max\{|x|, |y|\} \le \xi$, then

$$|v| \le (\underline{\qquad})\xi.$$

The greatest possible value of $|v|$ is attained for

$$[x, y] = \pm[\underline{\qquad}, \underline{\qquad}].$$

(f) Put the results of parts (d) and (e) together. Given A (i.e., given a, b, c, and d) in (1), then

$$\max\{|u|, |v|\} \le K \max\{|x|, |y|\},$$

where $K = \max\{\underline{\qquad}, \underline{\qquad}\}$. If $|a| + |b| \ge |c| + |d|$ and $\max\{|x|, |y|\} = 1$, then the greatest possible value for $\max\{|u|, |v|\}$ is attained for $[x, y] = \pm[\underline{\qquad}, \underline{\qquad}]$.

2. Since the solution of (1) is $\mathbf{X} = [x, y] = A^{-1}\mathbf{B}$, and you know the matrix of A^{-1}, you can apply the results of Exercise 1 to estimate $\mathbf{X}$ in terms of B:
   If A in (1) is given and $\Delta \ne 0$, then

$$\max\{|x|, |y|\} \le K_1 \max\{|u|, |v|\},$$

where $K_1 = |\Delta|^{-1} \max\{\underline{\qquad}, \underline{\qquad}\}$.

3. It is easy to estimate the error in the solution of (1) if A is fixed but $\mathbf{B}$ is known to within a given error. Let $\mathbf{X}_1 = [x_1, y_1]$ be the solution of

$$A\mathbf{X}_1 = \mathbf{B}_1,$$

where $\mathbf{B}_1 = [u_1, v_1]$, $|u_1 - u| \le \varepsilon$, and $|v_1 - v| \le \varepsilon$. What is the greatest possible value of $\max\{|x_1 - x|, |y_1 - y|\}$?
   (a) Let

$$\mathbf{X}_2 = \mathbf{X}_1 - \mathbf{X} = [x_1 - x, y_1 - y]$$

and

$$\mathbf{B}_2 = \mathbf{B}_1 - \mathbf{B} = [u_1 - u, v_1 - v].$$

Compute $A\mathbf{X}_2$. Now you can apply the result of Exercise 2.
   (b) Given A and $\varepsilon > 0$, and given that $\Delta \ne 0$, what is the largest possible value of

$$\max\{|x_1 - x|, |y_1 - y|\}$$

under the condition that

$$\max\{|u_1 - u|, |v_1 - v|\} \le \varepsilon?$$

4. Now let us investigate the error in the solution of (1) if B is fixed but A is known to within a given error. Let

$$E = \begin{pmatrix} \alpha & \beta \\ \gamma & \delta \end{pmatrix}$$

and assume that $\max\{|\alpha|, |\beta|, |\gamma|, |\delta|\} \le \varepsilon$. Let $\mathbf{X}_1 = [x_1, y_1]$ be the solution of the system $(A + E)X_1 = B$. What is the greatest possible value of

$$\eta = \max \{|x_1 - x|, |y_1 - y|\}?$$

Assume that A is given and that $\Delta \neq 0$. Imitate the procedure in Exercise 6 of Sec. 7.4.1. Find an ε_0 and a constant M (depending on the matrix A and the vector B) such that $\eta \leq M\varepsilon$ if $\varepsilon < \varepsilon_0$.

Let $X_2 = X_1 - X$, so that $X_1 = X +$ _____. Then you have

$$(A + E)X_1 = (A + E)(X + \text{\_\_\_\_})$$

$$= \text{\_\_\_\_} + \text{\_\_\_\_} + \text{\_\_\_\_} + \text{\_\_\_\_} = B,$$

or

$$AX_2 = - \text{\_\_\_\_} - \text{\_\_\_\_} = B_2 = [u_2, v_2].$$

You can apply the result of Exercise 2 if you can estimate the components of B_2:

$$\eta \leq K \max \{|u_2|, |v_2|\}.$$

(a) You can estimate the components of EX in two steps: If

$$\max \{|x|, |y|\} = \xi,$$

then each component of EX is at most _____$\varepsilon\xi$. (Use Exercise 1.)
Now you need only estimate ξ. If $B = [u, v]$ and $\zeta = \max \{|u|, |v|\}$, then, by the result of Exercise 2(c),

$$\xi = \max \{|x|, |y|\} \leq \text{_____}.$$

Putting these results together, you find that each component of EX is at most $M_1\varepsilon$, where $M_1 = $ _____.

(b) You can estimate the components of EX_2 in terms of

$$\eta = \max \{|x_1 - x|, |y_1 - y|\}$$

by using the result of Exercise 1: If $X_2 = [x_1 - x, y_1 - y]$, then each component of EX_2 is at most _____η.

(c) Putting these results together, you can estimate the components of B_2:

$$\max \{|u_2|, |v_2|\} \leq M_1\varepsilon + \text{\_\_\_\_}\eta,$$

and therefore

$$\eta \leq K \max \{|u_2|, |v_2|\} \leq \text{\_\_\_\_} + \text{\_\_\_\_}\eta.$$

If $\varepsilon < \varepsilon_0 = $ _____, then you obtain $\eta \leq M\varepsilon$, where $M = $ _____.

5. Now you are prepared to handle the general case where both A and B in equation (1) are known to within given errors. Let E be a "small" matrix as in Exercise 2, and let $B_1 = [u_1, v_1]$ be given as in Exercise 1. We assume that

$$\max \{|\alpha|, |\beta|, |\gamma|, |\delta|, |u_1 - u|, |v_1 - v|\} \leq \varepsilon.$$

Let $X_1 = [x_1, y_1]$ be the solution of $(A + E)X_1 = B_1$. Assume that A and B are fixed and that $\Delta \neq 0$. Find constants ε_0 and M such that

$$\max \{|x_1 - x|, |y_1 - y|\} \leq M\varepsilon$$

if $\varepsilon < \varepsilon_0$.

[*Hint:* Break up the problem into two steps by letting X_2 be the solution of $AX_2 = B_1$. Then you can estimate the vector $X_2 - X$ by means of Exercise 3 and the vector $X_1 - X_2$ by means of Exercise 4.]

6. Consider the equation

$$(A + E)X = B,$$

where A is a given matrix such that A^{-1} is known and E is a small matrix as in Exercise 2. Show that

$$A^{-1}(A + E) = I - E_1,$$

where E_1 is also a small matrix. Under the assumptions of Exercise 4 about the matrices A and E, find a constant M such that the elements of E_1 are, in absolute value, at most $M\varepsilon$.

7. Let $A = I - E$, where E satisfies the conditions of Exercise 4. What is the smallest possible value of $|\Delta|$ for a given $\varepsilon > 0$? What is the smallest value of ε such that Δ can be equal to zero? It is sufficient if you solve this problem for $0 < \varepsilon \leq \frac{1}{2}$.

8. Let

$$A = \begin{pmatrix} a & b \\ c & d \end{pmatrix}$$

be a given matrix and $B = [u, v]$ be a given vector. Compare the solution of the equation $X = AX + B$ with the sequence of vectors defined by $X_{n+1} = AX_n + B$ for $n \geq 0$, X_0 given. Let $X_n = [x_n, y_n]$. Is X_n "close to" X for large n?

(a) Let $Y_n = X_n - X$. Find a formula for Y_{n+1} in terms of Y_n.

(b) We would like to estimate the size of Y_{n+1} in terms of the size of Y_n. This is a problem of the following type: In equation (1) above, if A is given and $\max \{|x|, |y|\}$ is given, what is the greatest possible value of $\max \{|u|, |v|\}$? [You may find Exercise 1(c) useful.]

(c) What is the condition on A that there be a constant $k < 1$ such that

$$\max \{|x_{n+1} - x|, |y_{n+1} - y|\} \leq k \max \{|x_n - x|, |y_n - y|\}?$$

(d) If

$$\max \{|a| + |b|, |c| + |d|\} \leq 0.9$$

and

$$\max \{|x_0 - x|, |y_0 - y|\} \leq 1,$$

what is the largest possible value of

$$\delta_n = \max \{|x_n - x|, |y_n - y|\}$$

for $n \geq 16$? What is the largest possible value of n for which δ_n can be greater than 0.1?

9. Consider the iteration process defined by

$$ax_{n+1} + by_n = u,$$

$$cx_n + dy_{n+1} = v,$$

for solving equation (1) approximately.

(a) Let $\mathbf{X}_n = [x_n, y_n]$. Find a matrix A_1 and a vector $\mathbf{B}_1$ such that this iteration process is equivalent to

$$\mathbf{X}_{n+1} = A_1\mathbf{X}_n + \mathbf{B}_1.$$

(b) What is the condition on a, b, c, and d that the matrix A_1 satisfy the condition of Exercise 6(c)?

8.3

Quadratic Equations   Let us begin with a very simple equation:

$$x^2 = 3,$$

whose solution is $x = \pm\sqrt{3}$. We want to examine certain methods for computing the solution approximately.

In Sec. 7.9 and in Exercise 3 of Sec. 7.8.2, we found that this equation is equivalent to the equation

$$x = \frac{1}{2}\left(x + \frac{3}{x}\right) = f(x),$$

and our graphical discussion suggested that the iteration procedure

$$x_{n+1} = f(x_n) = \frac{1}{2}\left(x_n + \frac{3}{x_n}\right) \qquad \text{for } n \geq 0,$$

where x_0 is any positive number, will work.

In discussing this process we shall use methods that apply to many other problems.

We can test whether x is close to the exact solution $\sqrt{3}$ by computing $g(x) = x^2 - 3$. Indeed, if $\theta = \sqrt{3}$, so that $g(\theta) = 0$ and $\theta > 0$, then

$$g(x) = g(x) - g(\theta) = x^2 - \theta^2 = (x - \theta)(x + \theta)$$

and

$$|x - \theta| = \frac{|g(x)|}{|x + \theta|}.$$

We can estimate this fraction from above if we can estimate the denominator from below. The simplest result is that if $x > 0$, then

$$|x + \theta| = x + \theta > \theta > 1.$$

Hence we have

$$|x - \theta| \le \frac{|g(x)|}{\theta} \le |g(x)|$$

if $x > 0$.

The advantage of this estimate is that we do not need to know the value of θ in order to compute it.

Let us apply this test to x_{n+1}. Is $g(x_{n+1})$ smaller than $g(x_n)$? Let us see:

$$g(x_{n+1}) = x_{n+1}^2 - 3 = \frac{\overline{\qquad}}{4x_n^2}. \qquad\qquad (g(x_n))^2$$

This identity has many valuable consequences. First, the smallest possible value of $g(x_{n+1})$ is _____. Now, 0
if $x_0 > 0$, then $x_n > 0$ for all n. If $g(x_{n+1}) \ge 0$ and $x_{n+1} > 0$, then

$$x_{n+1} \underline{\qquad} \theta \qquad (\ge \text{ or } \le). \qquad\qquad \ge$$

In other words, no matter which positive x_0 we begin with, for $n \ge 1$ all our approximations are from _____   *above*
(above/below).

Now let us examine

$$\frac{g(x_{n+1})}{g(x_n)} = \frac{\overline{\qquad}}{4x_n^2} \qquad\qquad x_n^2 - 3$$

$$= \frac{1}{4} - \underline{\qquad}. \qquad\qquad \frac{3}{4x_n^2}$$

If $n \ge 1$, then $g(x_n) \ge$ _____, so that this ratio is non- 0
negative, and is at most _____. Therefore, $\frac{1}{4}$

$$0 \le g(x_{n+1}) \le \underline{\qquad} g(x_n) \qquad\qquad \frac{1}{4}$$

for $n \ge 1$.

It follows that

$$g(x_2) \le \underline{\qquad} g(x_1) \qquad\qquad \frac{1}{4}$$

and

$$g(x_3) \le \underline{\qquad} g(x_2) \qquad\qquad \frac{1}{4}$$

$$\le (\underline{\qquad})^2 g(x_1), \qquad\qquad \frac{1}{4}$$

and in general

$$0 \le g(x_n) \le \underline{\qquad} g(x_1). \qquad\qquad (\tfrac{1}{4})^{n-1}$$

Therefore,

$$|x_n - \theta| \leq \underline{\hspace{1cm}} g(x_1).$$

The method in Exercise 3(e) of Sec. 7.7.2 gives a more precise result but cannot be generalized so easily.

8.3.1
EXERCISES

1. (a) What are the fixed points of the transformation

$$f: x \rightarrow \frac{1}{2}\left(x + \frac{a}{x}\right),$$

where $a > 0$?

(b) Let $f(\theta) = \theta$, $\theta > 0$. Express a in terms of θ. Choose any positive x_0 and define a sequence by iterating f:

$$x_{n+1} = f(x_n) = \frac{1}{2}\left(x_n + \frac{a}{x_n}\right) \qquad \text{for } n \geq 0.$$

Find an estimate for $|x_n - \theta|$ for $n \geq 1$. Is this difference large or small for large values of n?

2. (a) What are the fixed points of the transformation

$$f: x \rightarrow \frac{3 + 2x}{2 + x}?$$

(b) Let $f(\theta) = \theta$, $\theta > 0$. Choose $x_0 > 0$ and define a sequence by iterating f:

$$x_{n+1} = f(x_n) \qquad \text{for } n \geq 0.$$

Find an estimate for $|x_n - \theta|$ for $n \geq 1$. Is this difference large or small for large values of n?

(c) More generally, what are the fixed points of the transformation

$$f: x \rightarrow \frac{\theta^2 + 2x}{2 + x}?$$

Find a constant k such that

$$\frac{f(x) - \theta}{f(x) + \theta} = k\left(\frac{x - \theta}{x + \theta}\right).$$

(d) In part (b) let

$$z_n = \frac{x_n - \theta}{x_n + \theta}.$$

Find a formula for z_{n+1} in terms of z_n. What is the value of z_n/z_0? What is the largest value of n for which z_n/z_0 is greater than 0.01?

(e) Apply the methods of this exercise to the transformation

$$f: x \to \frac{4x + 10}{x + 4},$$

$x_0 = 3$. For any $k \in \mathscr{Z}^+$, find $N \in \mathscr{Z}^+$ such that $|x_n - \theta| < 2^{-k}$, for $n > N$.

3. Compare $g(x_{n+1})/g(x_n)$ in Exercise 2 with the same ratio for the problem in the text. Which is smaller for large values of n?

4. (a) Given $k > 0$, a, and c, find b and d such that the fixed points of the transformation

$$f: x \to \frac{ax + b}{cx + d}$$

are the solutions of the equations $g(x) = x^2 - k = 0$.
(b) Let $g(\theta) = 0$, $\theta > 0$, and assume that $a/c > 0$. Choose $x_0 > 0$ and define a sequence by iterating f:

$$x_{n+1} = f(x_n) \qquad \text{for } n \geq 0.$$

Find an estimate for $|x_n - \theta|$ for $n \geq 1$. Is this difference large or small for large values of n?

(c) Give a favorable choice for a and c for the purpose of computing $\sqrt{19}$.

5. (a) Given $B > 0$, $C > 0$, $c > 0$, and $d > 0$. Find a and b such that the fixed points of the transformation

$$f: x \to \frac{ax + b}{cx + d},$$

are the solutions of the equation $g(x) = x^2 - Bx - C = 0$.
(b) Let θ and θ_1, $\theta > 0$, be the solutions of $g(x) = 0$, so that $f(\theta) = \theta$, $f(\theta_1) = \theta_1$. Find a constant k such that

$$\frac{f(x) - f(\theta)}{f(x) - f(\theta_1)} = k\left(\frac{x - \theta}{x - \theta_1}\right).$$

Is it possible that $|k| \geq 1$?
(c) Choose $x_0 > 0$ and define the sequence $\{x_n\}$ by: $x_{n+1} = f(x_n)$ for $n \geq 0$. Let

$$z_n = \frac{x_n - \theta}{x_n - \theta_1}.$$

Compute z_{n+1}/z_n. Compute z_n/z_0. Is $|z_n|$ large or small for large values of n?
(d) Solve for x_n in terms of z_n. Is $|x_n - \theta|$ large or small for large values of n?
(e) Apply the process in part (c) to compute the positive solution of the equation $x^2 - x - 1 = 0$. What are favorable and convenient choices for c and d? Choose $x_0 = 1$. What is the largest value of n such that $|x_n - \theta| \geq 0.01$?

6. (a) Let $g(x) = x^2 - x - 5$. Find an integer k such that

$$g(k) < 0 < g(k + 1).$$

(b) Let $x_0 = k + 1$. Find numbers a, b, and c such that

$$g(x_0 + h) = a + bh + ch^2 \qquad \text{for all } h.$$

(c) We may expect that there is a solution $\theta > 0$ of the equation $g(\theta) = 0$, and that $\theta = x_0 + h$ where h is small. Since, for small h, $g(x_0 + h)$ is approximately $a + bh$:

$$g(x_0 + h) \sim a + bh,$$

we suspect that $x_1 = x_0 + h_0$, where $a + bh_0 = 0$, is a good approximation to θ. Compute h_0, x_1, and $g(x_1)$. Is $|g(x_1)|$ small in comparison with $|g(x_0)|$?

(d) Find numbers a_1, b_1, and c_1 such that

$$g(x_1 + h) = a_1 + b_1 h + c_1 h^2 \qquad \text{for all } h.$$

Find h_1 such that $a_1 + b_1 h_1 = 0$. Compute h_1, $x_2 = x_1 + h_1$, and $g(x_2)$.

(e) Find θ_1 such that $g(x) = (x - \theta)(x - \theta_1)$. If $x > 0$ and $g(x) > 0$, can x be less than θ? Find a number C such that $x - \theta \le Cg(x)$. Use this result to estimate $x_2 - \theta$.

(f) Suppose x is any approximation to θ. Find polynomials a, b, and c such that

$$g(x + h) = a(x) + b(x)h + c(x)h^2 \qquad \text{for all } x, h.$$

Solve the equation $a(x) + b(x)h = 0$ for h, and define the transformation $f: x \to x + h$. What are the fixed points of f?

(g) Starting with $x_0 = k + 1$, construct a sequence

$$x_{n+1} = f(x_n) \qquad \text{for } n \ge 0.$$

(h) For which values of x is $g(f(x)) < 0$? If $x \ge 2$, can $f(x)$ be negative? Can $f(x)$ be less than 2? If $x \ge 2$, what is the greatest possible value of $g(f(x))/g(x)^2$? Find an estimate for $g(x_n)$. Is $g(x_n)$ small for large values of n?

(i) Can $x_n - x_{n+1}$ be negative? What is the greatest possible value of $(x_n - x_{n+1})/g(x_n)$? Obtain an estimate for $x_n - x_{n+1}$. [NOTE: If $x_0 \ge 0$, can x_n be less than 2 for any n?] If $m > n$, compute

$$(x_n - x_{n+1}) + (x_{n+1} - x_{n+2}) + \cdots + (x_{m-1} - x_m)$$

and, from your estimate of each term in this sum, find an estimate for $x_n - x_m$. (The result of Exercise 5, page 354, may be useful to you.) Note that the reasoning in parts (h) and (i) does not ever use the fact that the number θ exists. Apply the method in Exercise 5 to the equation $x^2 - x - 5 = 0$. Compare this method with the one in this exercise. For which one is $g(x_2)$ smaller?

8.4

Computation of Roots. Newton's Method   The method of Exercise 6 of Sec. 8.3.1, called *Newton's method*, can be applied to a wide variety of problems. Let us apply it to compute the positive solution θ of the equation

$$g(x) = x^3 - 5 = 0,$$

so that $\theta = \sqrt[3]{5}$.

Since $g(1) = -4$ and $g(2) = 3$, we expect to find a solution between 1 and 2. Let $x_0 = 2$, and let us look for an approximate solution of the form $x_0 + h$, where h is small. We find that

$$g(x_0 + h) = a + bh + ch^2 + dh^3 \qquad \text{for all } h,$$

for certain numbers $a, b, c,$ and d. As before, we take as a correction to x_0 the solution, h_0, of the equation $a + bh_0 = 0$, and form the new approximation

$$x_1 = x_0 + h_0.$$

Let us just check by computing $g(x_1)$. Is this much smaller than $g(x_0)$?

In the computation of $g(x_0 + h)$, we need for our purposes only the coefficients a and b, and may ignore c and d. The terms involving c and d are at most *of the order of magnitude of h^2* if h is small; i.e.,

$$|ch^2 + dh^3| = |h^2\|c + dh|$$

$$\leq (|c| + |d|)|h^2|, \qquad \text{if } |h| \leq 1,$$

$$\leq K|h^2|, \qquad \text{if } |h| \leq 1,$$

for a certain constant K. We can indicate this by writing

$$g(x_0 + h) = a + bh + O(h^2),$$

where "$O(h^2)$" stands for a quantity which is equal to h^2 times a bounded quantity. Just what the quantity denoted by "$O(h^2)$" is, in detail, is irrelevant to us.

More generally, there are polynomials $a(x)$ and $b(x)$ such that

$$g(x + h) = a(x) + b(x)h + O(h^2)$$

for small h. If x is an approximate solution of our equation, we can obtain a correction h by solving the equation

$$a(x) + b(x)h = 0.$$

Then $x + h$ will be, in general, a better approximation.

The mapping

$$f : x \to x + h = x - \frac{a(x)}{b(x)}$$

transforms each number x into a new approximate solution.

The iteration process $x_{n+1} = f(x_n)$ for $n \geq 0$, where x_0 is chosen suitably, often gives a very efficient method for computing a solution of the equation $g(x) = 0$.

In applying this method to other equations, it is useful to work out the following pattern:

$$(x + h)^2 = x^2 + 2xh + O(h^2),$$

$$(x + h)^3 = (x + h)(x^2 + 2xh + O(h^2))$$

$$= x^3 + 3x^2h + 2xh^2 + (x + h)O(h^2)$$

$$= x^3 + 3x^2h + O(h^2),$$

$$(x + h)^4 = \underline{\hspace{1cm}} + \underline{\hspace{1cm}}h + O(h^2), \qquad \text{and so on.}$$

If

(1) $$(x + h)^k = a_k(x) + b_k(x)h + O(h^2)$$

then

(2) $$(x + h)^{k+1} = (x + h)[a_k(x) + b_k(x)h + O(h^2)]$$

$$= xa_k(x) + [a_k(x) + xb_k(x)]h + O(h^2),$$

so that [comparing (1) with (2)] we have the recursion relations:

$$a_{k+1}(x) = xa_k(x), \qquad b_{k+1}(x) = a_k(x) + xb_k(x).$$

Since $a_2(x) = x^2$ and $a_3(x) = x^3$, we have

$$a_4(x) = xa_3(x) = \underline{\hspace{1cm}}, \qquad a_5(x) = xa_4(x) = \underline{\hspace{1cm}}, \qquad\qquad x^4, x^5$$

and, in general,

$$a_k(x) = \underline{\hspace{1cm}}. \qquad\qquad x^k$$

Similarly, we find that $b_2(x) = 2x$ and $b_3(x) = 3x^2$, so that

$$b_4(x) = a_3(x) + xb_3(x) = \underline{\hspace{1cm}}, \qquad\qquad 4x^3$$

$$b_5(x) = a_4(x) + xb_4(x) = \underline{\hspace{1cm}}, \qquad\qquad 5x^4$$

and, in general,

$$b_k(x) = \underline{\hspace{1cm}}. \qquad\qquad kx^{k-1}$$

Note that in the above calculations terms like $2xh^2$ and $b_k(x)h^2$ are absorbed in the terms $O(h^2)$. Terms like $xO(h^2)$ and $hO(h^2)$ are also of the form $O(h^2)$.

A facility in working with this "O" notation will be useful.

8.4.1

EXERCISES

1. (a) If $g(x) = x^3 - 5$ for all x and $g(x) > 0$, is h as calculated above positive or negative? Is $f(x)$ greater or less than x? If $x > 0$ and $g(x) > 0$, can $f(x)$ be negative?

(b) If $0 < y < x$, find Q such that

$$x^3 - y^3 = (x - y)Q$$

For given x, what is the greatest possible value of Q? For given y, what is the least possible value of Q?

(c) Apply the result of part (b) to $y = f(x) = x + h$. Is $g(y)$ positive or negative? Is $g(y)$ greater or less than $g(x)$?

(d) Suppose that $x > 0$ and $g(x) > 0$ and that h is defined as above. (Is h positive or negative?) Then

$$g(x + h) = a(x) + b(x)h + c(x)h^2 + d(x)h^3$$

where $a(x) =$ _____, $b(x) =$ _____, $c(x) =$ _____, $d(x) =$ _____. By the definition of h, you know that

$$a(x) + b(x)h = \underline{\qquad}.$$

Is $d(x)h^3$ positive or negative? Find a constant K such that

$$g(x + h) \le Kxh^2.$$

(e) If $x > 0$ and $g(x) > 0$, what is the greatest possible value of $g(f(x))/g(x)$? Use the result of part (d) and the fact that $h = -g(x)/b(x)$, where $b(x) =$ _____.
Find a constant M such that

$$\frac{g(x_{n+1})}{g(x_n)} \le M \qquad \text{for all } n \ge 0.$$

Find an estimate for $g(x_n)/g(x_0)$. Is this small or large when n is large?

Find an estimate for $x_n - x_{n+1}$ for $n \ge 0$. Is this small or large for large values of n?

(f) If $x_0 > 0$ and $g(x_0) < 0$, can $g(x_1)$ be negative? [What is the sign of h_0? Use the formula for $g(x_0 + h)$ on page 366.]

2. Do the analogue of Exercise 1 for $g(x) = x^3 - a$, where a is a given positive constant.

3. (a) Let $g(x) = x^4 - a$. Find a formula for f as outlined in the text.

(b) Use this method to compute $\sqrt[4]{80}$ approximately.

4. (a) Let g be defined by $g(x) = x^k - a, \forall x \in \mathcal{R}$, where $a > 0$ and $k \in \mathscr{Z}^+, k \ge 2$. Find a formula for f as defined in the text.

(b) Let $x > 0$, $x + h \ge 0$, and define

$$z_k = (x + h)^k - (x^k + kx^{k-1}h) \qquad \text{for } k \ge 1.$$

Compute z_k for $k = 1, 2, 3$. Compute $z_{k+1} - (x + h)z_k$. Can this quantity be negative? What is the smallest value of k for which z_k can be negative?

(c) Let $x > 0$, $x + h > 0$, $h \le 0$, and define

$$w_k = z_k - \frac{k(k-1)}{2}x^{k-2}h^2.$$

Compute w_k for $k = 1, 2, 3$. Compute $w_{k+1} - (x + h)w_k$. Can this quantity be positive? What is the smallest value of k for which w_k can be positive?

(d) Do the analogue of Exercise 1(c)–(f) for the choice of g in part (a) of this exercise. In doing the analogue of part (f), use the formula for $f(x)$:

$$f(x) = x + h = \frac{\underline{} + \underline{}}{\underline{}},$$

and

$$g(f(x_0)) = f(x_0)^k - a.$$

It is helpful to introduce the number $t = a/x_0^k$, so that $a = tx_0^k$. Then the problem of the sign of $g(x_1)$ can be reduced to that of the sign of

$$\left(1 + \frac{t-1}{k}\right)^k - t.$$

If $(t-1)/k = u$, then this expression is a special case of one you have already examined.

5. Let P be a polynomial of degree 2 defined by

$$P(x) = x^2 + bx + c, \qquad \forall x \in \mathscr{C},$$

and let r_1 and r_2 be the solutions of the equation $P(x) = 0$.

(a) Using the relation $P(x) = (x - r_1)(x - r_2)$, $\forall x \in \mathscr{C}$, find formulas for b and c in terms of r_1 and r_2.

(b) Let $z_n = r_1^n + r_2^n$ for $n \geq 0$. Compute $z_2 + bz_1 + cz_0$. Find formulas for z_n, $3 \leq n \leq 5$, in terms of b and c. Check your results for $b = -3$ and $c = 2$.

(c) Suppose that $|r_2/r_1| \leq \frac{1}{2}$. What is the approximate value of z_n/r_1^n for large values of n? What is the largest value of n for which

$$\left| \frac{z_{n+1}}{r_1^{n+1}} - \frac{z_n}{r_1^n} \right|$$

can be at least 0.001? What is the approximate value of z_{n+1}/z_n? Set $r_2/r_1 = k$, $|k| \leq \frac{1}{2}$, and estimate

$$\left| \frac{z_{n+2}z_n}{z_{n+1}^2} - 1 \right| \qquad \text{for } n \geq 10.$$

(d) Use the method suggested in parts (b) and (c) to compute approximately the positive solution of the equation

$$x^2 - 9x - 8 = 0.$$

Let r_1 and r_2 be the solutions of this equation, and let $|r_1| > |r_2|$.

(e) Define the sequence y_n by

$$y_0 = 0, \quad y_1 = 1, \quad y_{n+2} = 9y_{n+1} + 8y_n \qquad \text{for } n \geq 0.$$

Compute y_n and y_{n+1}/y_n for $2 \leq n \leq 10$. Solve the equations

$$y_n = Ar_1^n + Br_2^n \qquad (n = 0, 1)$$

for the coefficients A and B. What is the smallest n such that $y_n = Ar_1^n + Br_2^n$? What is the approximate value of y_{n+1}/y_n for large values of n? What is the approximate value of

$$\frac{y_{n+2} - r_1 y_{n+1}}{y_{n+1} - r_1 y_n}$$

for large values of n?

Compare the work of part (e) with the Bernoulli iteration method in the previous chapter.

Chapter Nine Convergence *The limit concept which lies at the basis of calculus is the subject of Sec. 9.1. From the study of limits, the reader will see the need for additional postulates to describe adequately the real number system $\mathcal{R}$. Sections 9.2 and 9.3 represent the culmination of our discussion of the real numbers, in that the characterization of $\mathcal{R}$ is completed with the addition of two postulates (to those for an ordered field). Equivalents of the two new postulates are discussed in Sec. 9.4. The discussion and exercises of the chapter are aimed at giving the reader an understanding of convergence and a facility in working with limits. The theorems that constitute the main instruments for this work are developed in Sec. 9.5.*

9.1

The Limit Concept   In the course of the last two chapters you constructed many sequences $\{x_n\}$ in order to approximate solutions to various problems. The aim was to construct sequences that approached—or converged upon—the root of a polynomial or the solution to a system of equations. What, precisely, do we mean by the statement that the sequence elements x_n approach A as n increases?

Example 1: We take the sequence defined by

$$x_1 = 2,$$

$$x_{n+1} = \frac{1}{2}\left(x_n + \frac{3}{x_n}\right),$$

which we used to approximate $\sqrt{3}$. We spoke of the x_n *approaching* $\sqrt{3}$ because the error $|x_n - \sqrt{3}|$ could be made as small as we pleased by taking n large enough. In fact, we showed that

$$|x_n - \sqrt{3}| < (\tfrac{1}{2})^n;$$

so that if you wish the error to be less than $\frac{1}{1000}$, all you need to do is restrict yourself to $n \geq 10$. That is,

$$|x_n - \sqrt{3}| < \tfrac{1}{1000}, \qquad \forall\, n > 9.$$

More generally, if a maximum error of $\varepsilon > 0$ is prescribed we can find an integer n_0 so that

$$|x_n - \sqrt{3}| < \varepsilon, \qquad \forall\, n > n_0.$$

The above procedure of locating the first integer n_0 so that $(\tfrac{1}{2})^{n_0} \leq \varepsilon$ (i.e., $\varepsilon^{-1} \leq 2^{n_0}$) is one way to guarantee that

$$|x_n - \sqrt{3}| < \varepsilon, \qquad \forall\, n > n_0.$$

This is what we mean by the symbolism

$$\lim_{n \to \infty} x_n = \sqrt{3},$$

read: "The limit of x_n, as n approaches infinity, equals $\sqrt{3}$."

In general, we make the following *definition of limit*:

$$\lim_{n \to \infty} x_n = A$$

if and only if, for any $\varepsilon > 0$, there is an $n_0 \in \mathscr{Z}^+$ such that

$$|x_n - A| < \varepsilon$$

for all $n > n_0$. In addition to the terminology, "The limit of x_n, as n approaches infinity, equals A," we will also use the descriptive:

"x_n *approaches* A as n approaches infinity," or simply, "x_n *approaches* A."

[NOTE: In order to prove that $\lim_{n \to \infty} x_n = A$, you must find, *for each* $\varepsilon > 0$, an $n_0 \in \mathscr{Z}^+$ so that the implication

$$n > n_0 \Rightarrow |x_n - A| < \varepsilon$$

is true. It is quite reasonable to expect that you will have to go out further in the sequence if you decide that your error should be smaller. The integer n_0 usually depends on ε. For this reason you will often see the definition written "...if for every $\varepsilon > 0$, there is an $n_0(\varepsilon)$ such that ...." Writing "$n_0(\varepsilon)$" serves to emphasize the fact that n_0 depends on ε. Thus, a definite set of choices of n_0, corresponding to a given set of ε values, defines n_0 as a function of ε.]

Example 2: The sequence $\{x_n\}$ defined by

$$x_1 = 3,$$

$$x_{n+1} = \frac{4x_n + 10}{4 + x_n}$$

may be used to approximate $\sqrt{10}$. In Exercise 2(e) of Sec. 8.3.1 you proved that the error at the nth step of iteration is less than $(\frac{1}{7})^n$. To prove that $\lim_{n \to \infty} x_n = \sqrt{10}$, we must find, for every $\varepsilon > 0$, an integer n_0 so that

$$n > n_0 \Rightarrow |x_n - \sqrt{10}| < \varepsilon.$$

Looking at your result on the error, you see that if $1/7^n < \varepsilon$, then $|x_n - \sqrt{10}| < \varepsilon$. But the inequality $1/7^n < \varepsilon$ is equivalent to $1/\varepsilon < 7^n$. We may take n_0 to be *the largest integer* such that $7^{n_0} \leq 1/\varepsilon$.

If we merely want to prove that x_n approaches $\sqrt{10}$, but do not care about the best possible estimate for n_0, we may use the fact that

$$7^n = (1 + 6)^n > 1 + 6n;$$

and this is greater than ε^{-1} if $n >$ _____ . We have then found an n_0, depending on ε, such that

$$\frac{1 - \varepsilon}{6\varepsilon}$$

$$n > n_0 \Rightarrow |x_n - \sqrt{10}| < \varepsilon,$$

namely $n_0 = [$_____$]$. This proves $\lim_{n \to \infty} x_n = \sqrt{10}$.

$$\frac{1 - \varepsilon}{6\varepsilon}$$

Notice that n_0 is defined by the *greatest integral function* [ ], this guarantees $n_0 \in \mathscr{Z}$.

Example 3: In the preceding example we used the result of Exercise 3 of Sec. 8.1.1, that

$$(1 + h)^n \geq 1 + nh \qquad \text{if } h \geq -1.$$

In Exercise 4 of Sec. 8.1.1 you used this important inequality to prove that if $|a| < 1$, then

$$|a|^n \leq \frac{|a|}{|a| + n(1 - |a|)}.$$

This implies that if $|a| < 1$, then

$$\lim_{n \to \infty} a^n = \underline{\quad}.$$

In fact, if $\varepsilon > 0$, then

$$|a^n - 0| = |a^n| = |a|^n \le \frac{|a|}{|a| + n(1 - |a|)} < \varepsilon$$

if

$$n > \frac{|a|}{1 - |a|} (\underline{\quad}).$$

At this point, we see that we should choose $\varepsilon < 1$. (Why?) Thus, we may take

$$n_0 = \left[\frac{|a|}{1 - |a|} \left(\frac{1}{\varepsilon} - 1 \right) \right],$$

provided $0 < \varepsilon < 1$.

However, we can simplify the appearance of our choice of n_0 if we are not interested in finding the "best possible," or smallest satisfactory value for n_0. For if

$$n > n_0 \Rightarrow |x_n - A| < \varepsilon,$$

then surely

$$m \ge n_1 > n_0 \Rightarrow |x_m - A| < \varepsilon.$$

Thus, for a given $\varepsilon > 0$, any n_0 larger than the "best possible" will satisfy the requirements. In this example, for instance, we may take

$$n_0 = \left[\frac{|a|}{\varepsilon(1 - |a|)} \right],$$

and we can be sure that this choice will satisfy the criterion to prove $\lim_{n \to \infty} a^n = 0$.

Example 4: We again consider a sequence whose nth term is given explicitly rather than recursively. Consider the sequence $\{x_n\}$, where $x_n = \sqrt[n]{2}$. What guess would you make for $\lim_{n \to \infty} \sqrt[n]{2}$? Let's investigate.

It is clear that $\sqrt[n]{2} > 1$, so we write

$$\sqrt[n]{2} = 1 + h, \qquad h > \underline{\quad}.$$

Observe that the value of h depends on n, whereas the value of h was constant in the last example. We now analyze the behavior of h, for it may give a clue to the limit of $\sqrt[n]{2}$ as $n \to \infty$. (For example, if $\lim_{n \to \infty} h = \pi$, then you might guess that $\lim_{n \to \infty} \sqrt[n]{2} = 1 + \pi$. This is, of course, not the case but it illustrates the possible advantage of analyzing h.)

The equation $\sqrt[n]{2} = 1 + h$ can be put in manageable form by raising both members to the power n. This gives $2 = (1 + h)^n$. (What justifies this step?)

But the inequality proved in the last example tells you

$$2 > 1 + \underline{\qquad} h.$$

Then

$$1 > \underline{\qquad} h.$$

Solving for h, you get

$$h < \frac{1}{\underline{\qquad}}.$$

What happens as n gets large? h approaches _____. That is,

$$\lim_{n \to \infty} h = \underline{\qquad}.$$

This insight leads you to believe that

$$\lim_{n \to \infty} \sqrt[n]{2} = \underline{\qquad}.$$

In order to prove this, suppose $\varepsilon > 0$ is given. Try to find n_0 so that $n > n_0 \Rightarrow |\sqrt[n]{2} - \underline{\qquad}| < \underline{\qquad}$. Since $\sqrt[n]{2} > 1$, the inequality to be proved is equivalent to $\sqrt[n]{2} - 1 < \underline{\qquad}$. According-ing to your estimate of h,

$$\sqrt[n]{2} - 1 = h < \underline{\qquad},$$

and this is less than ε for $n > \underline{\qquad}$.
You have thus proved that

$$\text{if } n > \underline{\qquad}, \qquad \text{then } |\sqrt[n]{2} - 1| < \varepsilon.$$

This means that you can choose $n_0 = [1/\varepsilon]$. You have shown that

$$\lim_{n \to \infty} \sqrt[n]{2} = \underline{\qquad}.$$

Example 5 : Consider the sequence $\{1/\sqrt{n}\}$. As n increases, the terms of the sequence _____ (increase/decrease). Make a guess at $\lim_{n \to \infty} 1/\sqrt{n}$.

If your guess is correct, and you wish to prove that it is correct, you must be able to show that $|(1/\sqrt{n}) - \underline{\qquad}|$ can be made arbitrarily small by choosing n sufficiently large. That is, given any $\varepsilon > 0$, you must prove the existence of $n_0 \in \mathscr{Z}$ so that

$$\underline{\qquad} > n_0 \Rightarrow \left| \frac{1}{\sqrt{n}} - \underline{\qquad} \right| < \underline{\qquad}.$$

We'll approach the problem just a little differently this time.

Answer
n
n
n
0
0
1
1, ε
ε
1/n
1/ε
1/ε
1
decrease
0
n, 0, ε

We shall begin with $|(1/\sqrt{n}) - 0| < \varepsilon$ and find the condition (on n) so that this inequality is true.

$$\left| \frac{1}{\sqrt{n}} - 0 \right| = \left| \frac{1}{\sqrt{n}} \right| = \frac{1}{\sqrt{n}} < \underline{\quad}.$$

ε

This is equivalent to $\sqrt{n} > \underline{\quad}$, which follows from $n > \underline{\quad}$. $\varepsilon^{-1}, \varepsilon^{-2}$
Therefore, $n > n_0$ if $n_0 = [\underline{\quad}]$ (last answer), and this implies ε^{-2}
$|(1/\sqrt{n}) - 0| < \underline{\quad}$. Thus ε

$$\lim_{n \to \infty} \frac{1}{\sqrt{n}} = 0.$$

If you wanted to carry the reasoning back to the definition, explicitly, you would write: Take $n_0 = [1/\varepsilon^2]$. Then

$$n > n_0 \Rightarrow n > \frac{1}{\varepsilon^2}$$

$$\Rightarrow \frac{1}{n} < \underline{\quad}$$

ε^2

$$\Rightarrow \frac{1}{\sqrt{n}} < \underline{\quad}. \qquad \text{(Justify!)}$$

ε

If $x_n = 1/(\sqrt{n} + \sqrt{n+1})$, the same reasoning shows that $|x_n - 0| < \varepsilon$ if $\sqrt{n} + \sqrt{n+1} > \varepsilon^{-1}$. You must show that $\sqrt{n} + \sqrt{n+1}$ is large when n is large by estimating this quantity from below:

$$\sqrt{n} + \sqrt{n+1} > \sqrt{n} + \sqrt{n} = 2\sqrt{n}.$$

This is greater than ε^{-1} if $n > 1/(4\varepsilon^2)$.

Example 6: Consider the sequence $\{(3n^2 + 1)/(2n^2 - 1)\}$. Let us first guess at the behavior of this sequence. If n is large, the dominant term in the numerator is $\underline{\quad}$. The other term is small $3n^2$
in comparison. In the same way, the dominant term in the denom-
inator is $\underline{\quad}$. Therefore, if n is large the ratio $(3n^3 + 1)/(2n^2 - 1)$ $2n^2$
is approximately equal to

$$\frac{\text{dominant term in numerator}}{\text{dominant term in denominator}} = A = \underline{\quad}.$$

$\dfrac{3}{2}$

We suspect, then, that

$$\lim_{n \to \infty} \frac{3n^2 + 1}{2n^2 - 1} = A = \underline{\quad}.$$

$\dfrac{3}{2}$

Let us prove it.

We must estimate the error

$$\left| \frac{3n^2 + 1}{2n^2 - 1} - A \right| = \left| \frac{\underline{} n^2 + \underline{}}{2(2n^2 - 1)} \right|.$$

0, 5

If $n \geq 1$, then $2n^2 - 1$ is \underline{\hspace{3cm}} (positive/negative), so that

positive

$$\left| \frac{3n^2 + 1}{2n^2 - 1} - A \right| = \frac{\underline{}}{2(2n^2 - 1)} < \varepsilon$$

5

if \underline{} $< 2n^2 - 1$ or $n > \frac{1}{2}\sqrt{\underline{}}$. If $\varepsilon > 0$ and $n_0 = $ [this last number], then

5/2ε, (5/ε) + 2

$$n > n_0 \Rightarrow \left| \frac{3n^2 + 1}{2n^2 - 1} - A \right| < \varepsilon.$$

This proves that

$$\lim_{n \to \infty} \frac{3n^2 + 1}{2n^2 - 1} = \underline{}.$$

3
2

In each of the examples above we were given a sequence $\{x_n\}$ and we were able to prove that there was a real number A such that

$$\lim_{n \to \infty} x_n = A.$$

If this is so, we say that the sequence $\{x_n\}$ is *convergent*, and has the *limit* A. If a sequence is not convergent, then it is called *divergent*. The iteration methods that we studied earlier lead to a practical interpretation of limit: *if* $\lim_{n \to \infty} x_n = A$, *then the numbers* x_n *approximate A to within as small an error as we please.* It is sometimes said that x_n *approximates A to within an arbitrarily small error*. On the other hand, if $\{x_n\}$ is divergent, then x_n does not get—*and stay*—arbitrarily close to any real number.

Let's look at another interpretation of $\lim_{n \to \infty} x_n = A$. As you recall, the set $\{x \mid a < x < b\}$ is called an *open interval,* and is also designated (a, b). The midpoint or *center* of this open interval is \underline{\hspace{1.5cm}}.

(a + b)/2

An open interval whose center is A is called a *neighborhood* of A. Some examples are:

$\{x \mid 1 < x < 5\}$ is a neighborhood of 3;
$\{x \mid -\frac{1}{2} < x < \frac{1}{2}\}$ is a neighborhood of 0;
$\{x \mid -3 < x < -1\}$ is a neighborhood of -2;
$(-1, 4)$ is a neighborhood of $\frac{3}{2}$;
If $\varepsilon > 0$, $(2 - \varepsilon, 2 + \varepsilon)$ is a neighborhood of \underline{};

2

If $\eta > 0$, $(\sqrt{2} - \eta, \underline{})$ is a neighborhood of $\sqrt{2}$;

$\sqrt{2} + \eta$

$\{x \mid |x - 1| < 2\}$ is a neighborhood of \underline{};

1

$\{x \mid |x + 3| < 3\}$ is a neighborhood of ____;
$\{x \mid 0 < |x - A| < \varepsilon\}$ is a neighborhood of ____.

| -3
| A

Then, in the language of neighborhoods,

$$\lim_{n \to \infty} x_n = A$$

if and only if for *any* neighborhood U of A, there is an $n_0 \in \mathscr{Z}$ such that $x_n \in U$ for all $n > n_0$. Pictorially, if $n > n_0$, then x_n is in here.

One can think of a neighborhood of A as marked off by a compass; the metal point of the compass is fixed at A, while the pencil point marks off the boundaries $A - \varepsilon$ and $A + \varepsilon$. This provides the motivation for calling the neighborhood $(A - \varepsilon, \ A + \varepsilon)$ a neighborhood of *radius* ε *centered* at A.

9.1.1
EXERCISES

1. Consider the constant sequence $\{x_n\}$, where $x_n = 3$. If U is any neighborhood of 3, then for all $n > 0$, x_n is in U. This shows that

$$\lim_{n \to \infty} x_n = \text{\_\_\_\_}.$$

| 3

Now verify that the original definition is satisfied. Let $\varepsilon > 0$ be given. Then

$$\left| x_n - \text{\_\_\_} \right| = |3 - \text{\_\_\_}| = \text{\_\_\_},$$

| 3, 3, 0

for every positive integer n. Therefore

$$\left| x_n - \text{\_\_\_} \right| < \varepsilon$$

| 3

for every positive integer n. Thus n_0 can be chosen to equal any positive integer.

2. Below you are given convergent sequences.
(a) Give the limit of each of these.
(b) If A denotes the limit of $\{x_n\}$, find n_0 so that

$$|x_n - A| < \tfrac{1}{10} \qquad \text{for } n > n_0,$$

for each of the given sequences.

(i) $\left\{ \dfrac{1}{n} \right\}$,

(iv) $\left\{ \dfrac{2}{n} \right\}$,

(ii) $\left\{ 3 + \dfrac{1}{n} \right\}$,

(v) $\left\{ \dfrac{-3}{n} \right\}$,

(iii) $\left\{ 3 - \dfrac{1}{n} \right\}$,

(vi) $\left\{ \dfrac{(-1)^n}{n} \right\}$,

(vii) $\left\{\left(\frac{1}{6}\right)^n\right\}$,

(ix) $\left\{\frac{n}{n^2 + 1}\right\}$,

(viii) $\left\{3\left(\frac{1}{6}\right)^n\right\}$,

(x) $\{x_n\}$, where $\begin{cases} x_{2k} = 1, \\ x_{2k+1} = \dfrac{2k + 1}{2k + 2}. \end{cases}$

3. For each of the sequences in Exercise 2, suppose ε is a given positive number. Find an n_0 so that if $n > n_0$, then x_n is in a neighborhood of radius ε of the limit.

4. (a) Consider the sequence: $1, -1, 1, -1, \ldots$. This sequence can be defined by stating that $x_n = (-1)^{-n+1}, n = 1, 2, 3, \ldots$. The even-numbered terms are always in a neighborhood of _____, and the odd-numbered terms are always in a neighborhood of _____. All the terms of the sequence are in a neighborhood of 0, provided the radius of the neighborhood is greater than _____. If the sequence has a limit A, then for *every* neighborhood U of _____, there is an $n_0 \in \mathcal{Z}$ so that $n > n_0 \Rightarrow x_n$ is in _____. Can this be true if $A = 0$? _____ (Yes/No). Considering only the odd-numbered terms, you have

n
-1
1
1
A
U
No

$$|x_{2k+1} - 0| = |1 - 0| = 1.$$

This means that the inequality $|x_{2k+1} - 0| < \varepsilon$ is never satisfied if $\varepsilon \le$ _____. The definition requires an inequality of this sort to be satisfied *for all* $\varepsilon > 0$ and *all* sufficiently large k. All you need to

1

do to *disprove* $\lim\limits_{n \to \infty} x_n = A$ (i.e., to prove the negation of $\lim\limits_{n \to \infty} x_n = A$) is to exhibit a single $\varepsilon > 0$ for which the inequality cannot be satisfied.

[NOTE: In order to disprove the statement,

"All humans are less than eight feet tall,"

you need only exhibit *one* human eight or more feet tall. The negation of the given statement is:

"There is a human who is not less than eight feet tall."

In mathematical notation, suppose $P(x)$ is a proposition concerning x. The negation of the statement,

"For all x, $P(x)$ is true,"

is the statement,

"There is an x, such that $P(x)$ is not true."

Similarly, the negation of the statement,

"There is an x such that $P(x)$ is true,"

is the statement,

"For all x, $P(x)$ is not true."

The statement,

"$\lim\limits_{n \to \infty} x_n = A$,"

means

"For all $\varepsilon > 0$, there is an n_0 such that for all n

$P(\varepsilon, n_0, n)$: if $n > n_0$, then $|x_n - A| < \varepsilon$."

This has the form,

"For all $\varepsilon > 0$, there is an n_0 such that for all n
$$P(\varepsilon, n_0, n)."$$

The negation of this statement is,

"There is an $\varepsilon > 0$ such that for all n_0 there is an n such that $P(\varepsilon, n_0, n)$ is not true."

To say that $P(\varepsilon, n_0, n)$ is not true is the same as saying,

"$n > n_0$ and $|x_n - A| \geq \varepsilon$."

Therefore, the negation of the statement,

"$\lim_{n \to \infty} x_n = A$,"

is the statement,

"There is an $\varepsilon > 0$ such that for all n_0 there is an n such that $n > n_0$ and $|x_n - A| \geq \varepsilon$."

(Note that *only a single n need exist*, such that $n > n_0$ and $|x_n - A| \geq \varepsilon$.)]

If $\lim_{n \to \infty} x_n = A(\neq \pm 1)$ then $\exists n_0 \in \mathscr{Z}$ so that if $n > n_0$ then all x_n are in

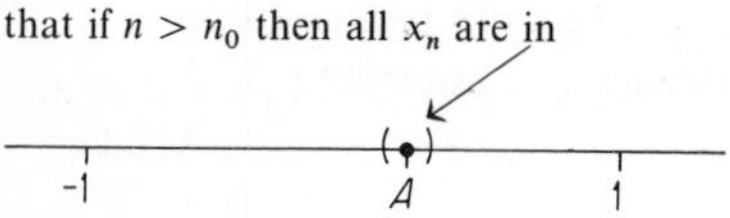

Figure 9-1

You have already shown that 0 cannot be the limit of the sequence $\{(-1)^{n+1}\}$. Show that 1 cannot be the limit by *exhibiting* a value for ε so that $|x_n - 1| < \varepsilon$ cannot be satisfied for every n greater than some n_0. Similarly, prove that -1 also cannot be the limit. Finally, prove that $A(\neq \pm 1)$ cannot be the limit either, using Fig. 9-1 as a hint.

After this you may finally conclude that the sequence is *divergent*. Can you trim down the proof by eliminating any of the steps we asked you to carry out?

[NOTE: Recall the intuitive description of divergence given on page 377, and note that the x_n of the sequence under discussion "get to 1" but don't "stay there"; and the x_n "get to -1" but they don't "stay there."]

(b) Let

$$y_{2n-1} = 1 + \frac{1}{2^n}, \qquad n \in \mathscr{Z}^+,$$

$$y_{2n} = 2 - \frac{1}{2^n}, \qquad n \in \mathscr{Z}^+.$$

Write the first six terms of the sequence $\{y_k\}$. Does the sequence converge or diverge? Prove.

5. Suppose that $\lim_{n \to \infty} x_n = A$.

(a) What is $\lim_{n \to \infty} (x_{n+1} - x_n)$?

(b) If $|x_n - A| < \varepsilon$ for $n > n_0(\varepsilon)$, estimate

$$|x_{n+1} - x_n| = |(x_{n+1} - A - (x_n - A)|$$

for $n > n_0(\varepsilon)$; that is, prove an inequality of the form $|x_{n+1} - x_n| < ?$.

(c) This gives a *necessary* condition for convergence which we can apply without knowing the value of A. Apply this criterion to the sequence in Exercise 4.

(d) Generalize the result:

$$\lim_{n \to \infty} (x_{n+2} - x_n) = \underline{\quad}.$$

(e) Let $n_0(\varepsilon)$ be as in part (b). Find an integer $n_1(\varepsilon)$ (defined for $\varepsilon > 0$) such that

$$|x_m - x_n| < \varepsilon \qquad \text{for } m > n_1(\varepsilon) \quad \text{and} \quad n > n_1(\varepsilon).$$

In fact, you can choose $n_1(\varepsilon) = n_0(\delta)$, where $\delta = \underline{\quad}$.

In other words, if the numbers x_n are all close to some number A for large n, then the numbers x_n must be close to each other.

6. A geometric progression (sequence) is given as

$$2, \quad \frac{2}{10}, \quad \frac{2}{10^2}, \quad \frac{2}{10^3}, \quad \dots \qquad \left| \quad \frac{2}{10^{n-1}} \right.$$

If $x_1 = 2$ is the first term, then $x_n = \underline{\quad}$. We form a new sequence $\{S_n\}$ whose nth term S_n is the sum of the first n terms of this sequence.

(a) Give an explicit formula for S_n. Compute S_n for $1 \le n \le 5$.

(b) Determine whether $\{S_n\}$ is convergent or divergent, and prove your answer.

(c) Give a recursive definition for the sequence $\{S_n\}$ by filling the blanks:

$$S_1 = \underline{\quad}.$$

$$S_{n+1} = S_n + \underline{\quad}.$$

Obtain another recursive definition for S_n by computing $S_{n+1} - S_n/10$. Check your results by computing $S_{n+1} - S_n$ and $S_{n+1} - S_n/10$ for $1 \le n \le 5$.

(d) The sequence $\{a_n\}$, where $a_n = 2 + (n-1)/2$, is an example of an arithmetic sequence whose *difference* is $a_{n+1} - a_n = \underline{\quad}$. Give a recursive definition of the sequence.

(e) When is a geometric sequence convergent? When is an arithmetic sequence convergent?

7. Use the definition of limit to prove the convergence of

(a) $\left\{ \dfrac{1}{\sqrt{n+1}} \right\}$,

(c) $\left\{ \dfrac{1}{n^{1/2}} + \dfrac{1}{n^{2/3}} \right\}$, (See Example 5, page 376.)

(b) $\left\{ \dfrac{1}{n^{2/3}} \right\}$,

(d) $\left\{ \dfrac{2}{n^{1/2}} + \dfrac{3}{n^{2/3}} \right\}$.

8. The sequence $\{x_n\}$, where $x_n = \sqrt{n+1} - \sqrt{n}$, can be analyzed by multiplying x_n by $\sqrt{n+1} + \sqrt{n}$. This is a standard algebraic technique. Have you seen it before in some related form? Find n_0 such that $|x_n - 0| \le 10^{-6}$ for $n \ge n_0$.

9. Use the hint in Exercise 8 to analyze the sequence

$$\{\sqrt[3]{n}(\sqrt{n+1} - \sqrt{n})\}.$$

10. Find the limit of

(a) $\left\{\dfrac{n^2 + 1}{n^2 - 1}\right\}$,

(b) $\left\{\dfrac{2n^2 + 1}{n^2 - 1}\right\}$,

(c) $\left\{\dfrac{3n^3 + 2}{n^2 - 1}\right\}$.

11. Let the sequence $\{x_n\}$ be given by

$$x_n = \frac{1}{n^2} + \frac{2}{n^2} + \cdots + \frac{n}{n^2}.$$

(a) Write the nth term in the form $x_n = B/n^2$.

(b) The numerator B is a familiar progression. Find its sum and simplify.

(c) Compute several values of x_n by means of your simplified formula and guess at

$$\lim_{n \to \infty} \left(\frac{1}{n^2} + \frac{2}{n^2} + \cdots + \frac{n}{n^2}\right).$$

(d) Prove that your guess of part (c) is correct.

(e) If $\varepsilon = \frac{1}{100}$, what is a value of n_0 so that: If $n > n_0$, x_n is in a neighborhood of radius $\frac{1}{100}$ centered about the limit.

12. (a) Let

$$x_n = \frac{1}{n} + \frac{1}{n^2} + \cdots + \frac{1}{n^{10}} \qquad \text{for } n \geq 1.$$

Compute nx_n and $nx_n - x_n$. What is the smallest constant C such that

$$(n - 1)x_n < C, \qquad \forall n \in \mathscr{Z}^+?$$

(b) Let

$$y_n = \frac{b_1}{n} + \frac{b_2}{n^2} + \cdots + \frac{b_{10}}{n^{10}}, \qquad \forall n \in \mathscr{Z}^+,$$

and assume that $|b_k| \leq B$ for $1 \leq k \leq 10$. What is the greatest possible value of $|y_n|/x_n$? Given $\varepsilon > 0$, find n_0 such that $|y_n| < \varepsilon$ for $n > n_0$.

(c) Let P be the polynomial defined by

$$P(x) = b_0 x^{10} + b_1 x^9 + \cdots + b_9 x + b_{10},$$

and assume that $|b_k| \leq B$ for $1 \leq k \leq 10$. Then

$$P(n)/n^{10} = \underline{\quad\quad} + y_n.$$

What is

$$\lim_{n \to \infty} \frac{P(n)}{n^{10}} = A?$$

Given $\varepsilon > 0$, find n_0 such that

$$\left|\frac{P(n)}{n^{10}} - A\right| < \varepsilon \qquad \text{for } n > n_0.$$

13. In the text we showed you how to prove that $\lim\limits_{n \to \infty} \sqrt[n]{2} = 1$. Extend this result by proving the following theorem: If the constant k is greater than or equal to 1, then $\lim\limits_{n \to \infty} \sqrt[n]{k} = 1$.

14. (a) Given $\varepsilon > 0$, find the largest $\delta > 0$ such that

$$|x - 1| < \delta \Rightarrow \left| \frac{1}{x} - 1 \right| < \varepsilon.$$

(b) Given K such that $0 < K < 1$, find k such that $\sqrt[n]{k} = 1/\sqrt[n]{K}$. Use the results of part (a) and Exercise 13 to compute

$$\lim_{n \to \infty} \sqrt[n]{K} = A$$

for $0 < K < 1$, and to find, for given $\varepsilon > 0$ and K, a number n_0 such that

$$\left| \sqrt[n]{K} - A \right| < \varepsilon \qquad \text{for } n > n_0.$$

15. The iteration formula

$$x_{n+1} = \frac{1}{3}\left(2x_n + \frac{10}{x_n^2} \right) = f(x_n)$$

defines a sequence $\{x_n\}$ provided the first term x_1 is also specified.

(a) Find a $\theta > 0$ such that $f(\theta) = \theta$. If $x_1 > 0$, what number do you think the iteration is approximating?

(b) To prove your guess in part (a), compute the error

$$\left| x_{n+1} - \sqrt[3]{\underline{\quad}} \right| = \left| \frac{1}{3}\left(2x_n + \frac{10}{x_n^2} \right) - \underline{\quad} \right| \qquad\qquad 10, \sqrt[3]{10}$$

$$= \left| \frac{1}{3}\left(2x_n + \frac{\theta^3}{x_n^2} \right) - \theta \right|$$

$$= \left| \frac{2x_n^3 - (\underline{\quad})x_n^2 + \underline{\quad}}{3x_n^2} \right|. \qquad\qquad 3\sqrt[3]{10}, 10$$

The numerator has the factor $x_n - \theta$, so you can imitate the procedure used in Chapter 8 to prove the convergence of the analogous iteration for square roots.

(c) If $x_1 = 1$, find the maximum error after n steps.

(d) If $\varepsilon > 0$ is given, what is a value of n_0 that assures

$$|x_n - \theta| < \varepsilon, \qquad \forall n > n_0?$$

(e) Compute

$$\lim_{n \to \infty} \frac{x_{n+1} - \theta}{(x_n - \theta)^2}.$$

16. Prove that the iteration formula

$$x_{n+1} = \frac{1}{3}\left(2x_n + \frac{k}{x_n^2} \right)$$

converges to the real cube root of k, for $k \in \mathcal{R}$.

17. Investigate the general progression

$$a, ar, ar^2, \ldots, ar^n.$$

Call $S_n = a + ar + \cdots + ar^n$. Under what condition(s) does $\{S_n\}$ converge? In high school you learned that the sum of an "infinitely decreasing" geometric progression is $S = \underline{\hspace{1cm}}$. In order for the terms of the progression to be decreasing in absolute value the ratio r must satisfy the inequality $\underline{\hspace{1cm}} < r < \underline{\hspace{1cm}}$. So a reasonable guess is that

$$\lim_{n \to \infty} S_n = \frac{\rule{0.8cm}{0.4pt}}{1-r} \qquad \text{if } |r| < \underline{\hspace{1cm}},$$

$$\left| S_n - \frac{a}{1-r} \right| = \left| \frac{a - (\underline{\hspace{0.6cm}})}{1-r} - \frac{a}{1-r} \right| = \left| \frac{\rule{0.8cm}{0.4pt}}{1-r} \right|.$$

If $|r| < 1$, $\displaystyle\lim_{n \to \infty} r^n = \underline{\hspace{1cm}}$. Therefore, for $\delta > 0$ there is an integer n_0 so that $|r^n| < \delta$ for all $n > n_0$.

Hence

$$\left| S_n - \frac{a}{1-r} \right| < \frac{|\rule{0.6cm}{0.4pt}|\delta}{|1-r|}, \qquad \text{if } n > n_0.$$

Now find the largest δ such that the right member of this inequality is less than ε: $\delta = \underline{\hspace{1cm}}$.

Suppose that $\varepsilon > 0$, a, and r are given. Find n_0 so that

$$\left| S_n - \frac{a}{1-r} \right| < \varepsilon \qquad \text{for all } n > n_0.$$

Prove that $\{S_n\}$ diverges if $|r| \geq 1$ and $a \neq 0$.

18. If p is a proposition, then the negation of p is denoted by "$\sim p$," which may be read, "It is false that p."

    (a) If p is true, then $\sim p$ is false. Is the converse of this statement true?
    (b) If p is false, then $\sim p$ is true. Is the converse of this statement true?
    (c) Show that $[\sim(\sim p)] \Leftrightarrow p$.
    (d) In Exercise 4 you learned that

$$[\sim(\forall\, x, P(x))] \Rightarrow [\underline{\hspace{1cm}}, \sim P(x)]$$

and

$$[\sim(\exists\, x, P(x))] \Rightarrow [\underline{\hspace{1cm}}, \sim P(x)].$$

19. Let p and q be propositions.
    (a) $[\sim(p \lor q)] \Leftrightarrow [\underline{\hspace{1cm}} \land \underline{\hspace{1cm}}]$.
    (b) $[\sim(p \land q)] \Leftrightarrow [\underline{\hspace{1cm}} \lor \underline{\hspace{1cm}}]$.
    (c) $[\sim(p \Rightarrow q)] \Leftrightarrow [p \land \underline{\hspace{1cm}}]$.
    (d) The statement $(\sim q) \Rightarrow (\sim p)$ is called the *contrapositive* of the implication $p \Rightarrow q$. Show that an implication and its contrapositive are equivalent, i.e.,

$$(p \Rightarrow q) \Leftrightarrow [(\sim q) \Rightarrow (\sim p)].$$

(Answer column, right margin:)

$\dfrac{a}{1-r}$

$-1, 1$

$a, 1$

ar^n, ar^n

0

a

$\dfrac{|1-r|\varepsilon}{|a|}$

Explain the importance of this equivalence in indirect proofs (proofs by contradiction).

(e) Use part (d) to show that either of the implications in Exercise 18(d) implies the other.

20. In logical symbols, $\lim_{n \to \infty} x_n = A$ may be stated

$$\forall \varepsilon \; \exists n_0 \; \forall n [n > n_0 \Rightarrow |x_n - A| < \varepsilon],$$

where $\varepsilon \in \mathscr{R}^+, n_0 \in \mathscr{Z}^+, n \in \mathscr{Z}^+$. Write the negation by manipulating the logical symbols in accordance with what you have learned in the last several exercises; then translate the symbolism into informal (necessarily messy) English.

9.2

The Cauchy Criterion Investigate the sequence $\{x_n\}$ where

$$x_n = \frac{1}{0!} + \frac{1}{1!} + \frac{1}{2!} + \cdots + \frac{1}{n!},$$

by computing x_n for $n = 1, 2, 3, 4, 5, 6, 7, 8, 9$, and 10. Does $\{x_n\}$ appear to be convergent? The values of x_n agree to more and more decimal places as n gets larger. In fact, we can prove a stronger result. If $m > n$, then

$$|x_m - x_n| = \frac{1}{(n+1)!} + \cdots + \frac{1}{m!}$$

$$= \frac{1}{(n+1)!}\left(1 + \frac{1}{n+2} + \frac{1}{(n+2)(n+3)} + \cdots + \frac{1}{(n+2)(n+3)\cdots m}\right)$$

$$< \frac{1}{(n+1)!}\left(1 + \frac{1}{n+1} + \frac{1}{(n+1)^2} + \cdots + \frac{1}{(n+1)^{m-n-1}}\right).$$

The expression in parentheses is the sum of a geometric progression, so we have

$$|x_m - x_n| < \frac{1}{(n+1)!}\left(\frac{1}{1 - 1/(n+1)}\right) = \frac{1}{n!n}.$$

The difference between *any pair* of terms can be made arbitrarily small if we go out far enough in the sequence. However, even this knowledge does not help us prove $\{x_n\}$ convergent because we need to have the limit before we can apply the definition. We need to prove that for any $\varepsilon > 0$ there is an $n_0 \in \mathscr{Z}$ so that

$$|x_n - A| < \varepsilon \qquad \text{for } n > n_0,$$

but we don't know what number to use for A. How can we tell whether a sequence is convergent when we don't know or can't guess what the limit is?

For all practical purposes the above sequence does determine a definite number, called e. For, if $m \geq 30$, then

$$|x_m - x_{30}| < \frac{1}{30!30} < 10^{-33},$$

so all numbers x_m, for $m \geq 30$, agree in the first 32 decimal places, and agree within 1 in the 33rd decimal place. It is hard to imagine a measuring device that would distinguish between two numbers that were equal in the first 32 decimal places. If we compute x_{29}, it suggests that

$$e = 2.71828182845904523536\ldots.$$

Certainly the first 20 decimal places ought to be safe for any physical measurements.

Common sense would seem to indicate that when we have a computation process like this, where the results agree with each other very closely as we continue, then the numbers must approach a definite number. More formally, we expect that if the sequence $\{x_n\}$ has the property:

(1) For every $\varepsilon > 0$, there is an $n_0 \in \mathscr{Z}$ such that $|x_m - x_n| < \varepsilon$ for every pair of integers $m, n > n_0$,

then the sequence $\{x_n\}$ has a limit. Any sequence that has this property (1) is said to be a *Cauchy sequence*. Common sense tells us that a Cauchy sequence must have a limit.

The trouble with this common-sense observation is that we can't prove it! Common sense often leads to valid propositions, but the test is mathematical proof. It is easy to prove that *if a sequence converges, then it must be a Cauchy sequence*. You may have already done this in Exercise 5 of Sec. 9.1.1. For completeness, we give the proof here:

Suppose $\lim\limits_{n \to \infty} x_n = a$. Then for every $\delta > 0$, there is an n_0 such that

$$|x_n - a| < \delta \qquad \text{for } n > n_0.$$

Then if $m, n > n_0$,

$$\begin{aligned}
|x_m - x_n| &= |(x_m - a) + (a - x_n)| \\
&\leq |x_m - a| + |a - x_n| \\
&< \delta + \delta = 2\delta.
\end{aligned}$$

If we set $2\delta = \varepsilon$, so that $\delta = \varepsilon/2$, we see that the sequence $\{x_n\}$ is a Cauchy sequence.

Thus, we have proved that *the Cauchy criterion is a necessary condition for convergence*:

$$\{x_n\} \text{ converges} \Rightarrow \{x_n\} \text{ is a Cauchy sequence.}$$

The converse cannot be proved without an additional assumption! In fact, without an additional assumption, we can't even prove that the decimal

$$0.1101000100000001\ldots,$$

with 1 in the 2^nth decimal place for all $n \geq 0$ and 0's in all other places, represents a number. (This decimal can be thought of as coming from the sequence defined recursively by $x_1 = 0.1$, $x_{n+1} = x_n + 1/10^{2^n}$.) That is, we can't prove that the sequence $\{x_n\}$ converges to some number.

We are thus led to *postulate* that the Cauchy criterion, (1), is a *sufficient* criterion for convergence.

Postulate C: *If $\{x_n\}$ is a Cauchy sequence of real numbers, then $\{x_n\}$ is convergent.*

In other words, if $\{x_n\}$ is a *Cauchy* sequence then there exists $A \in \mathscr{R}$ such that

$$\lim_{n \to \infty} x_n = A.$$

Postulate C is, then a postulate concerning $\mathscr{R}$.

We can see the meaning of the postulate intuitively on the number line. Let us take the sequence defined by

$$x_n = \frac{1}{10^1} + \frac{1}{10^2} + \cdots + \frac{1}{10^{2n}}.$$

(Where did you see this sequence before?) If $m > n$, then

$$|x_m - x_n| = \left(\frac{1}{10^1} + \frac{1}{10^2} + \cdots + \frac{1}{10^{2n}} + \cdots + \frac{1}{10^{2m}} \right)$$

$$- \left(\frac{1}{10^1} + \frac{1}{10^2} + \cdots + \frac{1}{10^{2n}} \right)$$

$$= \frac{1}{10^{2n+1}} + \frac{1}{10^{2n+2}} + \cdots + \frac{1}{10^{2m}}.$$

We can obtain an estimate of $|x_m - x_n|$ by converting the right member to a geometric progression according to the inequality:

$$|x_m - x_n| \leq \frac{1}{10^k} + \frac{1}{10^{k+1}} + \cdots + \frac{1}{10^l}, \quad k = 2^{n+1}, \quad l = 2^m.$$

Then, using the formula $S = a/(1 - r)$ for the sum of an infinite geometric progression, we obtain

$$|x_m - x_n| < \frac{1/10^k}{1 - \frac{1}{10}}.$$

Therefore,

$$|x_m - x_n| < \frac{1}{9 \cdot 10^{2^{n+1}-1}} \leq \frac{1}{9 \cdot 10^{2^n}}$$

$$< \frac{1}{9 \cdot 10^{2^n}},$$

which is true for all x_m, if $m > n$. Thus, if $m > n$, all numbers x_m lie in the *closed interval*

$$\mathcal{I}_n = \left[x_n - \frac{1}{9 \cdot 10^{2^n}}, \quad x_n + \frac{1}{9 \cdot 10^{2^n}} \right].$$

The intervals

$$\mathcal{I}'_n = \left[x_n - \frac{2}{9 \cdot 10^{2^n}}, \quad x_n + \frac{2}{9 \cdot 10^{2^n}} \right]$$

have a simple geometric property: $\mathcal{I}'_{n+1}$ is contained in $\mathcal{I}'_n$ for all n. (To prove this, you need only prove that

$$x_n - \frac{2}{9 \cdot 10^{2^n}} \leq x_{n+1} - \frac{2}{9 \cdot 10^{2^{n+1}}}$$

and

$$x_{n+1} + \frac{2}{9 \cdot 10^{2^{n+1}}} \leq x_n + \frac{2}{9 \cdot 10^{2^n}}.$$

But you just saw that

$$|x_{n+1} - x_n| < \frac{1}{9 \cdot 10^{2^n}} = \varepsilon_n$$

so you need only prove that $\varepsilon_n \leq 2\varepsilon_n - 2\varepsilon_{n+1}$, or $2\varepsilon_{n+1} \leq \varepsilon_n$.)

The inclusion relationship of these intervals is shown, with some slight distortion, in Fig. 9-2. It seems obvious, geometrically, that the intervals shrink down to a common point. A sequence of intervals of this type having the property that each interval is contained in the preceding interval ($\mathcal{I}'_{n+1}$ is contained in $\mathcal{I}'_n$, for all n), is called a sequence of *nested* intervals.

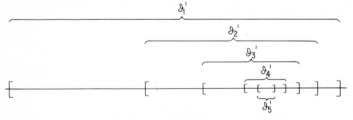

Figure 9-2

An alternative geometric form of our postulate is:

Postulate C′:   If $\{\mathscr{I}_n\}$ is a sequence of nested closed intervals, then there is a point x such that $x \in \mathscr{I}_n$ for all n.

Example 1: With the Cauchy criterion, which is both necessary and sufficient for convergence, it is easy to prove the divergence of many sequences. We begin with the trivial sequence $\{n\}$.

Since $|x_m - x_n| = |m - n|$ is never less than 1 if $m \neq n$, the Cauchy criterion can never be satisfied. (Actually $|m - n|$ can be made as *large* as you please.)

Example 2: $x_1 = 1$, $x_{n+1} = x_n + 1/(n + 1)$. The first five terms of this sequence are: $1, \underline{\qquad}, \underline{\qquad}, \underline{\qquad}, \underline{\qquad}$. An explicit formula for the nth term is $x_n = \underline{\qquad}$. Does x_n get larger than 2? Give a value for n which guarantees $x_n > 3$. Do you think the sequence diverges or converges?

We look at $|x_m - x_n|$, assuming $m > n$:

$$|x_m - x_n| = \frac{1}{n+1} + \frac{1}{n+2} + \cdots + \frac{1}{m} > \frac{1}{m} + \frac{1}{m} + \cdots + \frac{1}{m}.$$

How many terms are there in the sum and on the right? It seems that if the difference $m - n$ is taken to be large, then $|x_m - x_n|$ cannot be made arbitrarily small. For example, take $m = 2n$. Then

$$|x_m - x_n| = x_{2n} - x_n = \frac{1}{n+1} + \frac{1}{n+2} + \cdots + \frac{1}{2n}$$

$$> \frac{1}{2n} + \frac{1}{2n} + \cdots + \frac{1}{2n} = \frac{n}{2n}.$$

Thus,

$$x_m - x_n > \frac{1}{2}.$$

Once again the Cauchy criterion cannot be satisfied, since the inequality $|x_m - x_n| < \varepsilon$ must be satisfied *for all* m and n larger than some n_0.

Example 3: We return to the sequence $\{(-1)^{n+1}\}$. Recall how laborious it was to prove divergence by resorting to the definition of limit. You had to go back to first principles to prove that no real number A could satisfy the limit inequality. See, now, how simple it is by the Cauchy criterion.

$$|x_{n+1} - x_n| = 2 \qquad \text{for all } n.$$

Example 4: Imagine that we toss a coin infinitely many times. The sequence $\{x_n\}$ is defined by:

$$x_0 = 1, \qquad x_n = x_{n-1} + \frac{\varepsilon_n}{n!} \qquad \text{for } n \geq 1,$$

where $\varepsilon_n = +1$ or -1 according to whether the nth toss is heads or tails. Thus x_n is determined by chance events. Is $\{x_n\}$ certain to converge or diverge, or is either outcome possible?

For $m > n$, let us estimate

$$|x_m - x_n| = \left| \frac{\varepsilon_{n+1}}{(n+1)!} + \frac{\varepsilon_{n+2}}{(n+2)!} + \cdots + \frac{\varepsilon_m}{m!} \right|.$$

Using the fact that $|\varepsilon_k| = 1$ for all k, we find that

$$|x_m - x_n| < \frac{1}{(n+1)!} + \frac{1}{(n+1)!(n+1)} + \frac{1}{(n+1)!(n+1)^2}$$

$$+ \cdots + \frac{1}{(n+1)!(n+1)^{m-1}} < \frac{1}{n!\,n},$$

so that $\{x_n\}$ is a Cauchy sequence, no matter how the tosses come out. By Postulate C, we conclude that

$$\lim_{n \to \infty} x_n = A$$

exists, although we do not know what A is. The value of A is determined by chance. Still, if we toss the coin 30 times, we can compute A to within an error of less than 10^{-33}.

The first of these examples is a sequence in which x_n increases, getting larger than any fixed number M. If $M = 1000$, it is easy to see (in the first example) that $x_n > 1000$ for all $n > 1000$. In the second example $x_{2n} - x_n > \frac{1}{2}$ for all n. So

$$x_2 - x_1 > \underline{\hspace{1cm}},$$

$$x_4 - x_2 > \underline{\hspace{1cm}},$$

$$x_8 - x_4 > \underline{\hspace{1cm}}.$$

How large must n be to guarantee that $x_n > 1000$ for all n? Taking $M = 1000$ should be sufficient to show you how to prove that the sequences in both of these examples have the following property: For every fixed number M, no matter how large, there is an n_0 so that $x_n > M$ for all $n > n_0$. A sequence $\{x_n\}$ satisfying this property is said to *approach infinity* as n increases. We write

$$\lim_{n \to \infty} x_n = \infty.$$

Similarly, if the sequence decreases so that x_n becomes less than any number (such as -10^{10}), then we write

$$\lim_{n \to \infty} x_n = -\infty.$$

(Read: "The limit of x_n, as n approaches infinity, is minus infinity.") In formal terms, $\lim_{n \to \infty} x_n = -\infty$ means that for every fixed real number N, no matter how small, there is an n_0 so that $x_n < N$ for all $n > n_0$. Note that even though we write $\lim_{n \to \infty} x_n = \infty$ (or $\lim_{n \to \infty} x_n = -\infty$), and speak of the sequences as approaching infinity (or minus infinity) they are nevertheless *divergent* sequences. They do not converge to a real number, for ∞ *is not a real number*.

Historical note: The notion of limit has been used in mathematics for many centuries. It appeared in Greek mathematics two thousand years ago and was used by Newton and Leibniz for the development of calculus. However, careful mathematical proofs could not be given until Auguste Louis Cauchy (1789–1857) first formulated a definition of limit. It is he who deserves the credit for first developing a clear and mathematically rigorous treatment of the theory of limits, which, as we indicated earlier, is one of the central ideas of the course. The criterion which bears his name was given by Cauchy as a necessary and sufficient condition for convergence.

   The ideas concerning nested intervals are usually credited to Georg Cantor (1845–1918), who also used the Cauchy criterion as a basis for developing an axiomatic treatment of the real numbers. A recent exposition that utilizes Cantor's method is contained in *Foundations of Analysis* by E. J. Cogan.†

   Both Cauchy and Cantor were giants in the history of mathematics. Cauchy contributed to many branches of mathematics and to the application of mathematics to physics and engineering. In 1816 the French Academy awarded him its prize for his memoir on optics. Cantor deserves the credit for clearing up many of the mysteries of the infinite. His work on the theory of sets included the first careful analysis of infinite sets, which finally put to rest questions posed by Zeno, in his famous paradoxes, over two thousand years earlier. A very interesting discussion of Cantor's theory of the infinite appears in *Mathematics and the Imagination* by Edward Kasner and J. R. Newman.‡

9.2.1
EXERCISES

1. (a) In the text we proved, for the sequence defining e, that

$$|x_m - x_n| < \frac{1}{n!n} \qquad \text{if } m > n.$$

† E. J. Cogan, *Foundations of Analysis* (Englewood Cliffs, N.J.: Prentice Hall, Inc., 1962). See Chapter 2.
   ‡ Edward Kasner and J. R. Newman, *Mathematics and the Imagination* (New York: Simon and Schuster, 1940). See the chapter entitled, "Beyond the Googol."

We now ask you to complete the proof that this sequence is a Cauchy sequence. In other words, if $\varepsilon > 0$ is given, how large would you choose n_0 so that

$$\forall \, m, n > n_0 \Rightarrow |x_m - x_n| < \varepsilon?$$

(b) If you did not exhibit an explicit formula for n_0 in part (a), we will now help you obtain one. Fill in the relation:

$$\frac{1}{n_0!n_0} \, ? \, \frac{1}{n_0 \cdot n_0} = \frac{1}{n_0^2}.$$

If n_0 is taken so large that $1/n_0^2 < \varepsilon$, you will have

$$|x_m - x_n| < \varepsilon \qquad \text{for all } m, n > n_0.$$

2. Using the Cauchy criterion, establish the divergence of the following sequences and state which approach infinity, which approach minus infinity, and which approach neither plus nor minus infinity.

(a) $\left\{\dfrac{n}{2}\right\}$,

(f) $\left\{1 + \dfrac{1}{2^{2/3}} + \cdots + \dfrac{1}{n^{2/3}}\right\}$,

(b) $\{(-1)^n (\tfrac{3}{2})^n\}$,

(g) $\{3 + (-1)^n \sqrt{n}\}$,

(c) $\{(3n^2 + 1)/2n\}$,

(h) $\{3 + (-1)^{n+1} \sqrt{n}\}$,

(d) $\{1 - \sqrt{n}\}$,

(i) $\{1/(2 - (-1)^n)\}$,

(e) $\left\{(-1)^n \left(1 + \dfrac{1}{2} + \cdots + \dfrac{1}{n}\right)\right\}$,

(j) $\left\{\dfrac{1}{n} - n\right\}$.

3. One method of constructing a sequence that approaches $\sqrt{2}$ (from below) is to take $x_1 = 1$, $x_2 = 1 \cdot a_1 = 1 + (a_1/10)$, where a_1 is the largest integer $(0 \le a_1 \le 9)$, so that $(1 \cdot a_1)^2 \le 2$. In general, x_i is defined recursively by

$$x_{n+1} = x_n + \frac{a_n}{10^n},$$

where a_n is the largest integer $(0 \le a_n \le 9)$ so that $(x_{n+1})^2 < 2$.

(a) Find x_2, x_3, x_4, x_5.

(b) Construct a sequence $\{y_n\}$ so that the y_n approach $\sqrt{2}$ from above.

(c) Are the closed intervals $[x_n, y_n]$ a set of nested intervals?

(d) Prove that the sequence: $x_1, y_1, x_2, y_2, \ldots, x_n, y_n, \ldots$ satisfies the Cauchy criterion.

4. (a) What is $\lim\limits_{n \to \infty} \dfrac{2n + 1}{n}$?

(b) Find $\lim\limits_{n \to \infty} \dfrac{6n + 3}{n}$.

(c) Find $\lim\limits_{n \to \infty} \dfrac{-4n - 2}{3n}$.

5. (a) If $\{a_n\}$ is a Cauchy sequence, prove that $\{3a_n\}$ is also a Cauchy sequence. You know that for $\varepsilon > 0$ there is $n_0(\varepsilon)$ so that $|a_m - a_n| < \varepsilon$ for all $m, n > n_0$. Find an integer $n_1(\varepsilon)$ such that $|3a_m - 3a_n| < \varepsilon$ for all $m, n > n_1(\varepsilon)$. In fact, $n_1(\varepsilon) = n_0(\delta)$, where $\delta = $ _____.

   (b) Let $b_n = 2a_n + 5$. For $\varepsilon > 0$ find an integer $n_2(\varepsilon)$ such that $|b_m - b_n| < \varepsilon$ for all $m, n > n_2(\varepsilon)$.

6. Let the sequence $\{x_n\}$ be defined by the formulas $x_{2k} = 1$, $k = 1, 2, 3, \ldots$, and $x_{2k+1} = 2k/(2k + 1)$.
   (a) Write out the first ten terms.
   (b) Prove $\{x_n\}$ converges, using the Cauchy criterion.
   (c) Find $\lim_{n \to \infty} x_n$, and prove that your answer is correct.
   (d) Give a set of nested intervals $\mathscr{I}_n$ so that $x_n \in \mathscr{I}_n$.

7. (a) What is $\lim_{n \to \infty} \dfrac{2n}{2n + 1}$?

   (b) What is $\lim_{n \to \infty} \left(1 - \dfrac{2n}{2n + 1}\right)$?

   (c) What is $\lim_{n \to \infty} \left(\dfrac{2n}{2n + 1} + 3\right)$?

   (d) What is $\lim_{n \to \infty} \left(\dfrac{2n}{2n + 1} + k\right)$, where k is a constant?

8. If $\lim_{n \to \infty} a_n = A$, and k is a constant, what is B in

$$\lim_{n \to \infty} (a_n + k) = B?$$

If for $\varepsilon > 0$ and $n > n_0(\varepsilon)$ and $|a_n - A| < \varepsilon$, find an integer $n_1(\varepsilon)$ such that $|(a_n + k) - B| < \varepsilon$ for $n > n_1(\varepsilon)$.

9. Let $\mathscr{I}_n = \{x \mid 0 \le x \le 2/n\}$.
   (a) Is $\{\mathscr{I}_n\}$ a sequence of closed nested intervals?
   (b) Give a formula for the elements of some sequence $\{x_n\}$, where $x_n \in \mathscr{I}_n$.
   (c) Is the sequence $\{x_n\}$ convergent? Why?
   (d) What is $\lim_{n \to \infty} x_n$? Although different readers may have different answers for part (c), all the answers to this part must be the same. Why?
   (e) Suppose your answer is $\lim_{n \to \infty} x_n = A$ and someone else's answer is $\lim_{n \to \infty} x_n = B$. Does $A \in \mathscr{I}_1$? Does $A \in \mathscr{I}_2$? Does $A \in \mathscr{I}_n$? Is the same true of B?
   (f) Let $l_n = $ length of $\mathscr{I}_n$. Give a formula for l_n, and find $\lim_{n \to \infty} l_n$.
   (g) Assume $A \ne B$. Is there an interval $\mathscr{I}_m$ so that $l_m < |A - B|$?
   (h) Can A and B both belong to $\mathscr{I}_m$?
   (i) Compare your answer to part (h) with the answers to (e). What do you observe?

10. Let $\mathscr{I}_n = \{x \mid 0 < x < 2/n\}$, and call l_n the length of $\mathscr{I}_n$.
   (a) Let $x_n \in \mathscr{I}_n$. Give a formula for some such x_n.

(b) What is $\lim_{n \to \infty} x_n$?

(c) If your answer to (b) is $\lim_{n \to \infty} x_n = A$, we ask: Does A belong to $\mathcal{I}_1$? Does A belong to any $\mathcal{I}_n$?

(d) Why is the result of this exercise so different from that of Exercise 9? Check back to the Postulate C' and explain.

11. Postulate C' asserts the existence of at least one point in each of the closed nested intervals $\mathcal{I}_n$.

(a) If l_n denotes the length of $\mathcal{I}_n$, and $\lim_{n \to \infty} l_n = 1$, how many points x are there such that $x \in \mathcal{I}_n$ for all n?

(b) If $\lim_{n \to \infty} l_n = 0$, how many points x are there such that $x \in \mathcal{I}_n$ for all n? [*Hint:* See Exercise 9(g).]

12. (a) Using the method described in Exercise 3, construct the first five of a sequence of closed nested intervals $\{[x_n, y_n]\}$ such that $\sqrt{3} \in [x_n, y_n]$ for all n. (Note that the postulate is asserting the existence of $\sqrt{3}$. You satisfy the hypothesis by providing the sequence $\{[x_n, y_n]\}$, and the postulate then gives you the existence of $A \in \mathcal{R}$ so that $x_n \leq A \leq y_n$.)

(b) What is $\lim_{n \to \infty} (y_n - x_n)$?

(c) What does the result of Exercise 11(b) tell you about the number of A's such that $x_n \leq A \leq y_n$, for all n?

13. *Can there be two different limits to the same sequence?*

(a) Suppose $\lim_{n \to \infty} x_n = A$, $\lim_{n \to \infty} x_n = B$, and $A \neq B$. Then $|A - B|$? 0. (Fill in symbol.)

(b) If U is a neighborhood of A,

then there is $n_0 \in \mathscr{Z}$ so that $x_n \in U$ for all $n > n_0$. If V is a neighborhood of B, then there is an $n_1 \in \mathscr{Z}$ such that .... What radii would you choose for U and V so that U and V have no common points?

(c) If $n > $ maximum $\{n_0, n_1\}$, then $x_n \in$ _____ and $x_n \in$ _____. Is there anything wrong with this?

14. We have called Postulate C' an alternative form of Postulate C. Prove that these two postulates are logically equivalent. This is, prove:

$$\text{Postulate C} \Rightarrow \text{Postulate C'}$$

and

$$\text{Postulate C'} \Rightarrow \text{Postulate C.}$$

(a) To prove that $C \Rightarrow C'$: Assume C. Let $\{\mathcal{I}_n\}$ be a sequence of closed nested intervals whose lengths approach 0:

$$\mathcal{I}_n = [a_n, b_n], \qquad \lim_{n \to \infty} (b_n - a_n) = 0.$$

You wish to prove that there is a number x such that $x \in \mathscr{I}_n$ for all $n \in \mathscr{Z}^+$.

What does $\lim\limits_{n \to \infty} (b_n - a_n) = 0$ mean? If $\varepsilon > 0$, then there is an $n_0(\varepsilon)$ such that

$$|\underline{\hspace{4cm}}| < \varepsilon \qquad \text{for } n > n_0(\varepsilon).$$

Does this imply that $\{a_n\}$ is a Cauchy sequence?

You know that for $m > n$, $\mathscr{I}_m \underline{\hspace{1cm}} \mathscr{I}_n$ (what relation?). Since $a_m \in \mathscr{I}_m$, then certainly $a_m \underline{\hspace{1cm}} \mathscr{I}_n$ (what relation?). Therefore, $a_n \underline{\hspace{1cm}} a_m \underline{\hspace{1cm}} b_n$ (what order relations?), so that

$$|a_m - a_n| \underline{\hspace{1cm}} |b_n - a_n| < \underline{\hspace{2cm}}$$

for $m > n > n_0(\varepsilon)$.

By Postulate C, it follows that $\lim\limits_{n \to \infty} a_n = x$ exists. You have shown that for $m > n$,

$$a_n \underline{\hspace{1cm}} a_m \underline{\hspace{1cm}} b_n.$$

In this relation let $m \to \infty$. What information do you obtain about x? Is x in $\mathscr{I}_n$ or not?

(b) To prove that $C' \Rightarrow C$. Assume C'. Let $\{a_n\}$ be a Cauchy sequence. You wish to prove that $\lim\limits_{n \to \infty} a_n = x$ exists. Try to construct a sequence of nested intervals which "squeeze down" on x.

You know that for $\varepsilon > 0$ there is an $n_0(\varepsilon)$ such that for $m > n \geq n_0(\varepsilon)$, $|a_m - a_n| < \varepsilon$. Let us try a sequence of intervals of the form

$$\mathscr{I}_n = [a_n - \varepsilon_n, a_n + \varepsilon_n],$$

and investigate whether we can choose ε_n suitably.

If $\{\mathscr{I}_n\}$ is to be a sequence of nested intervals, then for $m > n$ we must have $\mathscr{I}_m \underline{\hspace{1cm}} \mathscr{I}_n$ (what relation?). This means that

$$a_n - \varepsilon_n \underline{\hspace{1cm}} a_m - \varepsilon_m \underline{\hspace{1cm}} a_m + \varepsilon_m \underline{\hspace{1cm}} a_n + \varepsilon_n,$$

and this is true if $-(\varepsilon_n - \varepsilon_m) \underline{\hspace{1cm}} a_m - a_n \underline{\hspace{1cm}} \varepsilon_n - \varepsilon_m$, or $|a_m - a_n| < \underline{\hspace{2cm}}$.

In general, it is not obvious how to choose ε_n so that the *whole* sequence $\{\mathscr{I}_n\}$ is nested.

But if we choose $\varepsilon_k = 2^{1-k}$ and let $n_k = n_0(2^{-k})$, then the *subsequence* $\{\mathscr{I}_k\}$, where $\mathscr{I}_k = \mathscr{I}_{n_k} = [a_{n_k} - \varepsilon_k, a_{n_k} + \varepsilon_k]$, is a sequence of nested intervals.

If $x \in \mathscr{I}_k$ for all k, then

$$|a_{n_k} - x| \leq \varepsilon_k \qquad \text{for all } k \in \mathscr{Z}^+.$$

But for $m > n \geq n_k = n_0(2^{-k})$, you know that $|a_m - a_n| < \underline{\hspace{2cm}}$. Choose $n = n_k$. Then for $m > n_k$

$$|a_m - a_{n_k}| = |(a_m - x) + (x - a_{n_k})|$$

$$\leq \underline{\hspace{2cm}} + \underline{\hspace{2cm}}$$

$$= (\underline{\hspace{1cm}} + \underline{\hspace{1cm}})2^{-k} = \underline{\hspace{1cm}} \cdot 2^{-k}.$$

Now it is easy to complete the proof that $\lim\limits_{n \to \infty} a_m = x$.

15. By means of logical symbols the Cauchy criterion may be written

(1) $\qquad \forall \varepsilon \; \exists \, n_0 \; \forall \, m \; \forall \, n \, [(m > n_0 \wedge n > n_0) \Rightarrow |x_m - x_n| < \varepsilon],$

where it is understood that $\varepsilon \in \mathscr{R}^+$ and $n_0, m, n \in \mathscr{L}^+$.

(a) Show that the formulation (1) is equivalent to

$$\forall \varepsilon \; \exists \, k \; \forall \, m \, [m > k \Rightarrow |x_m - x_k| < \varepsilon].$$

(b) Show how to negate (1) by filling the blanks:

$$\underline{\qquad\qquad} [(m > n_0 \wedge n > n_0) \underline{\qquad\qquad} |x_m - x_n| \geq \varepsilon].$$

Research Problem

16. Statements (i) and (ii) below define a method of measuring the magnitude of rational numbers that is analogous to measuring magnitude by absolute value.

(i) $\left\| \dfrac{m}{n} \right\| = 2^{-k}$ if $\dfrac{m}{n} = 5^k \dfrac{p}{q}$, where neither p nor q has 5 as a factor.

(ii) $\|0\| = 0$.

Suppose you define $\underset{n \to \infty}{L^*}(x_n) = A$ to mean:

$$\lim_{n \to \infty} \|x_n - A\| = 0.$$

For practice, compute $\|x\|$ for these values of x: $1, 5, 25, \frac{1}{5}, \frac{1}{15}, 2, 3, 4, \frac{17}{100}, \frac{100}{17}$.

(a) Is there a sequence $\{r_n\}$ of rationals such that $\underset{n \to \infty}{L^*}(r_n^2) = -1$? First, try to find an integer r_0 such that $\|r_0^2 + 1\| < 1$. Now, can you find an integer x_1 such that

$$\|r_1^2 + 1\| < \|r_0^2 + 1\|,$$

where $r_1 = r_0 + 5x_1$? Can you find an integer x_2 such that

$$\|r_2^2 + 1\| < \|r_1^2 + 1\|,$$

where $r_2 = r_1 + 25x_2$?

How can you continue this process to construct $\{r_n\}$?

(b) Is there a sequence $\{r_n\}$ of rationals such that $\underset{n \to \infty}{L^*}(r_n^2) = 2$? Where does the process in part (a) break down in constructing a sequence $\{r_n\}$ such that $\lim_{n \to \infty} \|r_n^2 - 2\| = 0$? Is there an integer m such that $m^2 - 2$ is divisible by 5?

(c) Suppose we define a "Cauchy (*) sequence" as a sequence of rationals $\{x_n\}$ which satisfies the definition of a Cauchy sequence, except that the absolute value is replaced by $\|\dots\|$. If the answer to (a) or (b) is "yes," can you find $\{r_n\}$ such that $\{r_n\}$ is a Cauchy (*) sequence?

(d) Suppose we replace Postulate C by Postulate C(*): If $\{x_n\}$ is a Cauchy (*) sequence, then there is an $A \in \mathscr{R}$ such that $\underset{n \to \infty}{L^*} x_n = A$.

Does the equation $A^2 = -1$ have a solution in a field which obeys Postulate C(*)?

Suppose we assume also Postulate C(∗∗): If A is any element of the field, then there is a sequence $\{x_n\}$ of rational numbers such that $\underset{n \to \infty}{L^*} x_n = A$.

Does the equation $A^2 = 2$ have a solution?

(e) If you replace the prime number 5 by the prime number 7 in the above definition of the magnitude of a rational number, which of the numbers ± 1, ± 2, and ± 3 have square roots in the resulting number system?

Is there a number system of this type, corresponding to some prime number, in which both -1 and 2 have square roots?

(f) Examine the properties of absolute value listed on page 119. Which of these properties hold if the absolute value is replaced by $\| \ldots \|$?

9.3

Monotonic Sequences   The sequence that defines the number e has some special properties that can easily be gleaned from its definition:

(1)
$$x_n = 1 + \frac{1}{1!} + \frac{1}{2!} + \cdots + \frac{1}{n!}, \qquad n = 0, 1, 2, \ldots..$$

First, the terms are *increasing*, since

(2)
$$x_{n+1} > x_n;$$

and the fact that this characteristic persists at every step, i.e., (2) holds for every n, is described by saying the sequence is *monotonic*. Thus (1) is an example of a *monotonic increasing* sequence.

Second, we note that

$$x_n < 1 + 1 + \frac{1}{2} + \frac{1}{2^2} + \cdots + \frac{1}{2^{n-1}} < 3, \qquad \text{for } n \geq 1,$$

so the terms are *bounded above* by 3 (Fig. 9-3).

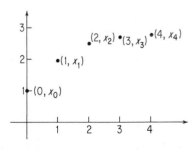

Figure 9-3

It seems obvious that any monotonic increasing sequence converges if it is bounded above, for there must be a bunching up of terms in smaller and smaller intervals. This is a crude but intuitive way of saying that the Cauchy criterion ought to be satisfied. We shall investigate this more closely.

Let $\{a_n\}$ be a monotonic increasing sequence that is bounded above, and suppose it does not converge. Then the Cauchy criterion must be contradicted by $\{a_n\}$. If we wish to state this precisely, we apply the results of Sec. 9.1 to obtain the negation of the Cauchy criterion:

There is $\varepsilon > 0$, so that for all $n_0 \in \mathscr{Z}^+$ there are $m, n \in \mathscr{Z}$, with $m > n > n_0$ such that $|a_m - a_n| \geq \varepsilon$.

(See also Exercise 16 of Sec. 9.2.1.)

It seems that if enough differences $a_m - a_n$ are greater than or equal to ε, we can go out far enough in the sequence to get above the bound. That is:

(3)   If $\varepsilon > 0$, no matter how small, and b is any positive real number, no matter how large, there is some positive integer N such that $N\varepsilon > b$.

The idea expressed by (3) appears to be true from our experience with real numbers. In fact, we assume it in measuring length; for, in measuring a long table with a short ruler (Fig. 9-4), we go ahead with complete assurance that we can mark off the length of the ruler a sufficient number of times to get from one end of the table to the other. So, for the moment, let's continue to assume (3) and come back to it after we complete the investigation of $\{a_n\}$.

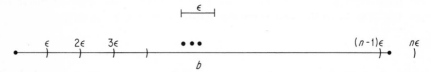

Figure 9-4

Take $n_0 = 0$. From our assumption that $\{a_n\}$ diverges, we conclude that

$$\exists \, n_1 > n_0 \quad \text{such that} \quad |a_{n_1} - a_{n_0}| = a_{n_1} - a_{n_0} \geq \varepsilon.$$

Also,

$$\exists \, n_2 > n_1 \quad \text{such that} \quad a_{n_2} - a_{n_1} \geq \varepsilon,$$

and

$$\exists \, n_3 > n_2 \quad \text{such that} \quad a_{n_3} - a_{n_2} \geq \varepsilon.$$

This process can be continued as many times as we like. If we take as our last step $a_{n_k} - a_{n_{k-1}} \geq \varepsilon$, then

$$a_{n_k} = (a_{n_k} - a_{n_{k-1}}) + (a_{n_{k-1}} - a_{n_{k-2}}) + \cdots + (a_{n_1} - a_{n_0}) + a_{n_0}$$

$$\geq k\varepsilon + a_{n_0}.$$

But, by (3), k can be chosen so that $k\varepsilon$ is as large as we please. Thus, a sequence element, a_{n_k}, can be found to exceed the bound. Herein lies the contradiction we expected. Thus, if (3) is assumed, we have the result that $\{a_n\}$ converges; that is, every monotonic increasing sequence that is bounded above is convergent.

To keep our promise, we return to a discussion of (3):

If $\varepsilon, b \in \mathscr{R}^+$, then there exists $N \in \mathscr{L}^+$ such that $N\varepsilon > b$.

This is a statement about order in $\mathscr{R}$. It is generally referred to as the *Archimedean property of order*, for Archimedes (287–212 B.C.), who, not seeing how to prove it from Euclid's postulates, assumed it and made extensive use of it in his work that anticipated some of the discoveries of integral calculus approximately two thousand years later. (See Exercise 9 of Sec. 10.1.1.) However, it was Eudoxus (400–355 B.C.) who first stated and used the property. Eudoxus, a powerful intellect of antiquity, has never quite achieved the fame he deserves. Among his great accomplishments is the development of the theory of proportion (and similarity) which is incorporated in Euclid's *Elements*. In fact, Euclid makes explicit use of the misnamed Archimedean property in *Elements, Book X*.

Earlier, it was mentioned that we assume the Archimedean property when we measure length; but we have also been tacitly assuming it for our most elementary work on limits. For example, if we want to prove that $\lim_{n \to \infty} (1/n) = 0$, we must show the existence of $n_0 \in \mathscr{L}^+$ such that

$$ n > n_0 \Rightarrow \frac{1}{n} < \varepsilon. $$

In order to do this we *assume* that there is $n_0 \in \mathscr{L}^+$ such that $n_0 \varepsilon > 1$. This is precisely the *Archimedean property*.

Strangely enough, this apparently simple order property cannot be proved from our present assumptions concerning $\mathscr{R}$, namely Postulate OF ($\mathscr{R}$ is an ordered field) and Postulate C (every Cauchy sequence converges). Therefore, we add to our assumptions

Postulate A: $\mathscr{R}$ *satisfies the Archimedean order property, i.e.,*

$$ a, b \in \mathscr{R}^+ \Rightarrow \exists n \in \mathscr{L}^+, \ na > b. $$

Armed with this new postulate, we can assert our result on monotonic sequences as a theorem. But let's first formalize the notions we used, and later state the theorem.

Definition:

(i) *If* $x_{n+1} \geq x_n$ *for all* n, *the sequence* $\{x_n\}$ *is called a* monotonic increasing *sequence* (*sometimes called* monotonic nondecreasing).

(ii) *If* $x_{n+1} \leq x_n$ *for all* n, *the sequence* $\{x_n\}$ *is called a* monotonic decreasing *sequence* (*sometimes called* monotonic nonincreasing).

(iii) *If $x_{n+1} > x_n$ for all n, the sequence is called* strictly increasing.
(iv) *If $x_{n+1} < x_n$ for all n, the sequence is called* strictly decreasing.

Definition: *The sequence $\{x_n\}$ is called* bounded *if there exists a real number B such that $|x_n| \leq B$ for all n. If there is a real number U such that $x_n \leq U$ for all n, then $\{x_n\}$ is said to be* bounded above *and U is called an* upper bound. *Similarly, if there is a real number L such that $x_n \geq L$ for all n, then $\{x_n\}$ is said to be* bounded below *and L is called a* lower bound.

Now, with precise meanings given to the terms, we state the result that we have already proved:

Theorem: *Every monotonic increasing sequence that is bounded above is convergent.*

9.3.1
EXERCISES

1. (a) Using the definitions just given, prove a generalization of the theorem proved in the text:

Theorem: *Every monotonic bounded sequence is convergent.*

(b) Give an example of a bounded sequence that is not convergent.
(c) Give an example of a monotonic sequence that is not convergent.

2. Which of the following sequences are monotonic? Which are bounded above? bounded below? bounded?

(a) $\left\{ \dfrac{1}{3^n} \right\}$,

(b) $\left\{ \dfrac{n+1}{n} \right\}$,

(c) $\{e^n\}$,

(d) $\left\{ \dfrac{n^2 + 5n}{n} \right\}$,

(e) $\{x_n\}$, where $x_1 = 5$, $x_{n+1} = \dfrac{1}{2}\left(x_n + \dfrac{10}{x_n}\right)$.

3. Suppose $x_1 < x_2 < x_3$, and $0 \leq x_{n+1} \leq x_n$ for all $n \geq 3$. That is, the sequence is monotonic decreasing from the 3rd term onward, and the sequence is bounded.
(a) $|x_n| \leq |\underline{\hspace{2cm}}|$ for all n. (Booby.)
(b) Is $\{x_n\}$ convergent?
(c) In considering whether any sequence is convergent, are the first three terms of consequence? Explain.
(d) Are the first 100 terms of consequence?
(e) Are the first 10,000,000 terms of consequence?

4. Which of the sequences in Exercise 2 converge?

5. We will help you to examine the behavior of the sequence $\{\sqrt[n]{n}\}$, first for monotonicity and finally for convergence. In each part proceed on your own as far as you can before going on to accept the next hint.

(a) Compute the first four terms of $\{\sqrt[n]{n}\}$ to two decimal places.

(b) Consider the two terms $x_n = \sqrt[n]{n}$ and $x_{n+1} = \sqrt[n+1]{n+1}$ with the idea of comparing magnitudes. If an inequality relation holds between these numbers, it will not be destroyed by raising both to the same power. Justify this statement and raise both to the power $n(n + 1)$. Then

$$x_n^{n(n+1)} = \underline{\hspace{1cm}} \quad \text{and} \quad x_{n+1}^{n(n+1)} = \underline{\hspace{1cm}}.$$

(c) Expand $x_{n+1}^{n(n+1)}$ by the binomial theorem.

(d) Prove that

$$x_{n+1}^{n(n+1)} \leq n^n + \frac{1}{1!}n^n + \frac{1}{2!}n^n + \cdots + \frac{1}{n!}n^n.$$

(e) Simplify the result of (d) to read

$$x_{n+1}^{n(n+1)} \leq n^n\left(1 + \frac{1}{1!} + \frac{1}{2!} + \cdots + \frac{1}{n!}\right).$$

Where have you seen the quantity in parentheses before? What is the least integer larger than this quantity?

(f) You now have $x_{n+1}^{n(n+1)} \leq 3n^n$. But $3n^n \leq x_n^{n(n+1)}$ for $n \geq \underline{\hspace{1cm}}$.

(g) You have shown that $x_{n+1}^{n(n+1)} \leq x_n^{n(n+1)}$ for $n \geq \underline{\hspace{1cm}}$.

(h) Finish the proof that $\{\sqrt[n]{n}\}$ is monotonic decreasing for $n \geq 3$.

(i) Give a lower bound for $\{\sqrt[n]{n}\}$ so that you may conclude that the sequence converges.

6. A recursive definition for a sequence $\{s_n\}$ is given by $s_1 = \sqrt{2}$, $s_{n+1} = \sqrt{2s_n}$.

(a) Write out the first five terms of the sequence.

(b) Is the sequence monotonic? Prove!

7. You have already proved that $\lim_{n \to \infty} (1 + \frac{1}{2} + \cdots + 1/n) = \infty$. (Do you recall how?) Comparing the sequence terms, prove that

$$\lim_{n \to \infty} \left(1 + \frac{1}{2^p} + \frac{1}{3^p} + \cdots + \frac{1}{n^p}\right) = \infty \qquad \text{for } 0 \leq p < 1.$$

8. (a) Let $0 < a < b$. Show that there is an $n \in \mathcal{R}a^+$, such that $nb < a$.

(b) Explain why Postulate A $\Rightarrow \mathcal{Z}^+$ is unbounded.

9. In Sec. 9.2 we stated that we required Postulate C to prove that the sequence $\{x_n\}$, where

$$x_n = 1 + \frac{1}{1!} + \frac{1}{2!} + \cdots + \frac{1}{n!},$$

converges.

In terms of logic we say that Postulate C is independent of the previous assumptions concerning $\mathscr{R}$, i.e., Postulate C cannot be proved from the remaining postulates. Prove that this is the case by showing that the field $\mathscr{R}a$ obeys Postulate OF but does not obey Postulate C. [*Hint:* All you need is one counterexample to Postulate C, i.e., one Cauchy sequence of rational numbers which does not converge to a rational number.]

10. The fact that Postulate A is independent of Postulate OF can be proved by exhibiting an ordered field that is non-Archimedean.

Let $\mathscr{Q}$ be the set of *rational functions*:

$$\mathscr{Q} = \{P/Q \mid P \text{ and } Q \text{ real polynomials, } Q \pm 0\}.$$

(a) Prove that $\mathscr{Q}$ is a field relative to ordinary algebraic addition and multiplication.

(b) An element $P_1/P_2 \in \mathscr{Q}(P_1, P_2$ polynomials) is called *positive* if and only if the product of the leading coefficients of P_1 and P_2 is positive. Show that this definition of *positive* satisfies the requirements for the set of positive elements of an ordered field (in Exercise 8 of Sec. 3.9.2).

(c) Part (b) shows that $\mathscr{Q}$ satisfies Postulate OF. Show by an example that $\mathscr{Q}$ is non-Archimedean.

Research Problem

11. Construct an example that shows Postulate A is independent of Postulate C.

Two ideas that we encountered—somewhat incidentally—in the first part of this section are worth pursuing a bit further. First, the notion of *boundedness*, which we defined for sequences, applies to sets in general:

(i) $\mathscr{S}$ is said to be *bounded above* if and only if there exists $U \in \mathscr{R}$ such that

$$\forall x \in \mathscr{S}, \qquad x \leq U.$$

U is called an *upper bound* for $\mathscr{S}$.

(ii) $\mathscr{S}$ is said to be *bounded below* if and only if there exists $L \in \mathscr{R}$ such that

$$\forall x \in \mathscr{S}, \qquad x \geq L.$$

L is called a *lower bound* for $\mathscr{S}$.

(iii) Finally, $\mathscr{S}$ is said to be *bounded* if and only if there exists $M \in \mathscr{R}$ such that

$$\forall x \in \mathscr{S}, \qquad |x| \leq M.$$

Second is the notion of *subsequence*. In the proof of the principal theorem of the section we used a subset $\{a_{n_0}, a_{n_1}, \ldots, a_{n_k}\}$ of the sequence $\{a_n\}$. If this subset is extended so that it, too, is a sequence, then we shall refer to it as a subsequence $\{a_{n_i}\}$ of the original sequence $\{a_n\}$.

The definition of subsequence can be made precise by recalling that a sequence is a function on $\mathcal{Z}^+$. Let the sequence $\{a_n\}$ be defined by f, so that

$$f(n) = a_n, \qquad n \in \mathcal{Z}^+.$$

Then a subsequence of $\{a_n\}$ is the function f on an infinite subset of $\mathcal{Z}^+$.

Example: Let $f(n) = a_n = (-1)^n$. We shall exhibit several subsequences:

$$\{a_{n_i}\}: \quad 1, 1, 1, \ldots; \qquad \text{i.e.,} \quad a_{n_i} = a_{2i} = 1.$$

$$\{a_{n_j}\}: \quad -1, -1, -1, \ldots; \quad \text{i.e.,} \quad a_{n_j} = a_{2j-1} = -1.$$

$$\{a_{n_k}\}: \quad 1, 1, -1, -1, \ldots; \quad \text{i.e.,} \quad a_{n_1} = a_2, a_{n_2} = a_4, a_{n_3} = a_5,$$

$$a_{n_4} = a_7, \ldots.$$

We shall make use of these notions in the exercises below.

9.3.2
EXERCISES

1. Let $A = \{x \mid x^2 < 2\}$.
(a) Is A bounded above? Is A bounded below?
(b) Find the smallest integer k_1 such that $k_1/1$ is an upper bound for A.
(c) Find the smallest integer k_2 such that $k_2/2$ is an upper bound for A.
(d) Find the smallest integers k_3, k_4 such that $k_3/3$ and $k_4/4$ are upper bounds for A.
(e) Is the sequence $\{k_n/n\}$ bounded? Is $\{k_n/n\}$ monotonic?
(f) What would you guess for $\lim_{n \to \infty} (k_n/n)$?
(g) The sequence $\{x_v\}$, where $x_v = k_{10^v}/10^v$, is obtained by taking the 1st, 10th, 100th, and 10^vth terms of $\{k_n/n\}$. $\{x_v\}$ is an example of a *subsequence* of $\{k_n/n\}$. Concerning $\{x_v\}$, answer the questions: Is it bounded? monotonic? convergent?
(h) Write out the terms of $\{x_v\}$ for $v = 1, 2, 3, 4, 5$.

2. Which of the following sequences are monotonic? bounded above? bounded below? bounded? convergent?
(a) $\{3^{1/n}\}$,
(b) $\{1 - (n + 1)/n\}$,
(c) $\{e^{1/n}\}$,
(d) $\{a_n\}$, where $a_1 = 1$, $a_2 = 2$, $a_{n+2} = (a_n + a_{n+1})/2$,
(e) $\{b_n\}$, where $b_n = [\sqrt{n}]$.

3. (a) Does $\{a_n\}$ converge if $a_n = (-1)^n(n - 1)/n$. Is $\{a_n\}$ bounded?
(b) Exhibit three convergent subsequences of $\{a_n\}$.

4. Let A be any set of real numbers bounded from above. For any n, let k_n be the smallest integer such that k_n/n is an upper bound of A. Show that $x_v = k_{10^v}/10^v$ is a monotonic decreasing sequence that is bounded below.

403

(a) Restate the definition of k_n: k_n is an integer, na _____ k_n for all $a \in A$ (what relation?), and if k is an integer such that $na \leq k$ for all $a \in A$, then k_n _____ k (what relation?)

(b) Apply this definition to $n = 10^v$ and to $n = 10^{v+1}$. How, then, do x_v and x_{v+1} compare?

(c) Let a_0 be any fixed element of A. What is the relation between a_0 and x_v for any v?

5. Let $\lim_{n \to \infty} x_n = A$.

(a) If $\{x_{n_k}\}$ converges, what is $\lim_{n_k \to \infty} x_{n_k}$?

(b) Does $\{x_{n_k}\}$ necessarily converge?

6. A sequence that converges to zero is called a *null sequence*.

(a) State the neighborhood definition of *limit* for null sequences.

(b) If $\{x_n\}$ and $\{y_n\}$ are null sequences, prove that $\{z_n\}$, where $z_n = x_n + y_n$, is also a null sequence. (It is easier to write $\{z_n\}$ simply as $\{x_n + y_n\}$.)

(c) Is $\{x_n - y_n\}$ also a null sequence if $\{x_n\}$ and $\{y_n\}$ are both null sequences?

(d) Give an example of a null sequence that is not monotonic.

(e) Give an example of a null sequence in which the terms alternate in sign.

(f) If $\{a_n\}$ is the sequence you used in (d) and $\{b_n\}$ the sequence you used in (e), find $\lim_{n \to \infty} a_n b_n$.

7. Let $\{a_n\}$ be a null sequence, and let $\varepsilon > 0$. Then there exists n_0 so that $|a_n - \underline{\quad}| < \varepsilon$ for $n > n_0$. Therefore, $\{a_{n_0}, a_{n_0+1}, \ldots\}$ is a bounded set.

Give a bound (the smallest number you can) so that $|a_n| < \underline{\quad}$. Is the set $\{a_1, a_2, \ldots, a_{n_0-1}\}$ bounded?

Let $|a_m|$ be the largest of $|a_1|, |a_2|, \ldots, |a_{n_0-1}|$. We write as usual: $|a_m| = \max \{|a_1|, |a_2|, \ldots, |a_{n_0-1}|\}$. Then $\{a_n\}$ is a bounded sequence, a bound for which is

$$M = \max \{|a_m|, \underline{\quad}\}.$$

8. (a) Prove that every convergent sequence is bounded. (If you need a hint, look at Exercise 7.)

(b) If $\lim_{n \to \infty} x_n = x$, prove that $\{y_n\}$, where $y_n = x_n - x$, is a null sequence. ($\{y_n\}$ could have been written $\{x_n - x\}$.)

9. Let $\{b_n\}$ be a bounded sequence that is not necessarily convergent, and let $\{a_n\}$ be a null sequence. Investigate $\{a_n b_n\}$. Let $|b_n| < K$ for all n, and let $\delta > 0$ be given. There is an n_0 so that $|a_n - \underline{\quad}| < \delta$. Then

$$|a_n b_n - \underline{\quad}| = |b_n| \, |a_n - \underline{\quad}| < \underline{\quad} \delta.$$

What is $\lim_{n \to \infty} a_n b_n$? Given $\epsilon > 0$, prove that there is $n_1 \in \mathscr{Z}^+$ so that $|a_n b_n - \underline{\quad}| < \varepsilon$ for $n > n_1$.

10. Let $\{x_n\}$ be convergent and *not* a null sequence.

(a) Can $x_n = 0$ for any n?

(b) Can $x_n = 0$ for five or more values of n?

(c) Prove that the set of integers $\{i \mid x_i = 0\}$ is bounded.

(d) The result of (c) states: At most a finite number of x_n can be zero if $\{x_n\}$ is convergent and not null. If you omit from $\{x_n\}$ all the terms which are zero, you still have an infinite sequence. Explain.

(e) Assuming $\{x_n\}$ has no zeros, prove that the sequence $\{x_n^{-1}\}$ is bounded. (Do you think $\{x_n^{-1}\}$ is convergent?)

11. The Snowflake Curve (see Fig. 9-5). Begin with an equilateral triangle F_1, and call the perimeter P_1. On the middle third of each side, erect an equilateral triangle pointing outward. Then erase the common parts of the old triangle and the three newly constructed triangles. Call P_2 the perimeter of the newly obtained figure F_2. On the middle third of each side of F_2, erect an equilateral triangle and erase the parts common to F_2 and the new triangles. Call F_3 the figure obtained and call the perimeter P_3. Continuing the process you get closer to the so-called *snowflake curve*.

F_1 F_2 F_3

Figure 9-5

Let each side of F_1 be unit length. Then $P_1 = 3$.
(a) Find P_2, P_3, P_4.
(b) Find a general formula for P_n.
(c) Is $\{P_n\}$ a bounded sequence?
(d) The length of the snowflake curve is defined as $\lim_{n \to \infty} P_n$. What is the length of the snowflake curve?
(e) Let A_n be the area of F_n. Is $\{A_n\}$ bounded?

12. The sequence $(1 + \frac{1}{2})$, $(1 + \frac{1}{2})(1 - \frac{1}{3})$, $(1 + \frac{1}{2})(1 - \frac{1}{3})(1 + \frac{1}{4}), \ldots$, can be defined precisely by the recursive definition:

$$x_1 = 1 + \tfrac{1}{2},$$

$$x_n = \left(1 + \frac{(-1)^{n+1}}{n+1}\right) x_{n-1}.$$

(a) Experiment to determine guesses for the formulas for the odd and even terms, x_{2k+1} and x_{2k}. Then verify your guesses.
(b) Find the limits of the subsequences $\{x_{2k+1}\}$ and $\{x_{2k}\}$.
(c) What is $\lim_{n \to \infty} x_n$?

13. (a) Let s be a nonzero constant and suppose $\{(x_n - s)/(x_n + s)\}$ is a null sequence. Prove that $\{x_n\}$ converges to s.
(b) Let $\lim_{n \to \infty} |x_{n+1}/x_n| = r < 1$. Prove x_n is a null sequence.

405

14. (a) If A and B are finite sets of real numbers and A is contained in B, and

$$\max_{x \in B} x = 1,$$

what is the greatest possible value for $\max_{x \in A} x$?

    (b) If $\{x_n\}$ is a sequence and $y_n = \max_{1 \le k \le n} x_k$, can y_{n+1} be less than y_n?

15. (a) Suppose $x_n \ge 0$ for all n, and $\{x_n\}$ is convergent. Can $\lim_{n \to \infty} x_n < 0$? If $A < 0$, what is the least possible value of $|x_n - A|$?

    (b) If $x_n \le A$ for all n and $\{x_n\}$ is convergent, what is the greatest possible value of $\lim_{n \to \infty} x_n$?

    (c) Suppose $x_n \le A$ for all $n > 100$ and $\{x_n\}$ is convergent, what is the greatest possible value of $\lim_{n \to \infty} x_n$?

9.4

Least Upper Bound Let the sequence $\{x_n\}$ be defined by

$$k_n = [2^n \sqrt{2}] \qquad \text{for } n \ge 1.$$

The integer k_n can also be defined as the largest integer k such that $k^2 \ge 2^{2n+1}$. For example, $k_1 = 2$ $(2^2 < 2^3 = 8 < 3^2)$, $k_2 = 5$, $k_3 = \underline{\hspace{2cm}}$.
Practically no laws of regularity are known about the integers k_n. For example, what proportion of them are odd? Nobody knows.

Let us formulate the question precisely. Let

$$x_n = \frac{\text{number of odd } k_r\text{'s}}{n}, \qquad 1 \le r \le n.$$

Does $\{x_n\}$ have a limit as n increases? We might expect that $\lim_{n \to \infty} x_n = \frac{1}{2}$.

Make a table:

n	2^{2n+1}	k_n	x_n
1	8	2	0
2	32	5	$\frac{1}{2} = 0.5$
3	128	11	$\frac{2}{3} = 0.666\ldots$
4	512	22	$\frac{1}{2} = 0.5$
5	2048	45	$\frac{3}{5} = 0.6$
6	——	—	——
7	——	—	——
8	——	—	——
9	——	—	——
10	——	—	——

Does there appear to be any pattern in the behavior of the numbers x_n? Certainly $x_n \le 1$ for all n. In other words, 1 is an upper bound of the sequence $\{x_n\}$. What is the *least* upper bound?

No one knows, but we can compute it to any required degree of accuracy. Let

$$y_1 = x_1, \quad y_2 = \max \{x_1, x_2\}, \quad y_3 = \max \{x_1, x_2, x_3\},$$

and, in general,

$$y_n = \max \{x_1, \ldots, x_n\} = \max \{x_r \mid 1 \le r \le n\} \quad (\text{or } \max_{1 \le r \le n} x_r).$$

Compute y_n for $1 \le n \le 10$. Do you notice anything about this sequence?

Can y_2 be less than y_1? _____ (yes/no). Can y_{11} be less than y_{12}? _____. Can the tallest student in your class be taller than the tallest student in your school? _____. Can the largest of the first 100 x_n's be larger than the largest of the first 101 x_n's? _____.	*no* *no* *no* *no*

In general, we have

$$y_n \underline{\hspace{1cm}} y_{n+1}, \quad \forall\, n \in \mathscr{Z}^+. \quad (\le/\ge)$$

<table>
<tr><td>The sequence $\{y_n\}$ is monotonic _____ (increasing/decreasing).</td><td>increasing</td></tr>
</table>

Is the sequence $\{y_n\}$ bounded? Since

$$x_n \le \underline{\hspace{1cm}}, \quad \forall\, n \in \mathscr{Z}^+,$$

we have

$$y_n \le \underline{\hspace{1cm}}, \quad \forall\, n \in \mathscr{Z}^+.$$

Therefore, $y = \lim_{n \to \infty} y_n$ exists, and

$$y_n \underline{\hspace{1cm}} y, \quad \forall\, n \in \mathscr{Z}^+. \quad (\le/\ge)$$

$$\text{But } x_n \underline{\hspace{1cm}} y_n \ (\le/\ge), \quad \forall\, n \in \mathscr{Z}^+; \text{ so that}$$

$$x_n \underline{\hspace{1cm}} y \quad \forall\, n \in \mathscr{Z}^+. \quad (\le/\ge)$$

Therefore, y is a(n) _____ (upper/lower) bound of sequence $\{x_n\}$. Is it the *least*?

Suppose that A is an upper bound of $\{x_n\}$, i.e.,

$$x_n \underline{\hspace{1cm}} A, \quad \forall\, n \in \mathscr{Z}^+. \quad (\le/\ge).$$

Can y_n be greater than A? We have

$$y_n \underline{\hspace{1cm}} A, \quad \forall\, n \in \mathscr{Z}. \quad (\le/\ge).$$

Therefore, we conclude that

$$y = \lim_{n \to \infty} y_n \underline{\hspace{1cm}} A. \quad (\le/\ge).$$

Can any upper bound of $\{x_n\}$ be smaller than y? _____ (yes/no).	*no*

Therefore, y is the *least upper* bound of $\{x_n\}$. We denote it by

$$y = \operatorname*{lub}_{n \ge 1} x_n \quad (\text{or } \operatorname{lub} \{x_n \mid n \ge 1\}.$$

The right-margin answers, in order: $\le$, 1, 1, $\le$, $\le$, $\le$, *upper*, $\le$, $\le$, $\le$.

It has the following properties:

(a) $x_n \leq y$, $\forall\, n \in \mathscr{Z}^+$.

(b) If $x_n \leq A$, $\forall\, n \in \mathscr{Z}^+$, then $y \leq A$.

Property (b) can be rephrased:

(b) If $A < y$, then there is an n such that $A < x_n$.

In the same way we can prove that if $\{x_n\}$ is any sequence which is bounded from above, then $\{x_n\}$ has a *least upper bound*, which can be defined by properties (a) and (b).

For the sequence $\{x_n\}$ discussed above, we do not know the value of $\operatorname*{lub}_{n \geq 1} x_n$.

We can give another proof which applies to an arbitrary nonempty bounded set $\mathscr{S}$ of real numbers. While this method could be used computationally in theory, there are steps which would be difficult to carry out in practice. This approach is based on the principle that *every non-empty set of positive integers has a smallest member*. We shall have more to say about this principle in Chapter 10.

By shifting the origin if necessary, we may assume that $\mathscr{S}$ contains some positive number c. For $n > 0$, let $x_n = k_n/10^n$, where k_n is the smallest integer such that x_n is an upper bound of $\mathscr{S}$. For example, if $\mathscr{S} = \{x \mid x < e\}$, then

$$x_1 = \frac{28}{10}, \qquad k_1 = 28,$$

$$x_2 = \frac{272}{10^2}, \qquad k_2 = 272,$$

$$x_3 = \frac{2719}{10^3}, \qquad k_3 = 2719,$$

and so on. In other words, k_n is the smallest member of the set $\mathscr{B}_n$ of integers k such that $k \geq 10^n s$, $\forall\, s \in \mathscr{S}$. (Why is $\mathscr{B}_n$ nonempty? We assumed that $\mathscr{S}$ is bounded, so that there is an A such that $A \geq s$, $\forall\, s \in \mathscr{S}$. Therefore,

$$10^n A \geq 10^n s, \qquad \forall\, s \in \mathscr{S},$$

so that $\mathscr{B}_n$ contains all integers $k \geq 10^n A$.)

The integer k_n has the two properties:

(a) $k_n \underline{\qquad} 10^n s$, $\forall\, s \in \mathscr{S}$, $(\leq/\geq)$ $\geq$

(b) $k_n - 1 \underline{\qquad} 10^n s$ for some $s \in \mathscr{S}$. $(\leq/\geq)$ $\leq$

What is the relation between x_n and x_{n+1}? The relation $x_n \geq x_{n+1}$ is equivalent to $\underline{\qquad} k_n \geq k_{n+1}$. By property (a), 10

$$10 k_n \underline{\qquad} 10^{n+1} s, \qquad \forall\, s \in \mathscr{S}.$$ $\geq$

Therefore $10k_n \in \mathscr{B}_{n+1}$. But the smallest member of $\mathscr{B}_{n+1}$ is ______. This implies the desired relation between k_n and k_{n+1}, and, therefore, the desired relation between x_n and x_{n+1}. In other words, $\{x_n\}$ is monotonic ______________ (increasing/decreasing). | k_{n+1}

decreasing

Is $\{x_n\}$ bounded? Since x_n is an ______ bound of $\mathscr{S}$, and $c \in \mathscr{S}$, we know | *upper*

$$x_n ____ c, \qquad \forall n. \qquad (\leq/\geq).$$ | $\geq$

Therefore, the sequence $\{x_n\}$ is ______________. Let $x = \lim_{n\to\infty} x_n$. Since x_n is an ______ bound of $\mathscr{S}$, we have | *convergent* | *upper*

$$x_n ____ s, \qquad \forall s \in \mathscr{S} \qquad (\leq/\geq).$$ | $\geq$

Hold s fixed, and let $n \to \infty$. We obtain

$$____ \geq s, \qquad \forall s \in \mathscr{S}.$$ | x

Hence, x is an ______ bound of $\mathscr{S}$. Is it the *least*? | *upper*

Suppose that A is any upper bound of $\mathscr{S}$. We want to prove that A ____ x $(\leq/\geq)$. Since $y \geq s$ for the particular s mentioned in property (b), we find that | $\geq$

$$A > \frac{____}{10^n} = x_n - ____.$$ | $k_n - 1$, 10^{-n}

Letting $n \to \infty$, we obtain

$$A \geq ____.$$ | x

We have thus proved the following:

Theorem L: *Every nonempty bounded set of real numbers has a least upper bound.*

If x is the least upper bound of $\mathscr{S}$, then
(a) *$x \geq s$ for all s in $\mathscr{S}$ and*
(b) *if $y \geq s$ for all s in $\mathscr{S}$, then $y \geq x$.*

9.4.1 EXERCISES

1. Let $\mathscr{S}$ be the set of numbers

$$x_n = \frac{1}{0!} + \frac{1}{1!} + \frac{1}{2!} + \cdots + \frac{1}{n!}$$

and k_n be defined as in the text. Call $u_n = k_n/10^n$ and $\lim_{n\to\infty} u_n = U$.

(a) Give a lower bound for $\{u_n\}$.
(b) Is x_3 a lower bound for $\{u_n\}$?
(c) Is x_{100} a lower bound for $\{u_n\}$?

(d) Is U a lower bound for $\{u_n\}$?

(e) Is U the greatest lower bound for $\{u_n\}$?

(f) Recall that we defined the number e as $e = \lim\limits_{n \to \infty} x_n$. Is e an upper bound for $\{x_n\}$?

(g) If $\varepsilon > 0$, can $e - \varepsilon$ be an upper bound for $\{x_n\}$?

(h) Only one of the following can be true: $e < U$, $e = U$, $e > U$. Which one? Check to see if you have proved your answer in the course of answering previous parts of this question. If you haven't, then prove it now!

2. In Exercise 1, use your estimate of $x_m - x_n$ for $m > n$ to obtain an upper bound for the numbers x_m, $m > n$. Apply this result to obtain an estimate for $U - x_m$. Does this difference approach 0?

3. *Prove:* The limit of a bounded monotonic increasing function is its least upper bound.

4. A sequence $\{\mathscr{I}_n\}$ of closed intervals is given by

$$\mathscr{I}_n = \left[2 + \frac{n}{n+1},\ 3 + \frac{1}{n}\right].$$

(a) Prove that the $\mathscr{I}_n$ are nested.

(b) What is the least upper bound of the left-hand endpoints?

(c) What is the greatest lower bound of the right-hand endpoints?

5. *Is e a rational number?* We shall help you to investigate. Let

$$x_n = \frac{1}{0!} + \frac{1}{1!} + \frac{1}{2!} + \cdots + \frac{1}{n!}.$$

Then $e = \lim\limits_{n \to \infty} x_n$. At the outset of Sec. 9.2, we showed that if $m > n$, then

$$x_m - x_n < \frac{1}{n!\,n}.$$

(Can you prove this inequality without referring to the text?) Now justify the related inequality:

$$e - x_n < \frac{1}{n!\,n}.$$

You already know that $e > x_n$, so the number e is "trapped," as described by the inequality,

$$x_n < e < x_n + \frac{1}{n!\,n}.$$

(Is this true for all n?) Now suppose $e = p/q$, where p and q are positive integers. Then

$$x_q < \frac{p}{q} < x_q + \frac{1}{q!\,q}.$$

If you want to multiply x_q by A to get an integer Ax_q, what would be the smallest positive number you could use for A? Use it to write

$$Ax_q < \frac{Ap}{q} < Ax_q + \frac{A}{q!\,q}.$$

Which terms in this inequality are integers and which are not? What is the smallest possible difference between distinct integers? Can $A/q!q$ be as large as that?

6. From Postulate OF alone we are guaranteed only the existence of rational numbers in $\mathscr{R}$. Even $\sqrt{3}$ does not exist as a consequence of the ordered field postulate, for without Postulate C we cannot be sure that the iteration

$$x_1 = 2, \qquad x_{n+1} = \tfrac{1}{2}\left(x_n + \frac{3}{x_n}\right)$$

converges. So it may justifiably be said that Postulate C can be used to *define* irrational numbers. In fact, every irrational number can be defined as the limit of a convergent sequence of rationals. For this reason, the assumption of a limit for every Cauchy sequence is called a *completeness postulate*; it is used to *complete* the system $\mathscr{R}$ from $\mathscr{R}a$.

(a) Give a sequence of rationals that you can use to define $\sqrt{2}$. Do the same for $\sqrt{5}$.

(b) Give a sequence of rationals that define $\sqrt[3]{2}$. Do the same for $\sqrt[3]{5}$.

(c) What sequence of rationals can you use to define e?

(d) Can a sequence of rationals be used to define a rational?

(e) How would you go about determining a sequence of rationals that would define π?

7. In Exercise 6 you learned that real numbers can be defined as limits of convergent sequences. In particular, you can choose monotonic sequences: If $\{a_n\}$ is monotonic increasing and bounded, then the number r defined by $\{a_n\}$ is $\lim\limits_{n \to \infty} a_n = r$. The least upper bound of $\{a_n\}$ is _____.

(a) Define $\sqrt[3]{2}$ by some monotonic sequence; i.e., exhibit a sequence, the limit of which is $\sqrt[3]{2}$.

(b) What is the least upper bound of $\mathscr{S} = \{x \mid x^3 < 2\}$?

(c) Isn't it just as simple to define $\sqrt[3]{2}$ as the least upper bound of $\mathscr{S}$?

(d) Define $\sqrt[3]{2}$ as the greatest lower bound of some set.

8. Some authors prefer to take as a postulate our Theorem L: *Every nonempty bounded set of real numbers has a least upper bound.* We proved Theorem L on the basis of Postulates A and C:

$$\text{(Postulate A} \land \text{Postulate C)} \Rightarrow \text{Theorem L.}$$

Is the converse true (assuming $\mathscr{R}$ is an ordered field)?

(a) First, we shall help you to prove the Archimedean property: If $a > 0$ and b any number in $\mathscr{R}$, then there is an $n \in \mathscr{Z}^+$ such that $na > b$.

Suppose there is not such an n. Then

$$na \underline{\quad\quad} b, \qquad \forall\, n \in \mathscr{Z}^+.$$

Is the set $\{na\}$ bounded? What does Theorem L tell you?

(b) If $\alpha = \text{lub}\,\{na\}$ and $\varepsilon > 0$, then there is an integer m such that

$$\alpha - \varepsilon \,?\, ma \qquad \text{(fill in the relation),}$$

$$\alpha \,?\, ma + \underline{\quad\quad}.$$

The only restriction on ε is that it be positive. So if $0 < \varepsilon \le a$, you have

$$\alpha \, ? \, (m + 1)a.$$

What's the matter with this statement? What can you conclude?

(c) Prove that Theorem L $\Rightarrow$ Postulate C. [*Hint:* Show that any Cauchy sequence is bounded.]

9. In the previous section, we proved Theorem M: *Every monotonic bounded sequence of real numbers converges.* In this section we proved that

$$\text{Theorem M} \Rightarrow \text{Theorem L}.$$

(a) Prove that the converse is also true, completing the set of equivalences

$$(\text{Post. A} \wedge \text{Post. C}) \Leftrightarrow (\text{Post. A} \wedge \text{Post.C}')$$

$$\Leftrightarrow \text{Theorem M} \Leftrightarrow \text{Theorem L}.$$

These logical equivalences indicate why it is possible to take any one of Postulate C, Postulate C', Theorem M, or Theorem L as a *completeness postulate*. The first person to successfully meet the logical need for such a postulate, which distinguishes $\mathscr{R}$ from $\mathscr{R}a$, was Richard Dedekind (1831–1916).† The postulate he used is different from— but equivalent to—Theorem L and, of course, also Theorem M.

(b) Look up Dedekind's work and find out what he used as a completeness postulate.

10. Let $\{x_n\}$ be a bounded sequence. Define the sequence $\{y_n\}$ by

$$y_n = \operatorname*{lub}_{k \ge n} x_k.$$

(a) Under what circumstances is $y_1 > y_2$?
(b) Under what circumstances is $y_1 < y_2$?
(c) Is the sequence $\{y_n\}$ monotonic? If so, is it increasing or decreasing? Is it bounded?
(d) Let $y = \lim_{n \to \infty} y_n$. (Why does y exist?) Suppose that

$$|y_n - y| < \varepsilon \qquad \text{for } n > n_0.$$

For which values of n is $x_n < y + \varepsilon$? For how many values of n is $x_n > y - \varepsilon$?

11. In proving Theorem L in the text, did we use fully the assumption that $\mathscr{S}$ is bounded? If $\mathscr{S}$ has an upper bound but not a lower bound, must $\mathscr{S}$ still have a least upper bound?

12. If x is the least upper bound of $\mathscr{S}$, when does x belong to $\mathscr{S}$? Give examples where x is in $\mathscr{S}$ and where x is not in $\mathscr{S}$.

A Word on Notation: The word *supremum* is preferred by many mathematicians as a synonym for *least upper bound*. Its only advantage is that a single word replaces three words. Even this Latin word is considered too long so we abbreviate and write *sup* (pronounced "soup"). The standard abbreviation for least upper bound is *lub*, which you might pronounce to rhyme with "rub"—but then how would you pronounce

† Richard Dedekind, *Stetigkeit und Irrationale Zahlen* (1872). Translated as "Continuity and Irrational Numbers," in *Essays on the Theory of Numbers* (New York: Dover, 1963).

glb (greatest lower bound)? For those who prefer Latin, the alternative to greatest lower bound is *infinimum*, abbreviated *inf* and pronounced as it reads.

It is often useful, as in Exercise 8, to have a simple notation for the *sup* of a set $\mathscr{S}$. Very simply we could write: sup $\mathscr{S}$. However, sometimes special conditions require modifications. For example, in Exercise 8 we could have written

$$\alpha = \sup_{n \in \mathscr{Z}^+} \{na\} \quad \text{or} \quad \alpha = \operatorname*{lub}_{n \in \mathscr{Z}^+} \{na\}.$$

13. Compute the following:

(a) $\displaystyle\sup_{n \in \mathscr{Z}^+} \left\{ 1 + \frac{1}{n} \right\}$,

(f) $\displaystyle\operatorname*{glb}_{-1 \le x \le 1} \{2x - 3\}$,

(b) $\displaystyle\inf_{n \in \mathscr{Z}^+} \left\{ 1 + \frac{1}{n} \right\}$,

(g) $\displaystyle\sup_{-1 \le x < 1} |2x - 3|$,

(c) $\displaystyle\inf_{x \in \mathscr{R}} \{x^2 + 1\}$,

(h) $\displaystyle\inf_{-2 < x < 5} |2[x] - 3|$,

(d) $\displaystyle\sup_{x \in \mathscr{R}} \{1 + 3x - x^2\}$,

(i) $\displaystyle\operatorname*{glb}_{-2 < x < 5} [2x - 3]$,

(e) $\displaystyle\operatorname*{lub}_{-1 \le x \le 1} \{2x - 3\}$,

(j) $\displaystyle\sup_{\substack{-1 < x < 1 \\ -1 < y < 1}} (x^2 + y^2)$.

14. Find $\displaystyle\lim_{n \to \infty} x_n$ if you are given that $\displaystyle\sup_{n \ge 1} \left| \frac{x_{n+1}}{x_n} \right| < 1.$

9.5

Limit Theorems Suppose we have two convergent sequences $\{x_n\}$ and $\{y_n\}$. Can we be sure that $\{x_n + y_n\}$ is also convergent? And, if so, can we get $\displaystyle\lim_{n \to \infty} (x_n + y_n)$ if we know $\displaystyle\lim_{n \to \infty} x_n$ and $\displaystyle\lim_{n \to \infty} y_n$? For example, suppose that you know the limits

$$\lim_{n \to \infty} \frac{3n^2 - 2n + 1}{n^2 - 3} \quad \text{and} \quad \lim_{n \to \infty} \frac{2n + 3}{\sqrt{n^2 + 1}}.$$

Is this any help in determining

$$\lim_{n \to \infty} \left(\frac{3n^2 - 2n + 1}{n^2 - 3} + \frac{2n + 3}{\sqrt{n^2 + 1}} \right)?$$

The operation of taking the limit yields a real number for every convergent sequence. So the limit operation is a function which, for the moment, we will call L. The domain of L is the set of convergent sequences. In order to simplify the discussion in this section we will find it convenient to designate a sequence $\{x_n\}$ by the single letter x. Similarly $\{y_n\}$ may be designated by y; and so on. In this shorthand, $\displaystyle\lim_{n \to \infty} x_n$ will be written $L(x)$.

What are the properties of the limit function L?

Question 1:   If $L(x)$ and $L(y)$ are defined, is $L(x + y)$ also defined?

If $L(x)$ is defined, then for every $\varepsilon > 0$, there is an n_0 such that

$$|x_n - L(x)| < \underline{\qquad}, \qquad \forall \underline{\qquad} > n_0.$$ ε, n

Also, since $L(y)$ is defined, there is an m_0 such that

$$|y_n - L(y)| < \varepsilon, \qquad \forall \underline{\qquad} > \underline{\qquad}.$$ n, m_0

How will we know whether $L(x + y)$ is defined? $L(x + y)$ exists if $\lim_{n \to \infty} (x_n + y_n)$ exists. What does your experience tell you about the existence of $\lim_{n \to \infty} (x_n + y_n)$? And what would you guess it to be? If your guess is correct, then: For every $\varepsilon > 0$, there is k_0 such that

$$\left|(x_n + y_n) - (\underline{\qquad})\right| < \varepsilon, \qquad \forall n > k_0.$$ $L(x) + L(y)$

Let's try to prove this.

$$\left|(x_n + y_n) - (\underline{\qquad})\right| = \left|(x_n - L(x)) + (y_n - \underline{\qquad})\right|$$ $L(x) + L(y),$ $L(y)$

$$\leq |x_n - L(x)| + \left|y_n - \underline{\qquad}\right|.$$ Ly

But for $n > n_0$ and $n > m_0$, you already have a bound for the right member. Therefore, for $n > k_0 = \max\{n_0, m_0\}$,

$$\left|(x_n + y_n) - (L(x) + \underline{\qquad})\right| < \underline{\qquad} + \underline{\qquad} = 2\underline{\qquad}.$$ $L(y), \varepsilon, \varepsilon, \varepsilon$

The number $2\underline{\qquad}$ is arbitrarily small, so this actually proves ε

$$L(x + y) = L(x) + L(y).$$

Although it is not logically necessary, some people prefer to have their inequalities conform to the letter of definition of limit. They would therefore prefer to conclude with an inequality

$$|x_n + y_n - (L(x) + L(y))| < \varepsilon.$$

If you are in this camp, you can see how to manage this by reviewing your argument and making the necessary alterations. You go back and say: Let $\varepsilon > 0$ be given. Call $\delta = \varepsilon/2$. Then there is n_0 such that

$$|x_n - L(x)| < \delta, \qquad \forall n > n_0$$

and there is m_0 such that

$$|y_n - L(y)| < \delta, \qquad \forall n > m_0.$$

Now taking $k = \max\{n_0, m_0\}$, we have

$$\left|x_n + y_n - (L(x) + L(y))\right| \le \left|x_n - L(x)\right| + \left|y_n - L(y)\right| < \delta + \delta = \varepsilon.$$

Here you have the answer to Question 1, but you also have much more! You know that

$$\lim_{n \to \infty} (x_n + y_n) = \lim_{n \to \infty} \underline{\qquad} + \lim_{n \to \infty} \underline{\qquad}.$$

Now, as an exercise, you carry out a similar proof for $\lim_{n \to \infty} (x_n - y_n)$.

Question 2:   If $L(x)$ and $L(y)$ are defined, is $L(x \cdot y)$ also defined? ($x \cdot y$ stands for the sequence $\{x_n y_n\}$.)

In answering Question 1, you discovered that the limit of the sum of two sequences is the _____ of the limits of the two sequences. If this result carries over to products, you will have: The limit of the product of two sequences is the _____ of the limits of the sequences.

sum

product

Let's try to prove this. We can use the fact that $L(x)$ and $L(y)$ exist, and we have to prove that

(1) $\left|x_n y_n - L(x)L(y)\right|$

can be made arbitrarily small by taking n large. At our disposal are the expressions

(2) $\left|x_n - L(x)\right|$ and $\left|y_n - L(y)\right|$,

which can be made arbitrarily small. So let's manipulate the absolute value (1) in order to be able to use the expression (2). We can write

$$
\begin{aligned}
\left|x_n y_n - L(x)L(y)\right| &= \left|(x_n - L(x))y_n + \underline{\quad}(y_n - L(y))\right| && L(x) \\
&\le \left|(x_n - L(x))y_n\right| + \left|\underline{\quad}(y_n - L(y))\right| && L(x) \\
&\le \left|x_n - L(x)\right|\left|y_n\right| + \underline{\quad}\left|y_n - L(y)\right|. && |L(x)|
\end{aligned}
$$

If $\delta > 0$ is given, then there is a $k_0 = k_0(\delta)$ such that

$$\left|y_n - L(y)\right| < \delta, \qquad \forall\, n > k_0(\delta),$$

and an $m_0 = m_0(\delta)$ such that

$$\left|x_n - L(x)\right| < \delta, \qquad \forall\, n > m_0(\delta).$$

To complete the estimate of $x_n y_n - L(x)L(y)$, we note that $\{y_n\}$ is bounded (see Exercise 8 of Sec. 9.3.2): There exists $B > 0$ such that $\left|y_n\right| \le B$. Therefore, if $n > \max\{k_0(\delta), m_0(\delta)\}$, we have

$$
\begin{aligned}
\left|x_n y_n - L(x)L(y)\right| &< \underline{\quad}\delta + \underline{\quad}\delta. && B, |L(x)| \\
&< (\underline{\quad})\delta. && B + |L(x)|
\end{aligned}
$$

So, if $\varepsilon > 0$ is given, we choose $\delta = \dfrac{\varepsilon}{B + |L(x)|}$ and $n_0 = \max\{k_0, m_0\}$.
This assures that

$$|x_n y_n - L(x)L(y)| < \varepsilon, \qquad \forall\, n > n_0.$$

Question 3: If $L(x)$ and $L(y)$ are defined, is $L(x/y)$ defined? (x/y represents $\{x_n/y_n\}$.)

Let's confine our attention to the special case $\{1/y_n\}$. If you have the answer in this special case, you can easily go to the general case. How?

If the pattern of answers to our questions continues, you would suppose that: The limit of the quotient of two sequences is the _____ of the limits of the sequences. This will be established if you can show that $|1/y_n - 1/L(y)|$ can be made arbitrarily small by taking n sufficiently large. We might expect this to be true only if $L(y) \neq$ _____. Let's investigate.

quotient

0

$$\left|\frac{1}{y_n} - \frac{1}{L(y)}\right| = \left|\frac{\rule{1.5cm}{0.4pt}}{y_n L(y)}\right|.$$

$L(y) - y_n$

Can the numerator be made arbitrarily small? What must be true of the denominator in order to know that the entire fraction becomes arbitrarily small?

First we need a lower bound for $|y_n|$. If $\delta > 0$, there is $k_0(\delta) \in \mathscr{L}^+$ such that

$$|y_n - L(y)| < \delta, \qquad \forall\, n > k_0(\delta).$$

Therefore,

$$
\begin{aligned}
|y_n| &= |L(y) - (L(y) - y_n)| \\
&\geq |L(y)| \,\underline{\quad}\, |L(y) - y_n| \quad (+/-) \\
&> \underline{\quad} - \delta \quad \text{for } n > k_0(\delta).
\end{aligned}
$$

$-$

$|L(y)|$

Then

$$|y_n| > \frac{|L(y)|}{2}, \qquad \text{provided} \quad \delta \leq \underline{\quad}.$$

$\dfrac{|L(y)|}{2}$

We can certainly place such a restriction on δ, so we have obtained a bound for $|y_n|$, $n > k_0(\delta)$.
This means that

$$n > k_0(\delta) \Rightarrow \left|\frac{1}{y_n} - \frac{1}{L(y)}\right| \leq \underline{\quad}\delta,$$

$\dfrac{2}{|L(y)|^2}$

which is less than ε if $\delta <$ _____ . Thus, if

$$\delta < \min\left\{\frac{|L(y)|}{2}, \underline{\hspace{1cm}}\right\},$$

we have

$$\left|\frac{1}{y_n} - \frac{1}{L(y)}\right| < \varepsilon \qquad \text{for } n > k_0(\delta).$$

These theorems enable us to use simple results about limits to obtain limits of more complicated sequences, without always returning to the original definition.

Now that we have these results, let's apply them to some problems.

Example 1:

$$\lim_{n \to \infty} \left(\frac{1}{n} + \frac{3}{n^2}\right).$$

This is of the form $L(x + y)$, where

$$x_n = \frac{1}{n} \quad \text{and} \quad y_n = \frac{3}{n^2}, \qquad n \in \mathscr{L}^+.$$

What is $L(x)$? What is $L(y)$? Now use the fact that

$$L(x + y) = \underline{\hspace{1cm}} + \underline{\hspace{1cm}}$$

to obtain

$$\lim_{n \to \infty} \left(\frac{1}{n} + \frac{3}{n^2}\right) = \underline{\hspace{1cm}}.$$

Example 2:

$$\lim_{n \to \infty} \frac{3n^2 - n + 1}{-2n^2 + n}.$$

A standard practice for manipulating rational expressions of this type in order to apply the limit theorems is to divide numerator and denominator by the highest power of n appearing in the expression. This results in

$$\lim_{n \to \infty} \frac{3n^2 - n + 1}{-2n^2 + n} = \lim_{n \to \infty} \frac{3 - \underline{\hspace{0.5cm}} + \underline{\hspace{0.5cm}}}{-2 + 1/n}.$$

The limit theorems allow you to simplify the calculation by computing

$$\frac{\lim_{n \to \infty} 3 - \lim_{n \to \infty} \underline{\hspace{0.5cm}} + \lim_{n \to \infty} \underline{\hspace{0.5cm}}}{\lim_{n \to \infty} (-2) + \lim_{n \to \infty} (1/n)} = \frac{3 - \underline{\hspace{0.5cm}} + \underline{\hspace{0.5cm}}}{-2 + \underline{\hspace{0.5cm}}} = \underline{\hspace{0.5cm}}.$$

Margin notes:

$\dfrac{\varepsilon|L(y)|^2}{2}$

$\dfrac{\varepsilon|L(y)|^2}{2}$

$L(x), L(y)$

0

$\dfrac{1}{n}, \dfrac{1}{n^2}$

$\dfrac{1}{n}, \dfrac{1}{n^2}, 0, 0, -\dfrac{3}{2}$

417

If you understand that you are using the limit theorem's, and if you understand how you are using them, you may be safe in taking shortcuts such as:

$$\lim_{n \to \infty} \frac{3n^2 - n + 1}{-2n^2 + n} = \lim_{n \to \infty} \frac{3 - \dfrac{1}{n} + \dfrac{1}{n^2}}{-2 + \dfrac{1}{n}} = \frac{3 - 0 + 0}{-2 + 0} = -\frac{3}{2}.$$

9.5.1
EXERCISES

1. Find the following limits, if they exist:

(a) $\displaystyle\lim_{n \to \infty} \frac{n + 1}{n^2 + 2}$,

(b) $\displaystyle\lim_{n \to \infty} \frac{n^2 + 3}{n^2 + 2}$,

(c) $\displaystyle\lim_{n \to \infty} \frac{3n^2 + 1}{n^2 + 4n}$, $(n > 4)$,

(d) $\displaystyle\lim_{n \to \infty} \frac{4n^3 + 6n - 7}{n^3 + 2n^2 + 1}$,

(e) $\displaystyle\lim_{n \to \infty} \frac{3n^{45} - 6n^{23} + n}{-2n^{45} + 3}$,

(f) $\displaystyle\lim_{n \to \infty} (-1)^n \frac{n^2 - 1}{n^2 + 1}$,

(g) $\displaystyle\lim_{n \to \infty} \frac{a_p n^p + a_{p-1} n^{p-1} + \cdots + a_0}{b_p n^p + b_{p-1} n^{p-1} + \cdots + b_0}$, $(b_p \neq 0)$, $p \in \mathscr{Z}^+$,

(h) $\displaystyle\lim_{n \to \infty} \frac{P(n)}{Q(n)}$, where P and Q are polynomials of degrees p and q, respectively,

and where Q is not the zero function.

2. There are often more ways than one to crack a nut.

(a) In proving the limit theorem for quotients,

$$\lim_{n \to \infty} \frac{1}{y_n} = \frac{1}{\displaystyle\lim_{n \to \infty} y_n},$$

we assumed $\displaystyle\lim_{n \to \infty} y_n \neq 0$, and had as our hardest task the problem of finding a lower bound for $|y_n|$. A more direct and intuitive method of obtaining such a bound is provided by the neighborhood concept.

State the neighborhood definition of

$$\lim_{n \to \infty} y_n = L(y).$$

If you take a neighborhood of the limit of radius $L(y)/2$, what can you conclude about the y_n? How does this give you a lower bound for $|y_n|$?

(b) In the text we proved that $\exists\, k_0 \in \mathscr{Z}^+$, such that

$$|y_n| > \frac{L(y)}{2}, \qquad \forall n > k_0.$$

Is there an $n_0 \in \mathscr{Z}^+$ such that

$$|y_n| > \frac{L(y)}{3}, \qquad \forall\, n > n_0?$$

Is there an $m_0 \in \mathscr{Z}^+$ such that

$$|y_n| > \frac{L(y)}{10^6}, \qquad \forall\, n > m_0?$$

Explain.

(c) In proving $\lim\limits_{n \to \infty} x_n y_n = \lim\limits_{n \to \infty} x_n \lim\limits_{n \to \infty} y_n$, we needed to estimate

$$|x_n y_n - L(x)L(y)| = |(x_n - L(x))y_n + L(x)(y_n - L(y))|.$$

For $\delta > 0$, $\exists\, k_0, m_0 \in \mathscr{Z}^+$ such that

$$n > k_0 \Rightarrow |y_n - L(y)| < \delta,$$
$$n > m_0 \Rightarrow |x_n - L(x)| < \delta.$$

A variation of the remainder of the proof is the following:

$$|y_n| = |(y_n - L(y)) + \underline{\qquad}| < \delta + |\underline{\qquad}|, \quad \text{if } n > \underline{\qquad}.$$

Therefore, if $n > m_1 = \max\{k_0, m_0\}$, then

$$|x_n y_n - L(x)L(y)| < \delta(\underline{\qquad}) + \underline{\qquad}\delta$$

$$< \delta^2 + \delta(\underline{\qquad} + \underline{\qquad}) = \delta(\delta + \underline{\qquad} + \underline{\qquad}).$$

There is no loss of generality in taking $\delta \le 1$ (why?), in which case

$$|x_n y_n - L(x)L(y)| < \delta(\underline{\qquad} + \underline{\qquad} + \underline{\qquad}), \quad \text{for } n > m_1.$$

Then, for $n > m_0$,

$$|x_n y_n - L(x)L(y)| < \varepsilon$$

if we choose $\delta = \min\{1, \underline{\qquad}\}$.

3. You have theorems on sums, products, and quotients of limits. We now ask you to investigate limits involving roots.

(a) What is $\lim\limits_{n \to \infty} \dfrac{2n + 1}{n}$?

(b) What would be your guess for $\lim\limits_{n \to \infty} \sqrt{\dfrac{2n + 1}{n}}$?

(c) Suppose $x = \{x_n\}$ is convergent and $x_n \ge 0$ for $n \in \mathscr{Z}^+$. What is

$$L(\sqrt{x}) = \lim\limits_{n \to \infty} \sqrt{x_n}?$$

(Use Exercise 8(h) of Sec. 7.4.1.)

4. Generalize Exercise 3(c). If $x = \{x_n\}$ is convergent and $x_n \geq 0$, $\forall n$, what is $L(\sqrt[k]{x}) = \lim_{n \to \infty} \sqrt[k]{x_n}$?

5. Still another definition of subsequence is the following: If $\{n_k\}$ is a strictly increasing sequence of positive integers (i.e., $n_1 < n_2 < \cdots < n_k < \cdots$), then $\{x_{n_k}\}$ is called a *subsequence* of $\{x_n\}$.

(a) Every sequence has infinitely many subsequences. Given the sequence $\{1/2^n\}$, write the general term for a subsequence which skips every other term of the original sequence. Write the term of a subsequence that skips every third term of the original sequence.

(b) Find $\lim_{n \to \infty} (1/2^{2n})$.

(c) Find $\lim_{n \to \infty} (1/2^{2n+1})$.

(d) Find $\lim_{n_k \to \infty} (1/2^{n_k})$.

6. (a) If $\lim_{n \to \infty} a_n = A$, every neighborhood of A contains *all* but a finite number of the a_n. Show why this follows from the definition of limit.

(b) If $\lim_{n \to \infty} a_n = A$, make a conjecture: $\lim_{n_k \to \infty} a_{n_k} = $ _____.

(c) Prove your conjecture of part (b).

7. (a) The sequence $\{(-1)^n\}$ has subsequences $\{x_k\}$ and $\{y_k\}$, where $x_k = (-1)^{2k}$ and $y_k = (-1)^{2k+1}$.

$$\lim_{k \to \infty} (-1)^{2k} = \underline{\qquad} \quad \text{and} \quad \lim_{k \to \infty} (-1)^{2k+1} = \underline{\qquad}.$$

(b) If $\lim_{n \to \infty} a_n = A$ and $\lim_{n \to \infty} a_n = B$, prove $A = B$.

(c) If $\{b_{n_k}\}$ and $\{b_{n_p}\}$ are two subsequences of $\{b_n\}$ that have different limits, prove $\{b_n\}$ diverges.

8. (a) In Exercise 5 of Sec. 9.3.1 you proved that $\{\sqrt[n]{n}\}$ converges. Let's call $\lim_{n \to \infty} \sqrt[n]{n} = A$, and try to find A by looking for a subsequence that is easier to work with than the original sequence. Any subsequence $\{n_k^{1/n_k}\}$ also converges to the limit _____. Try the even terms $\{(2n)^{1/2n}\}$. You know that

$$\lim_{n \to \infty} (2n)^{1/2n} = \lim_{n \to \infty} (2)^?(n)^? = \lim_{n \to \infty} (2^{1/2})^?(n^{1/n})^?.$$

But $\lim_{n \to \infty} (\sqrt{2})^{1/n} = \underline{\qquad}$, and Exercise 4 tells you that

$$\lim_{n \to \infty} (n^{1/n})^? = (\lim_{n \to \infty} n^{1/n})^? = A^?.$$

Therefore,

$$A = \lim_{n \to \infty} (2n)^{1/2n} = \underline{\qquad} A^?.$$

Solve for A. How many answers do you get? Which is (are) extraneous to the problem and why? Finally,

$$\lim_{n \to \infty} n^{1/n} = \underline{\qquad}.$$

(b) Using the idea of part (a), consider the sequence $\{a^{1/n}\}$ if $a > 1$. Prove that it converges and call its limit A. Then, by examining the particular subsequence for n even, prove that $\lim_{n \to \infty} a^{1/n} = 1$.

(c) Using the result of (b), prove that $\lim_{n \to \infty} a^{1/n} = 1$ if $0 < a < 1$.

9. You already have results about the limit function L. You know, for example, that $L(x + y) = \underline{\hspace{1cm}} + \underline{\hspace{1cm}}$.

(a) Let x denote the convergent sequence $\{x_n\}$ and λ a constant, so that λx denotes the sequence $\{\lambda x_n\}$. Prove $L(\lambda x) = \underline{\hspace{1cm}} L(x)$.

(b) If λ and μ are both constants, derive a result of the form

$$L(\lambda x + \mu y) = \underline{\hspace{1cm}} L(x) + \underline{\hspace{1cm}}.$$

Does this property of the function L look familiar?

(c) If you don't recall, check back to Sec. 7.6 to find the name we gave to functions that satisfy the result you proved in part (b). What did x and y represent in Sec. 7.6?

(d) If x and y are vectors, and λ and μ are scalars, you proved in earlier sections results of the form

(i) $x + y$ is a vector;

(ii) $x + y = y + x$;

(iii) there is a *zero* vector 0 such that $x + 0 = x$;

(iv) λx is a vector;

(v) $\lambda(\mu x) = (\lambda \mu)x$.

Let x and y be real sequences, λ and μ real constants. Determine which of these five properties hold and which fail to hold. What sequence did you use for 0?

(e) If you confine attention to null sequences, are the five properties in part (d) still satisfied? Do the null sequences form a vector space? Generalize.

10. (a) Let $L(x) = A$ and $\sup x = B$. Suppose $A > B$. Let η be a neighborhood of radius $(A - B)/2$ about A.

Are there points (numbers) of $\{x_n\}$ in η? What's wrong?

(b) Prove: $\inf x \le L(x) \le \sup x$.

(c) Prove: $|L(x)| \le \sup |x|$.

(d) Prove: If $\{x_n\}$ is convergent, then $\{|x_n|\}$ is convergent.

(e) Consider the converse to part (d). If true, prove it so; if false, give a counter-example.

(f) Prove: $L(x) \le \lim_{n \to \infty} |x_n|$.

11. (a) $\lim_{n \to \infty} \dfrac{n + 1}{1} = \underline{\hspace{1cm}}.$ (c) $\lim_{n \to \infty} \dfrac{2n + 1}{n} = \underline{\hspace{1cm}}.$

(b) $\lim_{n \to \infty} \dfrac{n + 2}{n + 1} = \underline{\hspace{1cm}}.$ (d) $\lim_{n \to \infty} \dfrac{2n + 3}{n + 1} = \underline{\hspace{1cm}}.$

(e) $\lim_{n \to \infty} x_n = A \Rightarrow \lim_{n \to \infty} x_{n+1} = \underline{\hspace{1cm}}.$ Prove.

12. Let $x_1 = \sqrt{2}$ and $x_{n+1} = \sqrt{2 + x_n}$, and assume $\{x_n\}$ converges to A.

(a) $x_{n+1}^2 = ?$.

(b) $\lim_{n \to \infty} x_{n+1}^2 = ?$.

(c) Find $\lim_{n \to \infty} x_n$.

13. We define a new function L_1 which operates on sequences (not necessarily convergent):

$$L_1(x) = \lim_{n \to \infty} \frac{x_n + x_{n+2}}{2}.$$

(a) Prove: $\{x_n\}$ convergent $\Rightarrow L_1(x) = L(x)$.

(b) Suppose $x_n = (-1)^n$, $L_1(x) = ?$.

(c) If $x_n = 1 + (-1)^{n+1}$, find $L_1(x)$.

(d) Let $\{x_n\}$ be a given sequence such that

$$\lim_{k \to \infty} x_{2k} = A \qquad \text{and} \qquad \lim_{k \to \infty} x_{2k+1} = A.$$

What can you say (and prove) about $\lim_{n \to \infty} x_n$?

(e) The sequence $1, \frac{1}{2}, \frac{2}{3}, \frac{1}{2}, \ldots$ is given by

$$x_{2k} = \frac{1}{2} \qquad \text{and} \qquad x_{2k+1} = \frac{k+1}{2k+1}.$$

Find $\lim_{k \to \infty} x_{2k}$ and $\lim_{k \to \infty} x_{2k+1}$. What is $\lim_{n \to \infty} x_n$?

14. From a given sequence $\{x_n\}$ we define a new sequence $\{\sigma_n\}$, where

$$\sigma_n = \frac{x_1 + x_2 + \cdots + x_n}{n}$$

is the *arithmetic mean* of the first n terms of $\{x_n\}$. Find $\lim_{n \to \infty} \sigma_n$ if it exists for the following:

(a) $x_n = (-1)^n$.

(b) $x_n = 1 + (-1)^n$.

(c) $x_{3n} = 0$, $x_{3n+1} = 0$, $x_{3n+2} = 1$. [*Suggestion:* First find $\sigma_{3n}, \sigma_{3n+1}, \sigma_{3n+2}$.]

(d) Suppose $\varepsilon > 0$ and $|x_n - a| \le \varepsilon$ for $n > 100$, and $|x_n| \le M$ for $1 \le n \le 100$. For any given $n > 100$, what is the greatest possible value of $|\sigma_n - a|$? Find an n_0 such that $|\sigma_n - a| < 2\varepsilon$ for $n > n_0$.

For investigation: If $\{x_n\}$ is convergent, can you conclude that $\{\sigma_n\}$ is also convergent? If so, how are the limits related?

15. If you think of x_n as an approximation to $\lim_{v \to \infty} x_v$, the error is $|x_n - \lim_{v \to \infty} x_v|$. Suppose you take $x_k (k \ge n)$ as your approximation. What is the maximum error ε_n you might encounter? It can be written

$$\varepsilon_n = \sup_{k \ge n} |x_k - \lim_{v \to \infty} x_v|.$$

Since this error depends upon the sequence $\{x_n\}$, we can write $\varepsilon_n(x)$, denoting the fact that ε_n is a function which operates on convergent sequences.

(a) If you are given $\varepsilon_n(x)$ and $\varepsilon_n(y)$, how would you estimate $\varepsilon_n(x + y)$?

$$\sup_{k \geq n} |(x_n + y_n) - (L(x) + L(y))| \leq \sup_{k \geq n} (|x_n - \underline{\hspace{1cm}}| + |y_n - \underline{\hspace{1cm}}|).$$

If you can make the right member $\leq \sup_{k \geq n} |x_n - L(x)| + \sup_{k \geq n} |y_n - L(y)|$, then you could conclude

$$\varepsilon_n(x + y) \leq \varepsilon_n(x) + \varepsilon_n(y),$$

a useful formula for approximating errors (if true). We shall therefore help you to investigate $\sup \{a_n + b_n\}$.

$$a_k \leq \sup \{a_n\}, \qquad \forall\, k \in \mathscr{L}^+,$$
$$b_k \leq \sup \{b_n\}, \qquad \forall\, k \in \mathscr{L}^+.$$

Therefore, $\underline{\hspace{1cm}} \leq \sup \{a_n\} + \sup \{b_n\}$, for all $\underline{\hspace{1cm}}$. Thus

$$\sup \{\underline{\hspace{1cm}}\} \leq \sup \{a_n\} + \sup \{b_n\}.$$

(b) Estimate $\varepsilon_n(xy)$ if given $\varepsilon_n(x)$ and $\varepsilon_n(y)$. Begin with

$$|x_k y_k - L(x)L(y)| = |(x_k - L(x))y_k + \underline{\hspace{1cm}}|,$$

taking a hint from the proof that $L(xy) = L(x)L(y)$. Prove that

$$\varepsilon_n(xy) \leq \varepsilon_n(x) \sup_{n > 0} |y_n| + \varepsilon_n(y) \sup_{n > 0} |x_n|.$$

(c) For convenience here we denote $\sup_{n > 0} |y_n|$ by $\|y\|$. Then the result of part (a) can be written

$$\varepsilon_n(xy) \leq \|y\| \varepsilon_n(x) + \|x\| \varepsilon_n(y).$$

Prove:

$$\varepsilon_n\!\left(\frac{1}{x}\right) \leq \left\|\frac{1}{x}\right\|^2 \varepsilon_n(x).$$

(d) Recall that the sequence $\{x_n\}$ is really a function on the positive (or nonnegative) integers; i.e.,

$$x : n \rightarrow x_n = x(n).$$

The terms x_n of the sequence $\{x_n\}$ are the function values. We transform x into another function on the positive integers:

$$Tx : n \rightarrow x_{n+1}$$

so that $(Tx)(1) = x_2, (Tx)(2) = x_3, \ldots$, and

$$(T^2 x)(1) = (T(Tx))(1) = (Tx)(2) = x(3) = x_3,$$
$$(T^3 x)(1) = \underline{\hspace{2cm}}, \quad \ldots.$$

The quantity $\|(T^n x)(k) - L(x)\|$ is equal to an error estimate. Fill in the question mark and prove the result.

$$\varepsilon_n(x) = \|(T^n x)(k) - L(x)\|.$$

(e) Prove: $\inf\{a_n + b_n\} \geq \inf\{a_n\} + \inf\{b_n\}$, if $\{a_n\}$ and $\{b_n\}$ are bounded sequences.

16. If A is the limit of a subsequence $\{x_{n_k}\}$ of $\{x_n\}$, then A is called a *limit point* of $\{x_n\}$.
One of the subsequences of $\{(-1)^n\}$ is $\{(-1)^{2n}\}$, which converges to ____; another subsequence $\{(-1)^{2n+1}\}$ converges to ____. Therefore $\{(-1)^n\}$ has ____ and ____ as limit points. Construct a sequence with three limit points. A neighborhood of limit points contains ____ (how many) numbers of the sequence. A convergent sequence has at least ____ (how many) limit (point(s) and at most ____ limit points.

(a) If $x_{2n} = (1/3^n)^{1/n}$ and $x_{2n+1} = (1/2^n)^{1/n}$, how many limit points does the $\{x_n\}$ have? What are they?

(b) If $x_{2n+1} = 1/2^{2n+1}$ and $x_{2n} = 1/4^{n-1}$, find all the limit points of $\{x_n\}$.

(c) The least upper bound of the set of limit points of $\{x_n\}$ is called the *limit superior* of $\{x_n\}$ and is written

$$\limsup_{n \to \infty} x_n.$$

Similarly, the greatest lower bound of the set of limit points is called the *limit inferior* of $\{x_n\}$ and is denoted

$$\liminf_{n \to \infty} x_n.$$

Find the limit superiors and limit inferiors of the sequences in (a) and (b).

(d) If the set of limit points is unbounded above, we write $\limsup_{n \to \infty} x_n = \infty$, and if unbounded below we write $\liminf_{n \to \infty} x_n = -\infty$. Prove that: If $\{x_n\}$ converges,

$$\limsup_{n \to \infty} x_n = \liminf_{n \to \infty} x_n = \lim_{n \to \infty} x_n.$$

(e) Find the $\limsup_{n \to \infty} x_n$ and $\liminf_{n \to \infty} x_n$ for (i) $x_n = (-1)^{n+1} n$, (ii) $x_n = (-1)^n/n$, and (iii) $x_n = (-1)^n - 1/2^n$.

(f) Assuming $\{x_n\}$ and $\{y_n\}$ are bounded, compare $\limsup_{n \to \infty}\{x_n + y_n\}$ with $\limsup_{n \to \infty}\{x_n\} + \limsup_{n \to \infty}\{y_n\}$. Investigate with examples before attempting a proof.

Research Problem

17. Let $\{a_n\}$ be a bounded sequence. Must $\{a_n\}$ have at least one limit point? [*Hint:* Note that all the a_n are in some closed interval $\mathscr{I}_1$. If $\mathscr{I}_1$ is divided into two subintervals, is it possible that both contain a_n for only finitely many values of n? Can you utilize the nested interval postulate?]

Chapter Ten Mathematical Induction *The idea of mathematical induction has been implicit in our work since Chapter 5, when we introduced recursive definition. In Sec. 10.1, the principle of induction is made explicit and formal and is applied in many different ways. Section 10.2 treats the notion of well-ordering and its relationship to the principle of induction. Finally, Sec. 10.3 treats another form of induction and applications to elementary number theory, viz. divisibility. The exercises of the chapter reinforce much of the earlier work on inequalities, iterations, and limits. Section 10.2.1, particularly, gives attention to sequences that define e and applications thereof.*

10.1

The Principle of Induction   The sequence $\{x_n\}$ given recursively by

$$x_1 = \sqrt{2},$$

$$x_{n+1} = \sqrt{2 + x_n}$$

appeared in Exercise 12 of Sec. 9.5.1. You calculated the limit of $\{x_n\}$ *on the assumption that the sequence is convergent.* Is this assumption valid or invalid? If you try to apply the definition of limit, you will find that an explicit formula for x_n is required, and this presents difficulties. Similarly, you will probably have trouble applying the Cauchy criterion. (Try it.) There is still another way out if we can prove the sequence monotonic and bounded. We shall attempt this approach.

$$x_1 = \sqrt{2}, \quad x_2 = \sqrt{2 + \sqrt{2}}, \quad x_3 = \sqrt{2 + \sqrt{2 + \sqrt{2}}}, \quad \ldots$$

It appears that x_n increases as n gets larger, although this may not be obvious. It is clear that $x_1 < x_2 < x_3$.

Suppose that for some index $k \in \mathscr{Z}^+$,

(1) $x_k < x_{k+1}.$

Does this inequality continue to hold as you go out further in the sequence? In particular, can you prove $x_{k+1} < x_{k+2}$? Let's see.

$$x_{k+2} = \sqrt{2 + x_{k+1}},$$

but by the supposition (1), we have

$$x_{k+2} = \sqrt{2 + x_{k+1}} > \sqrt{2 + x_k} = x_{k+1},$$

which shows that from the assumption that $x_k < x_{k+1}$, it follows that

$$x_{k+1} < x_{k+2}.$$

If the sequence is strictly increasing at some point in the sequence, it continues to be strictly increasing. But we do know that it is strictly increasing at some point! In fact, we know that $x_1 < x_2$. Therefore, what we just proved is that $x_2 < x_3$, and, therefore, $x_3 < x_4$, $x_4 < x_5$, and so on. We can summarize the result by stating $x_n < x_{n+1}$ for all $n \in \mathscr{Z}^+$, which is merely the statement that $\{x_n\}$ is a strictly increasing sequence.

If we can prove that $\{x_n\}$ is bounded above, we will know that the sequence is convergent. Any upper bound will do, so let's look for one which is an integer.

$$x_1 = \sqrt{2} < 2, \qquad x_2 = \sqrt{2 + \sqrt{2}} = \sqrt{3.41\ldots} < 2.$$

Let's try 2 as an upper bound. If it doesn't work, we'll try a larger number in the hope that $\{x_n\}$ is bounded. Let's repeat the type of argument used in proving the sequence monotonic. Suppose

(2) $$x_k < 2 \qquad \text{for some index } k.$$

Does this situation continue? That is, can you show $x_{k+1} < 2$?

$$x_{k+1} = \sqrt{2 + x_k}.$$

From supposition (2), we infer that

$$x_{k+1} = \sqrt{2 + x_k} < \sqrt{2 + 2} = 2.$$

From the assumption that $x_k < 2$, it follows that $x_{k+1} < 2$. But we know that $x_1 < 2$. We can therefore conclude that $x_2 < 2$, $x_3 < 2$, and so on. In general, we have $x_n < 2$, so $\{x_n\}$ has 2 as an upper bound. We can also infer, as a corollary, that

$$\lim_{n \to \infty} x_n = \sup \{x_n\} \leq 2.$$

(Check the answer you gave to the $\lim_{n \to \infty} x_n$ when you worked the problem earlier.)

The technique of proof that we exhibited in proving $\{x_n\}$ monotonic and also proving $\{x_n\}$ bounded can be summarized as follows:

Let $P(n)$ represent a proposition defined on the domain of positive integers such that
   (i) $P(1)$ is true and
   (ii) if $P(k)$ is true, then $P(k + 1)$ is also true.
Conclusion: $P(n)$ is true for every positive integer n.

This technique of proving propositions for positive integers is called *proof by mathematical induction.* It rests on a property of the natural numbers $\mathscr{Z}^+$, which can be stated as follows: Let $\mathscr{M}$ be a subset of the natural numbers $\mathscr{Z}^+$, such that
   (i) $1 \in \mathscr{M}$ and
   (ii) if a natural number $k \in \mathscr{M}$, then $(k + 1) \in \mathscr{M}$ also.
Then $\mathscr{M} = \mathscr{Z}^+$. That is, $\mathscr{M}$ is the entire set of natural numbers.

This property of the natural numbers was used by the Italian mathematician Guiseppe Peano (1858–1932) as a postulate in the first axiomatic development of the real number system, published in 1889. Dedekind, whom we mentioned earlier, carried out the first logical extension from the rationals to the reals. But Peano started with much less, five postulates for the natural numbers. He then carried out the program of extending the system to include the negative integers and zero, obtaining thereby all the integers. Then he extended the system of integers to the rationals, and finally called upon Dedekind's ideas for obtaining the irrationals. You can read an account of Peano's program, including all the theorems and proofs, in *Foundations of Analysis.†*

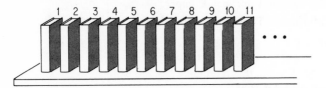

Figure 10-1

The principle of mathematical induction can be illustrated by a set of books standing loosely on a shelf as shown in Fig. 10-1. Suppose there are infinitely many books, perhaps labeled "1," "2," "3," .... If they are close

enough together and if one is knocked over, it will surely knock down an adjacent book (Fig. 10-2). How can you knock down all the books with a minimum of effort? Just push over the first in the direction of the second. In summary: If

Figure 10-2

(i) the first is pushed over in the direction of the second, and

(ii) the books are placed so that if one falls, the next one will also fall, *then all the books* will fall.

Any time you wish to prove that a proposition $P(n)$, $n \in \mathscr{Z}^+$, is true for all $n \in \mathscr{Z}^+$, you may find it helpful to call on mathematical induction.

Example 1: You have already proved and used the inequality

$$(1 + h)^n \geq 1 + nh \qquad \text{if } h > 0 \quad \text{and} \quad n \in \mathscr{Z}^+.$$

(See Exercise 3 of Sec. 8.1.1 and also Sec. 9.1.) Can this inequality be strengthened to *strict* inequality? Since $(1 + h)^1 = 1 + 1 \cdot h$, the answer is *no*. Let's find out then if strict inequality $(1 + h)^n > 1 + nh$ holds for any values of n; if so, which values?

Try $n = 2$:

$$(1 + h)^2 = 1 + 2h + \underline{\qquad} > 1 + 2h. \qquad \qquad \bigg| \quad h^2$$

(Was it necessary for h to be positive?)

For $n = 3$,

$$(1 + h)^3 = 1 + \underline{\qquad}h + \underline{\qquad}h^2 + h^3. \qquad \bigg| \quad 3, 3$$

† E. G. H. Landau, *Foundations of Analysis* (New York: Chelsea Publishing Company, 1951). [NOTE: The edition in German, *Grundlagen der Analysis* (Chelsea Publishing Company, 3rd ed., 1960), with a German-English glossary, is excellent practice for scientific German.]

Since $h > 0$,

$$(1 + h)^3 > 1 + \underline{\qquad}h.$$

3

Maybe the second part of mathematical induction will work. Does the validity of the inequality for $n = k$ imply that the inequality holds for $n = k + 1$? Suppose

(3) $(1 + h)^k > 1 + kh$ for $k \in \mathcal{Z}^+$.

Does it follow that $(1 + h)^{k+1} > 1 + (k + 1)h$? Let's find out by examining $(1 + h)^{k+1}$, and *remember that (3) is available as hypothesis*. From $(1 + h)^k$, you can obtain $(1 + h)^{k+1}$ if you multiply by _____. Begin with

1 + h

$$(1 + h)^k > \underline{\qquad} + \underline{\qquad}.$$

1, kh

Then

$$(1 + h)^{k+1} > (\underline{\qquad} + kh)(1 + \underline{\qquad}),$$

1, h

since $1 + h > \underline{\qquad}$.

0

Therefore,

$$(1 + h)^{k+1} > 1 + \underline{\qquad}h + \underline{\qquad}h^2,$$

(k + 1), k

and

$$(1 + h)^{k+1} > 1 + \underline{\qquad}h.$$

(k + 1)

But this is precisely the original inequality with $n = k + 1$. You have proved that: If the inequality holds for $n = k$, it must also hold for $n = k + 1$. Therefore, it holds for $n = 3$, since you proved it holds for $n = 2$. It also must hold for $n = 3 + 1 = 4$, $n = 4 + 1 = 5$, and so on. Finally, the inequality must hold for all integers greater than 1.

Questions. Where did you need the information that $h > 0$? Can you strengthen the result by proving that the inequality holds for a larger set of values for h, when $n = 2, 3, 4, \ldots$?

NOTE: The preceding example uses the principle of mathematical induction for sets other than the set of positive integers. Reviewing the method, you should observe that two things are required of a set before induction may be applied to it:

(i) there must be a starting element;
(ii) there must be a definite procedure for going from each element to the next one, and this procedure must enable you to exhaust the set.

Implicit in (ii) is the idea that there is some order relation in the set. We will return to this idea shortly.

429
PROGRAMMED TEXT
FOLLOWS

Example 2: We shall try to find and prove a formula for the sum of the squares

$$1^2 + 2^2 + 3^2 + \cdots + n^2.$$

Before you can attempt to prove anything by mathematical induction, you must have the proposition $P(n)$. This proposition is called the *induction hypothesis*. Often the major battle is to determine the induction hypothesis. In this case, we want an expression $S(n)$ for the sum, so that $P(n)$ would be

$$1^2 + 2^2 + 3^2 + \cdots + n^2 = S(n).$$

The sum $1 + 2 + 3 + \cdots + n$ can be determined from the formula for the sum of an _____ progression. Accordingly,

$$1 + 2 + 3 + \cdots + n = \text{\_\_\_\_}.$$

| *arithmetic* |
| $\dfrac{n(n+1)}{2}$ |

But the problem at hand is more difficult, so we perform some experiments. Make a table:

n	1	2	3	4	5	$\cdots$
$1 + 2 + \cdots + n$	1	3	___	___	___	$\cdots$
$1^2 + 2^2 + \cdots + n^2$	1	5	___	___	___	$\cdots$

Do you see any relationship between the sum of the integers and the sum of the squares? Experiment for at least a few values of n before reading further.

Suppose you look at the ratio of the rows: $\frac{1}{1}, \frac{3}{5}$, ___, ___, ___. Do you see any pattern? If all the numerators are made equal to 3, then the denominators are $3, 5$, ___, ___, ___. What would be your guess for the next denominator? Test it. What would you guess for the nth denominator? Accumulating your computations and guesses, it looks very much like

$$\frac{1 + 2 + \cdots + n}{1^2 + 2^2 + \cdots + n^2} = \frac{3}{2n + 1}.$$

Solving for $1^2 + 2^2 + \cdots + n^2$, you get

(H)
$$1^2 + 2^2 + \cdots + n^2 = \frac{(1 + 2 + \cdots + n)(2n + 1)}{3}$$

$$= \frac{n(n + 1)(2n + 1)}{6}.$$

Here is an induction hypothesis! Now to test it.

Suppose it holds for $n = k$. That is, suppose that

(4)
$$1^2 + 2^2 + \cdots + k^2 = \frac{k(k + 1)(2k + 1)}{6}.$$

If the formula is correct for $n = k + 1$, you should be able to prove that

$$1^2 + 2^2 + \cdots + k^2 + (k + 1)^2$$

(5)
$$= \frac{(k + 1)(\text{\_\_\_\_})(2k + \text{\_\_\_\_})}{6} \qquad \text{(Careful!)}$$

| $k + 2, 3$ |

How can you deduce (5) from (4)? The left member of (5) can be obtained from the left member of (4) by adding (_____)². Adding this to both members of (4) gives

$k + 1$

$$1^2 + 2^2 + \cdots + k^2 + (k + 1)^2 = \frac{k(k + 1)(2k + 1)}{6} + (k + 1)^2.$$

Is the right member of this equation equal to the right member of (5)? If it is, then our proof is complete; if it is not, then our induction hypothesis is false. Let's see.

$$\frac{k(k + 1)(2k + 1)}{6} + (k + 1)^2$$

$$= \frac{k(k + 1)(2k + 1) + \underline{\quad}(k + 1)^2}{6} \qquad 6$$

$$= \frac{(k + 1)(\underline{\quad}k^2 + \underline{\quad}k + \underline{\quad})}{6} \qquad 2, 7, 6$$

$$= \frac{(k + 1)(k + \underline{\quad})(2k + \underline{\quad})}{6}. \qquad 2, 3$$

You have proved: If $1^2 + 2^2 + \cdots + k^2 = \dfrac{k(k + 1)(2k + 1)}{6}$, then

$$1^2 + 2^2 + \cdots + k^2 + (k + 1)^2 = \frac{(k + 1)(k + 2)(2k + 3)}{6}.$$

In summary: The induction hypothesis, formula (H), holds for $n = 1, 2, 3, 4$, and 5. You have shown, in addition, that if it holds for $n = k$, it must also hold for $n = k + 1$. Therefore, it holds for all $n \in \mathscr{Z}^+$.

Example 3: This example will illustrate how important it is to carry out the first step in a mathematical induction proof. It is clear that the second step, showing that $P(k) \Rightarrow P(k + 1)$, is essential, but many beginners are too lax with regard to the first step, initiating the procedure. Let $P(n): 2^n < n!$ Assuming $P(k): 2^k < k!$, we try to prove

$$P(k + 1): 2^{k+1} < (k + 1)!.$$

Multiplying both members of $P(k)$ by $k + 1$, you get

$$2^k \cdot (k + 1) < (k + 1)!.$$

But if $k + 1 \geq 2$, you have

$$2^{k+1} \leq 2^k \cdot (k + 1) < (k + 1)!.$$

So it appears that $P(n)$ is true as long as $n + 1 \geq 2$, or $n \geq 1$. A careless (and lazy) student might conclude $2^n < n!, \forall n \in \mathscr{Z}^+$. But check $P(n)$ for $n = 1, 2, 3, 4, 5$. What is the smallest value of n for which $P(n)$ is true?

Example 4: Actually, we can go further and prove an entirely false proposition by disregarding the step that initiates the induction. Let the proposition be given by

$$P(n): n = n + 1, \qquad n \in \mathscr{L}^+.$$

Assuming $P(k): k = k + 1$, you can add 1 to both members, achieving

$$P(k + 1): k + 1 = k + 2.$$

This proves that if $P(n)$ is true for some integer $n = k$, it is true for the succeeding integer $k + 1$. But the proposition cannot be verified for a single integer, so the induction can never begin!

Example 5: This example is designed to bring your attention to possible pitfalls in the second stage of proof by mathematical induction.†
  The theorem we wish to prove states: *All gentlemen prefer blondes.* As a stepping-stone we prove a lemma‡, $P(n)$.

  $P(n)$: *If one of any collection of n gentlemen prefers blondes, then all n prefer blondes.*

  $P(1)$ is clearly true. Assume $P(k)$ is true; i.e., if one of any set of k gentlemen prefers blondes, then all k prefer blondes. Consider any collection G of $k + 1$ gentlemen, one of which, say Lee, prefers blondes. Now consider a collection G_1 of k gentlemen which includes Lee and any $k - 1$ others from G. (Let's call the one you left out Paul.) Then G_1 satisfies the induction hypothesis, so all k gentlemen in G_1 prefer blondes. Now form a collection G_2 of k gentlemen from G, this time including Paul. G_2 certainly has one gentleman who prefers blondes. (Actually there are at least $k - 1$ such gentlemen.) Therefore, G_2 also satisfies the induction hypothesis, so all k gentlemen in G_2 prefer blondes. In particular, Paul also prefers blondes. Thus, it seems that we have proved $P(k + 1)$ by assuming $P(k)$.
  How does the general theorem follow? If there is one gentleman in the world who prefers blondes, you can apply the lemma to the set of all gentlemen. There must be at least one gentleman who prefers blondes (*de gustibus non est disputandum*); hence, all do. Do all the gentlemen you know prefer blondes?

Definition by Induction:

The principle of induction, as a property of the natural numbers, enables you to give a definition of a concept for all natural numbers by
  (i) stating the definition for $n = 1$ and
  (ii) giving the definition for $n = k + 1$ in terms of the concept for $n = k$.
  This idea is really not new to you, because we have been using recursive definitions since Sec. 5.5. A recursive definition *is* a definition by mathematical induction. You've seen a definition of a^n for $n \in \mathscr{L}^+$ given recursively

  † The example is a variation of one given by George Polya (Professor Emeritus of Stanford University) in Vol. 1, *Induction and Analogy*, of *Mathematics and Plausible Reasoning* (2 vols.; Princeton, N.J.: Princeton University Press, 1954).
  ‡ The definition of *lemma* is given in the footnote on page 107.

as:

$$a^1 = 1,$$

$$a^{k+1} = a \cdot a^k, \qquad k \in \mathscr{L}^+.$$

This defines a^n for all positive integers n. The second part of the definition is called the *recursive relation* or the *recurrence relation*.

Scientists are always attempting to generalize their theories in order to be able to apply them as widely as possible. The extension (generalization) of the exponent theory is a simple example of this. Although you know about the extension of (6) to the definition of a^r, where r is any rational number (positive, negative, or zero), we'd like to point out something especially pertinent at this time. In order to have a true extension (generalization), the results (theorems, relations, and so forth) in the special case should extend to the general theory. More precisely, the extended theory should contain theorems, relations, and so forth, of which those in the special case are, indeed, special cases. As for exponents, the defining relation—the recursive relation—should hold in the extension of the theory. Accordingly, when mathematicians sought a fitting and useful definition for a^0, they investigated to see what a^0 should be in order that

$$a^{0+1} = a \cdot a^0 \qquad (a \neq 0).$$

Consequently, we have the definition: $a^0 = $ _____ if $a \neq 0$.

Would the following definition for a^n be all right for $n = 0, 1, 2, \ldots$? If $a \neq 0$,

$$a^0 = 1,$$

$$a^{k+1} = a^k \cdot a.$$

Of course, the earlier definition didn't exclude $a = 0$, but in all other cases ($a \neq 0$) do the results of the two definitions coincide?

Before reading on, give a definition by induction for $n!$ and show why $0!$ is defined as it has been in this and all other mathematics books.

The letter Σ (the Greek capital letter *sigma*) is universally used to represent *sum* or *summation*. The manner of its use can be defined most easily by induction. We will define $\sum_{i=1}^{n} a_i$, which is read "the sum of a_i for i running from 1 to n":

(i) $\sum_{i=1}^{1} a_i = a_1,$

(ii) $\sum_{i=1}^{k+1} a_i = a_{k+1} + \sum_{i=1}^{k} a_i.$

The letter i, in this case, is called the *index of summation*. It is not important which letter is used as an index of summation; any other letter not already in the statement would do just as well. If you write the sum in longhand, $a_1 + a_2 + \cdots + a_k$, the index has served its purpose and disappears. It is this point that explains why indices for summation are also referred to as *dummy indices*.

The summation notation is especially useful in writing long summands. For example, suppose you wanted to write the sum of the first 100 positive integers. You can write this:

$$\sum_{i=1}^{100} i. \qquad [\text{NOTE}: a_i = i.]$$

The sum of the integers from 137 to 1652 (inclusive) may be written:

$$\sum_{i=1}^{1516} (136 + i).$$

Earlier in the section, when we were summing squares, we wrote

$$1^2 + 2^2 + 3^2 + \cdots + n^2,$$

and asked what the sum is if $n = 1$ and $n = 2$. Writing the formula as we did with "..." is not very satisfactory; too much is taken for granted. Although you knew what we had in mind, it was not expressed by the notation. However, the summation notation does say it precisely.

$$\sum_{k=1}^{n} k^2 \qquad (\text{what is the index of summation?})$$

says, "the sum of k^2 for k running from 1 to n." This notation is valid even for $n = 1$, whereas the former notation was not.

10.1.1
EXERCISES

1. The inequality of Example 1 is due to James Bernoulli (1654–1705), another of the famous family of Swiss scientists. He proved a more general result, which was left for you to uncover in the example. The following result is the more usual form of the *Bernoulli inequality*: If $h > -1$ and $h \neq 0$ and $n \geq 2$, then

$$(1 + h)^n > 1 + nh.$$

(a) If you haven't already proved this, do so now.
(b) In Exercise 8 of Sec. 9.5.1 you found $\lim_{n \to \infty} \sqrt[n]{n}$ by means of subsequences. What did you get for the limit? We ask you to check your answer by another method, which relies on an inequality very much like Bernoulli's.

Proving that $\lim\limits_{n \to \infty} \sqrt[n]{n} = 1$ is equivalent to proving that $\{x_n\}$ is a null sequence where

$$x_n = \underline{\hspace{1cm}} - 1,$$

$$x_n \, ? \, 0, \qquad \forall n \in \mathscr{Z}^+, \qquad (\leq/\geq)$$

(7) $$(1 + x_n)^n = \underline{\hspace{1cm}}.$$

Expanding by the binomial theorem, you get

(8) $$(1 + x_n)^n = 1 + nx_n + \underline{\hspace{1cm}}x_n^2 + \cdots.$$

Therefore, combining the results of (7) and (8),

$$\underline{\hspace{1cm}} = (1 + x_n)^n \geq \underline{\hspace{1cm}}x_n^2.$$

(How did we determine the sense of the inequality after dropping terms?) Working only with the right and left members of the last inequality, you get

$$0 \leq x_n^2 \leq \underline{\hspace{1cm}}.$$

Therefore,

$$0 \leq x_n \leq \underline{\hspace{1cm}}.$$

Hence,

$$\lim\limits_{n \to \infty} x_n = \underline{\hspace{1cm}}.$$

You may now conclude, for the second time, that

$$\lim\limits_{n \to \infty} \sqrt[n]{n} = \underline{\hspace{1cm}}.$$

$\sqrt[n]{n}$
$\geq$
n
$\dfrac{n(n-1)}{2}$
$n, \dfrac{n(n-1)}{2}$
$\dfrac{2}{n-1}$
$\sqrt{\dfrac{2}{n-1}}$
0
1

(c) Look up James Bernoulli in an encyclopedia to find out some of his other contributions to science.

(d) Improve Bernoulli's inequality by proving: If $n \in \mathscr{Z}^+$ and x is *any* real number, then

$$(1 + x)^{2n} \geq 1 + 2nx + nx^2.$$

(e) **Research Problems.** What is the smallest number h_n such that

$$(1 + h)^n \geq 1 + nh \qquad \text{for } h \geq h_n?$$

For n even, part (d) shows that h_n does not exist. For n odd, Bernoulli's inequality shows that $h_n \leq -1$. Is it possible that $h_n \geq -2$? Compute h_3 and estimate h_5. Graph

$$y = (1 + x)^7 - 1 - 7x$$

and estimate h_7 graphically.

2. Find

    (a) $\displaystyle\sum_{i=1}^{9} i,$

(b) $\displaystyle\sum_{j=1}^{9} (2 + 3j)$,

(c) $\displaystyle\sum_{k=1}^{100} k^2$ (what shortcut did you use?).

3. (a) An appropriate definition for $\displaystyle\sum_{i=n}^{m} a_i$ would be:

$$\sum_{i=n}^{m} a_i = \sum_{i=1}^{?} a_i - \sum_{i=1}^{?} a_i.$$

(b) How would you interpret $\displaystyle\sum_{k=0}^{3} k^2$ and $\displaystyle\sum_{k=-2}^{5} k^2$? Have your extensions of the notation for summation satisfied the desirable properties of an extension?

(c) Find $\displaystyle\sum_{i=1}^{5} 2$. (What plays the role of a_i of the original definition?)

(d) Find $\displaystyle\sum_{n=0}^{5} 2(3^n)$.

(e) Find $\displaystyle\sum_{n=0}^{5} 3^n$. Compare with your answer to (d).

(f) Prove $\displaystyle\sum_{i=1}^{n} \lambda a_i = \lambda \sum_{i=1}^{n} a_i$. [*Hint:* You need mathematical induction.]

(g) Compare the following quantities:

$$\sum_{k=1}^{25} 3k, \quad 3\sum_{i=1}^{25} i, \quad \sum_{j=0}^{25} 3(25 - j), \quad \sum_{n=0}^{25} 3(25 - n),$$

$$3\sum_{a=-3}^{22} (a + 3), \quad \sum_{b=-2}^{22} 3(b + 3), \quad 3\left(\sum_{m=10}^{21} (m + 4) + \sum_{m=1}^{13} m\right).$$

4. (a) Let Σ be interpreted as an operation (or function) on the set of n-tuples $\{(a_1, a_2, \ldots, a_n)\}$. Is Σ a linear operation? Prove or disprove.

(b) $\displaystyle\sum_{k=1}^{n} (a_k - a_{k-1}) = a_? - a_?$. This is called the *telescoping property* of the Σ notation.

(c) Find $\displaystyle\sum_{k=1}^{100} \frac{1}{k(k + 1)}$. [*Hint:* Manipulate $\dfrac{1}{k(k + 1)}$ into a form so that the telescoping property can help you.]

5. (a) In the text you found a formula for $\displaystyle\sum_{k=1}^{n} k^2$ and you proved it by mathematical induction. We will now introduce you to another method of *discovering* the formula. Observing that $\displaystyle\sum_{k=1}^{n} k$ equals a quadratic in n, you might guess that $\displaystyle\sum_{k=1}^{n} k^2$ equals a cubic in n. To test this guess, begin by expanding:

$$(k + 1)^3 = \underline{\quad}k^3 + \underline{\quad}k^2 + \underline{\quad}k + 1.$$

Since it is squares that you wish to sum, it might be wise to concentrate on summing the right members. The right member has a bothersome cubic term, which you can eliminate by subtracting. This gives

$$(k + 1)^3 - \underline{\quad}k^3 = \underline{\quad}k^2 + \underline{\quad}k + 1.$$

Write this equation out for $k = 1, 2, \ldots, n$.

$$2^3 - (\underline{\quad})1^3 = \underline{\quad}1^2 + \underline{\quad}1 + 1,$$

$$3^3 - (\underline{\quad})2^3 = \underline{\quad}2^2 + \underline{\quad}2 + 1,$$

$$(n + 1)^3 - (\underline{\quad})n^3 = \underline{\quad}n^2 + \underline{\quad}n + 1.$$

Add and solve for $1^2 + 2^2 + \cdots + n^2$. Reviewing this procedure, you can see how the Σ notation would save a great deal of space. From

$$(k + 1)^3 - k^3 = 3k^2 + 3k + 1,$$

you can simply say: Sum both members over k from $k = 1$ to n. Then

$$\sum_{k=1}^{n} [(k + 1)^3 - k^3] = \sum_{k=1}^{n} (3k^2 + 3k + 1).$$

Does the telescoping property help? Does linearity help?

(b) Using either approach you have learned, find a formula for $\sum_{k=1}^{n} k^3$ and verify that it is correct by mathematical induction.

(c) Find a numerical value for $\sum_{j=1}^{10} (3j + 4j^2)$.

(d) Find a numerical value for $\sum_{j=1}^{10} (2j + 3j^2 + 4j^3)$.

6. (a) Discover and prove the validity of a formula for

$$\sum_{i=1}^{n} \frac{1}{(2i - 1)(2i + 1)}.$$

(b) The expression $x^{2n} - y^{2n}$ has a linear factor. Guess it, and prove by mathematical induction that it is a factor for all $n \in \mathscr{Z}^+$.

(c) The expression $x^{2n-1} + y^{2n-1}$ also has a linear factor. Guess it, and prove your guess is correct.

(d) Let a polygon of n sides be denoted P_n, and call its vertices $V_1, V_2, \ldots, V_n$. Any segment joining two nonadjacent vertices is called a *diagonal*. How many diagonals does a triangle have? How many diagonals does P_n have? Prove your last answer.

(e) The sum of the interior angles of a convex polygon P_n is (\underline{\quad})$180°$. Prove.

7. In much of our earlier work we took for granted that you were familiar with the binomial expansion

$$(a + b)^n = a^n + \frac{n}{1!}a^{n-1}b + \frac{n(n - 1)}{2!}a^{n-2}b^2 + \frac{n(n - 1)(n - 2)}{3!}a^{n-3}b^3 + \cdots + b^n.$$

In this exercise we will ask you to prove the validity of the binomial expansion, but first some preliminaries.

(a) The general term is given as

$$\frac{n(n-1)(n-2)\cdots(n-k+1)}{k!}a^{n-k}b^k.$$

Write the coefficient (of $a^{n-k}b^k$) in terms of factorials: $\dfrac{n!}{k!(\underline{\quad})!}$.

(b) A standard symbol for the *binomial coefficient* $\dfrac{n!}{k!(\underline{\quad})!}$ is $\binom{n}{k}$. You can now write the binomial expansion as

$$(a+b)^n = \sum_{k=?}^{?} \binom{n}{k}a^{n-k}b^?.$$

(Notice that this notation does not apply if $a = 0$ or $b = 0$.)

(c) Prove that

$$\binom{n}{k} + \binom{n}{k-1} = \binom{n+1}{k} \quad \text{and} \quad \binom{n}{k} = \binom{n}{n-k}.$$

(d) In order to prove that the binomial expansion is valid for the exponent $n+1$ if it holds for the exponent of n, you expand

$$(a+b)^{n+1} = (a+b)(a+b)^n = (a+b)\sum_{k=?}^{?} \binom{n}{k}a^{n-k}b^k$$

(i) $\quad a\displaystyle\sum_{k=?}^{?} \binom{n}{k}a^{n-k}b^k = a^{n+1} + \binom{n}{1}a^n b + \cdots + \binom{n}{k}a^2 b^? + \cdots + ab^n,$

(ii) $\quad b\displaystyle\sum_{k=?}^{?} \binom{n}{k}a^{n-k}b^k = a^n b + \underline{\qquad\qquad}.$

Add (i) and (ii), combining like-powered terms and finish the proof. What is the coefficient of $a^{n-k+1}b^k$?

(e) What is $\displaystyle\sum_{k=0}^{n} \binom{n}{k}$? [*Hint:* Make substitutions for a and b.] Also find $\displaystyle\sum_{k=0}^{n} (-1)^k \binom{n}{k}$.

8. *Blaise Pascal* (1623–1662), a French scientist and philosopher, was probably the first to use the principle of mathematical induction.

(a) Look up Pascal in an encyclopedia. What other scientific contributions did he make, and at what ages? What is *Pascal's principle* in physics?

(b) The famous *Pascal triangle* is shown below.

				0th row:	1					

0th row: 1
1st row: 1   1
2nd row: 1   2   1
                   1   3   3   1
                1   4   6   4   1
             1   5   10   10   5   1

It can be defined recursively. The symbol $a_{i,j}$ will stand for the jth number in the ith row, the counting starting with $i = 0$ and $j = 0$. Then $a_{0,0} = 1$ and $a_{0,j} = a_{i,i+1} = 1$ for all j and i. This merely says that the first and last number in each row is 1. Recursion enters in defining the other terms

$$a_{i+1,j+1} = a_{i,j} + a_{i,j+1}.$$

Expand $(a + b)^4$ and $(a + b)^5$. Examine the coefficients. Do you see any relationship between the coefficients and the entries in the Pascal triangle? Can you prove this is true in general?

9. The Method of Exhaustion. In an effort to determine the area of a region, Greek geometers used the idea of making approximations by inscribing polygonal regions. By suitably increasing the number of sides, better and better approximations were obtained. This is called the *method of exhaustion,* one of the essential ideas of integral calculus.

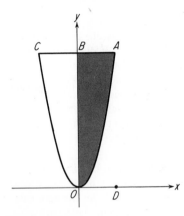

(a) Archimedes (287–212 B.C.) used the method of exhaustion to determine the area of a parabolic segment.

Let a parabola be given as the graph of $y = x^2$. The graph is symmetric with respect to the _____-axis. Therefore, the area enclosed by the parabolic arc AOC and segment AC equals _____ times the shaded region OAB in Fig. 10-3. Further, the area of the shaded region can be found by taking

area of rectangle $ODAB$ − area of region ODA (under the parabola).

Figure 10-3

So we turn attention to the region ODA (under the parabola), and apply the method of exhaustion. Let $D = (d, 0)$. Divide segment OD into n equal segments. The points of division are $0, d/n, \ldots, d$. Erect a vertical line at each of these points, between the first and the last, and inscribe rectangles as shown in Fig. 10-4. How many rectangles do you have? The width of every rectangle is the same. It is _____. The height of the first rectangle is _____. The height of the second rectangle is _____. The height of the kth rectangle is _____.

The area of the first rectangle is _____.

The area of the second rectangle is _____.

The area of the kth rectangle is _____.

The sum s_n of the areas of the rectangles under the parabola is _____. Writing this in Σ-notation, you get

Figure 10-4

$$s_n = \sum_{?=?}^{?} \left(\frac{kd}{n}\right)^2 \frac{d}{n}.$$

439

Using linearity of summation [Exercise 3(f), page 436], you can shift a common factor from one side of the Σ sign to the other. You can then compute the sum by applying one of the examples worked out in the text.

Find $\lim\limits_{n\to\infty} s_n$.

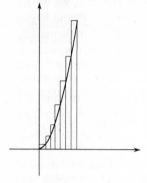

(b) Carry out a similar analysis for finding the area under the parabola by an overestimation with rectangles as shown in Fig. 10-5. If you use the points $(0,0), (d/n, 0), (2d/n, 0), \ldots, (nd/d, 0)$ to subdivide OD, call A_n the area obtained. Find $\lim\limits_{n\to\infty} A_n$ and compare with $\lim\limits_{n\to\infty} s_n$.

10. The Greek letter π is universally used to represent the ratio C/D, where C and D are, respectively, the circumference and diameter of a circle. If the circle is of diameter 1, then $C = \pi$. In fact, π was chosen to represent this ratio because it is the first letter of the Greek word περιφέρεια, which means *circumference*. The Old Testament (I Kings 7:23 and II Chronicles 4:2) gives π as 3. The Egyptian Ahmes (about 1600 B.C.)

Figure 10-5

gives π as 3.1605. Archimedes, by the method of exhaustion applied to perimeters, proved that $3\frac{1}{7} < \pi < 3\frac{10}{71}$, a remarkably accurate result. You can carry out part of Archimedes' approach by following the steps below.

(a) Let a circle of radius 1 be given. Find the perimeter of an inscribed square.

(b) Find the perimeter of an inscribed hexagon. (Use the law of cosines which was proved in Exercise 11 of Sec. 6.9.1.) Can you guess at a formula for the perimeter p_{2n} of an inscribed regular polygon of $2n$ sides? (Don't look at the next part until you have tried to get a general formula.)

(c) Prove by mathematical induction that

$$p_{2n} = \frac{n}{2}\sqrt{2 - 2\sqrt{1 - \left(\frac{2p_n}{n}\right)^2}}.$$

Let $q_n = p_k$, where $k = 2^n$.

(d) Prove that $\{q_n\}$ is a monotonic increasing sequence.

(e) Similarly, obtain a monotonic decreasing sequence $\{Q_n\}$ by using circumscribed regular polygons. Is the sequence $\{\mathscr{I}_n\}$, where $\mathscr{I}_n = [q_n, Q_n]$, a sequence of nested intervals? If it is, then, by Postulate C', you have proved the existence of π.

10.2

A Description of $\mathscr{X}^+$. Well-Ordering Before proceeding with more interesting applications of mathematical induction, we should discuss its logical basis! What postulates and/or theorems justify it? In order to find an answer, we should first answer the following more basic question: Since the principle of mathematical induction concerns the set $\mathscr{X}^+$ of positive integers, what do we know about $\mathscr{X}^+$? How have we defined or described $\mathscr{X}^+$?

The fact is that we have not constructed the set $\mathscr{L}$ of integers, but rather have assumed a knowledge of $\mathscr{L}$ as a special subset of $\mathscr{R}$. We then contented ourselves with a description of its properties (e.g., $\mathscr{L}$ is an abelian group with respect to $+$). If we had followed Peano's program (see the reference in Sec. 10.1) of *developing* or *constructing* $\mathscr{R}$ beginning with $\mathscr{L}^+$, we would have required a more explicit set of postulates for $\mathscr{L}^+$. In fact, Peano began with five assumptions for $\mathscr{L}^+$, and his fifth was the principle of mathematical induction. However, since our treatment of the real number system is different, let's look more closely at what we have assumed about $\mathscr{L}^+$, and try to move logically from there.

In Sec. 2.2, where we were interested in characterizing the real line $\mathscr{R}_1$, we began marking off successive unit lengths from a fixed origin, obtaining points corresponding to the positive integers $1, 2, 3, \ldots$. Thus, we used as our basic description of $\mathscr{L}^+$ the fact that it is generated by successive additions of 1. In the fancy language that you have learned since Chapter 2, we have taken as our definition: The set $\mathscr{L}^+$ is the smallest subset of $\mathscr{R}$ which contains the multiplicative identity and is closed under the operation of adding 1. Since we are working with a subset of the ordered field $\mathscr{R}$, we already have the order properties of $\mathscr{L}^+$, namely,

$$ 1 < 1 + 1 = 2 < 2 + 1 = 3 < \cdots < k < k + 1 < \cdots. $$

Exercise: Let r and ε be real numbers, such that $0 < r$ and $0 < \varepsilon < 1$. Prove that there is at most one positive integer in the set

$$ \{x \mid r \le x < r + \varepsilon\}. $$

Perhaps you might find it easy to prove the principle of mathematical induction directly from this definition of $\mathscr{L}^+$. This is certainly possible, but we choose to take an alternate route that will give us a view of another very important property of $\mathscr{L}^+$: *Every nonempty subset of $\mathscr{L}^+$ contains a smallest element.* This property is called the *well-ordering* or *well-ordered property* of $\mathscr{L}^+$. In general, a linearly ordered set $\mathscr{A}$ is called *well-ordered* if every nonempty subset of $\mathscr{A}$ contains a smallest element.

Thus, we ask your help in proving the following:

Theorem WO: $\mathscr{L}^+$ *is well-ordered with respect to* $<$.

Proof: Let $\mathscr{M}$ be a nonempty set of positive integers. We must show that $\mathscr{M}$ has a smallest element.

$\mathscr{M}$ is bounded below. (Explain why!) In fact, you know that a lower bound for $\mathscr{M}$ is the integer _____ (give the largest correct answer). Thus, $\mathscr{M}$ has a greatest lower bound, which we call m.

| *1* |

If $\varepsilon > 0$, then there is at least one integer of $\mathcal{M}$ in the set

$$\mathcal{I} = \{x \mid m \leq x < m + \varepsilon\}.$$

This follows because m is _____. If $0 < \varepsilon < 1$, then $\mathcal{I}$ | *glb $\mathcal{M}$*
contains _____ (how many?) element(s) of $\mathcal{M}$. This | *one*
integer is then the smallest element of $\mathcal{M}$. (Why?) Thus,
we may conclude that $\mathcal{Z}^+$ is well-ordered.

Query: Did we prove that $\mathcal{M}$ contains its glb?

Theorem MI: *The principle of mathematical induction.* Let $\mathcal{M}$ be a subset
of $\mathcal{Z}^+$, such that
(a) $1 \in \mathcal{M}$,
(b) $k \in \mathcal{M} \Rightarrow (k + 1) \in \mathcal{M}$.
Then $\mathcal{M} = \mathcal{Z}^+$.

Proof: Let $\mathcal{M}$ satisfy the conditions in the hypothesis, and call $\mathcal{M}'$ the
set of all positive integers not in $\mathcal{M}$:

$$\mathcal{M}' = \{k \mid k \in \mathcal{Z}^+ \wedge k \notin \mathcal{M}\}.$$

If we can show that $\mathcal{M}'$ is empty, i.e., $\mathcal{M}'$ contains no elements, then we
will have shown that $\mathcal{M} = \mathcal{Z}^+$, and the proof will be complete.

If $\mathcal{M}'$ is nonempty, then $\mathcal{M}'$ contains a smallest element (why?), say n.
We know that $n \neq 1$(why?) and that $(n - 1) \notin \mathcal{M}'$ (why?). Thus, $(n - 1) \in \mathcal{M}$.
But, according to (b),

$$(n - 1) \in \mathcal{M} \Rightarrow n \in \mathcal{M},$$

which is a contradiction. Thus $\mathcal{M}'$ must be empty.

In Sec. 10.1 we used induction on sets other than $\mathcal{Z}^+$. It was remarked
there that mathematical induction rests on
(i) a starting (smallest) element, and
(ii) an explicit procedure for passing from each element to the next,
and this procedure must exhaust the set.
A set satisfying (i) and (ii) is called *inductive*. This notion can be made
precise by the following:

Definition: *A set is called* inductive *if and only if it is the range of a one-to-one
function on* $\mathcal{Z}^+$.

How can we justify the extension of the principle of mathematical induction
from $\mathcal{Z}^+$ to inductive sets in general?
Let's look at an example. Consider the inductive set

$$\mathcal{T} = \{n \mid n \in \mathcal{Z}^+ \wedge n > 3\},$$

and suppose we are trying to prove proposition $P(n)$ for all $n \in \mathcal{T}$. This is the same as saying that we wish to prove the proposition

$$P(k + 3), \qquad \forall\, k \in \mathscr{Z}^+.$$

Thus, by means of the one-to-one function $f = I + 3$,

$$n = f(k), \qquad \forall\, k \in \mathscr{Z}^+,$$

we can relate the proof by induction from the basic set $\mathscr{Z}^+$ to the inductive set $\mathcal{T}$; i.e., a proof of

$$P(f(k)), \qquad \forall\, k \in \mathscr{Z}^+$$

is precisely a proof of

$$P(n), \qquad \forall\, n \in \mathcal{T}.$$

Returning to a study of the logic surrounding mathematical induction, recall that we proved

$$\text{well-ordering} \Rightarrow \text{mathematical induction.}$$

More precisely, we showed that

(1) $\qquad\qquad\qquad$ Theorem WO $\Rightarrow$ Theorem MI.

It is interesting that the converse of this implication is also true, so that *the principle of mathematical induction is logically equivalent to the well-ordering principle.* This means that Peano could have used the latter as a postulate in place of the former. It also means that we ought to be able to use the well-ordering principle directly as a basis for proving theorems about inductive sets. We shall explore this possibility in the exercises, but first we shall prove

(2) $\qquad\qquad\qquad$ Theorem MI $\Rightarrow$ Theorem WO.

Let $\mathscr{S}$ be a nonempty subset of $\mathscr{Z}^+$. We must prove that $\mathscr{S}$ has a smallest element.

If $1 \in \mathscr{S}$, then $\mathscr{S}$ clearly has 1 as its smallest member. We therefore direct attention to the case in which $1 \notin \mathscr{S}$. Call $\mathscr{S}'$ the subset of $\mathscr{Z}^+$ defined by

$$\mathscr{S}' = \{n \mid n < s, \quad \forall\, s \in \mathscr{S}\}.$$

For example, if $\mathscr{S} = \{3k \mid k \in \mathscr{Z}^+\}$, then $\mathscr{S}' = \{1, 2\}$; if

$$\mathscr{S} = \{5 + 10k \mid k \in \mathscr{Z} \wedge k \geq 0\},$$

then $\mathscr{S}' = \{1, 2, 3, 4\}$. Note that a positive integer may be in neither $\mathscr{S}$ nor $\mathscr{S}'$: in the first example, $4 \notin \mathscr{S}$ and $4 \notin \mathscr{S}'$; in the second example, $11 \notin \mathscr{S}$ and $11 \notin \mathscr{S}'$.

If $1 \notin \mathcal{S}$, then $1 \in \mathcal{S}'$. Thus, $\mathcal{S}'$ satisfies condition (a) of the principle of mathematical induction. It cannot also satisfy condition (b), for this would imply $\mathcal{S}' = \mathcal{Z}^+$, which would mean that $\mathcal{S}$ is empty. Therefore, denying (b), we have that there is a $k \in \mathcal{Z}^+$, such that

$$k \in \mathcal{S}' \wedge (k + 1) \notin \mathcal{S}'.$$

Thus, $\mathcal{S}$ doesn't contain the first k integers $1, 2, 3, \ldots, k$, but $(k + 1) \in \mathcal{S}$. This means that $\mathcal{S}$ contains a smallest member, namely $k + 1$.

In the exercises that follow, you will learn of still another proposition that is equivalent to the principle of mathematical induction.

10.2.1

EXERCISES

1. (a) Show that the following are inductive sets:

$$\mathcal{Z}^-, \quad \{x \mid x \in \mathcal{Z} \wedge x \geq 0\}, \quad n\left\{\frac{n}{2} \in \mathcal{Z}, n > -4\right\},$$

$$\{y \mid y = 2^n, n \in \mathcal{Z}, n \geq 0\}.$$

(b) In the text we showed, by example only, that the principle of induction holds for general inductive sets. Taking a hint from the example, prove the general result.

(c) Prove that $10n \leq 2^n$ for the inductive set

$$\{n \mid n \in \mathcal{Z}^+ \wedge n > k\},$$

where k is some integer. Find the smallest possible k.

2. (a) Which of the following sets are well-ordered, assuming their natural order in $\mathcal{R}$?

$$\{2n \mid n \in \mathcal{Z}^+\}, \quad \{3n \mid n \in \mathcal{Z}\}, \quad \mathcal{R}a, \quad \mathcal{Z},$$

$$\{k \mid k \in \mathcal{Z} \wedge |k| < 100\}.$$

(b) Define a new ordering for $\mathcal{Z}$ so that it becomes a well-ordered set.

(c) Is every well-ordered set inductive?

3. Let $S(n) = \sum_{k=1}^{n} \frac{2}{4k^2 - 1}$.

(a) Show that $S(n) = (3n - 1)/(2n + 1)$ satisfies only one of the conditions for proof by induction.

(b) Find and prove a correct formula for $S(n)$. [*Hint:* Use the telescoping property.]

4. In the text we indicated that the well-ordering property of an inductive set can be used as a basis for proof in place of using mathematical induction.

(a) Suppose you wish to prove that if $a, b \in \mathcal{R}^+$, then there is an integer q such that

$$0 \leq r = a - bq < b.$$

Let $\mathscr{S} = \{n \mid n \in \mathscr{Z}^+, nb > a\}$. By the Archimedean principle, $\mathscr{S}$ is nonempty. Let n be the smallest member of $\mathscr{S}$, and let $q = n - 1$. Since $q + 1 = n \in \mathscr{S}$, then

$$(q + 1)b \underline{\quad\quad} a. \qquad (</>)$$

Since $q < n$, then $q \notin \mathscr{S}$, so that

$$qb \underline{\quad\quad} a. \qquad (\leq/\geq)$$

Therefore, we have

$$0 \underline{\quad\quad} a - bq \underline{\quad\quad} b. \qquad \text{(What order relations?)}$$

(b) Now try to prove that if $n \in \mathscr{Z}^+$, $n > 1$, then there is a $p \in \mathscr{Z}^+$ such that $n/p \in \mathscr{Z}^+$, and if $1 < q < p$, $q \in \mathscr{Z}^+$, then $p/q \notin \mathscr{Z}^+$. [*Hint:* Let $\mathscr{S} = \{p \mid p \in \mathscr{Z}^+, p > 1,$ and $n/p \in \mathscr{Z}^+\}$. Can you exhibit a member of $\mathscr{S}$? If so, let p be the smallest member of $\mathscr{S}$. Compute $(n/p)(p/q) = \underline{\quad\quad}$. Is $\mathscr{Z}^+$ closed under multiplication?]

(c) Try to prove that $\sqrt{17}$ is irrational, i.e., that there are no positive integers m and n such that $m^2 = 17n^2$. Let

$$\mathscr{S} = \{n \mid n \in \mathscr{Z}^+ \quad \text{and} \quad \exists\, m \in \mathscr{Z}^+ \quad \text{such that } m^2 = 17n^2\}.$$

If $\mathscr{S}$ is nonempty, let n be its smallest member and let m be the positive integer such that $m^2 = 17n^2$.

By part (a), you can find a $q \in \mathscr{Z}$ such that

$$0 \underline{\quad\quad} m - qn \underline{\quad\quad} n. \qquad \text{(What order relations?)}$$

Is there an integer k such that

$$\frac{m}{n} = \frac{k}{m - qn}?$$

Is $m - qn \in \mathscr{S}$? Does this agree with the definition of n? If $m - qn = 0$, compute q^2. Is this possible?

(d) Prove that $\sqrt{6}$ is irrational in the same way.

5. (a) Let the recursive definition of $\{x_n\}$ be

$$x_1 = 1, \qquad x_{k+1} = x_k + 3.$$

Find the function f such that $x_n = f(n)$.

(b) Given that the terms of $\{y_n\}$ satisfy the recursion relation

$$y_{k+2} - 3y_{k+1} + 2y_k = 0,$$

and $y_1 = 1$, $y_2 = 2$. Find the function F such that $y_n = F(n)$. [*Hint:* You may discover an elementary method, but if you don't succeed, recall that recursion relation is a difference equation.]

(c) Work part (b) with different initial conditions: $y_1 = 2$, $y_2 = 3$.

6. Product Notation. Analogous to the Σ-notation for sums, the notation Π (capital Greek letter *pi*) is used to represent products. For example,

$$2 \cdot 4 \cdot 6 \cdot 8 \cdot 10 \cdot 12 \cdot 14 \cdot 16 \cdot 18 \cdot 20 \cdot 22$$

is written

$$\prod_{i=1}^{11} 2i.$$

(a) Define $\displaystyle\prod_{i=1}^{n} a_i$ by mathematical induction.

(b) Define $\displaystyle\prod_{i=k}^{n} a_i$ so that it is consistent with your definition in (a).

(c) What theorems can you prove about the use of Π-notation? (Use the properties of Σ-notation to give you a start in your thinking. Be careful in constructing the analogues.)

(d) What is the analogue of the telescoping property?

7. Let $\displaystyle p_n = \prod_{k=1}^{n} \left(1 - \frac{1}{k+1}\right)$.

(a) Compute p_n for $n = 1, 2, 3,$ and 4.

(b) Find and prove a simple formula for p_n. That is, find f such that $p_n = f(n)$.

8. Do parts (a) and (b) of Exercise 7 for

$$p_n = \prod_{k=1}^{n} \left(1 - \frac{1}{(k+1)^2}\right).$$

9. In the early work with inequalities we asked you to prove

(1) $$\sqrt{ab} \le \frac{a+b}{2},$$

provided $a > 0$ and $b > 0$. The right member of (1) is the average, or *arithmetic mean* of a and b, and the left member is called the *geometric mean* of a and b. What is a geometric interpretation of the inequality?

You know that averages can be taken of more than two numbers, so arithmetic mean has a more general definition. Similarly, geometric mean is also defined more generally:

Given $a_1, a_2, \ldots, a_n$, then

$$\frac{1}{n} \sum_{i=1}^{n} a_i$$

is called the *arithmetic mean* and

$$\sqrt[n]{a_1 \cdot a_2 \cdots a_n} = \left(\prod_{i=1}^{n} a_i\right)^{1/n}$$

is called the *geometric mean* of $a_1, a_2, \ldots, a_n$.

A generalization of the inequality you proved is the following

Theorem: Let $a_1, a_2, \ldots, a_n$ be n positive numbers. Then

$$\left(\prod_{i=1}^{n} a_i\right)^{1/n} \le \frac{1}{n} \sum_{i=1}^{n} a_i.$$

(That is, the geometric mean is less than or equal to the arithmetic mean.)

This theorem is obvious for $n = 1$ and already proved for $n = 2$. Assume that it is true for a given value of $n \in \mathscr{Z}^+$, and try to prove it for $n + 1$.

(a) Let A be the arithmetic mean of $a_1, \ldots, a_n$, and let $a_{n+1} = xA$, $x \geq 0$. Express the geometric mean of $a_1, \ldots, a_{n+1}$ in terms of G, the geometric mean of $a_1, \ldots, a_n$, and $a_{n+1} = xA$. Use the assumption that $G \leq A$.

(b) Express the arithmetic mean of $a_1, \ldots, a_{n+1}$ in terms of A and x. Use the result of part (a) to reduce the problem to that of proving a simple inequality for all $x \geq 0$.

(c) Let $h = (x - 1)/(n + 1)$ and state the inequality to be proved in terms of h. Have you seen it before? For which values of h does the equality sign hold? What does this imply about the conditions under which the equality sign holds in the theorem?

(d) The *harmonic mean* H of $a_1, a_2, \ldots, a_n$ is defined as

$$H = \frac{n}{1/a_1 + 1/a_2 + \cdots + 1/a_n}.$$

It is related to the arithmetic mean of the reciprocals because

$$\frac{1}{H} = \frac{1}{n} \sum_{i=1}^{n} \frac{1}{a_i}.$$

Prove that $H \leq G$.

(e) A plane flies around a square 100 miles on a side. It flies 100 mph on the first side, 200 mph on the second side, 300 mph on the third side, and 400 mph on the fourth side. What is the average speed of the plane over its complete flight? What does this problem have to do with any of the foregoing parts of this exercise? Explain algebraically.

(f) Compare the magnitudes of $n!$ and $\left(\dfrac{n+1}{2}\right)^n$, and prove an inequality that holds for n sufficiently large. State how large.

10. The Sequence $\{(1 + 1/n)^n\}$

(a) Expand $x_n = (1 + 1/n)^n$ by the binomial theorem writing out the terms explicitly.

$$x_n = 1 + \underline{\hspace{0.8cm}} \frac{1}{n} + \underline{\hspace{0.8cm}} \frac{1}{n^2} + \underline{\hspace{0.8cm}} \frac{1}{n^3} + \cdots + \underline{\hspace{0.8cm}} \frac{1}{n^{n-1}} + \frac{1}{n^n}.$$

Then

$$x_n = 1 + \underline{\hspace{0.8cm}} + \underline{\hspace{0.8cm}} \left(1 - \frac{1}{n}\right) + \underline{\hspace{0.8cm}} \left(1 - \frac{1}{n}\right)\left(1 - \frac{2}{n}\right) + \cdots$$
$$+ \left[\underline{\hspace{0.8cm}}\left(1 - \frac{1}{n}\right) \cdots \left(\frac{2}{n}\right)\left(\frac{1}{n}\right)\right].$$

(b) Write x_{n+1} in the same form. Is the sequence monotonic?

(c) Prove that $\{x_n\}$ is convergent.

11. Another Look at $\{(1 + 1/n)^n\}$

(a) Find the geometric mean G of the numbers

$$a_1 = 1, \quad a_2 = a_3 = \ldots = a_{n+1} = 1 + \frac{1}{n}.$$

(b) Find the arithmetic mean A of the $\{a_i\}$ and write explicitly the inequality that holds between A and G.

(c) Simplify to prove that $x_n < x_{n+1}$. Do you prefer this method of proof to the one suggested in Exercise 10?

(d) Prove that $\{(1 - 1/n)^n\}$ is monotonic strictly increasing.

(e) Let $y_n = (1 + 1/n)^{n+1}$. Then

$$y_n = \left(\frac{\underline{\quad} + \underline{\quad}}{n}\right)^{n+1} = (1 - \underline{\quad})^{-(n+1)}.$$

Now write

$$y_n = (1 - \underline{\quad})^{-(n+1)} = \frac{1}{(1 - \underline{\quad})^{n+1}}.$$

Can you make use of anything you learned in this problem to prove that $\{y_n\}$ is monotonic?

(f) If $\mathscr{I}_n = [x_n, y_n]$, then $\{\mathscr{I}_n\}$ is a sequence of closed intervals. Prove that the $\mathscr{I}_n$ are nested. You must show that $\mathscr{I}_{n+1}$ is contained in $\mathscr{I}_n$. What does this mean about the order of the numbers x_n, y_n, x_{n+1}, and y_{n+1}?

(g) *For investigation.* You have shown that $\{x_n\}$ and $\{y_n\}$ are convergent and, in fact, that

$$\lim_{n \to \infty} x_n = \lim_{n \to \infty} \sup x_n = \lim_{n \to \infty} \inf y_n = \lim_{n \to \infty} y_n.$$

You should also have an idea about the magnitude of the limit. Is it close to any number you have discussed in this chapter? Recall Exercise 10(a). Try and prove that

$$x_n < \sum_{k=0}^{n} \frac{1}{k!} < y_n.$$

If you can do this, you will know that $\lim_{n \to \infty} x_n = \lim_{n \to \infty} y_n = \underline{\quad}$. This would give you three different ways of getting this number!

(h) Use the result of (g) to find $\lim_{n \to \infty} (1 - 1/n)^n$.

(i) Find $\lim_{n \to \infty} (1 + a/n^2)^n$ for a any real number.

(j) Prove by mathematical induction that $e^n > n^n/n!$, $\forall n \in \mathscr{Z}^+$.

12. Gauss' Arithmetic-Geometric Mean. Carl Friedrich Gauss (1777–1855), often called the "Prince of Mathematicians," defined two functions based on arithmetic and geometric means of pairs of numbers. These functions were invented by him for their usefulness in advanced analysis.

We start with two positive numbers a and b. Let's assume $0 < a < b$, and define two sequences by induction as follows:

$$a_0 = a, \qquad\qquad b_0 = b,$$

$$a_1 = \sqrt{a_0 b_0}, \qquad b_1 = \frac{a_0 + b_0}{2},$$

$$a_{n+1} = \sqrt{a_n b_n}, \qquad b_{n+1} = \frac{a_n + b_n}{2}.$$

(a) Prove that $\{a_n\}$ is monotonic and bounded.

(b) Prove $\{b_n\}$ is also convergent.

(c) Prove that $\{b_n - a_n\}$ is a null sequence. [*Hint*:

$$b_{n+1} - a_{n+1} = \frac{(\underline{\quad} - \underline{\quad})^2}{2} = \frac{(\underline{\quad})^2}{2(\sqrt{a_n} + \sqrt{b_n})^2} < \frac{b_n - a_n}{2}.]$$

The limit of $\{a_n\}$ and $\{b_n\}$ depends on the numbers a and b. Gauss' arithmetic-geometric mean function F is defined by

$$F(a, b) = \lim_{n \to \infty} a_n \qquad (= \lim_{n \to \infty} b_n).$$

The domain of F is the set of ordered pairs of real numbers. If λ is positive, express $F(\lambda a, \lambda b)$ in terms of λ and $F(a, b)$.

13. Other Sequences of Arithmetic and Geometric Means

(a) In an earlier exercise (14 of Sec. 9.5.1) you were to show that

$$\lim_{n \to \infty} x_n = A \Rightarrow \lim_{n \to \infty} \frac{1}{n} \sum_{i=1}^{n} x_i = A.$$

Now prove that this result is true even when $A = \pm \infty$. (Is the converse true?)

(b) Let $a_n > 0$ and $\lim_{n \to \infty} a_n = A$. Prove that the geometric mean also converges to A. That is,

$$\lim_{n \to \infty} \left(\prod_{i=1}^{n} a_i \right)^{1/n} = A.$$

There are two easy ways to do this. One is to imitate the solution of Exercise 14 of Sec. 9.5.1

$$\left(\lim_{n \to \infty} x_n = A \Rightarrow \lim_{n \to \infty} \sum_{k=1}^{n} \frac{x_k}{n} = A \right).$$

For this you need to solve such a problem as: Find the greatest possible value of $\left(\prod_{2}^{n} a_k \right)^{1/n}$ for a given n, given that $|a_k| \le M$ for all $k \in \mathcal{Z}^+$ and $a_k \le A + \varepsilon$ for $k \ge 100$.

An alternative method is to use the results of Exercise 10, and to apply the result of part (a) of this exercise.

Does this result hold if $A = \pm \infty$?

(c) Prove: If $\lim_{n \to \infty} (x_{n+1} - x_n) = A$, then $\lim_{n \to \infty} (x_n/n) = A$. [*Hint*: Use the telescoping property backwards. Define y_n, so that

$$\frac{1}{n} \sum_{i=1}^{n} y_n = \frac{x_n}{n},$$

and apply an earlier result of this exercise.]

(d) Prove: If $x_n > 0$ and $\lim_{n \to \infty} (x_{n+1}/x_n) = A$, then $\lim_{n \to \infty} \sqrt[n]{x_n} = A$. Is the converse true?

(e) Using the results of this exercise, prove for the third time that $\lim_{n \to \infty} \sqrt[n]{n} = 1$.

(f) Find $\lim_{n\to\infty} \sqrt[n]{n!}$ and $\lim_{n\to\infty} (1/n)\sqrt[n]{n!}$.

(g) Let $x_n = (n^n/n!)$. Find $\lim_{n\to\infty} (x_{n+1}/x_n)$. Using this fact, prove that

$$\lim_{n\to\infty} \frac{n}{(n!)^{1/n}} = e.$$

14. (a) Prove: If $|x_{n+1} - x_n| \le r^n$ for $n \in \mathscr{Z}^+$, where $0 \le r < 1$, then $\{x_n\}$ is convergent. [*Hint*: Estimate $|x_m - x_n|$ for $m > n$.]

(b) Let $\theta = 2 - \sqrt{3}$ and $\theta^n = a_n - b_n\sqrt{3}$. Find recursive formulas for a_n and b_n. Although you used a_n/b_n as an approximation to $\sqrt{3}$ in earlier sections, you were never asked to prove $\{a_n/b_n\}$ convergent. We now ask you to prove

$$\lim_{n\to\infty} \frac{a_n}{b_n} = \sqrt{3}.$$

15. (a) If $\lim_{n\to\infty} |x_n|^{1/n} < 1$, what is $\lim_{n\to\infty} x_n$?

(b) If $\lim_{n\to\infty} |x_n|^{1/n} > 1$, is $|x_n|$ large or small for large n? What is $\lim_{n\to\infty} |x_n|$?

(c) Give an example of a sequence $\{x_n\}$ such that $\lim_{n\to\infty} x_n^{1/n} = 1$ and $\lim_{n\to\infty} x_n = 0$. For this sequence, let $y_n = 1/x_n$. What are $\lim_{n\to\infty} y_n^{1/n}$ and $\lim_{n\to\infty} y_n$?

16. Find the following limits.

(a) $\lim_{n\to\infty} \dfrac{a^n}{n!}$ if $a > 0$.

(b) $\lim_{n\to\infty} \dfrac{n!}{n^n}$.

(c) $\lim_{n\to\infty} \dfrac{n^p}{a^n}$ if $a > 1$ and p is any constant.

(d) $\lim_{n\to\infty} \left(\dfrac{1}{\sqrt{n^2 + 1}} + \dfrac{1}{\sqrt{n^2 + 2}} + \cdots + \dfrac{1}{\sqrt{n^2 + n}} \right)$.

17. (a) If $0 \le a \le \frac{1}{4}$ and $x_1 = a$, $x_{n+1} = a + x_n^2$, find $\lim_{n\to\infty} x_n$. [*Hint*: Find the fixed points of $f: x \to a + x^2$. Which fixed point do you think x_n approaches? If ξ is your guess, let $\varepsilon_n = \xi - x_n$, $\varepsilon_{n+1} = \xi - x_{n+1}$, and investigate the behavior of the error ε_n as n increases.]

If $a = \frac{1}{4}$, prove by induction an estimate of the form $0 \le \varepsilon_n \le C/(n + 1)$ for some constant C.

(b) Find $\lim_{n\to\infty} (n^2 - n + 100)^{1/n}$. [You may find it helpful to write

$$(n^2 - n + 100)^{1/n} = (n^2)^{1/n}(1 - \cdots)^{1/n}.]$$

18. Compound Interest. If you put $\$A$ in a bank that pays interest at an annual rate of r dollars per dollar (usually given as $100r$ per cent in bank advertisements), the interest at the end of a year would be Ar. How much would your account show at the end of one year? At the end of two years?

(a) Suppose your account is started with $\$A_0$, and $\$A_t$ is the total account at the end of t years, the interest compounded annually at the annual rate of r. Find a formula for A_t, and prove by mathematical induction that your formula is correct.

(b) Let the annual rate of interest be r dollars per year, but suppose it is compounded semiannually. Find a formula for A_t, the total account t years after the initial deposit of $\$A_0$. Prove your answer is correct.

(c) Now generalize your result of part (b). Suppose the annual rate of interest is r, and suppose the interest is compounded n times per year. Prove that

$$A_t = A_0 \left(1 + \frac{r}{n}\right)^{nt}.$$

(d) A_t can be written $A_t = A_0[(1 + r/n)^n]^t$. If we write $x_n = (1 + r/n)^n$, then $A_t = A_0 x_n^t$. How does x_n behave as n increase? [Do you recall finding any limit that would assist in analyzing $\lim_{n \to \infty} (1 + r/n)^n$?] Have you studied sequences like $\{x_n\}$ for any particular values of r?

(e) Suppose you have a choice of banks in which to deposit your money. The Chemical National Bank pays interest at the rate r, compounded n times per year. The Physical National Bank pays interest at the same rate r, but compounded $n + 1$ times per year. Which bank would you choose? Intuitively, you would expect that interest compounded more often would be to your advantage. Can you prove this, i.e., can you prove

$$\left(1 + \frac{r}{n}\right)^n < \left(1 + \frac{r}{n + 1}\right)^{n + 1} ?$$

This would follow, if you knew that

$$\left[\left(1 + \frac{r}{n}\right)^n\right]^{1/(n+1)} < 1 + \frac{r}{n + 1}.$$

The left members can be thought of as the geometric means of the $n + 1$ numbers $\{\underline{\quad}, \ldots, \underline{\quad}\}$. Can the right member be represented as an arithmetic mean? Complete the argument.

19. More on the Compound-Interest Sequence. In the last problem you analyzed the sequence $\{x_n\}$, where $x_n = (1 + r/n)^n$. Certain characteristics of the sequence can be learned from looking at the particular subsequences. Assume that $|r| \le 1$.

(a) First, prove that $(1 + r/n)^n < (1 + r/2n)^{2n}$ by considering the nth roots of both members. Is your argument valid for $r \le 0$?

(b) Call $y_n(r) = x_{2^n}$. That is, $y_n = (1 + r/2^n)^{2^n}$. $\{y_n\}$ is a strictly increasing sequence. How do you know this? $y_n(-r) = \underline{\quad}$.

$$y_n(r) y_n(-r) = \left(1 - \frac{r}{2^n}\right)^{2^n} (\underline{\quad})^{2^n} = (\underline{\quad})^{2^n}.$$

If n is sufficiently large, $2^n > |r|$. Under this hypothesis, prove that $y_n(r) y_n(-r) < 1$. Then

$$y_n(r) < \frac{1}{(\underline{\quad})}.$$

(c) If you are especially interested in the sequence $\{(1 + 1/n)^n\}$ (Is this a familiar sequence?), then you might learn something of interest from examining $y_n(1)$. You have

$$y_n(r) < \frac{1}{y_n(-r)} < \frac{1}{y_1(-r)} \qquad \text{if } 0 < r < ?.$$

Then

$$y_n(1) < \frac{1}{y_1(-1)} = \underline{\qquad}.$$

So you have an upper bound for $\{y_n\}$. Is this also a bound for $\{x_n\}$? How does this compare with upper bounds that you discovered in earlier work with this sequence?

10.3

Division in $\mathscr{L}$ How do you divide one integer by another? Suppose you want to divide 21 by 4; what is the procedure you follow? In elementary terms, you might explain that you consider the sequence

$$1 \cdot 4, \, 2 \cdot 4, \, 3 \cdot 4, \, 4 \cdot 4, \, 5 \cdot 4, \, 6 \cdot 4, \, \ldots$$

until you reach a number greater than 21, namely $6 \cdot 4$. You backtrack one step in the sequence, to $5 \cdot 4$, giving the result $21 \geq 5 \cdot 4$ or

$$21 = 5 \cdot 4 + \text{remainder}, \qquad 0 \leq \text{remainder} < 4.$$

From this point you go on to establish the equation

$$21 = 5 \cdot 4 + 1 \qquad \text{or} \qquad \tfrac{21}{4} = 5 + \tfrac{1}{4}.$$

The result of the division is a *quotient* of 5 and a *remainder* of 1.

We shall now discuss the procedure in general terms for elements of $\mathscr{L}$.

Let $a, b \in \mathscr{L}$. We want to consider the division of a by b. Therefore, we insist that $b \neq 0$. Following the above example, we consider the set

$$\mathscr{M} = \{mb \mid m \in \mathscr{L} \wedge a < mb\}.$$

From the Archimedean property, we know that there is an m_1 such that $m_1 b > a$; so $\mathscr{M}$ is not empty. From its definition, $\mathscr{M}$ is bounded below by a. Therefore, applying the well-ordered principle, $\mathscr{M}$ contains a smallest element, say $m_0 b$. If we call $q = m_0 - 1$, we have

$$qb \leq a < (q + 1)b = m_0 b.$$

This implies that

$$a = bq + r, \qquad 0 \leq r < b.$$

The procedure just described is generally called the *division algorithm*, and can be found in Euclid's *Elements*, Book VII. We shall state it formally as a theorem.

Division Algorithm: *Let $a, b \in \mathscr{Z}$ and $b > 0$. Then there exist $q, r \in \mathscr{Z}$, such that*

$$a = qb + r, \qquad 0 \le r < b.$$

Are the quotient and remainder uniquely determined? Can we prove that there is only one correct result for any division? We shall help you. Suppose

(1)	$a = bq + r,$	___ $\le r <$ ___,	$0, b$
(2)	$a = bq_1 + r_1,$	___ $\le r_1 <$ ___.	$0, b$
	$r - r_1 = b($___ $-$ ___ $).$		q_1, q

The right member is a multiple of b, but since $r, r_1 < b$, we know that $|r - r_1| <$ ___. Therefore,

$$r - r_1 = \text{\_\_\_},$$

b

which implies that $q_1 - q =$ ___.

0

0

We conclude that $q = q_1$ and $r = r_1$. so *the quotient and remainder are uniquely determined*!

If division of $a \in \mathscr{Z}$ by $b \in \mathscr{Z}$ results in a quotient q and remainder of zero, i.e. if $a = qb$, then we say that b *divides* a or that b is a *divisor* ($=$ factor) of a. The standard shorthand is $b \,|\, a$. In other words,

$$b \,|\, a \Leftrightarrow a = qb, \qquad \text{for some } q \in \mathscr{Z}.$$

If b does not divide a, we write $b \nmid a$.

Let's confine our attention to $\mathscr{Z}^+$ for a moment. If $a \in \mathscr{Z}^+$, it is clear that $1 \,|\, a$ and $a \,|\, a$. These divisors, 1 and a, might be called the trivial divisors of a. Are there integers $a > 1$ that have only trivial divisors? Name the first ten in increasing order:

$$\text{\_\_, \_\_, \_\_, \_\_, \_\_, \_\_, \_\_, \_\_, \_\_, \_\_, 31.}$$

Numbers of this sort are called *primes*. That is, an integer $p > 1$ is a *prime* (or *prime number*) if and only if its only positive divisors are 1 and p. If an integer $c > 1$ is not a prime, it is called *composite*.

Questions concerning prime and composite numbers have intrigued mathematicians and laymen alike for thousands of years. Perhaps the greatest intrigue results from the fact that the concepts are elementary— accessible to anyone who knows arithmetic— and the problems can often be stated in very simple terms; yet, there is a host of simply stated problems that remain unsolved, taunting the generations of mathematicians and, in fact, anyone with intellectual curiosity concerning the *theory of numbers*. Perhaps your curiosity will also be piqued by this fascinating subject.

453

It is quite likely that the first major number theory problem considered was: How many primes are there? It is reasonable to guess that prime numbers become more and more scarce as one goes out further in the sequence of natural numbers, because large numbers have more candidates available for divisors than do small numbers. One might even conjecture that all sufficiently large numbers are composite. Euclid settled this question in his *Elements*, Book IX, with a slight variation of the following argument.

If the set of all primes consists of k members, say $p_1, p_2, \ldots, p_k$, consider the number

$$N = p_1 \cdot p_2 \cdots p_k + 1.$$

Is N prime or composite? If N is a prime, then there is a contradiction of the fact that there are only k primes (why?). If N is composite, there is a prime p that divides N. But p cannot be equal to any one of $p_1, p_2, \ldots, p_k$, for division by any of these k leaves a remainder of 1. A contradiction is reached in either case, so the assumption of only a finite number of primes must be false. Hence, we have:

Euclid's Theorem: *The number of primes is infinite.*

G. H. Hardy (1877–1947), in his delightful book, *A Mathematician's Apology*,† uses this theorem and its proof as his first of four elementary examples of beautiful and significant mathematics. Although many mathematicians would disagree with Hardy's basic criteria for aesthetics in mathematics, there is probably no disagreement with his judgment in this case.

Before we present any more of the highlights of the subject of number theory, we suggest that you take a workout with the following exercises.

10.3.1
EXERCISES

1. (a) Find all the divisors of 12, 52, 243, 571.
(b) State which divisors are primes in each case.

2. Which of the following are primes: 41, 66, 1025, $(2^{41} + 4)$, $(2^{41} - 64)$, $(6^{41} - 3)$?

3. (a) Name primes p and q so that $100 < p < 200$ and $200 < q < 300$.
(b) Show that the set of even primes is bounded. Find the least upper bound.

4. (a) Prove: $2 \mid (n^2 + n)$, $\forall n \in \mathscr{Z}^+$.
(b) Prove: $3 \mid (n^3 + 2n)$, $\forall n \in \mathscr{Z}^+$.
(c) Prove: $4 \mid (n^4 + 2n^3 + n^2)$, $\forall n \in \mathscr{Z}^+$.

† G. H. Hardy, *A Mathematician's Apology* (New York: Cambridge University Press, 1941).

(d) Prove: $3 \mid (4^n - 1)$, $\forall\, n \in \mathcal{Z}^+$.

(e) Prove: $8 \mid (3^{2n} - 1)$, $\forall\, n \in \mathcal{Z}^+$.

(f) Prove: $30 \mid (n^5 - n)$, $\forall\, n \in \mathcal{Z}^+$.

(g) Prove: If n is odd, then $24 \mid n(n^2 - 1)$.

5. If $a \mid b$ and $a \mid c$, then a is called a *common divisor* of b and c.

(a) Find the common divisors of 66 and 42.

(b) Find the common divisors of 12 and 20.

(c) Find the common divisors of 54 and 12.

(d) Prove that: If a is a common divisor of b and c, then (i) $a \mid (mb + nc)$, $\forall\, m$, $n \in \mathcal{Z}^+$ and (ii) $a \mid bc$.

6. Let $a, b \in \mathcal{Z}^+$. Divide:

$$a = q_1 b + r_1, \qquad 0 \le r_1 < b.$$

If $r_1 > 0$, divide again:

$$b = q_2 r_1 + r_2, \qquad 0 \le r_2 < \underline{\qquad}.$$

If $r_2 > 0$, divide again:

$$r_1 = q_3 r_2 + r_3, \qquad 0 \le r_3 < \underline{\qquad}.$$

(a) Does this process end? In other words, do you always reach a step such that $r_{n-1} = q_{n+1} r_n + 0$? Prove!

(b) Let $a = 66$ and $b = 42$.

$$66 = \underline{\qquad} 42 + \underline{\qquad}.$$

Continue the process until you reach a remainder of 0. What is r_n, the last nonzero remainder?

(c) Let $a = 12$, $b = 54$. What is r_n?

(d) Prove that r_n is a common divisor of a and b. [*Hint:* Follow the procedure backwards.]

(e) Show that r_n can be expressed as $r_n = ma + nb$, for some m, $n \in \mathcal{Z}$.

(f) Suppose $a > b$ and $b \mid a$. Then

$$a - q_1 b = r_1 > 0.$$

If $k \mid a$ and $k \mid b$, then $k \mid \underline{\qquad}$. That is, any common divisor of a and b is a divisor of $\underline{\qquad}$.

(g) Show that the conclusion of (f) is true for every nonzero remainder in the process.

(h) If r_n is the last nonzero remainder, r_n must be the *greatest common divisor*. Prove this statement. [*Hint:* See (d) and (g).]

7. The procedure described in Exercise 6 is called *Euclid's algorithm* for determining the *greatest common divisor* (gcd) of a pair of integers. You will find this algorithm of help in finding the gcd's of

(a) 119 and 221,

(b) 245 and 732,

(c) 2387 and 7469,

(d) 8321 and 17,322.

8. In Exercise 6 you learned that if d is the gcd of a and b, then there are m, $n \in \mathscr{Z}$ such that $d = ma + nb$. In fact, you saw how Euclid's algorithm can be used to find a particular solution for m and n.

(a) Find integers m and n such that

$$119m + 221n = \text{(gcd of 119 and 221)}.$$

(b) Find integers m and n such that

$$8321m + 17{,}322n = \text{(gcd of 8321 and 17,322)}.$$

9. The notation (a, b) is standard for the gcd of a and b. We shall use it freely. You have, thus far, that $(a, b) = ma + nb$, for some m, $n \in \mathscr{Z}$. In this exercise, we look at the set

$$\mathscr{D} = \{xa + yb \mid x, y \in \mathscr{Z}\}$$

to see whether (a, b) is any special member of $\mathscr{D}$.

(a) Since we are dealing with a, $b > 0$, you know that $(a, b) > 0$. Are you sure that this information is enough for you to conclude that $\mathscr{D}$ always contains positive elements?

(b) Let $\mathscr{D}^{+}$ be the set of positive elements in $\mathscr{D}$. From (a) you know that $\mathscr{D}^{+}$ is nonempty. Therefore, it has a _____ member c. Suppose that

$$c = x_0 a + y_0 b.$$

Prove that any common divisor of a and b also divides c.

(c) Is c a common divisor of a and b? Let d be any element in $\mathscr{D}$, say $d = xa + yb$. Divide

$$d = qc + r, \qquad 0 \le r < \text{_____}$$

or

$$xa + yb = q(\text{\_\_\_\_}a + \text{\_\_\_\_}b) + r.$$

Solve for r and answer the question: Is $r \in \mathscr{D}$?

$$0 \le r < c \Rightarrow r = \text{\_\_\_\_\_}.$$

Therefore, $d = $ _____, which proves that _____ $\mid d$ for all $d \in \mathscr{D}$.

Since $a \in \mathscr{D}$ and $b \in \mathscr{D}$, you may conclude that _____ $\mid a$ and _____ $\mid b$, and, finally, that _____ $= (a, b)$.

10. If two integers a and b have no common divisors other than the trivial divisor 1, then $(a, b) = $ _____. In this case, we say that a and b are *relatively prime*, or that a is *relatively prime to b*.

(a) If $a > 0$, then $(a, 1) = $ _____.

(b) If p is a prime and $0 < a < p$, then $(a, p) = $ _____.

(c) If p is a prime, $(p, p^2) = $ _____.

(d) Let p be a prime. If $p \mid ab$ and $p \nmid a$, what can you conclude? Can you prove it [without looking at part (e)]?

(e) Let p be a prime.

$$p \nmid a \Rightarrow (p, a) = \text{\_\_\_\_\_}$$

$$\Rightarrow m, n \in \mathscr{Z} \text{ such that } mp + na = \text{\_\_\_\_\_}$$

$$\Rightarrow mpb + nab = \text{\_\_\_\_\_}.$$

p divides the right member of the last equation if it divides the left member. Show that $p \mid (mpb + nab)$.

(f) Generalize the result of (d) and (e); namely, prove: If $(a, b) = 1$ and $a \mid bc$, then $a \mid c$.

(g) Prove: If a prime p divides the product $\prod_{i=1}^{n} a_i$, $a_i \in \mathscr{Z}^+$, then p divides at least one of the a_i.

How do you decide whether two integers are equal? For example, how would you test the statement

(3) $10,640,452,333,896 = 7777 \cdot 2706 \cdot 5,060,708?$

Is "10,640,452,333,896" another name for the number "$7777 \cdot 2706 \cdot 5,060,708$"? Or is statement (3) false? In the study of any mathematical system, there is always the question of how one can decide whether two elements are the same—especially when the names used for them look so different. This question is easily answered for the system $\mathscr{Z}^+$. Can you guess the answer?

The analogous problem in trigonometry would be the following (see Fig. 10-6): Given $\triangle ABC$ such that $|\overline{AB}| = 17$, $\angle A = 30°$, $\angle B = 64°$; and given $\triangle ABC'$ such that $|\overline{AB}| = 17$, $\angle A = 30°$, $|\overline{AC'}| = 16$. Are the two triangles the same? You could answer the question by finding $|\overline{AC}|$, thus allowing you to compare

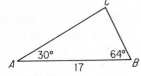

Figure 10-6

(4)   two sides and the included angle (s.a.s.) of the triangles;

or, you could find $\angle ABC'$, allowing you to compare

(5)   two angles and the included side (a.s.a.) of the triangles.

Both (4) and (5) are "standard forms" for the complete determination of a triangle. In other words, a triangle is uniquely determined (except for its position and orientation) by the data in (4) or (5).

In the chemistry of compounds—at least at the elementary level—the question of whether two samples are of the same compound can be decided by determining the chemical formula for each. The chemical formula is the "standard form," which exhibits the constituents of the compound in terms of the chemical elements.

Returning to the study of integers in $\mathscr{Z}^+$, we seek a "standard form" representing each integer so that we can compare two integers by inspecting them in "standard form." What would be the basic *words* of such a form? In chemistry, the basic words are the elements, the so-called building blocks of compounds. What are the building blocks of $\mathscr{Z}^+$? In some sense, the analogues of chemical elements are the primes in $\mathscr{Z}^+$, for primes cannot be decomposed into nontrivial factors, and it seems that integers are built of primes. Can we prove that every $n \in \mathscr{Z}^+$, $n > 1$, can be factored into a product of primes? Let's see.

The number 2 is already factored into a product of primes, namely the single prime 2. (Note that a "product" with only one factor is simply that factor.) So we have a start on induction. Let's try the following induction hypothesis:

$P(n)$: *If* $n \in \mathscr{Z}^+$ *and* $n > 1$, *then* n *can be factored into a product of primes.*

We attempt to prove that $P(k + 1)$ is true, assuming $P(k)$ is true. What we get from assuming the truth of $P(k)$ is

$$k + 1 = \prod_{i=1}^{n} p_i + 1,$$

where p_i are primes. This seems to tell us little, but let's proceed, anyway. If $k + 1$ is a prime, then $P(k + 1)$ is true. If $k + 1$ is composite, then there are $u, v \in \mathscr{Z}^+$ such that

(6) $$k + 1 = uv.$$

Equation (6) appears frustrating, since it shows that the problem is reduced to that of $P(u)$ and $P(v)$, *and not* to $P(k)$, our principal weapon. However, frustration can be averted if we take a hint from (6) and use the well-ordering principle:

Let $\mathscr{S}$ be the set of integers $n > 1$ such that n cannot be factored into a product of primes. Try to prove that $\mathscr{S}$ is empty.

If $\mathscr{S}$ is nonempty, it has a smallest member n. Then n cannot be expressed as a product of primes, but every smaller positive integer except 1 can.

Can n be a prime? No, for then it is a product of that single prime. Therefore, n is composite:

$$n = uv,$$

where $u, v \in \mathscr{Z}^+$, $1 < u < n$, and $1 < v < n$. But since n was the *smallest* member of $\mathscr{S}$, neither u nor v can be in $\mathscr{S}$. Therefore, each is expressible as a product of primes. Therefore, so can n be expressed as a product of primes. That is, $n \notin \mathscr{S}$, which is a contradiction. Thus $\mathscr{S}$ must be empty, so that we have proved:

Any integer $n > 1$ *can be factored into a product of primes.*

This gives us a start on a standard form. We can specify it more precisely by ordering the primes, so that

(7)
$$n = \prod_{i=1}^{s} p_i^{\alpha_i},$$

where $p_1 < p_2 < \cdots < p_s$ are primes and where each integer α_i is positive. Now the important question that remains is: Is the representation unique? If it is not, then (7) does not give a "standard form" with the desirable properties for comparison.

Suppose there is an $n \in \mathscr{Z}^+$ with two distinct factorizations into prime factors. We may cancel all the common factors of both representations until we obtain

$$\prod_{i=1}^{s} p_i^{\alpha_i} = \prod_{i=1}^{t} q_i^{\beta_i},$$

where no prime p_i in the left member occurs among the primes q_j in the right member and vice versa. This means that

$$p_1 \left| \prod_{i=1}^{t} q_i^{\beta_i}, \right.$$

which implies that p_1 divides some q_i (If you don't see why, check the exercises in Sec. 10.3.1 until you do.); that is, p_1 is equal to some q_j. But this is impossible. Hence, every $n \in \mathscr{Z}^+$ $(n > 1)$, has a unique representation as a product of primes. We shall make this statement precise.

Unique Factorization Theorem: *Every positive integer $n > 1$ can be factored uniquely, so that*

(8)
$$n = \prod_{i=1}^{s} p_i^{\alpha_i},$$

where $p_1 < p_2 < \cdots < p_s$ are primes and each $\alpha_i > 0$.

This theorem, which answers as the *standard form* (or *canonical form*) for integers, is sometimes called the *fundamental theorem of arithmetic*, for it lays the basis for many of the theorems in elementary number theory.

In the first part of the proof, we used an induction hypothesis **H** which asserts the truth of a proposition, namely $P(n)$, for all r, $1 < r \leq n$. This variation of mathematical induction is sometimes called the *second principle of mathematical induction*, which, for proofs, can be formulated as follows: If

(i) $P(1)$ is true,
(ii) $P(k + 1)$ is true if $P(k)$ is true for all integers r, $1 < r \leq k$,
then $P(n)$ is true for all $n \in \mathscr{Z}^+$.

Note that we avoided the need for a new principle by strengthening our induction hypothesis, incorporating into **H** all that the second principle of mathematical induction allows us to use. Thus, the second principle is deducible from the first.†

In applying the principle of mathematical induction and its variants, we are concerned with the question of whether a subset A of the set $\mathscr{Z}^+$ is all of $\mathscr{Z}^+$ or not; i.e., is $A = \mathscr{Z}^+$? This is equivalent to the question of whether the *complement* of A, namely

$$A' = \{m \mid m \in \mathscr{Z}^+ \wedge m \notin A\},$$

is empty or not. The principle of induction can then be formulated either as a criterion that A be all of $\mathscr{Z}^+$ ($A = \mathscr{Z}^+$) or that A' be empty ($A' = \varnothing$).

Assuming A and its complement A' to be subsets of $\mathscr{Z}^+$, we can state each variant of the induction principle in parallel versions:

1′. If
  (i) $1 \in A$, *and*
  (ii) $\forall n\,[n \in A \Rightarrow (n + 1) \in A]$,
     then $A = \mathscr{Z}^+$.

1″. If $A' \neq \varnothing$, then
  (i) $1 \in A'$, *or*
  (ii) $\exists n\,[n \notin A' \wedge (n + 1) \in A']$.

2′. If
  (i) $1 \in A$, *and*
  (ii) $\forall n\,[(\forall k(k < n \Rightarrow k \in A))$
    $\Rightarrow n \in A]$, then $A = \mathscr{Z}^+$.

2″. If $A' \neq \varnothing$, then $\exists n \in A'$ such that
$$\forall k\,[k \in A' \Rightarrow n \le k].$$

Without the succinctness of the logical symbolism, 1′ says that if a subset A of positive integers contains 1, and if A contains $n + 1$ whenever it contains n, then A is the set of all positive integers; 2′ says that if A contains 1, and if A contains n whenever it contains all positive integers k, $k < n$, then A is the set of all positive integers. (Now, you try and phrase 1″ and 2″ in words without the advantage of logical symbolism.)

The four statements 1′, 2′, 1″, and 2″ are logically equivalent. 1′ and 2′ are the "principle of mathematical induction" and the "second principle of mathematical induction," respectively. Did you notice that statement 2″ is "the well-ordering principle"? For, 2″ asserts that if a subset of positive integers is not empty, it must contain a least element. Should this be a surprise?

10.3.2
EXERCISES

  1. (a) Is (3) true? Prove or disprove.
     (b) Represent 5,217,520 in the canonical form (8).

    † The first form of induction also follows from the second, so that the two forms are logically equivalent. For a rather complete—but short—discussion of the relation between these two principles, see Arthur Schach, "Two Forms of Mathematical Induction," *Mathematics Magazine*, November–December 1958, pp. 83–85.

2. (a) Name five consecutive composite integers.
(b) Name ten consecutive composite integers.
(c) Are there 1000 consecutive composite integers?
(d) Generalize your conclusions of this exercise.

3. (a) Let $a, b \in \mathcal{Z}$. Before you heard about gcd's, how did you describe the fraction a/b, when $(a, b) = 1$?
(b) Let $(a, b) = 1$ and a/b be a root of the polynomial equation

$$c_n x^n + c_{n-1} x^{n-1} + \cdots + c_1 x + c_0 = 0, \qquad c_n \neq 0.$$

Show that $a \mid c_0$ and $b \mid c_n$.

(c) Prove, as a consequence of (b), that if $k \in \mathcal{Z}^+$, then

$$\sqrt[n]{k} \in \mathcal{Ra} \Leftrightarrow \sqrt[n]{k} \in \mathcal{Z}^+.$$

(d) Explain why $\pm \frac{3}{5}$ are two candidates for rational roots of the equation
$$30x^9 - 41x^8 + 2x^7 - 9x^3 + 12 = 0.$$

(e) Name the twelve integers that are candidates for roots of the equation in (d).

4. Let x be any integer greater than 1. Prove that
$$\forall n \in \mathcal{Z}^+, \qquad (x - 1) \mid (x^n - 1).$$

5. Let x be any nonnegative integer. Prove that
$$\forall n \in \mathcal{Z}^+, \qquad (x + 1) \mid (x^{2n} - 1).$$

6. Prove:
(a) $\forall n \in \mathcal{Z}^+, 5 \mid (8^n - 3^n)$.
(b) $\forall n \in \mathcal{Z}^+, 64 \mid (9^n - 8n - 1)$.
(c) $\forall n \in \mathcal{Z}^+, x_n = \dfrac{(1 + \sqrt{5})^n - (1 - \sqrt{5})^n}{2^n \sqrt{5}} \in \mathcal{Z}^+$. [Hint: $(1 \pm \sqrt{5})/2$ are the roots

of which quadratic equation? Find a recursion formula for x_n.]
(d) $\forall n \in \mathcal{Z}, 6 \mid n(n^2 + 5)$. [Hint: $n^2 + 5 = 6 + (\underline{\quad\quad})$.]

7. Since the earliest studies of number theory, people have attempted to find formulas that would generate primes:
(a) Examine the formula

$$f(n) = n^2 - n + 41$$

for $n = 1, 2, 3, 4, 5, 6, 7, 8, 9, 10$. How many of the $f(n)$ are primes?
(b) By now you know that the "physical induction" of part (a) is not sufficient to prove that $f(n)$ is a prime, for all $n \in \mathcal{Z}^+$. Find an integer n which proves that mathematical induction could not prove that $f(n)$ is always a prime.
[NOTE: There is no known elementary function F such that $F(n) = p_n$, where p_n is the nth prime. That is, there is no known formula that generates all primes.]

8. Prove the sum of all $k \in \mathcal{Z}^+$ such that $2 \nmid k$, $5 \nmid k$, and $k < 10n$ is $20n^2$.

9. Decimal Representation of Integers. If $n \in \mathbb{Z}^+$, the representation

(9) $n = \sum\limits_{i=0}^{s} a_i 10^i,$ $a_i \in \{0, 1, 2, 3, 4, 5, 6, 7, 8, 9\},$ $a_s \neq 0,$

is called the *decimal form* or *decimal representation* of n. (In practice we use only the sequence of digits in the order

$$a_s, a_{s-1}, \ldots, a_1, a_0$$

to represent n.)

(a) Does the integer 1 have a unique decimal representation? If so, what is it?

(b) Assume that all integers less than $k \in \mathbb{Z}^+$ have a unique decimal representation. Prove that there exists a unique integer m such that

$$10^m \leq k < 10^{m+1}.$$

Dividing k by 10^m, obtain

$$k = 10^m q + r,   \underline{\hspace{1cm}} \leq r < \underline{\hspace{1cm}}.$$

Why is $q > 0$? Why is $q < 10$?

If $r = 0$, then

$$k = \underline{\hspace{0.5cm}} 10^0 + \underline{\hspace{0.5cm}} 10^1 + \underline{\hspace{0.5cm}} 10^2 + \cdots + \underline{\hspace{0.5cm}} 10^{m-1} + q 10^m.$$

If $r \neq 0$, then r has a (unique) representation in the form

$$r = \sum\limits_{i=0}^{t} a_i 10^i,   a_t > 0,   0 \leq a_i < 10.$$

How do you know that $t < m$?

If you have answered all the questions, you may conclude that k has a decimal representation

$$k = a_0 \cdot 10^0 + a_1 \cdot 10^1 + \cdots + a_t \cdot 10^t + 0 \cdot 10^{t+1} + \cdots + 0 \cdot 10^{m-1} + q \cdot 10^m$$

$$= \sum\limits_{i=0}^{t} a_i \cdot 10^i + q \cdot 10^m.$$

(c) Is the decimal representation of an integer unique? Let

$$n = \sum\limits_{i=0}^{s} a_i \cdot 10^i = \sum\limits_{i=0}^{t} b_i \cdot 10^i,$$

$s, t \geq 0$; $a_s, b_t > 0$, $0 \leq a_i < 10$, and $0 \leq b_i < 10$, for all i.

Prove that $s = t$ and $a_i = b_i$, for all i. [*Hint:* Subtract one representation from the other and examine the coefficients in the resulting decimal.]

(d) Can you generalize the results of this problem?

10. (a) Let $s \in \mathbb{Z}^+$ be a square and

$$s = \sum\limits_{i=1}^{m} a_i \cdot 10^i,   a_m > 0,$$

be the decimal representation of s. What are the possibilities for the *units digit*, a_0?

(b) Prove that: $a_0 = 6 \Leftrightarrow a_1$ is odd.

11. (a) Is every pair of consecutive integers relatively prime?

    (b) Can $n(n + 1)(n + 2)$ be a perfect square, for $n \in \mathscr{Z}^+$?

    (c) Can $n(n + 1)(n + 2)(n + 3)$ be a perfect square, for $n \in \mathscr{Z}^+$?

12. Let $\mathscr{S} = \{1, 2, \ldots, n\}$.

    (a) Show that there is a unique $k \in \mathscr{Z}^+$ such that $2^k \leq n < 2^{k+1}$. [See Exercise 9(b).]

    (b) How many integers in $\mathscr{S}$ are divisible by 2^k?

    (c) Use (b) to show that

$$\sum_{j=1}^{n} \frac{1}{j} = \frac{a}{2^k b},$$

where $a, b \in \mathscr{Z}^+$. What else can you say about a and b? Can either be even?

    (d) Use part (c) to show that

$$\sum_{j=1}^{n} \frac{1}{j}$$

is not an integer if $n > 1$.

13. Recall the Fibonacci sequence $\{x_n\}$, where

$$x_1 = x_2 = 1, \qquad x_{n+1} = x_n + x_{n-1} \quad \text{for } n \geq 2.$$

    (a) Prove that $(x_n, x_{n+1}) = 1$, for every $n \in \mathscr{Z}^+$.

    (b) Prove: $3 \mid n \Leftrightarrow 2 \mid x_n$.

    (c) Prove the explicit formula:

$$x_n = \frac{1}{\sqrt{5}} \left(\left(\frac{1 + \sqrt{5}}{2} \right)^n - \left(\frac{1 - \sqrt{5}}{2} \right)^n \right).$$

[*Hint:* Among the ways to discover this formula is the observation that the recursive relation is a simple difference equation.]

14. Prove: If n is not divisible by a prime less than or equal to $\sqrt{n}$, then n is a prime. How does this help in factoring integers?

15. Imitate Euclid's proof (page 454) in these problems:

    (a) Prove that there are infinitely many primes of the form $6k - 1$, $k \in \mathscr{Z}^+$. [*Hint:* Use $P - 1$, where P is the product of all primes less than or equal to $6n - 1$.]

    (b) Prove that there are infinitely many primes of the form $4n - 1$. [*Hint:* Use $2Q - 1$, where Q is the product of all primes less than or equal to $4n - 1$.]

16. Refer to the parallel versions of mathematical induction on page 460.

    (a) Prove that the condition "(i) or (ii)" in $1''$ is the logical negation of "(i) and (ii)" of $1'$.

    (b) What is the negation of $2'(\text{ii})$? [*Hint:* Write $2'(\text{ii})$ as: $\forall n [p \Rightarrow q]$.]

    (c) Show that the negation of "(i) and (ii)" of $2'$ is logically equivalent to the conclusion of $2''$, namely

$$\exists n \in A' \quad \text{such that} \quad \forall k [k \in A' \Rightarrow n \leq k].$$

[*Hints:* The proposition $(k \in A' \Rightarrow n \leq k)$ is the contrapositive of $(k < n \Rightarrow k \in A)$. Also, note that the negation of 2'(ii) supersedes the negation of 2'(i); does this mean that 2'(i) is logically superfluous in the statement of the second principle of induction?]

With the completion of part (c), you will have established that *the principle of mathematical induction is logically equivalent to the well-ordering principle.*

A Few Unsolved Problems in Number Theory   Although a great deal is known about prime numbers, they still provide many of the open questions of number theory.

A renowned Russian mathematician, Chebyshev (1821–1894), proved an elegant result on the existence of primes: $\forall\, n \in \mathscr{Z}^+$ and $n > 1$, there is a prime p such that $n < p < 2n$. This prompted the ditty: "Chebyshev said it, and I say it again, there is a prime between n and $2n$." Sharper results than Chebyshev's have been discovered; for example, if $x > \frac{7}{2}$, there exists a prime p such that

$$x < p < 2(x - 1).$$

There is a related unsolved problem: If $x \in \mathscr{Z}^+$, is there always a prime such that

$$x^2 < p < (x + 1)^2?$$

Some other simply stated unsolved problems on the existence of primes are: Are there infinitely many primes of the form 111 ... 1, i.e., with all digits equal to 1 when the number is expressed in decimal notation? Are there infinitely many primes of the form $n^2 + 1$, $n \in \mathscr{Z}^+$? Are there infinitely many primes of the form $n! + 1$, $n \in \mathscr{Z}^+$?

In 1742 the German mathematician Christian Goldbach wrote to Euler conjecturing:

(a) Every even number $n \geq 6$ is the sum of two odd primes.

(b) Every odd number $m \geq 9$ is the sum of three odd primes.

[NOTE: (a) $\Rightarrow$ (b).] Euler, who was convinced of the truth of the Goldbach conjectures, was unable to find any proof. Neither has anyone else! The conjectures have been verified by "physical induction" up to 100,000. In this century, the Norwegian, Viggo Brun, and the Russian, I. Vinogradoff, have made some substantial progress, but the complete solution still seems far off.

An open question that has an appearance somewhat similar to the Goldbach problem is: Is every even integer a difference of two primes?

Two consecutive odd primes are called *twin primes*. It is conjectured that there are infinitely many twin primes. Again, no one has proved or disproved the conjecture.

A *diophantine problem* (after the Greek, Diophantus, approximately 250 A.D.) is an algebraic problem which demands integer solutions for the unknowns.† For example, the Babylonians and Greeks had many solutions to the diophantine problem,

$$x^2 + y^2 = z^2, \qquad x, y, z \in \mathscr{Z}^+,$$

for they were interested in the Pythagorean triangles. The most famous unsolved diophantine problem is the so-called *Fermat's last theorem*. Fermat (1601–1665), in the margin of one of his books, wrote that he had proved: There exist no nonzero integer solutions for x, y, and z in the equation

$$x^n + y^n = z^n$$

if the integer n is larger than 2. In the three hundred years since Fermat's death, no one has been able to discover a proof of his last theorem. It is therefore conjectured that Fermat had no proof, either. Thus far, Fermat's theorem has been established for $2 < n < 4002$ and for infinitely many other values of n. But, once again, it seems that the solution for all $n > 2$ is also beyond reach at the present time.

Another unsolved diophantine problem is:

$$x^3 + y^3 + z^3 = 30.$$

It is not known whether there are any integral solutions.

We close this short list with a simple question, whose answer is also elusive: Is $n! + 1$ a square for any integers $n > 7$?

---

† The concept of a *diophantine problem* has changed somewhat in recent times. Originally, *rational* solutions were admitted, for the work of Diophantus concerned algebraic problems which required *rational* solutions. Although one finds authors who still prefer the traditional meaning, we have given the more usual interpretation.

Index

C

Calculus, 11
Cancellation property, 71
Canonical form, 459
Cartesian coordinate system, 124
Cauchy criterion, 386
Cauchy inequality, 341
Cauchy sequence, 386
Chebyshev, 464
Closure postulate, 68
Cobweb solution, 313
Common divisor, 455
Commutative laws, 21
Commutative property, 62
Complement, 460
Completeness postulate, 411
Complex number system, 89
Component, 198, 235
Composition, 58, 158, 453
  of translations, 198
Compound interest, 450
Configuration-space, 138
Constant function, 161
Constant of proportionality, 143
Contrapositive, 384
Convergent sequence, 377, 400
Coordinate, 51
Coordinate system, 51
Cowles commission, 9
Current, 247

D

Debreau, Gerard, 35
Decimal form, representation, 462
Deduction, 2
Deductive inference, 2
Deductive reasoning, 2, 3
Degrees of freedom, 138
Demand function, 263
Derivative, 11, 15

Descartes, René, 37
Diagonal, 437
Difference equation, 346
Differential equation, 17
Diophantine problem, 464
Directed distance, 52
Directed line segment, 195
Direction, 195
Direction angles, 230
Direction cosines, 230
Discriminant, 340
Displacement, 196
Distance from point to a line, 243
Distributive laws, 22, 66, 73
Divergent sequences, 377, 391
Division algorithm, 452
Domain, 161, 190
Dominating main diagonal, 357
Dot product, 236, 241
Dummy indices, 434

E

e, 20, 21, 23, 386, 410
Eigenvalue, 293
Eigenvector, 293
Electromotive force, 247
Elimination, solution by, 253, 254
Equality, 60
  of translations, 194
Equilibrium point, 263
Equivalence relation, 267
Equivalent, 255
Euclid's algorithm, 455
Euclid's theorem, 454
Euler, 464
Exhaustion, method of, 439
Existential quantifier, 69
Exponential function, 165
Extreme point, 334
Extreme value, 334

Utility, 26, 27
Utility function, 27

V

Vector(s), 192, 195, 231
  change, 203
  geometric, 233
  invariant, 290
  inventory, 203, 233
  length of (notation), 204
  multiplication of, by a scalar, 206, 231
  position, 218
  price, 203
  radial, 221
  real multiple of, 209
  sum of, 200
    around closed polygon, 202
  unit, 214
  zero, 202
Vector addition, 231
Vector equation:
  of a circle, 229
  of the line, 220
Vector space, abstract, 231
  properties of, 231

Vector subtraction, 212
Velocity:
  average, 13
  instantaneous, 14
  uniform, 221
  wind, 195
Void set, 173
Voltage drop, 247
Voltage source, 247
Volts, 247
Von Neumann, John, 9, 35
Voters paradox, 29

W

Well-known Proposition, 95
Well-ordered property of $\mathbb{Z}^+$, 440, 441
Well-ordering principle, 443
Work, 234

Z

Zero matrix, 301
Zeros, 164

473